MEDICAL ASSISTING
Health Insurance Basics and
Claims Processing
Module H

MEDICAL ASSISTING
Health Insurance Basics and Claims Processing
Module H

Material Selected from:

Health Insurance Today: A Practical Approach
Second Edition
(textbook and workbook)
by
Janet I. Beik, AA, BA, MEd

SAUNDERS

ELSEVIER

11830 Westline Industrial Drive
St. Louis, Missouri 63146

Notice

Knowledge and best practice in this field are constantly changing. As new research and
experience broaden our knowledge, changes in practice, treatment, and drug therapy may
become necessary or appropriate. Readers are advised to check the most current information provided (i) on procedures featured or (ii) by the manufacturer of each product to be
administered, to verify the recommended dose or formula, the method and duration of
administration, and contraindications. It is the responsibility of practitioners, relying on
their own experience and knowledge of the patient, to make diagnoses, to determine
dosages and the best treatment for each individual patient, and to take all appropriate
safety precautions. To the fullest extent of the law, neither the Publisher nor the Authors
assume any liability for any injury and/or damage to persons or property arising out of or
related to any use of the material contained in this book.

The Publisher

Printed in Canada

Last digit is the print number: 9 8 7 6 5 4 3 2 1

ACKNOWLEDGMENTS

Thank you to our advisory board members and the CCi Medical Assisting Program community for your dedication, teamwork, and support over the years.

This textbook has been designed for your success. Each feature has been chosen to help you learn medical assisting quickly and effectively. Colorful boxes, tables, and illustrations will visually spark your interest, add to your knowledge, and aid in your retention of the material. All chapters end with a review that asks you to apply the terms and concepts you have learned.

USE ALL THE FEATURES IN THE CHAPTER

Key Terms

The key terms list provides you with a quick overview of the terms you will encounter as you work your way through the chapter. You can also use this page to help you review for tests.

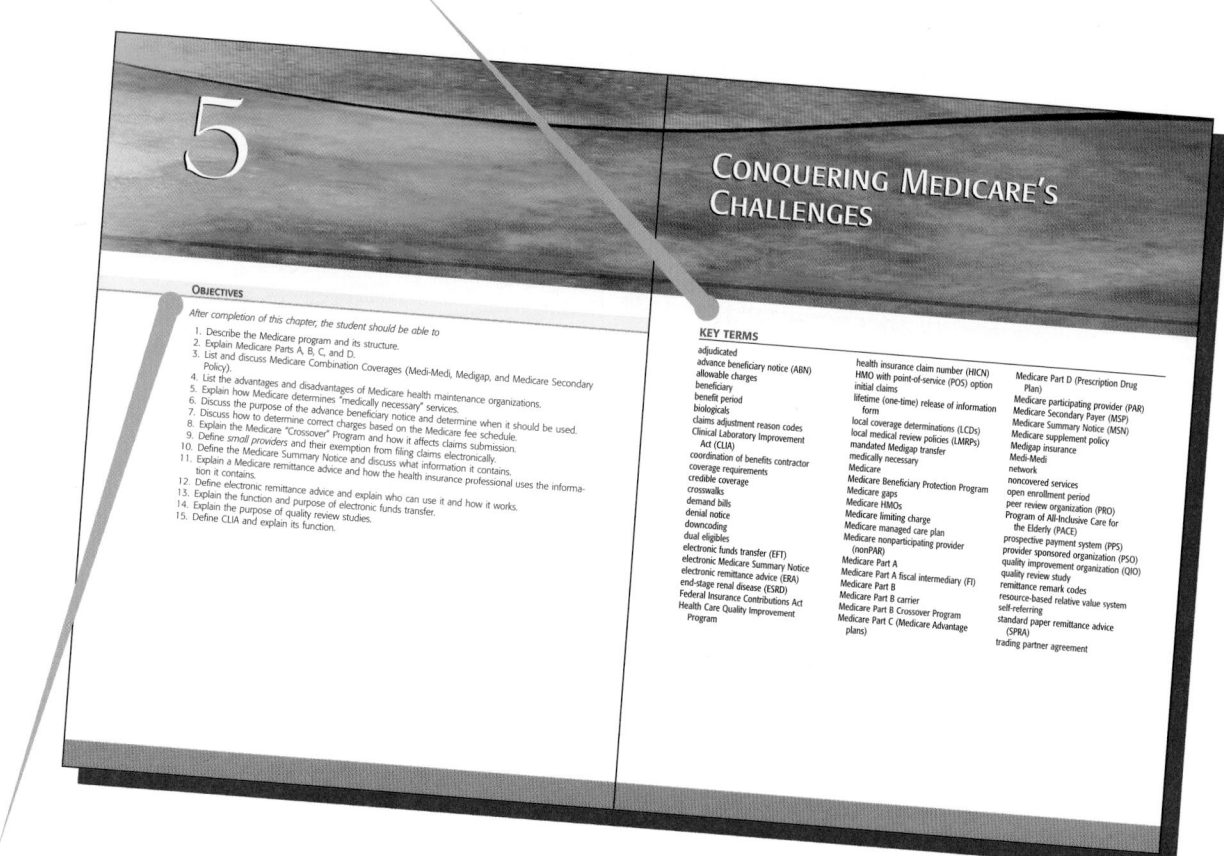

Objectives

Each objective is a goal for you. You should refer to these objectives before you study the chapter to see what your goals are and then again when you finish the chapter to see if you have accomplished them.

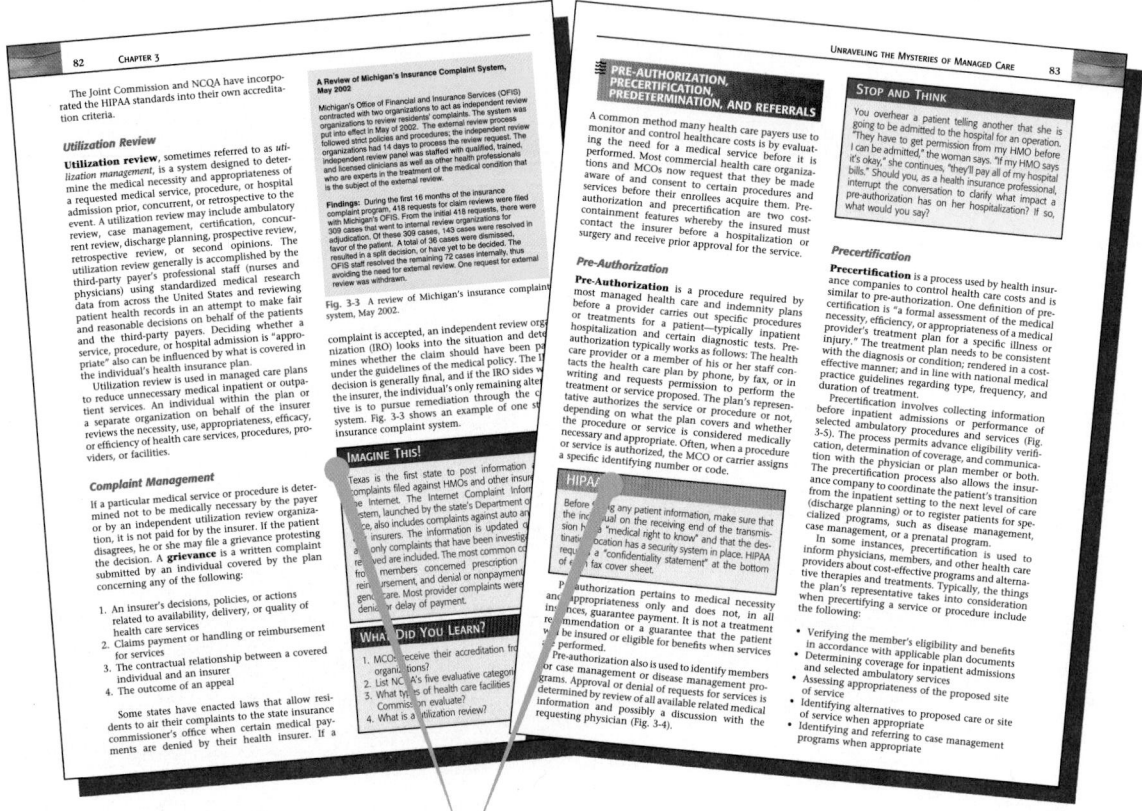

Special Information Boxes

Special information boxes are scattered throughout each chapter and offer different ways of thinking about the material you are learning.

- *What Did You Learn?* boxes contain review questions following each section within a chapter.
- *Imagine This!* boxes allow you to apply information you have just learned to real-life situations.
- *Stop and Think* boxes ask you to read and study a particular paragraph, then apply critical-thinking skills to resolve a problem or answer a question.
- *HIPAA Tips* boxes give periodic tips to help you better understand this very important piece of legislation, the Health Insurance Portability and Accountability Act (HIPAA).

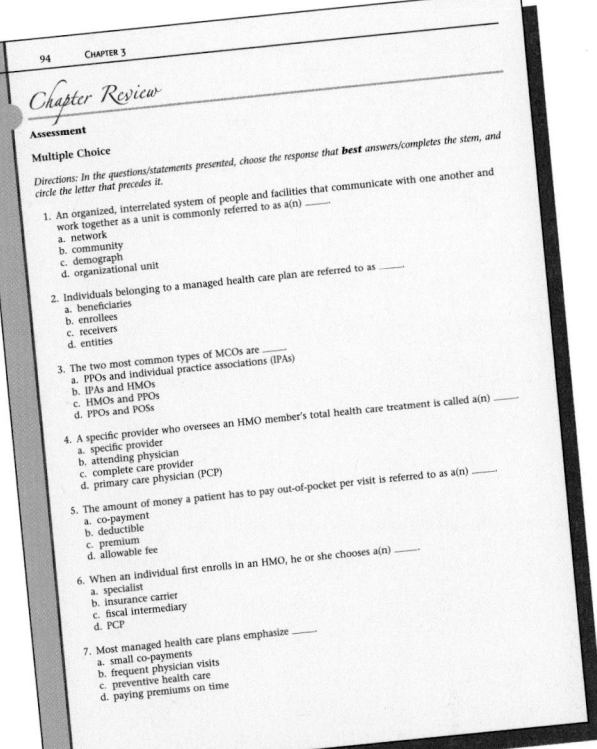

Chapter Review

A variety of exercises, including reviews of chapter terminology, theory, and critical-thinking, are included at the end of each chapter to help you test your knowledge. Many chapter reviews also include case studies to give you the opportunity to apply your recently gained knowledge to real-life situations. Your instructor can check your work on the chapter review section.

Appendixes

Appendixes include competency checklists. The competency checklists are organized into two groups. Core Competency Checklists should be used for the core skills that you will be practicing in every module, such as taking vital signs, giving injections, and using the *Physician's Desk Reference*. These are followed by the Procedure Competency Checklists, which are unique to the topics you are learning in this module. Each group of checklists comes with a Grade Sheet to summarize your performance scores when demonstrating your competencies to your instructor.

CONTENTS

MEDICAL ASSISTING
Health Insurance Basics and Claims Processing
Module H

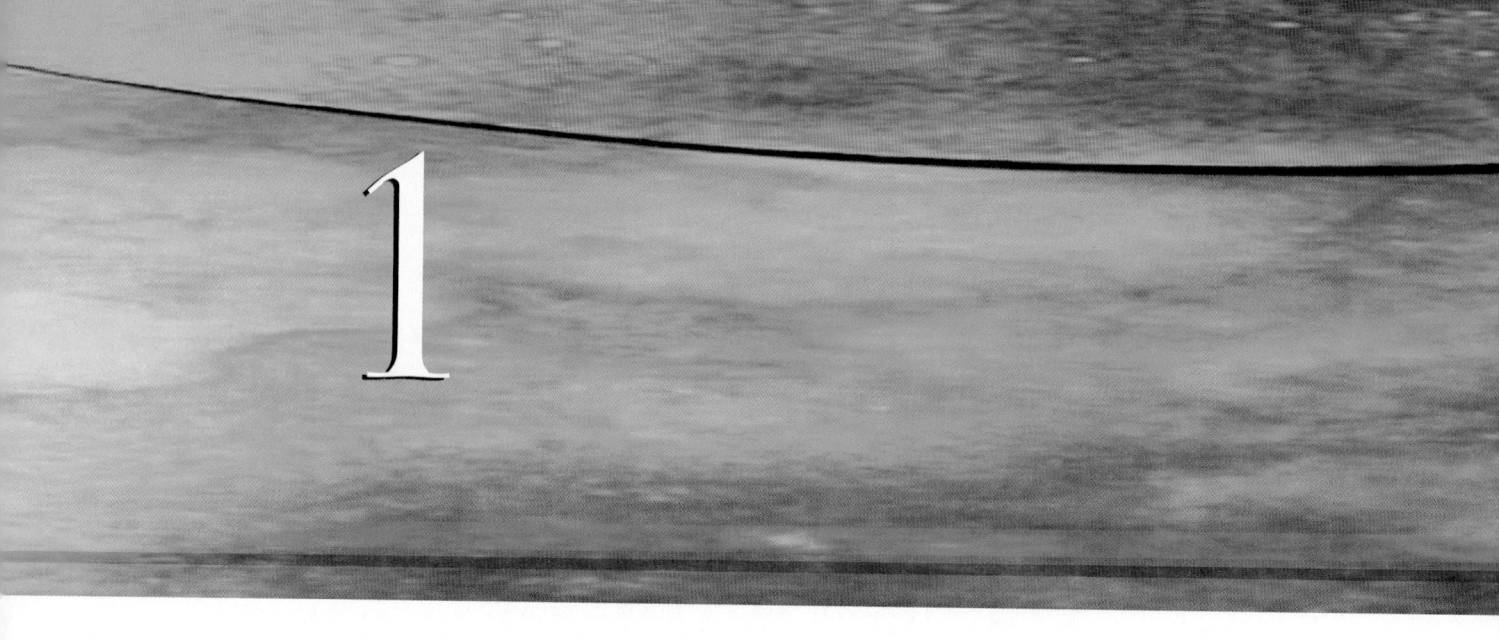

OBJECTIVES

After completion of this chapter, the student should be able to:

1. Explain how the CMS-1500 "universal" insurance claim form was developed.
2. Discuss the format of the form.
3. List the major rules necessary for optical character recognition.
4. Identify the necessary criteria for using the paper CMS-1500 form.
5. Describe each of the five documents needed for completion of the CMS-1500 form.
6. Apply general guidelines for completing a CMS-1500 paper form.
7. Discuss the importance of proofreading claims.
8. Explain the function of claims clearinghouses.
9. Compare and contrast the use of a clearinghouse versus direct claims submission.

The "Universal" Claim Form: CMS-1500

KEY TERMS

abstract
ASCII (American Standard Code for
  Information Interchange)
assign benefits
beneficiary
claims clearinghouse

clean claims
CMS-1500 (form)
demographic information
encounter form
mono-spaced fonts
OCR scannable

optical character recognition (OCR)
patient ledger card
release of information
small provider
waiver

Opening Scenario

Emilio Sanchez and Latisha Howard are enrolled in a health insurance course at a career school in their area. Emilio graduated from high school just last year and knew immediately what career path he wanted to pursue—health insurance administration. Latisha has worked in the health care field for 5 years as a nursing assistant, but she injured her back lifting a patient and had to give up her job at a long-term care facility. Because her experience lies in health care, she decided to stay in this discipline but pursue a different avenue that did not involve physical exertion.

In the class in which they are enrolled, the facilitator allows students to progress at their own speed; Emilio and Latisha found that they work well together, and they work at about the same pace. Both students feel comfortable that they know the material covered in Unit I well enough to move on to Unit II and continue with their learning experience in health insurance.

After reading over the outline for Chapter 1, Emilio and Latisha agree that the idea of using a universal form for all health insurance claims makes good sense, but knowing what information to enter in each of the 33 blocks is puzzling at this point. They also are curious to learn how information from a patient's health record can be adapted to this form. They reassure each other, however, that completing the CMS-1500 form should become routine with practice.

UNIVERSAL INSURANCE CLAIM FORM

A major innovation that made the process of health insurance claims submission simpler was the development of a universal form. Before the emergence of this universal form, every insurance carrier had its own specialized type of paperwork for submitting claims. Imagine the frustration a health insurance professional must have felt trying to figure out how to complete all these different forms properly. In the mid-1970s, the Health Care Financing Administration (HCFA [pronounced "hick-fa"]) created a new form for Medicare claims, called the HCFA-1500. The form was approved by the American Medical Association Council on Medical Services and subsequently was adopted by all government health care programs.

Although the HCFA-1500 originally was developed for submitting Medicare claims, it eventually was accepted by most commercial/private insurance carriers to facilitate the standardization of the claims process. Because HCFA is now called the Center for Medicare and Medicaid Services (CMS), the name of the form has been changed to **CMS-1500**; however, it is basically the same document.

The National Uniform Claim Committee (NUCC) and the National Uniform Billing Committee (NUBC) have revised the CMS-1500 universal form. The original form, initiated in 1990, was referred to as CMS-1500 (12-90). The revised version is called the CMS-1500 (08-05). The new form is very similar to the original form, but there are new areas to place national provider identifier (NPI) numbers for the Referring Provider (Box 17a), Service Facility Location Information (Box 32), and Billing Provider Information (Box 33). The NUCC established May 23, 2007, as the deadline for mandatory use of the revised CMS-1500 (08-05) form. After the new form is implemented, claims submitted on the CMS-1500 (12-90) form will be rejected.

Fig. 1-1 shows the front and back sides of the official CMS-1500 (08-05) form. Additional information regarding the revised form is available at the NUCC website listed under Websites to Explore at the end of this chapter.

HIPAA TIP

Any person or organization that furnishes bills or is paid for health care electronically in the normal course of business falls under HIPAA rules and regulations.

CMS-1500 Paper Form

Format of the Form

The CMS-1500 form is an 8½ × 11-inch, two-sided document. The front side is printed in **OCR scannable** red ink; the back side contains instructions

1500

HEALTH INSURANCE CLAIM FORM

APPROVED BY NATIONAL UNIFORM CLAIM COMMITTEE 08/05

PICA

PICA

1. MEDICARE MEDICAID TRICARE CHAMPUS CHAMPVA GROUP HEALTH PLAN FECA BLK LUNG OTHER
(Medicare #) (Medicaid #) (Sponsor's SSN) (Member ID#) (SSN or ID) (SSN) (ID)

1a. INSURED'S I.D. NUMBER   (For Program in Item 1)

2. PATIENT'S NAME (Last Name, First Name, Middle Initial)

3. PATIENT'S BIRTH DATE   SEX
MM   DD   YY   M   F

4. INSURED'S NAME (Last Name, First Name, Middle Initial)

5. PATIENT'S ADDRESS (No., Street)

6. PATIENT RELATIONSHIP TO INSURED
Self   Spouse   Child   Other

7. INSURED'S ADDRESS (No., Street)

CITY   STATE

8. PATIENT STATUS
Single   Married   Other

Employed   Full-Time Student   Part-Time Student

CITY   STATE

ZIP CODE   TELEPHONE (Include Area Code)
(   )

ZIP CODE   TELEPHONE (Include Area Code)
(   )

9. OTHER INSURED'S NAME (Last Name, First Name, Middle Initial)

10. IS PATIENT'S CONDITION RELATED TO:

11. INSURED'S POLICY GROUP OR FECA NUMBER

a. OTHER INSURED'S POLICY OR GROUP NUMBER

a. EMPLOYMENT? (Current or Previous)
YES   NO

a. INSURED'S DATE OF BIRTH   SEX
MM   DD   YY   M   F

b. OTHER INSURED'S DATE OF BIRTH   SEX
MM   DD   YY   M   F

b. AUTO ACCIDENT?   PLACE (State)
YES   NO

b. EMPLOYER'S NAME OR SCHOOL NAME

c. EMPLOYER'S NAME OR SCHOOL NAME

c. OTHER ACCIDENT?
YES   NO

c. INSURANCE PLAN NAME OR PROGRAM NAME

d. INSURANCE PLAN NAME OR PROGRAM NAME

10d. RESERVED FOR LOCAL USE

d. IS THERE ANOTHER HEALTH BENEFIT PLAN?
YES   NO   **If yes**, return to and complete item 9 a-d.

READ BACK OF FORM BEFORE COMPLETING & SIGNING THIS FORM.
12. PATIENT'S OR AUTHORIZED PERSON'S SIGNATURE I authorize the release of any medical or other information necessary to process this claim. I also request payment of government benefits either to myself or to the party who accepts assignment below.

SIGNED _____ DATE _____

13. INSURED'S OR AUTHORIZED PERSON'S SIGNATURE I authorize payment of medical benefits to the undersigned physician or supplier for services described below.

SIGNED _____

14. DATE OF CURRENT: ILLNESS (First symptom) OR INJURY (Accident) OR PREGNANCY(LMP)
MM   DD   YY

15. IF PATIENT HAS HAD SAME OR SIMILAR ILLNESS. GIVE FIRST DATE   MM   DD   YY

16. DATES PATIENT UNABLE TO WORK IN CURRENT OCCUPATION
MM   DD   YY   MM   DD   YY
FROM   TO

17. NAME OF REFERRING PROVIDER OR OTHER SOURCE

17a.
17b. NPI

18. HOSPITALIZATION DATES RELATED TO CURRENT SERVICES
MM   DD   YY   MM   DD   YY
FROM   TO

19. RESERVED FOR LOCAL USE

20. OUTSIDE LAB? $ CHARGES
YES   NO

21. DIAGNOSIS OR NATURE OF ILLNESS OR INJURY (Relate Items 1, 2, 3 or 4 to Item 24E by Line)

1. |___.___   3. |___.___

2. |___.___   4. |___.___

22. MEDICAID RESUBMISSION CODE   ORIGINAL REF. NO.

23. PRIOR AUTHORIZATION NUMBER

24. A. DATE(S) OF SERVICE		B. PLACE OF SERVICE	C. EMG	D. PROCEDURES, SERVICES, OR SUPPLIES (Explain Unusual Circumstances)		E. DIAGNOSIS POINTER	F. $ CHARGES	G. DAYS OR UNITS	H. EPSDT Family Plan	I. ID. QUAL.	J. RENDERING PROVIDER ID. #
From MM DD YY	To MM DD YY			CPT/HCPCS	MODIFIER						
1										NPI	
2										NPI	
3										NPI	
4										NPI	
5										NPI	
6										NPI	

25. FEDERAL TAX I.D. NUMBER   SSN EIN

26. PATIENT'S ACCOUNT NO.

27. ACCEPT ASSIGNMENT? (For govt. claims, see back)
YES   NO

28. TOTAL CHARGE
$

29. AMOUNT PAID
$

30. BALANCE DUE
$

31. SIGNATURE OF PHYSICIAN OR SUPPLIER INCLUDING DEGREES OR CREDENTIALS
(I certify that the statements on the reverse apply to this bill and are made a part thereof.)

SIGNED _____ DATE _____

32. SERVICE FACILITY LOCATION INFORMATION

a. NPI   b.

33. BILLING PROVIDER INFO & PH # (   )

a. NPI   b.

NUCC Instruction Manual available at: www.nucc.org

APPROVED OMB-0938-0999 FORM CMS-1500 (08/05)

CARRIER

PATIENT AND INSURED INFORMATION

PHYSICIAN OR SUPPLIER INFORMATION

Fig. 1-1 Front and back of a blank CMS-1500 (red ink) form.

Continued

BECAUSE THIS FORM IS USED BY VARIOUS GOVERNMENT AND PRIVATE HEALTH PROGRAMS, SEE SEPARATE INSTRUCTIONS ISSUED BY APPLICABLE PROGRAMS.

NOTICE: Any person who knowingly files a statement of claim containing any misrepresentation or any false, incomplete or misleading information may be guilty of a criminal act punishable under law and may be subject to civil penalties.

REFERS TO GOVERNMENT PROGRAMS ONLY

MEDICARE AND CHAMPUS PAYMENTS: A patient's signature requests that payment be made and authorizes release of any information necessary to process the claim and certifies that the information provided in Blocks 1 through 12 is true, accurate and complete. In the case of a Medicare claim, the patient's signature authorizes any entity to release to Medicare medical and nonmedical information, including employment status, and whether the person has employer group health insurance, liability, no-fault, worker's compensation or other insurance which is responsible to pay for the services for which the Medicare claim is made. See 42 CFR 411.24(a). If item 9 is completed, the patient's signature authorizes release of the information to the health plan or agency shown. In Medicare assigned or CHAMPUS participation cases, the physician agrees to accept the charge determination of the Medicare carrier or CHAMPUS fiscal intermediary as the full charge, and the patient is responsible only for the deductible, coinsurance and noncovered services. Coinsurance and the deductible are based upon the charge determination of the Medicare carrier or CHAMPUS fiscal intermediary if this is less than the charge submitted. CHAMPUS is not a health insurance program but makes payment for health benefits provided through certain affiliations with the Uniformed Services. Information on the patient's sponsor should be provided in those items captioned in "Insured"; i.e., items 1a, 4, 6, 7, 9, and 11.

BLACK LUNG AND FECA CLAIMS

The provider agrees to accept the amount paid by the Government as payment in full. See Black Lung and FECA instructions regarding required procedure and diagnosis coding systems.

SIGNATURE OF PHYSICIAN OR SUPPLIER (MEDICARE, CHAMPUS, FECA AND BLACK LUNG)

I certify that the services shown on this form were medically indicated and necessary for the health of the patient and were personally furnished by me or were furnished incident to my professional service by my employee under my immediate personal supervision, except as otherwise expressly permitted by Medicare or CHAMPUS regulations.

For services to be considered as "incident" to a physician's professional service, 1) they must be rendered under the physician's immediate personal supervision by his/her employee, 2) they must be an integral, although incidental part of a covered physician's service, 3) they must be of kinds commonly furnished in physician's offices, and 4) the services of nonphysicians must be included on the physician's bills.

For CHAMPUS claims, I further certify that I (or any employee) who rendered services am not an active duty member of the Uniformed Services or a civilian employee of the United States Government or a contract employee of the United States Government, either civilian or military (refer to 5 USC 5536). For Black-Lung claims, I further certify that the services performed were for a Black Lung-related disorder.

No Part B Medicare benefits may be paid unless this form is received as required by existing law and regulations (42 CFR 424.32).

NOTICE: Any one who misrepresents or falsifies essential information to receive payment from Federal funds requested by this form may upon conviction be subject to fine and imprisonment under applicable Federal laws.

NOTICE TO PATIENT ABOUT THE COLLECTION AND USE OF MEDICARE, CHAMPUS, FECA, AND BLACK LUNG INFORMATION
(PRIVACY ACT STATEMENT)

We are authorized by CMS, CHAMPUS and OWCP to ask you for information needed in the administration of the Medicare, CHAMPUS, FECA, and Black Lung programs. Authority to collect information is in section 205(a), 1862, 1872 and 1874 of the Social Security Act as amended, 42 CFR 411.24(a) and 424.5(a) (6), and 44 USC 3101;41 CFR 101 et seq and 10 USC 1079 and 1086; 5 USC 8101 et seq; and 30 USC 901 et seq; 38 USC 613; E.O. 9397.

The information we obtain to complete claims under these programs is used to identify you and to determine your eligibility. It is also used to decide if the services and supplies you received are covered by these programs and to insure that proper payment is made.

The information may also be given to other providers of services, carriers, intermediaries, medical review boards, health plans, and other organizations or Federal agencies, for the effective administration of Federal provisions that require other third parties payers to pay primary to Federal program, and as otherwise necessary to administer these programs. For example, it may be necessary to disclose information about the benefits you have used to a hospital or doctor. Additional disclosures are made through routine uses for information contained in systems of records.

FOR MEDICARE CLAIMS: See the notice modifying system No. 09-70-0501, titled, 'Carrier Medicare Claims Record,' published in the Federal Register, Vol. 55 No. 177, pages 37549, Wed. Sept. 12, 1990, or as updated and republished.

FOR OWCP CLAIMS: Department of Labor, Privacy Act of 1974, "Republication of Notice of Systems of Records," Federal Register Vol. 55 No. 40, Wed. Feb. 28, 1990, See ESA-5, ESA-6, ESA-12, ESA-13, ESA-30, or as updated and republished.

FOR CHAMPUS CLAIMS: PRINCIPAL PURPOSE(S): To evaluate eligibility for medical care provided by civilian sources and to issue payment upon establishment of eligibility and determination that the services/supplies received are authorized by law.

ROUTINE USE(S): Information from claims and related documents may be given to the Dept. of Veterans Affairs, the Dept. of Health and Human Services and/or the Dept. of Transportation consistent with their statutory administrative responsibilities under CHAMPUS/CHAMPVA; to the Dept. of Justice for representation of the Secretary of Defense in civil actions; to the Internal Revenue Service, private collection agencies, and consumer reporting agencies in connection with recoupment claims; and to Congressional Offices in response to inquiries made at the request of the person to whom a record pertains. Appropriate disclosures may be made to other federal, state, local, foreign government agencies, private business entities, and individual providers of care, on matters relating to entitlement, claims adjudication, fraud, program abuse, utilization review, quality assurance, peer review, program integrity, third-party liability, coordination of benefits, and civil and criminal litigation related to the operation of CHAMPUS.

DISCLOSURES: Voluntary; however, failure to provide information will result in delay in payment or may result in denial of claim. With the one exception discussed below, there are no penalties under these programs for refusing to supply information. However, failure to furnish information regarding the medical services rendered or the amount charged would prevent payment of claims under these programs. Failure to furnish any other information, such as name or claim number, would delay payment of the claim. Failure to provide medical information under FECA could be deemed an obstruction.

It is mandatory that you tell us if you know that another party is responsible for paying for your treatment. Section 1128B of the Social Security Act and 31 USC 3801-3812 provide penalties for withholding this information.

You should be aware that P.L. 100-503, the "Computer Matching and Privacy Protection Act of 1988", permits the government to verify information by way of computer matches.

MEDICAID PAYMENTS (PROVIDER CERTIFICATION)

I hereby agree to keep such records as are necessary to disclose fully the extent of services provided to individuals under the State's Title XIX plan and to furnish information regarding any payments claimed for providing such services as the State Agency or Dept. of Health and Human Services may request.

I further agree to accept, as payment in full, the amount paid by the Medicaid program for those claims submitted for payment under that program, with the exception of authorized deductible, coinsurance, co-payment or similar cost-sharing charge.

SIGNATURE OF PHYSICIAN (OR SUPPLIER): I certify that the services listed above were medically indicated and necessary to the health of this patient and were personally furnished by me or my employee under my personal direction.

NOTICE: This is to certify that the foregoing information is true, accurate and complete. I understand that payment and satisfaction of this claim will be from Federal and State funds, and that any false claims, statements, or documents, or concealment of a material fact, may be prosecuted under applicable Federal or State laws.

According to the Paperwork Reduction Act of 1995, no persons are required to respond to a collection of information unless it displays a valid OMB control number. The valid OMB control number for this information collection is 0938-0008. The time required to complete this information collection is estimated to average 10 minutes per response, including the time to review instructions, search existing data resources, gather the data needed, and complete and review the information collection. If you have any comments concerning the accuracy of the time estimate(s) or suggestions for improving this form, please write to: CMS, N2-14-26, 7500 Security Boulevard, Baltimore, Maryland 21244-1850.

Fig. 1-1, cont'd

for various government and private health programs. There are two sections to the CMS-1500 form; the top portion is for the patient/insured information (Blocks 1-13); the bottom portion is for the physician/supplier information (Blocks 14-33). Later, in the section titled "Completing the CMS-1500 Paper Form," the student learns what typically goes in each block. Keep in mind, however, that there are minor differences from one major payer to another; these are pointed out in the individual chapters pertaining to the particular major carrier.

Optical Character Recognition

In most instances, when the paper CMS-1500 form is prepared for submission, **optical character recognition (OCR)** formatting guidelines should be used. OCR is the recognition of printed or written text characters by a computer. This involves photo scanning of the text character by character, analysis of the scanned-in image, and translation of the character image into character codes, such as **ASCII (American Standard Code for Information Interchange)**. ASCII is the most common format used for text files in computers and on the Internet.

In OCR processing, the scanned-in image is analyzed for light and dark areas to identify each alphabetical letter or numerical digit. When a character is recognized, it is converted into an ASCII code. Special circuit boards and computer chips designed expressly for OCR are used to speed up the recognition process. The CMS-1500 form is printed in a special red ink to optimize this OCR process. When the form is scanned, everything in red "drops out," and the computer reads the information printed within the blocks.

Using Optical Character Recognition Format Rules

Because many third-party carriers use OCR scanning for reading health insurance claims, the health insurance professional should complete all paper CMS-1500 forms using the specific rules for preparing a document for OCR scanning. OCR works best with originals or very clear copies and **monospaced fonts** (in which each character takes up exactly the same amount of space); standard mono-

spaced type fonts (such as Courier) in 12-point font size and black text are recommended. No special formatting, such as bold, italics, or underline, should be used, and extreme care should be taken when keying the information. Type should be lined up so that all entries and characters fall within the spaces provided on the form.

The following are specific guidelines for preparing OCR scannable claims:

- Use all uppercase (capital) letters.
- Omit all punctuation.
- Use the MM DD YYYY format (with a space—not a dash—between each set of digits) for dates of birth.
- Use a *space* instead of the usual punctuation or symbols for
  - dollar signs and decimal points in fee charges and ICD-9 codes,
  - a dash preceding a procedure code modifier,
  - parentheses around the telephone area code, and
  - hyphens in Social Security and employer identification numbers.
- Omit titles and other designations, such as Sr., Jr., II, or III, unless they appear on the patient's identification (ID) card.
- Use two zeros in the cents column when the charge is expressed in whole dollars.
- Do not use lift-off tape, correction tape, or whiteout.
- Photocopied forms and forms printed from a color printer are unacceptable.

A section of the CMS-1500 form showing the proper OCR format is shown in Fig. 1-2.

When the health insurance professional has completed the claim form, the form needs to be examined thoroughly for errors and omissions. If you are new to the profession, it is recommended that you ask a co-worker or supervisor to proofread forms before submission until you acquire the necessary proficiency in the claims process. The most important task for which the health insurance professional is responsible is to obtain the maximum

Fig. 1-2 Section of the CMS-1500 form illustrating proper optical character recognition format.

- Improper identification of patient, either the insurance identification number or name
- Missing or invalid subscriber's name and/or birth date
- Missing or incomplete name, address, and identifier of an ordering provider, rendering, or referring provider (or others)
- Invalid provider NPI identifier (when needed) for rendering providers, referring providers, or others
- Missing "insurance type code" for secondary coverage (This information, such as a spouse's payer, is important for filing primary claims in addition to secondary claims.)
- Pre-authorization codes missing
- Missing payer name and/or payer identifier, required for both primary and secondary payers
- Invalid diagnostic and/or procedure code(s)
- Missing or invalid admission date for inpatient services
- Missing or incomplete service facility name, address, and identification for services rendered outside the office or home, including invalid Zip Codes or two-letter state abbreviations
- Failing to include necessary documentation when needed
- Filing the claim after the deadline date

Fig. 1-3 List of common errors and omissions on the CMS-1500 claim form.

amount of reimbursement in the minimal amount of time that the medical record supports. Fig. 1-3 shows common CMS-1500 claim form errors and omissions.

If a claim is being resubmitted, most carriers require a new one using the original (red print) CMS-1500 form. Additional tips for submitting paper claims include the following:

- Do not include any handwritten data (other than signatures) on the forms.
- Do not staple anything to the form.

Who Uses the Paper CMS-1500 Form?

To improve the efficiency and effectiveness of the health care system, the Health Insurance Portability and Accountability Act (HIPAA) includes a series of administrative simplification provisions that require the Department of Health and Human Services (HHS) to adopt national standards for electronic health care transactions. By ensuring consistency throughout the industry, these national standards presumably make it easier for health care carriers, physicians, hospitals, and other health care providers to submit claims and other transactions electronically.

The HIPAA Administrative Simplification Compliance Act (ASCA) set the deadline for compliance with the HIPAA Electronic Healthcare Transactions and Code Set standards as October 2003, meaning that providers' offices must be computerized and capable of submitting all claims electronically by that date. ASCA prohibits the HHS from paying Medicare claims that are not submitted electronically after this date, unless the secretary of the HHS

(hereafter referred to as the *Secretary*) grants a **waiver** for this requirement. A waiver, in this case, would be if the Secretary formally tells a provider (usually in writing) that he or she does not have to comply with this regulation.

ASCA further stated that the Secretary must grant such a waiver if a provider had no method available for the submission of claims in electronic form or if the facility submitting the claim was a **small provider** of services or supplies. ASCA, according to the Centers for Medicare and Medicaid Services' website, defines a small provider or supplier as *a provider of services with fewer than 25 full-time equivalent employees or a physician, practitioner, facility, or supplier (other than a provider of services) with fewer than 10 full-time equivalent employees.*

This provision does not prevent providers from submitting paper claims to other health plans. It also states that if a provider transmits any claim electronically, it is subject to the HIPAA Administrative Simplification requirements, regardless of size. In other words, if a provider's office submits any claims electronically, ASCA says it must submit all claims electronically. It cannot submit some claims on paper and some electronically.

So, who uses the paper CMS-1500 form? If the provider falls into one of the two following categories, the paper CMS-1500 form can be used—but, remember, it has to be used exclusively with all carriers that have the capability of receiving electronic transmissions:

1. Providers who are not computerized and do not have the capability of submitting claims electronically still can use the paper version of the form.
2. "Small providers" who fit the previous italicized description still can use the paper version of the form.

HIPAA TIP

The "under 10" rule applies only to Medicare/Medicaid. If a medical facility has only one employee but is doing *anything* electronic, the office must be in compliance with HIPAA's privacy rules and regulations.

STOP AND THINK

We learned in this section that two categories of providers are exempt from the ASCA mandate that by October 2003, all claims must be submitted electronically. In your opinion, why are providers falling into these categories allowed to use the CMS-1500 paper form?

DOCUMENTS NEEDED WHEN COMPLETING THE CMS-1500 CLAIM FORM

Several documents are needed when completing the CMS-1500 claim form.

Patient Information Form

A patient information form, sometimes referred to as a *patient registration form*, is a document (typically one page) that patients seeking care at a health care facility are asked to complete for the following reasons:

1. To gather all necessary demographic information to aid the health care professional in providing appropriate treatment
2. To have a record of current insurance information for claim preparation and submission
3. To keep health records up-to-date

When the form is completed, it becomes an integral part of the patient's health record. This information form is considered a legal document and should be updated at least once a year. It is a good idea to ask returning patients if there have been any changes since they were last in the office. Fig. 1-4 shows a typical patient information form.

New Patient Information

Look at this section in the sample patient information form (see Fig. 1-4). It asks for general **demographic information**, such as name, address, Social Security number, and employment.

Insurance Section

The second section contains questions regarding the patient's insurance. Having the patient fill out the blanks in this section is important, but it is necessary also to request and make photocopies of the front and the back of the patient's insurance ID card. The ID card often lists additional information that patients might not routinely include on the form, such as telephone numbers for preauthorization or precertification. Also, it is common for patients to transpose or omit identifying alpha characters or numbers or both.

Additional Insurance

In some cases, patients may be covered under more than one insurance policy. Most patient information forms have a separate section where additional insurance is listed. Information from a secondary insurance policy should be included in this section, including the name of the policy, the policyholder's name, and the policy numbers. It is important for the health insurance professional to confirm that the "additional insurance" is secondary. Some patients, particularly elderly patients, can become confused over the technicalities of dual insurance coverage. If the patient is uncertain which of the policies is primary and which is secondary, the health insurance professional may have to telephone one or both of the insuring agencies to find out.

Insurance Authorization and Assignment

The section on insurance authorization and assignment should be completed and signed by the patient or responsible party, in the case of a minor or mentally disabled individual. This section gives the health care professional the authorization to release the information necessary to complete the insurance claim form. It also "assigns benefits"—that is, it authorizes the insurance company to send the payment directly to the health care professional. This authorization should be updated at least once a year, unless it is a "lifetime" **release of information** worded specifically for Medicare claims.

Patient Insurance Identification Card

Every insurance company has a unique ID card that it issues to its subscribers. With Medicare, every individual (referred to as a **beneficiary**) has his or her own individual card. Other insurers, such as Blue Cross and Blue Shield, may issue a card that covers not only the subscriber but also his or her spouse and any dependents included on the policy. This coverage is referred to as a *family plan*. As mentioned previously, at the same time the patient completes the information form, the health insurance professional should ask to see the patient's insurance ID card and make a photocopy of it to keep in the health record.

It is important always to make sure you copy the front and the back of the ID card, if there is information on the back. On subsequent visits, ask the patient if there is any change in coverage. If so, ask for and make a copy of the new card. The rationale for this procedure is to have complete and correct insurance information on file for the purpose of

ACCOUNT # _____

PATIENT # _____

NEW PATIENT INFORMATION   DATE _____

PATIENT'S NAME (PLEASE PRINT)	S.S. #	MARITAL STATUS					SEX		BIRTH DATE	AGE
		S	M	W	D	SEP	M	F		
STREET ADDRESS PERMANENT TEMPORARY	CITY AND STATE						ZIP CODE		HOME PHONE#	
PATIENT'S EMPLOYER	OCCUPATION (INDICATE IF STUDENT)						HOW LONG EMPLOYED		BUS. PHONE # EXT. #	
EMPLOYER'S STREET ADDRESS	CITY AND STATE								ZIP CODE	
DRUG ALLERGIES, IF ANY	PHARMACY								PHARMACY PHONE #	
SPOUSE OR PARENT'S NAME	S.S. #								BIRTH DATE	
SPOUSE OR PARENT'S EMPLOYER	OCCUPATION (INDICATED IF STUDENT)						HOW LONG EMPLOYED		BUS. PHONE #	
EMPLOYER'S STREET ADDRESS	CITY AND STATE								ZIP CODE	
*SPOUSE'S STREET ADDRESS, IF DIVORCED OR SEPARATED	CITY AND STATE						ZIP CODE		HOME PHONE #	

PLEASE READ: ALL CHARGES ARE DUE AT THE TIME OF SERVICES. IF HOSPITALIZATION IS INDICATED, THE PATIENT IS RESPONSIBLE FOR FURNISHING INSURANCE CLAIM FORMS TO THE OFFICE PRIOR TO HOSPITALIZATION.

REFERRED BY	STREET ADDRESS, CITY, STATE		ZIP CODE	PHONE #
BLUE SHIELD (GIVE NAME OF POLICYHOLDER) ☐	☐ ALLIANCE ☐ OTHER ☐ ALLIANCE SELECT	BIRTH DATE	POLICY #	
OTHER (WRITE IN NAME OF INSURANCE COMPANY) ☐	NAME OF POLICYHOLDER	BIRTH DATE	POLICY #	
OTHER (WRITE IN NAME OF INSURANCE COMPANY) ☐	NAME OF POLICYHOLDER	BIRTH DATE	POLICY #	
MEDICARE # ☐	RAILROAD RETIREMENT # ☐		MEDICAID # ☐	
INDUSTRIAL ☐	WERE YOU INJURED ON THE JOB? ☐ YES ☐ NO	DATE OF INJURY	INDUSTRIAL CLAIM #	
ACCIDENT ☐	WAS AN AUTOMOBILE INVOLVED? ☐ YES ☐ NO	DATE OF ACCIDENT	NAME OF ATTORNEY	
WERE X-RAYS TAKEN OF THIS INJURY OR PROBLEM? ☐ YES ☐ NO	IF YES, WHERE WERE X-RAYS TAKEN? (HOSPITAL, ETC.)			DATE X-RAYS TAKEN
HAS ANY MEMBER OF YOUR IMMEDIATE FAMILY BEEN TREATED BY OUR PHYSICIAN(S) BEFORE? INCLUDE NAME OF PHYSICIAN AND FAMILY MEMBER.				
NEAREST RELATIVE OR FRIEND NOT RESIDING WITH YOU	STREET ADDRESS, CITY, STATE		ZIP CODE	PHONE #

ALL PROFESSIONAL SERVICES RENDERED ARE CHARGED TO THE PATIENT. NECESSARY FORMS WILL BE COMPLETED TO HELP EXPEDITE INSURANCE CARRIER PAYMENTS. HOWEVER, THE PATIENT IS RESPONSIBLE FOR ALL FEES, REGARDLESS OF INSURANCE COVERAGE. IT IS ALSO CUSTOMARY TO PAY FOR SERVICES WHEN RENDERED UNLESS OTHER ARRANGEMENTS HAVE BEEN MADE IN ADVANCE WITH OUR OFFICE BOOKKEEPER.

INSURANCE AUTHORIZATION AND ASSIGNMENT

Name of Policy Holder_____   HIC Number _____

I request that payment of authorized Medicare/Other Insurance company benefits be made either to me or on my behalf to _____ for any services furnished me by that party who accepts assignment/physician. Regulations pertaining to Medicare assignment of benefits apply. I authorize any holder of medical or other information about me to release to the Social Security Administration and Health Care Financing Administration or its intermediaries or carriers any information needed for this or a related Medicare claim/other Insurance Company claim. I permit a copy of this authorization to be used in place of the original, and request payment of medical insurance benefits either to myself or to the party who accepts assignment. I understand it is mandatory to notify the health care provider of any other party who may be responsible for paying for my treatment. (Section 1128B of the Social Security Act and 31 U.S.C. 3801-3812 provides penalties for withholding this information.)

Signature_____   Date_____

Accounts past 60 days will accrue an interest charge.   NEW PATIENT INFORMATION

Fig. 1-4 Typical patient information form.

completing the CMS-1500 claim. It also is helpful for obtaining telephone numbers to contact for pre-authorization/precertification from the carrier if certain procedures or inpatient hospitalization is required. Fig. 1-5 shows the front and back sides of a typical insurance ID card.

Patient Health Record

After the patient information form is completed, the health insurance professional should examine it to ensure that all necessary information has been entered and that the entries are legible. The form is

Iowa Med Co.

	HOSPITAL	EMERGENCY ROOM
GROUP NUMBER	CO-PAY	CO-PAY
17098-020-00004	$ .00	$ 50.00

MEMBER   MEMBER NUMBER
LINDA L. FUHR   H-550-XX-5072-02

PRIMARY CARE PHYSICIAN   OFFICE VISIT
GEOFF LOMAN   CO-PAY
                                $10.00

ABC INSURANCE COMPANY
P.O. BOX 12340   **IMPORTANT**
FRESNO   CA   93765   **INFORMATION**
                                        ON REVERSE

FOR BENEFITS, ELIGIBILITY AND
CLAIMS CALL MEMBER SERVICES: 1-800-XXX-XXXX
FOR PRECERTIFICATION AND
REFERRALS CALL: 1-800-XXX-XXXX

PAYER NUMBER   60054 0106

RX COPAY $10.00   RX GROUP NUMBER 0067-0000   PHARMACY
PLAN

For mental health services, call 1-800-424-4047

Member: Co-pays and higher benefits apply to services rendered by your
primary care physician (PCP) or through your PCP's referral. Call your PCP
in advance for an appointment. If a life threatening emergency exists, seek
immediate attention. If admitted, call Member Services within 48 hours.
When not referred by your PCP, you are responsible for any precertification
required by your plan. For you or your physician to obtain precertification,
call Member Services. Failure to obtain precertification may result in
reduced benefits.
Providers: Call Member Services to verify eligibility; this card does not
guarantee coverage. In case of an emergency, notify Member Services the
next business day.
This plan is administered by ABC Insurance Company.

Fig. 1-5 Insurance ID card.

customarily placed in the patient's health record near the front so that the health insurance professional has easy access to it when it is time to complete and submit a claim. Details of the patient medical record are discussed in Chapter 14. A medical record is an account of a patient's medical assessment, investigation, and course of treatment. It is a source of information and a vital component in quality patient care. A complete medical record should

- outline the reason for the patient's visit to the health care professional,
- document the health care professional's findings,
- include a detailed discussion of the recommended treatment,
- provide information to any referring physician or other health care provider,
- serve as a teaching or research tool (or both), and
- provide a means for assessing the quality of care by the practitioner or other health care provider.

The clinical chart note illustrated in Fig. 1-6 is a typical example taken from a patient's health record.

BROWN, SARA J.   DOB 11/27/1989   CURRENT DATE: 12/03/2001

HX: This 12-year-old white female presents to the clinic today for chief complaint of fever, chills, sweats, temperature recorded up to 101.5°, mild earache, stuffy nose, sinus pain and pressure, and an episodic cough that is worse in the evening, wheezing, shortness of breath, or dyspnea that started approximately five days ago.
PAIN ASSESSMENT: Scale 0-10, zero.
ALLERGIES: NKA.
CURRENT MEDS: None.
PE: NAD. Ambulatory. Appears well.
   VS: T: 98.2°
   ENT: TMs:The TMs appear dull, primarily on the left as opposed to the right but without erythema, bulging, or retraction.
   NOSE: Minimal nasal congestion, slightly inflamed nasal mucosa.
   SINUS: Mild tenderness in the maxillary and frontal sinus areas to palpation and percussion.
   THROAT: Clear without tonsillar enlargement, inflammation, or exudate.
   NECK: Supple, not rigid, without adenopathy or thyropathy.
   LUNGS: CTA all fields with good breath sounds heard throughout. No wheezes or rales. Occasional upper bronchial rhonchi noted on examination that clear with cough. Respiratory excursion is symmetric and equal. No respiratory stridor or costal retractions. Normal vocal fremitus without egophony change. Peak flow 300, 350, 350. O_2 saturation 98%.
   SKIN: Warm to touch, good turgor, without viral-like exanthemas, petechiae, or purpura.
IMP: URI with mild sinusitis, possibly allergy-related.
PLAN: The patient was started on Allegra 60 mg 1 p.o. b.i.d., given samples for 10 days, Septra DS 1 p.o. b.i.d. #20 given. Regular diet and activity as tolerated, force fluids. Recommended that they humidify the room. Routine follow up in 10 days or sooner if her symptoms worsen.
RTN PRN

Frank O. McDermott
Frank O. McDermott, M.D./jj

Fig. 1-6   Clinical (chart) notes from a patient's health record.

Tammy Butler visited Dr. Harold Norton, her family care provider, on February 10, for her yearly wellness examination plus routine diagnostics. Dr. Norton's health insurance professional submitted the claim the day after the visit. A month later, Tammy received an explanation of benefits (EOB) from her health insurer indicating that the services were not covered under her policy. Assuming that her policy did not cover wellness examinations, Tammy forgot about it. During Christmas vacation of that same year, Tammy again visited Dr. Norton for a case of sinusitis. The claim was denied again by her insurer. Puzzled that a second claim had been denied, Tammy contacted Dr. Norton's office and, after some extensive research, learned that they had filed her claims under an old ID number from a previous employer. The problem now was that it was now January of a new year—past the deadline for filing claims for the previous year. The health insurance professional at Dr. Norton's office informed Tammy that she was responsible for the charges.

STOP AND THINK

In the scenario in Imagine This!, do you agree with Dr. Norton's health insurance professional that Tammy is responsible for the charges on the two visits in question? What should the health insurance professional have done to prevent this?

Encounter Form

We have discussed three of the items necessary for completing the CMS-1500 form. Now we look at a document used by most medical practices, which is often referred to as the **encounter form**. This multipurpose billing form is known by many names (e.g., superbill, routing form, patient service slip). The encounter form can be customized to medical specialties and preprinted with common diagnoses and procedures for that particular specialty. Fig. 1-7 shows an example of an encounter form.

Typically, this form is clipped to the front of the patient's medical record before the patient is seen in the clinical area. A variety of information is included on the form shown in Fig. 1-7, including the following:

- Demographic
- Accounting
- Professional services rendered
- CPT and ICD-9 codes
- Professional fees
- Return appointment information

It is important that the sections dealing with professional services and diagnostic and procedure codes be updated annually so that revised codes are changed, new codes are added, and old codes are deleted.

The following is a typical routine in many medical offices. Each morning, the medical records clerk (or whichever member of the health care team is in charge of this task) prepares the health records for the patients who are to be seen that day. An encounter form is attached to the front of each record, and any areas on the form regarding the date of service, patient demographics, and accounting information are filled out. (If computerized patient accounting software is used, this is printed automatically on the form.) Each encounter form has a number (usually at the top), which serves as an identifier for that particular patient visit.

As each patient is seen in the clinical area, the health care provider indicates on the form what services or procedures were performed along with the corresponding fees. The provider signs the encounter form and indicates if and when the patient needs to return or have any follow-up tests. It is important that the encounter form be checked for accuracy, after which the medical receptionist totals the day's charges, enters any payment received, and calculates the balance due.

The patient receives a copy of the completed encounter form, and a copy is retained in the medical office for accounting purposes and future reference in case any question comes up regarding that particular visit. Many offices file these forms by number within files that are separated into months and days. Medical offices are subject to accounting and insurance audits. The original encounter form can be requested by auditors to verify services rendered on any patient or on any date of service. A few insurance companies still accept the original encounter form for claim payment; in some cases, an insurer asks that a copy of the encounter form be included with the CMS-1500 claim form.

Patient Ledger Card

In offices that do not use computerized patient accounting software, **a patient ledger card** (Fig. 1-8) is used to keep track of patient charges and payments. A ledger card is an accounting form on which professional service descriptions, charges, payments, adjustments, and current balance are posted chronologically. Although many medical professional offices are becoming computerized, there are still some offices that are not, so to become a well-rounded health care professional, you must be familiar with manual accounting methods.

Tri-State Medical Group

008112

400 North 4th Street • Anytown, Iowa 50622
Phone: 319-555-5734 • Fax: 319-555-5758
Fed. Tax I.D. # 42-1435XXX

ACCOUNT NO.		DOB		DATE OF SERVICE
PATIENT NAME		PROVIDER		
INSURANCE ID		SECONDARY		

DESCRIPTION	CODE		FEE
OFFICE VISIT	NEW	ESTAB.	
Minimum	99201	99211	
Brief	99202	99212	
Limited	99203	99213	
Extended	99204	99214	
Comprehensive	99205	99215	
Prenatal Care		59400	
Global		99024	
PREVENTIVE	NEW	ESTAB.	
Infant	99381	99391	
Age 1-4	99382	99392	
Age 5-11	99383	99393	
Age 12-17	99384	99394	
Age 18-39	99385	99395	
Age 40-64	99386	99396	
Age 65 & Over	99387	99397	
OFFICE CONSULTATION			
Limited		99241	
Intermediate		99242	
Extended		99243	
Comprehensive		99244	
Complex		99245	
LABORATORY PROCEDURES			
Venipuncture		36415	
Routine Urinalysis w/o Microscopy		81002	
Hemoccult		82270	
Glucose Blood Reagent Strip		82948	
Wet Mount		87210	
PAP Smear		88155	
Urine Pregnancy		81025	
Other:		99000	
X-RAY			
X-ray Cervical Spine		75052	
X-ray Thoracic Spine		72070	
X-ray Lumbar Spine (2)		72100	
X-ray Lumbar Spine (Comp)		72110	
X-ray Pelvis (1 view)		72170	
X-ray Sacrum & Coccyx		72220	
X-ray Clavicle (Complete)		73000	
X-ray Shoulder (2) or		73030	
X-ray Humerus (2 views)		73060	
X-ray Elbow (AP & LATE)		73070	
X-ray Forearm (AP & LA)		73090	
X-ray Wrist (AP & LATE)		73100	
X-ray Wrist (3 Views)		73110	
X-ray Hand (2 Views)		73120	
X-ray Hand (3 Views)		73130	
X-ray Finger (2 Views)		73140	
X-ray Hip (2 Views)		73510	
X-ray Hips (Bilateral)		73520	
X-ray Scoliosis (2 AP & LA)		72069	
X-ray Femur (AP & LATE)		73550	
X-ray Knee (AP & LATE)		73560	
X-ray Knee (3 Views)		73564	
X-ray Tibia & Fibula		73590	
X-ray Ankle (3 Views)		73610	
X-ray Foot (AP & LATER)		73620	
X-ray Foot (AP, LA.,)		73630	
X-ray Calcaneus (2 Views)		73650	
X-ray Toes		73660	
X-ray Pelvis & Hip Inf		73540	
Elbow, Minimum of 3 Views		73080	
IMMUNIZATIONS & INJECTIONS			
PPD Intradermal TB Tine		86580	
DTaP		90700	

DESCRIPTION	CODE	FEE
DT, Pediatric	90702	
MMR	90707	
Oral Polio	90712	
IVP Polio	90713	
Varicella	90716	
Td, Adult	90718	
DTP & HIB	90720	
Influenza	90659	
Hepatitis B, Newborn to 11 Years	90744	
Hepatitis B, 11-19 Years	90747	
Hepatitis B, 20 Years & Above	90746	
Pneumococcal	90732	
Hemophilus Infl. B	90645	
Therapeutic:	90782	
Allergy Inject Single	95115	
Allergy Inject Multiple	95117	
B-12	J3420	
Injection / Aspiration	20600	
Small joint-Finger, Toes, Ganglion		
Injection / Aspiration	20605	
Intermediate jt-Wrist, Elbow, Ankle		
Injection / Aspiration	20610	
Major jt. - Shoulder, Hip, Knee		
Inject Tendon/Ligament	20550	
Aristocort	J3302	
Depo Provera	J1055	
Rocephin	J0696	
OFFICE PROCEDURE / MINOR SURGERY		
I & D Abscess	10060	
Removal FB Subcutaneous	*10120	
I & D Hematoma	10140	
Puncture Aspiration Abscess	10160	
Exc. Ben. Lesion #:		
Location:		
Exc. Ben. Lesion #:		
Location:		

DESCRIPTION	CODE	FEE
Removal Skin Tags up to 15 Lesions	*11200	
Exc. Malignant Lesion, Trunk, Arm or Leg		
Exc. Malignant Lesion, Face, Ear, Eyelid, Nose		
Exc. Malignant Lesion, Scalp, Hand, Neck, Feet		
Lacer, Repair 2.5cm or Less/Location:	*12001	
Scalp, Nk, Axillae, Ext. Genitalia, Trk, Hands/Feet		
Lacer, Repair 2.5cm or Less/Location:	*12011	
Face, Ears, Eyelids, Nose, Lips & Mucous Mem.		
Burn w/Dressing, w/o Anesth. Small	16020	
Wart Removal	*17110	
Removal FB Conjunct. Ext. Eye	*65205	
Removal FB Ext. Auditory Canal	69200	
Ear Lavage	69210	
Tympanometry	92567	
EKG Tracing Only w/o Interp. & Rept	93005	
Nebulizer Therapy (x)	94640	
Pulse Oximetry	94760	
Cryosurgery		
Debridement	11041	
Excise Ingrown Toenail	11730	
Colposcopy w/Biopsy	57454	
LEEP	57460	
Endometrial Bx	58100	
Cryotherapy	57511	
Peak Flow Measurement	94160-52	
Intradermal Tests CMI # Doses =	95025	
Intradermal Tests/Allergens	95024	
Intravenous Access	36000	
Immunotherapy/Single Injection	95120	
Immunotherapy/Double Injection	95125	
Regular Spirometry	94010	
Spirometry Read by Physician	94010-26	
Spirometry w/pre & Post Bronchodilator	94060	
Spirometry/Bronchodilator read by Doctor	94060-26	
Skin Prick Test: # of Tests =	95004	
Vial Preparation	95165	

HOSPITAL ORDERS

OB Non-Stress Test	Cystogram	Physical Therapy
OB Ultrasound-Diagnostic	MRI	
OB Ultrasound-Routine	CT Scan _____	
Biophysical Profile	Chest X-ray	Diet Consultation
Mammogram-Diagnostic	X-ray _____	
Mammogram-Routine	Bone Densitometry	
	EKG	Laboratory
Ultrasound _____	Holter Monitor	
Gallbladder Ultrasound	Echocardiogram	
Pelvic Ultrasound	Treadmill _____	
Doppler Studies _____	Thallium Stress Test	
	Doppler Studies_____	
IVP	PFT-Partial	
Upper GI	PFT-Complete	
Lower GI	Cardiac Rehab	
Barium Enema		
Barium Swallow		

AUTHORIZATION TO PAY BENEFITS AND RELEASE INFORMATION TO TRI-STATE MEDICAL GROUP: I hereby authorize payment directly to the undersigned Physician of all Surgical and / or Medical Benefits, if any, otherwise payable to me for his / her services as described above. I have read and understand the Financial Policy and that I am financially responsible for charges not covered by this insurance. I also authorize the undersigned Physician to release any information acquired in the course of my examination or treatment.

Signed: _____

Date: _____

Provider's Signature   Date

PREVIOUS BALANCE	
CHARGES TODAY	
TOTAL	
AMOUNT PAID	
BALANCE DUE	

DX or Other Information

Samples:

Your next appointment is:

BILLING COPY

Fig. 1-7   Sample encounter form.

STATEMENT

Tri-State Medical Group
400 North 4th Street
Anytown, Iowa 50622
Phone: 319-555-5734
Fax: 319-555-5758

Mrs. Samantha Taylor
6345 Elm
Ames, Iowa 50010

| DATE | PROFESSIONAL SERVICE DESCRIPTION | CHARGE | CREDITS | | CURRENT BALANCE |
			PAYMENTS	ADJUSTMENTS	
12-15-xx	Init OV, D hx/exam, LC decision making.	95 00			95 00
12-15-xx	EKG c̄ interpret & report.	55 00			150 00

Due and payable within 10 days.   **Pay last amount in balance column** ⇧

Key: PF:	Problem-focused	SF:	Straightforward	CON:	Consultation	HCD:	House call (day)
EPF:	Expanded problem-focused	LC:	Low complexity	CPX:	Complete phys exam	HCN:	House call (night)
D:	Detailed	MC:	Moderate complexity	E:	Emergency	HV:	Hospital visit
C:	Comprehensive	HC:	High complexity	ER:	Emergency dept.	OV:	Office visit

Fig. 1-8 Sample patient ledger card. *(Modified from Fordney MT: Insurance handbook for the medical office, ed 9, St Louis, 2006, Saunders.)*

HIPAA TIP

A medical office can use sign-in sheets and announce names; however, reasonable safeguards still need to be used. This decision has been added to HIPAA's rules and regulations to address incidental disclosures of protected health information. Examples of safeguards used by some medical offices include the following:

1. Covering sign-in sheet with a separate, nontransparent sheet of paper
2. Using a heavy black marking pen to cross through names after the chart is verified, co pay is collected (if applicable), and patient is seated

A patient ledger card is prepared for each new patient. In some medical offices, particularly family practice facilities, one ledger card is set up for the head of household, and all dependent family members are included on it. This setup makes sense because not only does it save time and space in the ledger file, but also minor children usually are not responsible for their own bills, and statements are normally not addressed directly to them. One must be cautious, however, in the case of divorced parents because it is important that the parent who is financially responsible for the child be billed. More information is given on the maintenance of the patient ledger card as we proceed through the chapters on third-party payers and process insurance claims and reimbursements.

WHAT DID YOU LEARN?

1. List the documents needed for filing a paper CMS-1500 claim.
2. Explain why it is important to photocopy the back and front of the ID card.
3. What types of information are typically included on an encounter form?

COMPLETING THE CMS-1500 PAPER FORM

Before filling in any of the blocks, type the name and address of the insurance carrier to whom the form will be mailed. This information should appear in the upper right hand corner of the form as illustrated in Fig. 1-9.

The following instructions for completing the CMS-1500 form are nonspecific. For the most part, they do not include details specific to any one major carrier, such as Medicare or Medicaid. More detailed guidelines applicable to each of the major carriers are presented in later chapters. In these generic guidelines, we assume that the patient is covered by a private (commercial) insurance policy and has no secondary insurance coverage. These instructions were adapted from the *National Uniform Claims Committee's Reference Instruction Manual, Version 08/05.*

Patient/Insured Section

Information required in many of the blocks varies from claim to claim and from one insurance carrier to another. Blocks 9 through 9d are examples of this. For a patient who has no secondary coverage, blocks 9 through 9d are left blank. More detailed information is given as to how these blocks should be completed as each major carrier is discussed later in the text.

Block 1—Indicate the type of health insurance coverage applicable to the claim by checking the appropriate box. Usually, only one box is checked except when the claim involves dual coverage, such as Medicare and Medicaid or Group Health and Medicare, in which case more than one box is checked.

Block 1a—Enter the patient's health insurance claim number exactly as it appears on his or her ID card, including any alpha characters.

Fig. 1-9 How and where the name and address of the carrier should appear on the CMS-1500 form.

Block 2—Enter the patient's last name, first name, and middle initial (if any). Do not use shortened names or nicknames. (Remember to use uppercase letters and no punctuation.)

Block 3—Enter the patient's eight-digit birth date, using the MM DD YYYY format, and check the appropriate box under "sex." It is important to use this exact formatting style (the 4-digit year) for a birth date so that it is clear when the patient was born. Entering a birth date of 05 10 07 could represent a centenarian or a young child.

Block 4—Enter the policyholder's (subscriber's) name here exactly as it is listed on the insurance card. If the patient and the policyholder are the same, most carriers allow you to enter the word "SAME."

Note: On Medicare claims, the patient (referred to as the *beneficiary*) and the policyholder are the same. Sometimes there is insurance primary to Medicare, through the patient's or spouse's employment or some other source. If this is the case, list the insured's name from the primary policy here. If Medicare is primary, leave blank. (Instructions on how to fill out the CMS-1500 claim form for Medicare secondary claims are given in Chapter 5.)

Block 5—Enter the patient's mailing address (city, state, and Zip Code) and telephone number as the form indicates. Do not use punctuation or separate the telephone number groups with dashes.

Block 6—Check the applicable box for the patient's relationship to the insured when Block 4 is completed. (Do not use the box for "other.")

Block 7—Enter the policyholder's address and telephone number. If the address is the same as the patient's, enter "SAME." (Usually, this item is completed only when Blocks 4 and 11 are completed.)

Block 8—Check the appropriate box for the patient's marital status and whether employed or a student. Checking the "married" or "student" boxes is not mandatory for all carriers. Always check with the carrier if you have questions.

Blocks 9-9d—Rather than try to explain what information to enter here for various third-party carriers, these blocks are left blank for this generic run-through, and they are addressed individually in later chapters.

Blocks 10a-10c—This is a crucial area of the form. You must check "yes" or "no" to indicate whether the services or procedures listed in Block 24 are the result of an accident or illness resulting from employment, an auto accident, or other accident. If auto accident is checked, enter the two-letter code for the state in which the accident occurred. An item checked "yes" indicates that there may be another insurance carrier that is primary, such as workers' compensation or an auto insurance carrier.

Block 10d—This block is used when Medicaid is the secondary payer. If the patient is a Medicaid recipient, enter the patient's Medicaid ID number preceded by the letters "MCD." Otherwise, leave blank. (Verify this with your state Medicaid carrier.)

Block 11—The completion of this item, similar to Blocks 9 through 9d, depends on the guidelines of the carrier to whom the claim is being sent, or whether or not the patient is covered under another insurance policy. If there is a second health insurance policy, go back and complete Blocks 9 through 9d. In our generic case, the "patient" is covered by a private insurance company with no secondary coverage. In this case, Blocks 11 through 11c are left blank.

On Medicare claims, if there is no insurer primary to Medicare, enter the word "NONE." Completion of this item acknowledges that the physician/supplier has made a good faith effort to determine whether Medicare is the primary or secondary carrier. More detailed information is given in the sections of the text that deal with the various major carriers.

Block 11a—Enter the insured's eight-digit birth date and sex, *if different from Block 3.*

Block 11b—If this is an employer-sponsored group insurance, enter the employer's name. For Medicare claims, if the beneficiary is retired, enter the eight-digit retirement date preceded by the word "RETIRED."

Block 11c—For most claims, this item is left blank. For secondary claims, enter the primary insurance plan or program name of the insured (as indicated in Block 1a). Some payers require an identification number of the primary insurer rather than the name in this field. If you have questions, check with the applicable carrier.

Block 11d—Check "yes" or "no," whichever is applicable. If marked "YES," complete Blocks 9 and 9a-d. Only one box can be marked. Under most circumstances, leave blank on Medicare claims.

Block 12—The patient's or authorized individual's signature indicates there is an authorization on file for the release of any medical or other information necessary to process or adjudicate the claim. Enter "Signature on File," "SOF," or legal signature. When legal signature is used, enter date signed in six-digit format (MM DD YY) or eight-digit format (MM DD YYYY). If there is no signature on file, leave blank, or enter "No Signature on File." (Remember, for a release of information to be valid, it should not be more than 1 year old. On Medicare claims, a properly worded "lifetime" release of information is acceptable.) An example of a HIPAA-compliant release of information is shown in Fig. 1-10. A Medicare-approved lifetime release of information is shown in Chapter 5.

Block 13—A signature here tells the insurance carrier that the patient (or insured) authorizes them to **assign benefits** (send reimbursement check directly to the health care provider). If a separate signed authorization to assign benefits exists elsewhere (it is often included on a patient information form), the letters "SOF" can be entered here. In certain instances, a signature here is unnecessary, but there are some exceptions, as in the case of Medicaid and Medigap. (This information is discussed in more detail in later chapters.) If there is no signature on file, enter "NO SIGNATURE ON FILE."

What Did You Learn?

1. What is the rationale for using the MM DD YYYY date format?
2. When is it necessary to complete Blocks 9 through 9d?
3. Why is it important to check "yes" or "no" in all three boxes in Blocks 10a through 10c?

Physician/Supplier Section

We now turn our attention to the part of the CMS-1500 form that contains information the health insurance professional must **abstract** from the health record or the encounter form or both. Learning how to abstract, or pull out, information from the health record that is necessary for completing the CMS-1500 claim form takes some level of expertise, which the novice health insurance professional might not possess. This skill develops with experience and practice.

The new CMS-1500 form (08-05) accommodates the NPI numbers that all health care providers or organizations defined as "covered entities" under HIPAA must obtain. This unique 10-digit numerical identifier is considered permanent and, when assigned, is assigned for life. The NPI replaces all other provider identifiers previously used by health

care providers (e.g., UPIN, Medicare/Medicaid numbers).

When completing the CMS-1500 form, date fields (other than date of birth) should be one or the other format, six-digit (MM DD YY) or eight-digit (MM DD YYYY). Intermixing the two formats on the claim is not allowed. The date of birth must be in the eight-digit format.

The following guidelines for the Physician/Supplier section of the CMS-1500 form comply with those outlined in the April 2007 version of the National Uniform Claim Committee's (NUCC) *Reference Instruction Manual* using the following Web link: http://www.nucc.org/images/stories/PDF/claim_form_manual_v2-1_3-07.pdf. There may be subtle differences among carriers. Consult the specific carrier in your state/area for guidelines.

Block 14—Enter the date of the first symptom of the current illness or injury in this block (if one is documented in the health record) or the date of the last menstrual cycle if the claim is related to a pregnancy. Use the six-digit (MM DD YY) or eight-digit (MM DD YYYY) date format. Use caution here because an incorrect date could indicate a preexisting condition, and the claim could be rejected. *Example:* If a patient was treated for a back injury before the effective date of his or her existing health care policy, this policy might not cover charges stemming from this same back injury.

Block 15—Enter the first date the patient had the same or a similar illness using the six-digit or eight-digit format. Leave blank if unknown. Leave blank for Medicare claims. (*Note:* Previous pregnancies are not a similar illness.)

Block 16—If the patient is employed and is unable to work in current occupation, a six-digit or eight-digit date must be shown for the "from-to" dates that the patient is unable to work. An entry in this field may indicate employment-related (worker's compensation) insurance coverage. Completion of this block is not required for most other carriers.

Block 17—Enter the name (first, middle initial, last name) and credentials of the professional who referred, ordered, or supervised the services or supplies on the claim. Do not use periods or commas within the name. A hyphen can be used for hyphenated names. For laboratory and x-ray claims, enter the name of the physician who ordered the diagnostic services. *Example:* If Lewis L. Madigan orders an electrocardiogram, which is performed by a medical assistant but interpreted by Dr. Madigan, his name (Lewis L. Madigan MD) is entered into Block 17.

Authorization for Release of Information

I hereby authorize the use or disclosure of my individually identifiable health information as described below. I understand that this authorization is voluntary and that I may revoke it at any time by submitting my revocation in writing to the entity providing the information.

Participant Name: _____   ID Number: _____

Person(s) authorized to provide information:

_____

_____

Person(s) authorized to receive information:

_____

_____

Description of information to be used or disclosed:

_____

_____

(Facility Name) will not receive financial or in-kind compensation in exchange for using or disclosing the health information described above.

This authorization will expire _____ . (Indicate date, or an event relating to you personally or to the purpose of the authorization.)

IMPORTANT INFORMATION ABOUT YOUR RIGHTS

I have read and understood the following statements about my rights:

- I may revoke this authorization at any time prior to its expiration date by notifying (Facility Name) in writing, but the revocation will not have any affect on any actions the entity took before it received the revocation.

- I may see and copy the information described on this form if I ask for it.

- I am not required to sign this form to receive my benefits.

- The information that is used or disclosed pursuant to this authorization may be redisclosed by (Facility Name). I have the right to seek assurances from the above-named person(s) authorized to receive the information that they will not redisclose the information to any other party without my further authorization.

_____   _____
Signature of Participant   Date

_____   _____
Printed Name of Participant's Personal Representative   Relationship to the Participant

Fig. 1-10 Form for authorization for release of information.

Completion of this box also is required if billing for a consultation.

Block 17a—Block 17a is not to be reported after May 23, 2007.

Block 17b—The NPI of the provider reported in Block 17 should appear in this block.

Note: If a claim involves multiple referring or ordering physicians, a separate form should be used for each ordering or referring physician.

Block 18—If the claim is related to a hospital stay, enter the dates of hospital admission and discharge. If the patient has not yet been discharged, leave the "to" box blank.

Block 19—Refer to the most current instructions from the applicable public or private payer regarding the use of this field. Some payers ask for certain identifiers in this field. If identifiers are reported in this field, enter the appropriate qualifiers describing the identifier. Do not enter a space, hyphen, or other separator between the qualifier code and the number. The NUCC defines the following qualifiers, which are the same as those used in the electronic 837 Professional 4010A1:

0B—State License Number
1A—Blue Cross Provider Number
1B—Blue Shield Provider Number
1C—Medicare Provider Number
1D—Medicaid Provider Number
1G—Provider UPIN
1H—CHAMPUS Identification Number
EI—Employer's Identification Number
G2—Provider Commercial Number
LU—Location Number
N5—Provider Plan Network Identification Number
SY—Social Security Number (Social Security number may not be used for Medicare.)
X5—State Industrial Accident Provider Number
ZZ—Provider Taxonomy

Block 20—Complete this field only when billing for purchased services. A charge entered into this block indicates that services have been rendered by an independent provider. Enter an X in "YES" if the reported service was performed by an entity other than the billing provider. If "YES," enter the purchased price under "CHARGES." A "YES" mark indicates that an entity other than the entity billing for the service performed the purchased services. A "NO" mark indicates that no purchased services are included on the claim. When "YES" is annotated, Block 32 must be completed. When billing for multiple purchased services, each service should be submitted on a separate claim form. Only one box can be marked. When entering the charge amount, enter the amount in the field to the left of the vertical line. Enter the number right justified to the left of the vertical line. Do not use commas or a decimal point when reporting amounts. Negative dollar amounts are not allowed. Dollar signs should not be entered. Use 00 for the cents if the amount is a whole number. Leave the right-hand field blank. Leave this block blank if no laboratory or diagnostic tests were performed.

Block 21—Enter the patient's diagnosis using ICD-9-CM code numbers. If there is more than one diagnosis, list the primary diagnosis code first. List up to four ICD-9-CM diagnosis codes. Relate lines 1, 2, 3, 4 to the lines of service in 24E by line number. When entering the number, include a space (accommodated by the period) between the two sets of numbers. If entering a code with more than three beginning digits (e.g., E codes), enter the fourth digit on top of the period.

Block 22—This block is used only for Medicaid replacement claims. Medicaid resubmission means the code and original reference number assigned by the payer (or receiver) indicate a previously submitted claim. List the original reference number for resubmitted claims. Refer to the most current instructions from the applicable public or private payer regarding the use of this field.

Block 23—Enter any of the following: prior authorization number, referral number, mammography precertification number, or Clinical Laboratory Improvement Amendments (CLIA) number, as assigned by the payer for the current service. Do not enter hyphens or spaces within the number. The prior authorization number refers to the payer-assigned number authorizing the service. Consult the specific guidelines for the payer to whom the claim is being submitted.

Block 24a—Enter dates of service ("From" and "To"). If one date of service only, enter that date under "From." Leave "To" blank or re-enter "From" date. If grouping services, the place of service, procedure code, charges, and individual provider for each line must be identical for that service line. Grouping is allowed only for services on consecutive days. The number of days must correspond to the number of units in 24G. Submit each date of service on a separate line. Enter the month, day, and year (in the MM DD YYYY format) for each procedure, service, or supply. When "From" and "To" dates are shown for a series of identical services, enter the number of days or units in 24G.

Note: Only one procedure may be billed on each line. If there are more than six procedures, a second claim form needs to be used.

Block 24b—Enter the appropriate two-digit code from the Place of Service Code list (Table 1-1) for each item used or service performed. The Place of Service Code identifies the location where the service was rendered. A more detailed list of Place of Service Codes is available at www.cms.hhs.gov/PlaceofServiceCodes/Downloads/POSDataBase.pdf.

Block 24c—Check with the applicable carrier to determine if this element (emergency indicator) is necessary. If required, enter Y for "YES" or leave blank if "NO" in the bottom, unshaded area of the field. The definition of emergency would be determined by federal or state regulations or programs, payer contracts, or the electronic 837 Professional 4010A1 implementation guide.

TABLE 1-1   Frequently Used Place-of-Service Codes

Code	Description
11	Office
12	Home
21	Inpatient hospital
22	Outpatient hospital
23	Emergency department—hospital
24	Ambulatory surgical center
25	Birthing center
26	Military treatment facility
31	Skilled nursing facility
32	Nursing facility
33	Custodial care facility
34	Hospice
41	Ambulance—land
42	Ambulance—air or water
50	Federally qualified health center
51	Inpatient psychiatric facility
52	Psychiatric facility partial hospitalization
53	Community mental health center
54	Intermediate care facility/mentally retarded
55	Residential substance abuse treatment facility
56	Psychiatric residential treatment center
60	Mass immunization center
61	Comprehensive inpatient rehabilitation facility
62	Comprehensive outpatient rehabilitation facility
65	End-stage renal disease treatment facility
71	State or local public health clinic
72	Rural health clinic
81	Independent laboratory
99	Other unlisted facility

Block 24d—Enter the procedure, service, or supply code using appropriate five-digit CPT or Healthcare Common Procedure Coding System (HCPCS) procedure code. Enter the two-digit modifier when applicable. If using an unlisted procedure code (codes ending in "99"), a complete description of the procedure must be provided as a separate attachment. This field accommodates the entry of four two-digit modifiers. The specific procedure codes must be shown without a narrative description.

Block 24e—Enter the diagnosis code reference number (pointer) as shown in Block 21 to relate the date of service and the procedures performed to the primary diagnosis. When multiple services are performed, the primary reference number for each service should be listed first, and other applicable services should follow. The reference number should be a 1, 2, 3, or 4; or multiple numbers as explained. (ICD-9-CM diagnosis codes must be entered in Block 21 only. Do not enter them in Block 24e.) Enter numbers left justified in the field. Do not use commas between the numbers.

Block 24f—Enter the amount charged for each listed procedure, supply, or service. Enter numbers right justified in the dollar area of the field. Do not use commas when reporting dollar amounts. Negative dollar amounts or "no charge" services are not allowed. Dollar signs should not be entered. Enter 00 in the cents area if the amount is a whole number.

Block 24g—Enter the number of days or units. This field is most commonly used for multiple visits, units of supplies, anesthesia units or minutes, or oxygen volume. If only one service is performed, the number 1 must be entered. Enter numbers right justified in the field. No leading zeros are required. If reporting a fraction of a unit, use the decimal point. If only one service is performed, enter the number 1. Do not leave blank.

Block 24h—For Early and Periodic Screening, Diagnosis, and Treatment (EPSDT)–related services, enter the response in the shaded portion of the field. If there is no requirement (e.g., state requirement) to report a reason code for EPDST, enter Y for "YES" or N for "NO" only. If there is a requirement to report a reason code for EPDST, enter the appropriate reason code as noted in the following list. (A Y or N response is not entered with the code.) The two-character code is right justified in the shaded area of the field. The following codes for EPSDT are used in the electronic 837 Professional 4010A1:

AV—Available—Not Used (Patient refused referral.)

S2—Under Treatment (Patient is currently under treatment for referred diagnostic or corrective health problem.)

ST—New Service Requested (Referral to another provider for diagnostic or corrective treatment or scheduled for another appointment with screening provider for diagnostic or corrective treatment for at least one health problem identified during an initial or periodic screening service, not including dental referrals.)

NU—Not Used (Used when no EPSDT patient referral was given.)

If the service is Family Planning, enter Y ("YES") or N ("NO") in the bottom, unshaded area of the field.

Block 24i—Enter the ID qualifier 1C in the shaded portion for Medicare claims. See instructions for Block 19 for additional

24. A.	DATE(S) OF SERVICE					B. PLACE OF SERVICE	C. EMG	D. PROCEDURES, SERVICES, OR SUPPLIES (Explain Unusual Circumstances) CPT/HCPCS	MODIFIER	E. DIAGNOSIS POINTER	F. $ CHARGES		G. DAYS OR UNITS	H. EPSDT Family Plan	I. ID. QUAL.	J. RENDERING PROVIDER ID. #
	From MM	DD	YY	To MM	DD	YY											
7 Begin 1245 End 1415 Time 90 minutes														N	1B	12345678901
10	01	05	10	01	05	22		00770	P2	134	875	00	6	N	NPI	0123456789

Fig. 1-11 Completed Blocks 24a to 24j.

qualifiers, or contact the third-party payer for ID qualifiers for non-Medicare claims.

Block 24j—Report the individual rendering the service here. Enter the non-NPI ID number in the shaded area of the field if required by the carrier. Enter the NPI number in the unshaded area of the field. The Rendering Provider is the person or company (laboratory or other facility) who rendered or supervised the care. In the case where a substitute provider *(locum tenens)* was used, enter that provider's information here. Report the Identification Number in Blocks 24i and 24j only when different from data recorded in Blocks 33a and 33b. Enter numbers left justified in the field.

Fig. 1-11 provides an example of how Blocks 24a through 24j might be completed.

Block 25—Enter the unique nine-digit identifier assigned by a federal or state agency to that provider (or group), and check the appropriate box in this field. In the case of an unincorporated or individual practice, enter the provider's Social Security number. Do not enter hyphens with numbers. Enter numbers left justified in the field.

Block 26—Enter the patient's account number assigned by the provider of service's or supplier's accounting system. Do not enter hyphens with numbers. Enter numbers left justified in the field. Reporting the patient's account number in this block enables the insurer to print it on the explanation of benefits (EOB) and speeds data entry from the EOB.

Block 27—Check the appropriate block to indicate whether the provider accepts assignment of benefits. If the supplier is a participating provider, assignment must be accepted for all covered charges. For nonparticipating providers, this can be left blank. The accept assignment indicates that the provider agrees to accept assignment under the terms of the Medicare Program. Medicare nonparticipating providers can use this block to indicate assignment on a claim-by-claim basis. For Medicaid claims, check "Yes."

Block 28—Enter the total charges for services listed in Block 24f. Enter the number right justified in the dollar area of the field. Do not use commas when reporting dollar amounts.

Negative dollar amounts are not allowed. Dollar signs should not be entered. Enter 00 in the cents area if the amount is a whole number.

Block 29—Enter the total amount, if any, that the patient has paid or any payment from other payers. Leave blank if no payment has been made.

Block 30—Enter total amount due. Enter the number right justified in the dollar area of the field. Do not use commas when reporting dollar amounts. Negative dollar amounts are not allowed. Dollar signs should not be entered. Enter 00 in the cents area if the amount is a whole number. Balance Due does not exist in the electronic 837 Professional 4010A1.

Block 31—Enter the legal signature of the practitioner or supplier, signature of the practitioner or supplier representative, "Signature on File," or "SOF." Enter either the six-digit or eight-digit date or the alphanumerical date (e.g., JANUARY 1 2003) the form was signed.

HIPAA TIP

If providers choose to use electronic signatures, the signatures must comply with HIPAA standards.

Block 32—Enter the name, address, city, state, and Zip Code of the location where the services were rendered. Providers of service (i.e., physicians) must identify the supplier's name, address, Zip Code, and NPI number when billing for purchased diagnostic tests. When more than one supplier is used, a separate CMS-1500 form should be used to bill for each supplier. Enter the name and address information in the following format:
1st line—Name
2nd line—Address
3rd line—City, State, and Zip Code

Do not use commas, periods, or other punctuation in the address (e.g., 123 N MAIN STREET 101 instead of 123 N. Main Street, #101). Enter a space between town name and state code; do not include a comma. When entering a nine-digit Zip Code, include the hyphen.

Block 32a—Enter the NPI of the service facility. The NPI number refers to the HIPAA National Provider Identifier number.

Block 32b—Enter the two-digit qualifier identifying the non-NPI number followed by the ID number if required by the carrier. Do not enter a space, hyphen, or other separator between the qualifier and number. (See Block 19 for list of two-digit qualifiers.)

Note: After May 23, 2007, most carrier guidelines request Block 32b not to be reported.

Block 33—Block 33 identifies the provider that is requesting to be paid for the services rendered and should always be completed. Enter the provider's or supplier's billing name, address, Zip Code, and phone number. The phone number is to be entered in the area to the right of the field title. Enter the name and address information in the following format:
First line—Name
Second line—Address
Third line—City, State, and Zip Code

Do not use commas, periods, or other punctuation in the address. Enter a space between town name and state code; do not include a comma. When entering a nine-digit Zip Code, include the hyphen. Do not use a hyphen or space as a separator within the telephone number.

Block 33a—Enter the NPI number of the billing provider.

Block 33b—If required by the carrier, enter the two-digit qualifier identifying the non-NPI number followed by the ID number. The non-NPI ID number of the billing provider refers to the payer-assigned unique identifier of the professional. Do not enter a space, hyphen, or other separator between the qualifier and number. See Block 19 above for a list of qualifiers. Some carriers request this block not to be reported after May 23, 2007.

The physician/supplier portion of the CMS-1500 form is the most challenging part. There is so much to learn, and the fact that all major payers' guidelines are slightly different complicates the process. Be patient, however, because you will not be expected at this point to know everything.

Refer to the Websites to Explore section for more detailed instructions for completing the new CMS-1500 (08-05) claim form.

WHAT DID YOU LEARN?

1. When should a provider's name appear in Block 17?
2. If a provider's name appears in Block 17, what should be entered in Block 17a?
3. When is it acceptable to include "no charge" services on the CMS-1500?
4. How should Block 33 be completed if the provider is a member of a physician's group?

PREPARING THE CLAIM FORM FOR SUBMISSION

Proofreading

After the form has been completed according to the applicable payer guidelines, it should be meticulously proofread for accuracy. The goal is always to submit **clean claims**—claims that can be processed for payment quickly without being returned. Returned or rejected claims delay the payment process and cost the practice and the patient money. On average, nearly one quarter of the claims submitted by medical practices to insurers are rejected because they contain some type of error. One national professional association estimates that resubmitting a paper claim could cost a medical practice between $24 and $41.67.

A claim that is rejected for missing or invalid information must be corrected and resubmitted by the provider. Common examples of claim rejections include the following:

- Incomplete/invalid patient diagnosis code
- Diagnosis code that does not justify the procedure code
- Missing or improper modifiers
- Omitted or inaccurately entered the referring/ordering/supervising provider's name or NPI
- Insured's subscriber or group number missing or incorrect
- Charges not itemized
- Provider signature missing

Claim Attachments

Under certain circumstances, it may be necessary to include certain supporting documentation with a claim, as in the case in which an unlisted procedure code (a code ending in "99") is used or to justify certain procedures or charges or both. Attachments also might include laboratory reports, physician notes, and other documents, which explain further the medical appropriateness for the claim. When it

Patient Name	Carrier Name	Date Filed	Claim Amount	Date of Payment/EOB	Payment Amount	Claim Status	Action Taken/Date
Anderson, Joseph L.	Metropolitan Life	01/12/XX	1450.00			Pending	Telephone call to Met Life 2/12/XX
Siverly, Penelope R.	Medicare	01/23/XX	125.00	02/13/XX	64.50		
Loper, Michael C.	Medicaid	01/25/XX	65.00			Denied	Appeal Letter to Medicaid 2/16/XX
Carpenter, Susan	BCBS	01/27/XX	255.00			Lost Claim	Resubmitted on 2/22/XX

Fig. 1-12 Sample insurance claim tracking form.

is necessary to include an attachment with the claim, a complete description of the procedure must be provided as a separate document and included with the completed CMS-1500 form. Every carrier has specific guidelines for how to handle attachments. A carrier's guidelines may state that "all attachments must be at least 3 to 5 inches in size and clearly readable." Under most circumstances for paper claims, the attachment is paper-clipped behind each claim form when submitted. (Most carriers prefer that attachments not be stapled to the claim form.)

One last thing you must remember to do before mailing the claim is to make a copy of the completed form for your files. Some carriers require making and keeping copies of paper claims for a certain length of time (e.g., 5 years). Consult your carrier's guidelines to find out how long you must retain copies of paper claims.

Tracking Claims

Many practices use some sort of claims follow-up system so that claims can be tracked and delinquent claims resolved before it is too late to resubmit (as in the case of a lost claim). An example of a claims follow-up system is an insurance log or insurance register. The insurance log or register should include various entries, such as the patient's name, insurance company's name, date claim filed, status of the claim (e.g., paid, pending, denied), date of explanation of benefits (EOB) or payment receipt, and resubmitted date. A claims follow-up system can be set up manually or electronically. It is a helpful tool for the health insurance professional and the provider because it ultimately leads to an increase in payments to the practice. Insurance claims can be

overlooked if a tracking system is not in place, which can lead to lost revenue. Fig. 1-12 shows an example of an insurance log.

WHAT DID YOU LEARN?

1. What crucial function should be performed after the claim has been completed?
2. List four common reasons that claims are rejected.
3. Under what circumstances should supporting documents accompany a claim?

GENERATING CLAIMS ELECTRONICALLY

Many practices submit their claims electronically because of the time and money savings that result. Experts tell practitioners that processing insurance claims electronically (1) improves cash flow; (2) reduces the expense of claims processing; and (3) streamlines internal processes, allowing practitioners to focus more on patient care. On average, a paper insurance claim typically takes 30 to 45 days for reimbursement, whereas the average payment time for electronic claims is approximately 10 to 14 days. This reduction in insurance reimbursement time results in a significant increase in cash available for other practice expenses. As with everything, there is a tradeoff, however, because often the expense of setting up for an electronic process is not taken into account. The office has to purchase adequate equipment—computers, printers, and software programs. Additionally, everyone involved in the claim process must become computer literate.

Depending on the size and needs of the practice, computer hardware and software can cost from $10,000 to $250,000. Also, an intensive training program may be needed to teach staff how to use the equipment and become adept at operating the software.

There are basically two ways to submit claims electronically: through an electronic claims clearinghouse or directly to an insurance carrier. Many large practices can be set up to support both methods. Whether a practice chooses to use a clearinghouse or to submit claims directly to the carrier, it usually must go through an enrollment process before submitting electronic claims. The enrollment process is required so that the company the practice has hired can "set up" information about the practice on the computer system. Most government and many commercial carriers require such an enrollment. Some also require that the practice sign a contract with them. The enrollment process typically takes 6 to 7 weeks to complete. The largest obstacle in getting set up for electronic claims processing is the time that it takes for approval from state, federal, and (in some cases) commercial/health maintenance organization carriers.

HIPAA TIP

For entities that choose to transmit claims electronically, practice management software or a clearinghouse is needed to handle the conversion of data to meet the requirements of HIPAA.

≋ CLAIMS CLEARINGHOUSES

A **claims clearinghouse** is a company that receives claims from health care providers and specializes in consolidating the claims so that they can send one transmission to each third-party payer containing batches of claims. A clearinghouse typically is an independent, centralized service available to health care providers for the purpose of simplifying medical insurance claims submission for multiple carriers. HIPAA defines a health care clearinghouse as *"a public or private entity that processes or facilitates the processing of nonstandard data elements of health information into standard data elements."*

The clearinghouse acts as a simple point of entry for paper and electronic claims from providers. Clearinghouse personnel edit the claims for validity and accuracy before routing the edited claim on to the proper third-party carrier for payment. A medical practice can send all completed claims to one central location, rather than to multiple payers. If the clearinghouse finds errors on the claim that would cause the claim to be rejected or denied, it sends the claim back to the provider for correction and resubmission.

Clearinghouses also are capable of translating data from one format to another (e.g., electronic to paper or vice versa). Many private clearinghouses are available to health care providers and payers that facilitate electronic and paper claims processing. Payers also can act as clearinghouses for claims of other payers.

Most clearinghouses have the ability to meet the requirements of each insurance company using their specific computer formats. They can submit electronic claims to any insurance company in a format that exactly matches that of the insurance company's computers. This clearinghouse task is essential for electronic claims because it is usually too complex and costly for independent billing services to perform on each claim. Clearinghouse services are not free, however. Charges for paper claims vary from 25 to 75 cents each, but some providers believe the advantages outweigh the disadvantages. Electronically submitted claims are less costly (some cost only 5 cents each), and many clearinghouses do not charge for claims submitted in certain standard electronic formats.

Using a Clearinghouse

Here is how using a clearinghouse typically works. The medical practice subscribes to a clearinghouse. After this process is completed, the health insurance professional enters the practice's billing information in a preformatted template, and a file is created from this template that contains that practice's specific claim information. This file is transmitted through the modem to the clearinghouse using the clearinghouse's specific built-in functionality.

As the clearinghouse receives claims from the medical practice, they are checked for completeness and accuracy. If an error has been made, the practice is notified that there is a problem with a claim. Ideally, the claim information is corrected quickly, and the claim is resubmitted to the clearinghouse. This validation process normally takes just minutes, eliminating the costly delays associated with submitting "dirty" claims directly to the insurer. When submitted and validated for accuracy, claims are forwarded electronically (in most cases overnight) to the specific insurance carriers for reimbursement.

Direct Claims

Submitting electronic claims directly to an insurance carrier is a little more complicated. As explained previously, you first must enroll with the carrier.

Most government carriers and many commercial carriers require that you enroll with them before submitting claims electronically to them. You also need some additional software from each insurance carrier to which you wish to submit claims. Many carriers have their own software or can refer the health insurance professional to someone who supports direct transmissions in the area.

The most common direct claims submission method is done by creating a "print image" file of the claim and using the applicable direct claims software to send the claim to the proper insurance carrier. Printing claims to a file is as easy as printing claims to paper. The first step is to set up a printer properly that has the capability to designate "print to file." After completing the printer setup and entering the billing information, claims can be printed to the carrier transmission file. The health insurance professional would select an option such as "print insurance claims" and select which claims to send to a particular insurance carrier.

When prompted to select a printer to print claims, you simply select the printer that has been set up to print to file. A prompt screen appears requesting that you enter a filename. Enter the filename that was given to you by the direct claims software product. Then, using the direct claims software, transmit the file to the carrier. Some carriers may "edit" claims; the health insurance professional needs to work with that particular insurance carrier to determine how to identify and resubmit claims that contain errors.

Clearinghouses Versus Direct

When deciding whether to send claims electronically through a clearinghouse or direct to the carrier, you must consider several things. Carrier direct is usually less expensive if the medical practice submits most claims to just one carrier. When multiple carriers are used, however, a clearinghouse is generally less expensive. With a clearinghouse, the health insurance professional needs to dial into only one location. If the decision is made to go direct, there will be multiple dialups. When using a clearinghouse, all claims can be submitted in one transmission, and the convenience of sending all claims to one location should not be underestimated. Submitting claims to multiple insurance carriers requires members of the health insurance team to become experts in each of the claims submission software applications used. Because each one is unique, the health insurance professional must be adequately trained and available to submit all variety of claims. Clearinghouses typically generate a separate confirmation report for each carrier where claims are submitted directly.

Regarding which method of electronic claims submission is better, if a medical practice submits insurance claims to only multiple carriers and has someone who is well trained technically to handle the task of electronic claims submission, an electronic claims clearinghouse might be the better choice. If claims are sent primarily to one carrier, the practice should consider using direct submission to that carrier. Whichever method is selected, it is a proven fact that claims are processed much faster and reimbursement time is shortened using electronic claims submission.

SUMMARY CHECK POINTS

☑ In the mid-1970s, HCFA created a form for Medicare claims, which was approved by the American Medical Association Council on Medical Services. All government health care programs and most commercial/private carriers subsequently adopted this form, now referred to as the CMS-1500, to standardize the claims process.

☑ The CMS-1500 form is an 8½ × 11-inch, two-sided form printed in OCR scannable red ink. The top section of the form is for patient/insured information; the bottom section is for provider/supplier data.

☑ For the CMS-1500 form to be OCR "readable," certain rules must be followed. Some of the more important ones are as follows:
- Use all uppercase letters
- Omit all punctuation
- Use the MM DD YYYY format (with a space—not a dash—between each set of digits) for dates of birth

☑ HIPAA mandates that all providers must submit claims electronically unless the provider falls into either of the following categories:
- The health care provider has no method available for submitting claims in electronic format.
- The "small provider" criteria are met, which are defined as *a provider of services with fewer than 25 full-time equivalent employees or a*

physician, practitioner, facility, or supplier (other than a provider of services) with fewer than 10 full-time equivalent employees.

☑ In either of the aforementioned cases, the Secretary may grant a waiver from the mandatory electronic submission rule.

☑ The five documents typically needed for completion of the CMS-1500 are the following:
- The *patient information form* supplies demographic and insurance information and provides the necessary signed release of information.
- The *patient's insurance ID card* contains current subscriber numbers and other information necessary for pre-authorization of certain procedures and inpatient hospitalization.
- The *patient's health record* contains detailed documentation of the reason for the patient's visit, the physician's findings, and a discussion of the recommended treatment.
- The *encounter form* includes the professional services rendered and corresponding CPT and ICD-9 codes.

- The *patient ledger card* documents the fees charged for the services listed on the claim form.

☑ The primary objective in submitting claims is to submit "clean" claims. For this reason, thorough proofreading of each claim form is crucial to prevent claim rejection or denial.

☑ A claims clearinghouse is a company that receives multiple claims from health care providers, edits each for validity and accuracy, and routes the edited claims on to the proper carrier for payment.

☑ Studies have shown that a clearinghouse is the best method of submitting electronic claims if the provider submits claims to multiple carriers. Direct claim submission is the method of choice if most claims are being sent to a single carrier.

Closing Scenario

Studying the information in Chapter 1 one topic at a time and reviewing each main point proved helpful to Emilio and Latisha in comprehending the new material. The chapter contained a lot of information that could have proved difficult had they not adopted a structured method for studying. At the beginning of the chapter, the CMS-1500 form presented a challenging picture, as did the concept of OCR. The students worked through the "generic" guidelines many times, however, until they felt they understood them thoroughly. To get a better grasp of the OCR rules, they practiced lining up the forms and keying information into the blocks using the all caps, no punctuation OCR format.

Emilio preferred to learn how to generate claims using a computer; however, he realized it was important to understand what information should appear in each of the 33 blocks of the form, why the particular datum needed to be there, and how it was derived. Emilio and Latisha agree now that the best way to understand the intricacies of the CMS-1500 form is to abstract information from the five documents explained in the chapter and generate a paper claim. After completing this chapter, Latisha believes she is now ready to begin completing paper forms at the clinic where she volunteers.

WEBSITES TO EXPLORE

- For students who are interested in learning more about OCR technology, log on to the following website, key "OCR Technology" into the search block, and peruse articles of interest:
http://www.eric.ed.gov

- For tips on keeping up-to-date on CMS-1500 completion guidelines for Medicare and Medicaid, log on to the CMS website and type

"CMS-1500 Guidelines" into the search block:
http://www.cms.hhs.gov

- For specific instructions on completing a new CMS-1500 form for Medicare, refer to the Medicare Claims Processing Manual searchable by visiting this address:
http://www.cms.hhs.gov

- For additional information on the revised CMS-1500 form, visit the NUCC website at
http://www.nucc.org

- More information on electronic claims and clearinghouses is available on the *Federal Register*. Use the following web address, then key applicable words, such as "claims clearinghouse" or "electronic claims":

  http://www.gpoaccess.gov/fr/index.html

- Specific and detailed instructions for completing claims using the new CMS-1500 form are given in the National Uniform Claim Committee's instruction manual, which is searchable at this address:

  http://www.nucc.org

Chapter Review

Assessment

Multiple Choice

Directions: *In the questions/statements presented, choose the response that **best** answers/completes the stem, and circle the letter that precedes it.*

1. A major innovation that simplified the process of health insurance claims submission was the development of ___B___.
   A. HIPAA
   B. a universal form
   C. the American Medical Association
   D. optical character recognition (OCR) scanners

2. The front side of the CMS-1500 claim form is printed in ___C___.
   A. all italics
   B. two languages
   C. OCR scannable red ink
   D. Times New Roman, 12-point font

3. The most common *format* used for *text files* in computers and on the Internet is ___B___.
   A. OCR
   B. ASCII
   C. Universal 100
   D. Times New Roman

4. OCR formatting rules specify ___D___.
   A. all entries in uppercase
   B. no punctuation
   C. MM/DD/YYYY birth date format
   D. all of the above

5. A "small provider" of services is one with less than ___D___.
   A. five full-time equivalent employees
   B. 15 full-time equivalent employees
   C. 20 full-time equivalent employees
   D. 25 full-time equivalent employees

6. The patient information form is considered a legal document and should be updated no less often than ___B___.
   A. once a month
   B. once a year
   C. every 2 years
   D. every 5 years

7. A patient's name, address, Social Security number, and employment data are commonly referred to as ___D___.
   A. viable data
   B. pertinent facts
   C. transient statistics
   D. demographic information

8. An individual covered under Medicare is referred to as a(an) _B_.
   A. enrollee
   B. beneficiary
   C. recipient
   D. covered entity

9. An insurance policy that covers an individual, his or her spouse, and eligible dependents is referred to as a(n) _B_.
   A. dual plan
   B. family plan
   C. multiple plan
   D. individual plan

10. A multipurpose form used by most medical practices for billing is called a(an) _B D_
    A. superbill
    B. encounter form
    C. routing form
    D. all of the above

11. In noncomputerized practices, patient charges and payments can be tracked manually on a(an) _C_.
    A. encounter form
    B. CMS-1500 form
    C. patient ledger card
    D. patient information form

12. The CMS-1500 claim form has _D_ separate blocks.
    A. 24
    B. 28
    C. 30
    D. 33

13. After the health insurance professional has completed the claim form, it should be _A_.
    A. proofread
    B. mailed to the patient
    C. mailed to the insurance carrier
    D. submitted to the provider for signature

14. An example of a method for manual claims follow-up is using an _D_.
    A. insurance log
    B. encounter form
    C. insurance register
    D. A and C are correct

15. A company that receives claims, consolidates them, and transmits them in batches to third-party payers is called a _B_.
    A. third-party payer
    B. clearinghouse
    C. claims consolidator
    D. covered entity

True/False

Directions: *Read the following sentences. If it is true, place a "T" in the blank preceding the number. If it is false, place an "F" in the blank, and then rewrite the sentence in the space provided beneath so that it reads true. The first one is done for you as an example.*

_F_   1. The American Medical Association is responsible for creating the universal claim form known as the CMS-1500.

The Health Care Financing Administration is responsible for creating the universal claim form known as the CMS-1500.

_T_   2. The CMS-1500 form (originally known as the HCFA-1500) was developed for the purpose of submitting Medicare claims.

_T_   3. The federal government has passed a law mandating that the universal claim form be used for all third-party payers.

_F_   4. The CMS-1500 form is in two parts. The top portion is for the physician/supplier information, and the bottom portion is for the patient/insured information.

THE BOTTOM PART IS FOR PHYSICAN/SUPPLIER

_T_   5. The CMS-1500 form is composed of 33 blocks.

_____   6. Because the CMS-1500 is a "universal" form, every major payer has exactly the same guidelines for completing each block.

_F_   7. The use of OCR formatting guidelines is preferred, but not mandatory, when completing the CMS-1500 claim form.

_T_   8. Correct OCR guidelines require the use of the MM DD YY format for all dates.

_____   9. The health insurance professional's most important responsibility is to obtain the maximum amount of reimbursement in the minimal amount of time that the patient's health record would support.

_F_ 10. The HIPAA Administrative Simplification Compliance Act (ASCA) prohibits the Department of Health and Human Services (HHS) from paying all claims that are not submitted electronically, without exception.

_T_ 11. The patient information form lists demographic and insurance information.

_T_ 12. The health insurance professional must obtain written permission from the patient to release health care information to any person or business entity except the patient's insurance carrier.

Short Answer/Fill-in-the-Blanks

1. Name the two major sections of the CMS-1500 claim form.

   PATIENT/INSURANCE INFORMATION

   PHYSICAN/SUPPLIER INFO

2. List the situations when a space is required instead of the usual punctuation or symbols in OCR formatting.

3. When the health insurance professional has completed the claim form, it is crucial that the form be thoroughly examined for __MISTAKES__ and __LEGIBILITY__.

4. What is the health insurance professional's most important task?

   TO SUBMIT CLEAN CLAIMS.

5. Who uses the paper CMS-1500 form?

   SMALL PROVIDERS OF SERVICES/SUPPLIES

6. ASCA prohibits HHS from paying Medicare claims that are not submitted electronically, unless the Secretary grants a(an) __WAVIER__ for this requirement.

7. Define a "small provider."

   A PROVIDER WITH FEWER THAN 25 FULL-TIME EQUIV. EMPLOYEES

8. List three reasons that health care facilities use a patient information form.

TO KEEP RECORDS CURRENT

FOR CURRENT INSURANCE PREPARATION & SUBMISSION

CORRECT DEMOGRAPHIC INFO TO PROPERLY AID PATIENT

9. Explain the rationale for making a photocopy of both sides of a patient's insurance ID card.

THERE MAY BE PATIENT INFO ON THE BACK

10. What is the significance of a patient "assigning benefits"?

IT AUTHORIZES CARRIER TO ASSIGN BENEFITS

11. Define a medical record.

PATIENTS ASSESSMENT, COURSE OF TREATMENT & INVESTIGATION.

12. List six things a complete medical record should provide.

OUTLINE PATIENTS VISITS

DOCUMENT FINDINGS

DETAILED DISCUSSION OF TREATMENT

PROVIDE INFO TO ANY REFERRING PROVIDER

SERVE AS A TEACHING/RESEARCH TOOL

PROVIDE MEANS FOR ASSESING QUALITY CARE

13. List at least six types of information typically found on an encounter form.

ACCOUNTING

DEMOGRAPHIC

PROFESSIONAL SERVICES RENDERED

FEES

CPT & ICD-9 CODES

RETURN PATIENT INFO

14. List at least five reasons why a claim might be rejected.

INCOMPLETE/INVALID PATIENT INFO

DIAGNOSIS OF CORRECT PROCEDURAL CODE

MISSING/IMPROPER MODIFIERS

CHARGES NOT ITEMIZED

PROVIDER SIGNATURE MISSING

15. What are three advantages of electronic claims filing?

IMPROVES CASH FLOW

REDUCES COST OF PROCESSING

STREAMLINES INTERNAL PROCESSES

Critical Thinking Activities

A. You are employed as a health insurance professional in a family practice facility. Eloise Grafton, the office supervisor, asks you to generate a document for the Office Procedures Manual explaining the steps involved in the insurance claims and billing process. Begin with the patient's arrival at the office through the checkout process at the reception area when the encounter is concluded. Include a diagram or a flow chart to enhance understanding.

B. Write a paragraph explaining the purpose and function of the **encounter form.** Be specific and thorough. Use examples as necessary.

Problem-Solving/Collaborative (Group) Activities

A. Carefully examine the completed claim form (Adam Rogers) in Fig. 1-13. Highlight or circle any shaded blocks that contain errors. Then, in Table 1-2, insert a "C" in Column 2 if the information in the block is correct; insert an "I" if it is incorrect. Lastly, illustrate how the information should be entered correctly in Column 3.

1500

HEALTH INSURANCE CLAIM FORM

APPROVED BY NATIONAL UNIFORM CLAIM COMMITTEE 08/05

CARRIER

PICA | | | PICA | | |

1. MEDICARE (Medicare #) | MEDICAID (Medicaid #) | TRICARE CHAMPUS (Sponsor's SSN) | CHAMPVA (Member ID#) | GROUP HEALTH PLAN (SSN or ID) [X] | FECA BLK LUNG (SSN) | OTHER (ID) | 1a. INSURED'S I.D. NUMBER (For Program in Item 1) XQS123456789

2. PATIENT'S NAME (Last Name, First Name, Middle Initial) ROGERS ADAM L | 3. PATIENT'S BIRTH DATE MM 10 DD 21 YY 54 SEX M [X] F | 4. INSURED'S NAME (Last Name, First Name, Middle Initial) SAME

5. PATIENT'S ADDRESS (No., Street) 1500 WEST 50TH ST | 6. PATIENT RELATIONSHIP TO INSURED Self [X] Spouse Child Other | 7. INSURED'S ADDRESS (No., Street)

CITY MILTON | STATE XY | 8. PATIENT STATUS Single [X] Married Other | CITY | STATE

ZIP CODE | TELEPHONE (Include Area Code) ( ) | Employed Full-Time Student Part-Time Student | ZIP CODE | TELEPHONE (Include Area Code) ( )

9. OTHER INSURED'S NAME (Last Name, First Name, Middle Initial) | 10. IS PATIENT'S CONDITION RELATED TO: | 11. INSURED'S POLICY GROUP OR FECA NUMBER

a. OTHER INSURED'S POLICY OR GROUP NUMBER | a. EMPLOYMENT? (Current or Previous) YES NO | a. INSURED'S DATE OF BIRTH MM DD YY SEX M F

b. OTHER INSURED'S DATE OF BIRTH MM DD YY SEX M F | b. AUTO ACCIDENT? PLACE (State) YES NO | b. EMPLOYER'S NAME OR SCHOOL NAME RARITAN HYDRAULICS

c. EMPLOYER'S NAME OR SCHOOL NAME | c. OTHER ACCIDENT? YES NO | c. INSURANCE PLAN NAME OR PROGRAM NAME

d. INSURANCE PLAN NAME OR PROGRAM NAME | 10d. RESERVED FOR LOCAL USE | d. IS THERE ANOTHER HEALTH BENEFIT PLAN? YES NO *If yes,* return to and complete item 9 a-d.

READ BACK OF FORM BEFORE COMPLETING & SIGNING THIS FORM.

12. PATIENT'S OR AUTHORIZED PERSON'S SIGNATURE I authorize the release of any medical or other information necessary to process this claim. I also request payment of government benefits either to myself or to the party who accepts assignment below.
SIGNED *Adam L Rogers* DATE 9/10/XX

13. INSURED'S OR AUTHORIZED PERSON'S SIGNATURE I authorize payment of medical benefits to the undersigned physician or supplier for services described below.
SIGNED

PATIENT AND INSURED INFORMATION

14. DATE OF CURRENT: MM 09 DD 10 YY 20XX ILLNESS (First symptom) OR INJURY (Accident) OR PREGNANCY(LMP) | 15. IF PATIENT HAS HAD SAME OR SIMILAR ILLNESS. GIVE FIRST DATE MM DD YY | 16. DATES PATIENT UNABLE TO WORK IN CURRENT OCCUPATION FROM MM DD YY TO MM DD YY

17. NAME OF REFERRING PROVIDER OR OTHER SOURCE HORNER WILLIAMS MD | 17a. 655432112 17b. NPI 231314800 | 18. HOSPITALIZATION DATES RELATED TO CURRENT SERVICES FROM MM DD YY TO MM DD YY

19. RESERVED FOR LOCAL USE | 20. OUTSIDE LAB? YES NO $ CHARGES

21. DIAGNOSIS OR NATURE OF ILLNESS OR INJURY (Relate Items 1, 2, 3 or 4 to Item 24E by Line)
1. 892 . 0
2. .
3. .
4. .
| 22. MEDICAID RESUBMISSION CODE ORIGINAL REF. NO.
23. PRIOR AUTHORIZATION NUMBER

24. A. DATE(S) OF SERVICE From MM DD YY To MM DD YY	B. PLACE OF SERVICE	C. EMG	D. PROCEDURES, SERVICES, OR SUPPLIES (Explain Unusual Circumstances) CPT/HCPCS MODIFIER	E. DIAGNOSIS POINTER	F. $ CHARGES	G. DAYS OR UNITS	H. EPSDT Family Plan	I. ID. QUAL.	J. RENDERING PROVIDER ID. #
1	09 10 XX 09 10 XX	11		99202	1	60 00	1		NPI	0020202 231314800
2	09 10 XX 09 10 XX	11		90703	1	20 00	1		NPI	0020202 231314800
3									NPI	
4									NPI	
5									NPI	
6									NPI	

PHYSICIAN OR SUPPLIER INFORMATION

25. FEDERAL TAX I.D. NUMBER 42 1898989 SSN EIN [X] | 26. PATIENT'S ACCOUNT NO. | 27. ACCEPT ASSIGNMENT? (For govt. claims, see back) [X] YES NO | 28. TOTAL CHARGE $ 80 00 | 29. AMOUNT PAID $ | 30. BALANCE DUE $

31. SIGNATURE OF PHYSICIAN OR SUPPLIER INCLUDING DEGREES OR CREDENTIALS (I certify that the statements on the reverse apply to this bill and are made a part thereof.) HORNER WILLIAMS MD
Horner Williams MD 09/14/20XX SIGNED DATE | 32. SERVICE FACILITY LOCATION INFORMATION BROADMOOR MEDICAL CLINIC 4353 PINE RIDGE DRIVE MILTON XY 12345-0001 a. X100XX1000 b. | 33. BILLING PROVIDER INFO & PH # ( ) BROADMOOR MEDICAL CLINIC 4353 PINE RIDGE DRIVE MILTON XY 12345-0001 a. X100XX1000 b.

NUCC Instruction Manual available at: www.nucc.org | APPROVED OMB-0938-0999 FORM CMS-1500 (08/05)

Fig. 1-13 CMS-1500 form for Adam Rogers.

TABLE 1-2	Table of Corrections

Block No.	C/I	Corrected Information
2		
3		
5		
10		
11d		
17		
17a		
24b		
24g		
25		
32b		
33		
33a		
33b*		

*After May 23, 2007, Block 33b is not to be reported.

B. Study the insurance ID card in Fig. 1-14. Answer the following questions with regard to the information on the card.

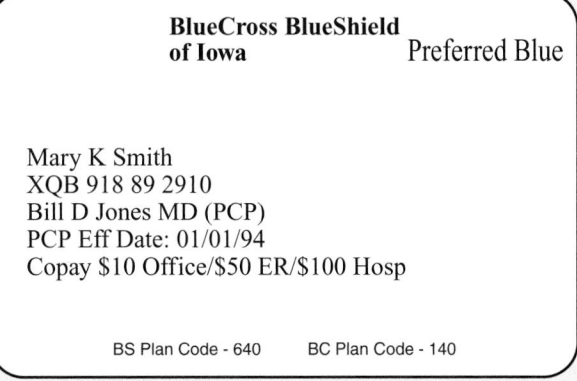

BlueCross BlueShield of Iowa   Preferred Blue

Mary K Smith
XQB 918 89 2910
Bill D Jones MD (PCP)
PCP Eff Date: 01/01/94
Copay $10 Office/$50 ER/$100 Hosp

BS Plan Code - 640   BC Plan Code - 140

Fig. 1-14 Insurance ID card for Mary K. Smith.

1. In whose name is this insurance policy written?
2. What identification code should be entered in Block 1a of the CMS-1500 form?
3. What is the name of the insured's primary care physician?
4. When was this primary care physician assigned to the insured?
5. Explain what the numbers mean in the last line of the card: **Copay $10 Office/$50 ER/$100 Hosp**

Case Studies

A. Using the information on Mary K. Smith's patient information form (Fig. 1-15) and her insurance ID card (see Fig. 1-14), complete Blocks 1 through 13 in the top half of the CMS-1500 claim form (Fig. 1-16).

PATIENT INFORMATION SHEET

Today's date: 6/12/XX

HEAD OF HOUSEHOLD

Head of household: Mary K. Smith

Social Security #: 918-89-2910

Sex: F   Date of birth: 7/24/68

Address: 409 Oak St.

City, St: Milton, XY   Zip 12345

Home phone #: SSS-765-1234

Occupation: Waitress

Employer's name: Grover's Pizza

Employer's address: 1516 Main St.

Employer's City, St: Milton, XY   Zip 12345

Employer's phone #: SSS-766-4321

PATIENT INFORMATION

Patient's legal name: Mary K. Smith   Nickname: —   Relationship to head of household: same

Date of birth _____ Age _____ Sex _____ Marital Status: S

Employer name _____ SAME AS ABOVE   Social Security _____

Employer address _____   Employer phone # _____

City, St: _____ Zip _____   Worker's Compensation Carrier (If applicable): -N/A

Referring Physician: none   Allergies _____

EMERGENCY INFORMATION

Other contact not living with you: Betty Keyes   Home phone# _____   Work phone# _____

Address: Rt 63 Box 112   City: Milton   St XY   Zip 12345

Patient relationship to other contact: daughter   If patient is a child, parent name: N/A

INSURANCE INFORMATION

Primary insurance: BlueCross/BlueShield   Subscriber: Mary K. Smith

ID #: XQB 918-89-2910   Relationship to subscriber: self

Secondary insurance: none   Subscriber _____

ID # _____   Relationship to subscriber _____

OTHER FAMILY MEMBERS:

Name: Darrell P. Beckett   Date of birth: 2/21/90

Name: Cathy M. Beckett   Date of birth: 4/6/95

Name _____   Date of birth: _____

Name _____   Date of birth: _____

I understand that it is my responsibility that any incurred charges are paid.

To the extent necessary to determine liability for payment to obtain reimbursement, process claim forms, I authorize the release of any medical information necessary to process claims.

I hereby assign all medical and/or surgical benefits, to include major medical benefits to whichI am entitled, including Medicare, private insurance, and other health plans to Family Medicine of Mt. Pleasant, P.C.

This assignment will remain in effect until revoked by me in writing, a photocopy of this assignment is to be considered as valid as an original. I hereby authorize said assignee to release all information necessary to secure the payment.

Signed: Mary K. Smith   Date: 6/12/04
If patient is a minor, parent or guardian signature.

Fig. 1-15 Patient information sheet for Mary K. Smith.

Fig. 1-16 Top half of CMS-1500 form (for Mary K. Smith).

B. Using the information in the encounter form (Mary K. Smith) shown in Fig. 1-17, complete the bottom half of the CMS-1500 claim form (Fig. 1-18). Use the following information:

Provider Block	
Broadmoor Medical Clinic	Clinic EIN # 42-1898989
4353 Pine Ridge Drive	Dr. R. L. Jones NPI 1234567890
Milton, XY 12345-0001	Dr. Marilou Lucerno NPI 2907511822
Clinic NPI # X100XX1000	Date claims 1 day after examination
Telephone: 555-656-7890	

BROADMOOR MEDICAL CLINIC

DATE OF SERVICE 6/12/XX

PATIENT ID#: 918892910

PATIENT NAME: Mary K. Smith

PROVIDER NAME: R.L. Jones, M.D.
NPI 1234567890

CHIEF COMPLAINT: Annual exam

CONFIDENTIAL: X

BILLED VISIT? X

Office Vs, New/Est	Code
99201	99211
99202	99212
99203	99213
99204	99214
99205	99215

Telephone Calls	Code
Intermediate	99372
Complex/Lengthy	99373

Prev Medicine, New	Code
5-11 yo	99383
12-17 yo	99384
18-39 yo 130.00	99385

Prev Medicine, Est.	Code
5-10 yo	99393
12-17 yo	99394
18-39 yo	99395

Counseling/Risk Fx	Code
Individual:	
15 min	99401
30 min	99402
45 min	99403
60 min	99404
Group:	
30 min	99411
60 min	99412
Health Risk Assess:	
Administer	99420

AdminVaccine	Code
Administer one:	99471
Admin, ea add'l:	90472
Admin, oral, one:	90473
Admin, oral, ea add'l:	90474

AdminTher Injection	Code
Therapeutic inj	90782
IM antibiotic	90788

Drugs Administered IM/SC	Code
Tetracycline 250 mg	J0120
Ampicillin Na 500 mg	J0290
Rocephin 250 mg	J0696
Depo-Provera 150 mg	J1055
Benadryl to 50 mg	J1200
Erythrocin 500 mg	J1364
Gentamicin to 80 mg	J1580
Wycillan 600,000 U	J2510
Pen G 600,000 U	J2540
Streptomy to 1 Gm	J3000

Vaccine(s)	Code
Adenovirus	90476
BCG/Tb	90585
Cholera	90724
Diptheria	90719
DT	90702
DTaP	90700
DTaP-HepB-IPV	90723
DTaP-HIB	90721
DTP	90701
DTP-HIB	90720
Flu, 3+ yo	90658
Hep A, 2ds	90633
Hep B 2ds	90743
Hep B 3ds	90744
Hep B adult	90746
Hep B/HIB	90748
Hib/HbOC, 4 ds	90645
Hib/PRP-D, boost	90646
Hib/PRP-OMP, 3 ds	90647
Hib/PRP-T, 4 ds	90648
IPV	90713
Measles	90705
Meningococcal	90733
MMR	90707
MMRV	90710
MR	90708
Mumps	90704
OPV	90712
Pneumococcal	90732
Rotavirus, live, oral	90680
Rubella	90706
Td	90718
Tetanus Tox	90703
Typhoid (AKD)	90693
Typhoid (ViCPS)	90691
Typhoid (H-P)	90692
Varicella	90716

Team Conference	Code
Pt not pres, 30 min	99361
Pt not pres, 60 min	99362

Respiratory SystemTx	Code
Peak flow	94200
Nebulizer demo	94664
Repeat neb Tx	94640-76
Pulse oximetry	94760

Inhaled Drugs	Code
Albuterol/0.5 mg	J7618

ScreeningTests	Code
Vision	99173
Hearing (air only)	92551

Allergy Injections	Code
Single inj (OV incl)	95115
2+ inj (OV incl)	95117

Health/Behavior Assess	Code
Initial, ea 15 min	96150
Re-assess	96151
Indiv int'vent/15"	96152
Group/15 min	96153
Family/15 min	96154
Fam w/o pt/15 min	96155

Education	Code
Group	99078
Supplies	99071

Surgical Procedures	Code
I & D:	
abscess	10060
foreign body	10120
Debridement:	
10% body surf	11000
ea add'l 10%	11000
Biopsy:	
lesion, skin	11100
ea add'l lesion	11001
Repair Wound:	
Trunk, ext, scalp, neck:	
2.5 cm or <	12001
Face, ears, nose, lips	
eyelids 2.5 cm or <	12011
Tx dehiscence	12020
Burns:	
1st deg, local	16000
Destruction lesion:	
Flat warts, up to 14	17110
Common warts, 1st	17000
ea add'l wart, 2-14	17003
Penis	54050
Vulva	56501
Removal foreign body:	
Eye, external	65205
Nose	30300
Skin	Office Vs
Removal ear wax	69210
Strain/Sprain	Office Vs

Laboratory:	Code
Venipuncture	36415

CLIAWaivedTests	Code
Glucometer	82962
Hematocrit	85014QW
Hemoglobin	85018QW
Mononucleosis	86308QW
Rapid strep test	87880QW
Urine dipstick	81002
Urine pregnancy	81025

CLIA Phys Perf Micro	Code
Wet mount-any	Q0111
KOH prep	Q0112
UA dip, non-auto, w/micro 15.00	81000
UA dip, auto, w/micro	81001

CLIA Intermediate	Code
CBC 15.00	85025
Chlamydia culture	87110
GC culture	87081
Lead	83655
Sickle cell screen	85660
TB intradermal	86580
Throat culture	87070
Urine culture	87086

CLIA Complex	Code
HIV	86703
PAP smear, thin prep 25.00	88144
VDRL	86592

Diagnosis(es):

1. V 70.0
2.
3.
4.

Signature of provider:

Bill Jones, MD

Return to clinic: 1 year

Fig. 1-17   Encounter form (for Mary K. Smith).

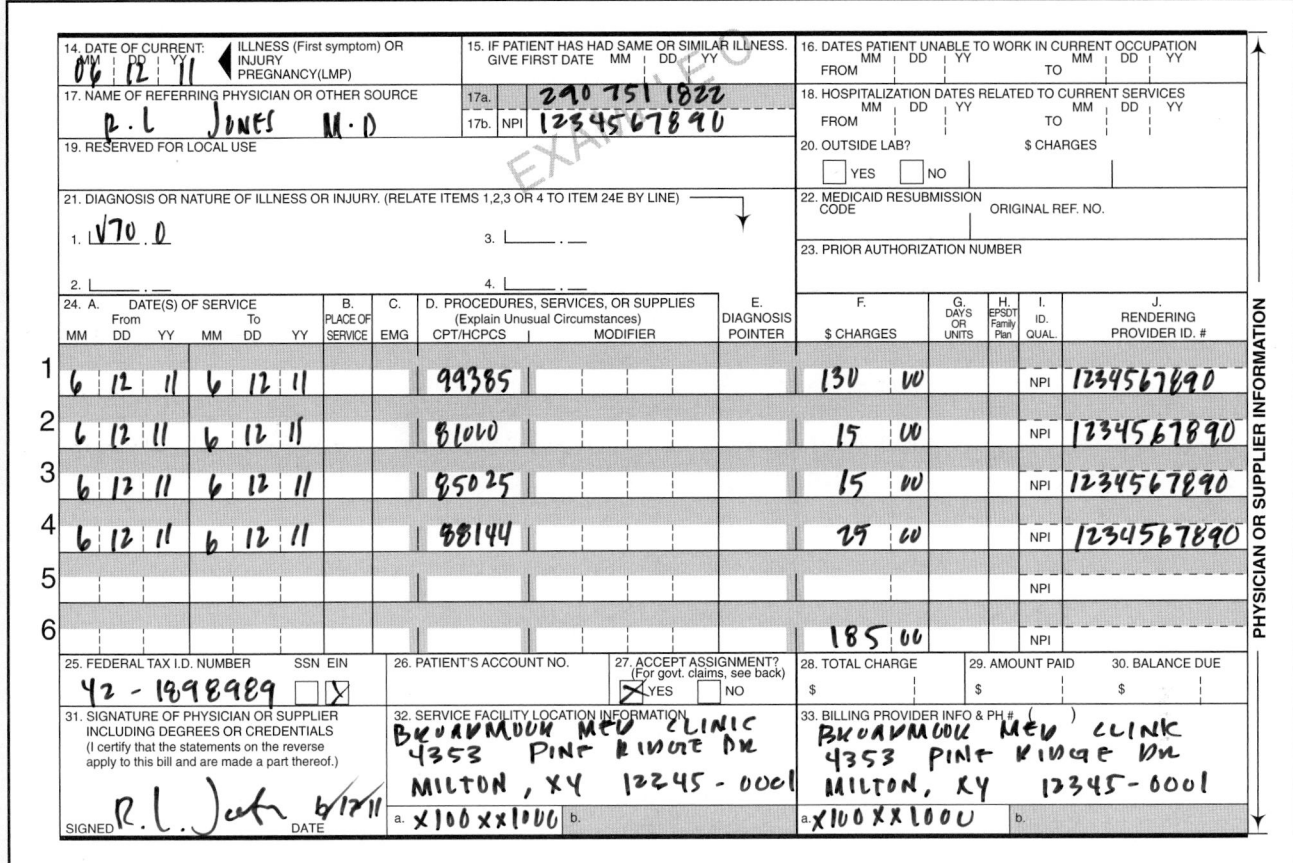

Fig. 1-18   Bottom half of CMS-1500 form (for Mary K. Smith).

Internet Exploration

A. Using the Internet research a specific example of a HIPAA-compliant authorization form for use or disclosure of protected health information (PHI).

B. Your office manager has informed you that the practice is considering electronic claims submission. She has asked you to do some research to find the names of two or three clearinghouses and compare what they have to offer, specifically considering services offered, software and equipment needed, and corresponding costs. Search the Internet using "claims clearinghouse" as your search word, and create a memo to your office manager providing him or her with at least two clearinghouse companies to show a comparison of services provided by the company, their costs, and required equipment/software.

2

OBJECTIVES

After completing this chapter, the student should be able to:

1. Describe fee-for-service (indemnity) insurance.
2. List the various levels of coverage available under a fee-for-service plan.
3. Discuss how a fee-for-service plan works.
4. Define commercial/private insurance.
5. Explain self-insurance.
6. Relate the functions of third-party administrators and administrative services organizations to self-insured organizations.
7. Summarize the Blue Cross and Blue Shield health insurance program.
8. List the various programs administered by Blue Cross and Blue Shield.
9. State the deadline for submitting Blue Cross and Blue Shield claims.

TRADITIONAL FEE-FOR-SERVICE/ PRIVATE PLANS

KEY TERMS

administrative services organization
  (ASO)
autonomy
basic health insurance
BlueCard Program
BlueCard Worldwide
Blue Cross and Blue Shield Federal
  Employee Program (FEP)
carve out
co-insurance
commercial health insurance
comprehensive insurance
covered expenses
deductible

Employee Retirement Income Security Act
  of 1974 (ERISA)
explanation of benefits (EOB)
Federal Employees Health Benefits (FEHB)
  Program
fee-for-service (FFS)/indemnity plan
fiscal intermediary
group insurance
health insurance policy premium
health maintenance organization (HMO)
health care service plans
insurance cap
lifetime maximum cap
major medical insurance

managed care plan
Medicare supplement plans
nonforfeitable interest
participating provider (PAR)
point-of-service (POS) plan
policyholder
preferred provider organization (PPO)
reasonable and customary fee
self-insured/self-insurance
single or specialty service plans
stop loss insurance
supplemental coverage
third-party administrator (TPA)
third-party payer

Opening Scenario

The subject matter of Chapter 2 is traditional fee-for-service insurance, sometimes referred to as indemnity, private, or commercial insurance. Traditional, indemnity, fee-for-service, private, commercial, self-insurance—Emilio and Latisha are amazed that so many different terms can be interrelated. Blue Cross and Blue Shield is a type of insurance they are both familiar with. As Emilio put it, "Who hasn't heard of 'The Blues'?" Emilio's parents currently have a Blue Cross and Blue Shield health insurance policy, and Emilio is still covered on it. Latisha's husband has a family plan with Liberty Value Insurance Company, a commercial carrier, through his employer. The term "commercial" did not have much meaning to Latisha until now, and she is looking forward to learning more about it.

TRADITIONAL FEE-FOR-SERVICE/ INDEMNITY INSURANCE

Fee-for-service (FFS), or **indemnity**, insurance is a traditional type of health care policy wherein the insurance company pays fees for the services provided to the individuals covered by the policy. This type of health insurance offers the most choices of physicians and hospitals. Typically, patients can choose any physician they want and can change physicians at any time. Additionally, they can go to any hospital in any part of the United States and still be covered.

To review, we know why people need health insurance. Today's health care costs are continually increasing, and individuals need to protect themselves from catastrophic financial losses that result from serious illnesses or injuries. If you have health insurance, a third-party payer covers a major portion of your medical expenses. A **third-party payer** is any organization (e.g., Blue Cross and Blue Shield, Medicare, Medicaid, or commercial insurance company) that provides payment for specified coverages provided under the health plan. Many Americans obtain health insurance through their employment, through what is referred to as *group insurance*. **Group insurance** is a contract between an insurance company and an employer (or other entity) that covers eligible employees or members. Group insurance is generally the least expensive kind. In many cases, the employer pays part of the cost, or in some cases, the employer pays all of the cost.

If an employer does not offer group insurance, or if the insurance offered is very limited, a wide variety of individual, private policies are available. Two basic categories of individual health insurance are available: FFS plan or some type of managed care plan. A **managed care plan** typically involves the financing, managing, and delivery of health care services and comprises a group of providers who share the financial risk of the plan or who have an incentive to deliver cost-effective, but quality, service. Options need to be weighed carefully when choosing an individual health care plan because coverage and costs and how comprehensive the coverage is vary considerably from one insurance company to another.

HIPAA TIP

Although HIPAA makes it much easier to get health insurance from a new employer when switching jobs, it does not guarantee the same level of benefits, deductibles, and claim limits the individual might have had under the former employer's health plan.

Looking more closely at these two broad categories of insurance, we find four basic types of plans, as follows:

1. Traditional FFS/indemnity plans
2. **Preferred provider organizations (PPOs)**
3. **Point-of-service (POS) plans**
4. **Health maintenance organizations (HMOs)**

No one type of health care plan is universally better than another. It depends on an individual's (or group's) needs and preferences. FFS health plans can cover everything, but the tradeoff is the cost.

The **autonomy**, or freedom to choose what medical expenses will be covered, offered by FFS plans is attractive to some, whereas others prefer the lower costs associated with most types of managed care.

Traditional FFS insurance is gradually becoming less popular as managed care moves to the forefront in health care. For individuals who value autonomy and flexibility of choices and can afford to spend a little extra money for the type of coverage they prefer, however, an individual health insurance policy may be the best policy for them.

FFS health care offers unlimited choices. The **policyholder** (the individual in whose name the policy is written) controls the choice of physician and facility, from primary caregiver to specialist, surgeon, and hospital. Flexible coverage offered by the FFS usually allows immediate treatment for medical emergencies or unexpected illness. FFS health plans do have restrictions, however. Often, they do not cover preventive medicine, so checkups, routine office visits, and injections are likely to be the patient's responsibility. This can make FFS insurance impractical for a large family that requires many routine visits and preventive care.

IMAGINE THIS!

Maria Solaris is 52 years old and has worked for Olympia Products for 10 years. Her husband, Alonzo, is a self-employed auto mechanic. Olympia offers a comprehensive group health plan to its employees and pays half of their health insurance premium costs. Maria's share of the family plan premium through Olympia is $240 per month. (They have no children eligible for the plan.) Maria and Alonzo decided to purchase a private policy from a company that offers a husband and wife–only plan with basically the same benefits as the group plan with Olympia at a monthly premium rate of $265. Although this private policy is more costly, Maria and Alonzo feel more secure with their new health care plan. If Maria loses her job at Olympia or retires, she and her husband don't have to worry about loss of benefits or preexisting conditions.

Choice does not come cheap. Although it is hard to predict the annual cost of health care under an FFS insurance plan, there are a few costs that are standard, as follows:

- A periodic payment (monthly or quarterly), called a **health insurance policy premium**
- A yearly **deductible** (out-of-pocket payment) before the health insurance carrier begins to contribute

- A per-visit **co-insurance**, or percentage of health care expenses

As a rule, health care services that are not covered by the health insurance policy (e.g., checkups) do not count toward satisfying the deductible. All FFS health plans are not created equal. There are three levels of coverage available:

1. **Basic health insurance**, which includes:
   - Hospital room and board and inpatient hospital care
   - Some hospital services and supplies, such as x-rays and medicine
   - Surgery, whether performed in or out of the hospital
   - Some physician visits
2. **Major medical insurance**, which includes:
   - Treatment for long, high-cost illnesses or injuries
   - Inpatient and outpatient expenses
3. **Comprehensive insurance**, which is a combination of the two

The cost of the FFS plan varies with the level of coverage chosen—the better the coverage, the higher the premiums, and the higher the deductible, the lower the premium. Although indemnity health insurance plans offer choice and security, these advantages are reflected in the cost of the coverage.

WHAT DID YOU LEARN?

1. Name the four basic types of insurance plans.
2. What main advantage does an individual (private) insurance plan offer?
3. List the various levels of coverage available under an FFS plan.

HOW A FEE-FOR-SERVICE PLAN WORKS

With an FFS type of plan, the policyholder pays a periodic fee, referred to as a *premium*. In addition to the premium, a specific amount of money must be paid out-of-pocket each year as costs are incurred before the insurance payments begin. This is called the *deductible*. In a typical plan, the deductible may range from $100 to $10,000. Most family plans require the deductible be paid on at least two people in the family. The deductible requirement applies each year of the policy, and not all health care expenses count toward the deductible—only the expenses specifically covered by the policy. After the deductible for the year has been met, the policyholder (or dependents) shares the cost of services with the insurance carrier. The patient might pay 20% of **covered expenses**—charges incurred that qualify for reimbursement under the terms of the policy contract—whereas the insurer pays 80%. This type of cost sharing is referred to as co-insurance.

Most FFS plans have an **insurance cap** (in some plans, it is called a "stop loss"), which limits the amount of money the policyholder has to pay out-of-pocket for any one incident or in any one year. The cap is reached when out-of-pocket expenses for deductibles and co-insurance total a certain amount. This amount may be $1000 or $5000. After the "cap" is reached, the insurance company pays the reasonable and customary amount in excess of the cap for the items the policy says it will cover and for which co-insurance provision does not apply. (The cap does not include the premiums.)

Also, many FFS policies have a **lifetime maximum cap** the insurer pays. This cap is an amount after which the insurance company would not pay any more of the charges incurred. Often this cap is quite high—$500,000 to $1 million. This can be a "per incident" cap or a "lifetime" cap, depending on the policy.

Most insurance plans pay the **reasonable and customary fee** for a particular service. The phrase "reasonable and customary" is used to refer to the commonly charged or prevailing fees for health services within a geographic area. A fee is generally considered to be reasonable if it falls within the parameters of the average or commonly charged fee for the particular service within that specific community. If the health care provider charges $1000 for a specific procedure, whereas most other providers in the same geographic area charge only $600, the policyholder may be billed for the $400 difference. If the provider is a **participating provider (PAR)**, one who participates through a contractual arrangement with a health care service contractor in the type of health insurance in question, he or she agrees to accept the amount paid by the carrier as payment in full. The policyholder does not have to pay the $400 difference—it is adjusted off, which means the provider absorbs this difference in cost.

IMAGINE THIS!

Jim Benson is seen in Dr. Mueller's office for the removal of a benign cyst of the right hand and is charged $125 for the procedure; however, his insurance carrier's allowed fee for this procedure is only $95. Jim has a 20/80 coverage plan and has met his yearly deductible. The difference between the two charges, or $30, is deducted from the original charged amount, resulting in an insurance payment of $76. If Dr. Mueller is PAR with Jim's insurance carrier, the $30 difference between the original charge and the insurance carrier's allowed charge would have to be adjusted off of Jim's bill. If Dr. Mueller is nonPAR, he can bill Jim for this difference. Jim is still responsible for his 20% share of the allowed charge, or $19.

STOP AND THINK

Dr. Mueller, a family practitioner, asks you, his health insurance professional, for your opinion as to whether or not he should sign a contract and become a PAR provider for Western United Insurance. Olympia Products, a manufacturing plant employing 1350 people in the same city, has a group policy with Western United. What is your opinion?

WHAT DID YOU LEARN?

1. What is an "insurance cap"?
2. How is a "lifetime maximum cap" different from an "insurance cap"?
3. With a PAR provider, what happens to any balance owing after the patient has paid his or her deductible and co-insurance, and the insurer has paid the "allowable" fee?

COMMERCIAL OR PRIVATE HEALTH INSURANCE

What Is Commercial Insurance?

Commercial health insurance (also called "private" health insurance) is any kind of health insurance paid for by someone other than the government. Medicare, Medicaid, TRICARE, and CHAMPVA all are government programs and do not fall into the category of commercial or private plans. There also is one kind of commercial insurance that the government does pay for—the **Federal Employees Health Benefits (FEHB) Program**, which is a government health insurance plan for its own civilian employees.

Government health insurance is standard for each program it sponsors, but commercial health insurance includes many variations in price and the kinds of benefits that the policy covers. The rules about a health insurance policy, such as what benefits are received and what rights the individuals covered under the policy have, depend on two things: the type of insurance (e.g., HMO, FFS) and who is paying for the insurance.

> ## HIPAA TIP
>
> HIPAA protects millions of American workers by offering portability and continuity of health insurance coverage when changing jobs.

Who Pays for Commercial Insurance?

Commercial health insurance usually is paid for by an employer, a union, an employee and employer sharing the cost, or an individual. When the cost of health insurance is shared, the cost to the patient is much less than if he or she is buying health insurance as an individual. Not all jobs come with health insurance, and sometimes individuals are between jobs and not eligible for coverage. In these situations, it may be necessary to consider a private insurance policy to maintain health care coverage.

> ## HIPAA TIP
>
> Under HIPAA, *group* health plans cannot deny an application for coverage based solely on the individual's health status. It also limits exclusions for preexisting conditions.

What Is Self-Insurance?

Some employers are **self-insured**, which means that when an employee needs health care, the employer—not an insurance company—is responsible for the cost of medical services. Most organizations that are self-insured are large entities, which can draw from hundreds or thousands of enrollees. Self-insured plans usually do not have to obey traditional laws governing insurance because they are technically not considered insurance companies.

Employee Retirement Income Security Act of 1974

Self-insured plans sometimes are called ERISA plans. The only law that governs self-insured plans is the federal law known as ERISA, an acronym for the **Employee Retirement Income Security Act of 1974**. ERISA sets minimum standards for pension plans in private industry, which is how most self-insured employers fund their programs.

Self-insured employers typically set up employee benefit plans that provide benefits to employees in the form of life insurance, disability insurance, health insurance, severance pay, and pensions. These benefits are funded through the purchase of insurance policies or through the establishment of trusts, paid for by the employer or the employer and employee. When the money is put into a trust, the employer takes a tax deduction for its contribution to the trust. The trust money is then invested. If an employer maintains a pension plan, ERISA specifies the following:

1. When an employee must be allowed to become a participant
2. How long an employee has to work before acquiring a **nonforfeitable interest** (an amount employees do not have to give up when quitting or retiring) in their pension
3. How long an employee can be away from the job before it affects benefits
4. Whether a spouse has a right to part of an employee's pension in the event of death

Most of these ERISA provisions are effective for plan years beginning on or after January 1, 1975.

Third-Party Administrators/Administrative Services Organizations

Many self-insured groups, such as employers and union trusts, hire **third-party administrators (TPAs)** or **administrative services organizations (ASOs)** to manage and pay their claims. A TPA is a person or organization who processes claims and performs other contractual administrative services. An ASO, similar to a TPA, provides a wide variety of health insurance administrative services for organizations that have chosen to self-fund their health benefits. TPAs and ASOs are neither health plans nor insurers but organizations that provide claims-paying functions for the clients they service. Although historically TPAs and ASOs paid claims only, their functions are expanding. Now these organizations typically perform some or all of the following functions:

- General administrative functions
- Planning
- Marketing
- Human resources management
- Financing and accounting

Many self-insured groups were pioneers in PPO development. As a result, a TPA or ASO may pay claims based on discounted rates negotiated by a PPO on behalf of a self-insured group. A self-insured group may contract directly with providers, or it may use the services of a managed care organization.

Instead of paying premiums to health insurers (who would charge group premiums to pay for the health care services rendered to the group's enrollees), self-insured groups assume the risk of providing such services on their own, usually with some kind of stop loss insurance. **Stop loss insurance** is protection from the devastating effect of exorbitant medical claims. Examples are claims resulting from prolonged or intense medical services resulting from premature births, multiple trauma, transplant, or any other extended care that can result in catastrophic medical fees. Stop loss insurance limits the amount the insurer has to pay to a specified amount.

Single or Specialty Service Plans

Single or specialty service plans are health plans that provide services only in certain health specialties, such as mental health, vision, or dental plans. These health plans developed as people realized that eliminating a specific category of health care (e.g., mental health services) might slow the rate of increasing costs for health care in general and facilitate the management of care within these specialties. Eliminating a certain specialty of health services from coverage under the health care policy is referred to as a **carve out**. Employers wanting to include these special carved-out coverages for their employees can contract with one of these single or specialty service plans that focus on the desired specialty service.

Vision and dental plans and prescription drug coverage often have been add-on or **supplemental coverage** to health plans. Supplemental coverage varies greatly in the benefit services offered and represents another example of single specialty service plans.

> ## HIPAA TIP
>
> There is one major exception to the HIPAA rule on insurance portability: It provides no protection switching from one individual health plan to another individual plan.

> ## WHAT DID YOU LEARN?
>
> 1. Explain the difference between traditional insurance and self-insurance.
> 2. What is the function of TPAs and ASOs?
> 3. How might a "single or specialty service plan" benefit an employee?

BLUE CROSS AND BLUE SHIELD

Overview

Blue Cross and Blue Shield (BCBS) is probably the best-known commercial insurance company in the United States. The Blue Cross and Blue Shield Association, created in 1982, is the result of a merger of the Blue Cross Association and National Association of Blue Shield Plans. The Blue Cross and Blue Shield Association is a national organization of 39 independent regional companies in the United States, including Puerto Rico. BCBS insurance companies are franchisees, independent of the association (and traditionally each other), offering insurance plans within defined regions under one or both of the association's brands. BCBS insurers also act as Medicare administrators in many states or regions of the United States. They also provide group coverage to state government employees and the federal government under a nationwide option of the FEHB Program established by the Association on their behalf. BCBS coordinates and oversees more than 40 independent local programs that provide health care coverage to more than 90 million Americans through indemnity insurance, HMOs, PPOs, POS plans, and FFS plans.

Blue Cross policies primarily cover inpatient hospital care, and Blue Shield policies cover surgery, physician services, and other aspects of medical care. BCBS plans, often referred to as "Blue Plans" or "The Blues," offer health insurance coverage in all 50 states, the District of Columbia, Puerto Rico, and Canada. These plans cover all sectors of the population, including large employer groups, small businesses, and individual consumers and their families. Most health care providers accept BCBS cards.

As mentioned, BCBS offers indemnity and managed care plans. One of their more popular types of managed care plans is referred to as a *preferred provider organization (PPO)*. Under this plan, members have the freedom to choose any provider, but they are encouraged to receive care from PPO network providers. The incentive to use PPO plan providers is that the out-of-pocket costs the member pays are typically less if they choose a provider within the network. Similar to Medicare, BCBS plans have provider identification (ID) numbers and PAR and nonparticipating (nonPAR) provider arrangements. Most plans pay participating providers directly, and the providers agree not to bill the patient for the difference between the plan's allowable charge and the actual fee charged.

History of Blue Cross

In 1929, Justin Ford Kimball, an official at Baylor University in Dallas, Texas, introduced a plan to guarantee schoolteachers 21 days of hospital care for $6 a year. Other groups of employees in Dallas soon joined the plan, and the idea quickly attracted nationwide attention. By 1939, the Blue Cross symbol was officially adopted by a commission of the American Hospital Association as the national emblem for plans that met certain guidelines. In 1960, the commission was replaced with the Blue Cross Association, and all formal ties with the American Hospital Association were severed in 1972.

History of Blue Shield

The Blue Shield concept grew out of the lumber and mining camps of the Pacific Northwest early in the 20th century. Employers wanted to provide medical care for their workers, so they paid monthly fees to "medical service bureaus" composed of groups of physicians. These pioneer programs led to the first Blue Shield Plan, which was founded in California in 1939. The Blue Shield symbol was informally adopted in 1948 by a group of nine plans known as the Associated Medical Care Plans. This group eventually became the National Association of Blue Shield plans.

Blue Cross and Blue Shield Programs

Local chapters of the independent BCBS plans offer products and services uniquely tailored to meet community and individual consumer needs. At the same time, their membership in the Blue Cross and Blue Shield Association enables these local chapters to serve large regional and national employers effectively. Although health care coverage options differ from region to region, they typically include FFS and managed FFS plans and PPO plans. The three-letter alpha prefix that precedes the subscriber number on the BCBS ID card identifies the plan to which the member belongs.

BlueCard and BlueCard Worldwide

The **BlueCard Program** and **BlueCard Worldwide** links independent BCBS plans so that members and their families can obtain health care services while traveling or working anywhere in the United States, receiving the same benefits they would receive if they were at home. The main identifiers for BlueCard members are the alpha prefix; a blank suitcase logo; and, for eligible PPO members, the "PPO in a suitcase" logo. BlueCard member ID

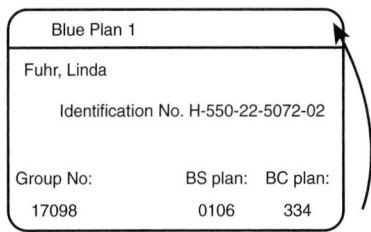

Fig. 2-1 Location on the ID card where suitcase can be found.

numbers also may include alpha characters within the body of the number; however, these alpha characters should not be confused with the three-character alpha prefix that precedes the member number. If the member belongs to a BlueCard PPO, the initials PPO appear inside the suitcase logo (Fig. 2-1).

BlueCard Worldwide provides BCBS plan members inpatient and outpatient coverage at no additional cost in more than 200 foreign countries. BlueCard Worldwide participating hospitals are located in major travel destinations and business centers around the world. When plan members travel or live outside the United States and require inpatient hospital care, all they have to do is show their ID card to any of these participating hospitals, and their claim is handled just as if they were at home. Plan members have the choice of using a nonparticipating hospital; however, they may have to pay the hospital directly and then file a claim with BCBS for reimbursement of covered expenses. The preferred form to file for BlueCard Worldwide claims is shown in Fig. 2-2.

Federal Employees Health Benefits

Congress instituted the FEHB Program in 1960. FEHB is the largest employer-sponsored group health insurance program in the world, covering more than 9 million federal civilian employees, retirees, former employees, family members, and former spouses. Under this program, eligible members of the participating insurance companies (of which BCBS is one) have access to a wide variety of health plans. Choices include various types of plans, as follows:

- FFS
- PPOs
- POS plans
- HMOs (if the individual works within an area serviced by an HMO plan)

Federal Employee Program

The Federal Employees Health Benefits Act is the law governing the FEHB Program. This program provides health benefits coverage for federal

Please see the instructions on the reverse side of this form before completing. Please type or print.

1. Patient Information– 1A. Alpha prefix   Identification number   *Copy this from your Blue Cross Blue Shield identification card.*

1B. Patient's name (First, middle initial, last)	**1C. Patient's date of birth** MM/DD/YY / /	**1D. Patient's sex** ☐ Male ☐ Female	
1E. Name of subscriber (First, middle initial, last)	**1F. Subscriber's date of birth** MM/DD/YY / /	**1G. Patient's relationship to subscriber** ☐ Self ☐ Spouse ☐ Child	

2. Other Health Insurance– Is the patient covered under other health insurance, including Medicare A or B? ☐ Yes   ☐ No
If yes, complete 2A through 2E below.

2A. Name and address of insuring company

2B. Type of policy ☐ Family ☐ Individual	**2C. Effective date** MM/DD/YY / /	**2D. Termination date** MM/DD/YY / /	**2E. Policy or identification number of other coverage**

3. Diagnosis – 3A. Describe illness, injury, or symptoms requiring treatment | **3B. Was patient's treatment due to a work-related accident or condition?** ☐ Yes ☐ No

3C. Complete for care related to accidental injuries
Date of accident _____   Location: ☐ At home ☐ Auto ☐ Other _____
Time of accident _____   *If the accident was caused by someone else, attach a statement describing the accident.*

4. Charges – Use a separate line to list each type of service or provider and attach itemized bills for all services.

4A. Type of provider	4B. Name of provider making charge	4C. Description of service	4D. Dates of service or purchase	4E. Charges

5. Payee– Select one of the following payment options:
5A. ☐ **Make payment to subscriber; provider has been paid.**
Currency– Do you want the check issued in the currency reflected on the itemized bill(s) or in U.S. dollars? ☐ Currency on itemized bill(s) ☐ U.S. dollars
Please specify subscriber name as it appears on bank account: _____

5B. ☐ **Make payment to provider (hospital, doctor). Please complete and sign.**
Authorization for Assignment of Benefits
I, the undersigned, authorize and request Blue Cross and Blue Shield to make payment for benefits due herein to:
Name of provider _____   Signature of subscriber or spouse _____   Date _____

6. Signature – I certify the above is complete and correct and that I am claiming benefits only for charges incurred by the patient named above.

Signature of subscriber or patient _____   Date _____

N20-00-155

Fig. 2-2 Sample international claim form.

General Information

The International Claim Form is to be used to submit institutional and professional claims for benefits for covered services received outside the United State, Puerto Rico, Jamaica and the U.S. Virgin Islands. For filing instructions for other claim types (e.g., dental, prescription drugs, etc.) contact your carrier.

The International Claim Form must be competed for each patient in full, and accompanied by fully itemized bills. It is not necessary for you to provide an English translation or convert currency.

Since the claim cannot be returned, please be sure to keep photocopies of all bills and supporting documentation for your personal records.

International Claim Form Instructions

Please complete all items on the claim form. If the information requested does not apply to the patient, indicate N/A (Not Applicable). Special care should be taken when completing the following items:

2. Other Health Insurance

If the patient holds other insurance coverage, please complete items A through E as completely as possible. It is especially important to indicate the name and address of the other insurance company and the policy or identification number of that coverage, as well as the name and birth date of the person who holds that policy.

In addition, if the patient is someone other than the subscriber and has received benefits from any other health insurance plan held by reason of law or employment, the Explanation of Benefits Form furnished by the other carrier pertaining to these charges must be included with the claim. A clear photocopy of the other carrier's Explanation of Benefits Form is acceptable in place of the original document.

Itemized Bill Information

Each provider's original itemized bill must be attached and must contain:

- The letterhead indicating the name and address of the person or organization providing the service
- The full name of the patient receiving the service
- The date of each service
- A description of each service
- The charge for each service

This completed claim form, together with itemized bills and supporting documentation, should be submitted to:

Smith & Co. Insurance
113 Waverton
Springfield, XY 33142 USA

Fig. 2-2, cont'd

employees. The Office of Personnel Management has overall administration responsibility for the FEHB Program. The Office of Personnel Management also receives and deposits payments to the FEHB Program and remits payment to the carriers. Each carrier is responsible for furnishing ID cards to enrollees, adjudicating claims, and maintaining and reconciling operational and enrollment records.

The **Blue Cross and Blue Shield Federal Employee Program (FEP)** enrolls several million federal government employees, retirees, and their dependents. FEP has covered federal workers and their families since the Federal Employees Health Benefits Act was adopted in 1960. Today, BCBS FEP covers nearly half of all people eligible for FEHB Program benefits. To examine sample BCBS FEP ID cards, refer to the Websites to Explore section at the end of this chapter.

Medicare

BCBS plans have partnered with the U.S. government in administering the Medicare program since its beginning in 1966. BCBS plans helped design the original infrastructure for tracking and processing Medicare payments. Today, the Blue System is the largest single processor (**fiscal intermediary**) of Medicare claims—handling most Part A claims (hospitals and institutions) and more than half of Part B claims from physicians and other health care practitioners. BCBS is not the fiscal intermediary for Medicare in all states, however. A fiscal intermediary is a commercial insurer or agent (e.g., Blue Cross) that contracts with the Department of Health and Human Services (Centers for Medicare and Medicaid Services) for the purpose of processing and administering Part A Medicare claims for reimbursement of health care coverage. In addition to handling financial matters, a fiscal intermediary may perform other functions, such as providing consultative services or serving as a center for communication with providers and making audits of providers' needs.

Health Care Service Plans

Health care service plans, typically operated by BCBS plans throughout the United States, have provided health care coverage for many years. Although they initially were involved in paying claims for indemnity carriers, many health care service plans have developed managed care products to compete with companies offering managed care plans.

Because the individual member BCBS organizations no longer are governed at a national level, each has its own specific guidelines for completing the CMS-1500 claim form. Although guidelines are similar, there may be subtle differences from one plan to the next. To make absolutely certain that

you follow the correct claims completion guidelines for the BCBS plan in your area, log on to the BCBS main website (http://www.bcbs.com/) and insert the appropriate area code.

Medicare Supplement Plans

In addition to indemnity and managed care plans, BCBS offers **Medicare supplement plans**. Medicare supplement insurance is designed specifically to provide coverage for some of the costs that Medicare does not pay, such as Medicare's deductible and co-insurance amounts, and for certain services not allowed by Medicare. If Medicare-eligible patients do not have supplemental coverage, they must pay the deductibles and co-insurance amounts themselves.

WHAT DID YOU LEARN?

1. What type of services does Blue Cross cover?
2. Explain the BlueCard Program.
3. List the various programs offered under the Blue Cross and Blue Shield system.
4. What role does Blue Cross and Blue Shield play in the FEP?

PARTICIPATING VERSUS NONPARTICIPATING PROVIDERS

We will discuss participating (PAR) providers and nonPAR providers in Chapter 15. A PAR provider enters into a contractual agreement with a carrier and agrees to follow certain rules involving claims and payment in return for advantages granted by the carrier. Not all insurance companies offer such contracts to health care providers, but BCBS does. A health care provider who is a PAR with BCBS agrees to

- file claims for all BCBS patients and
- accept the BCBS "allowed" fee as payment in full and write off (adjust) any differences between the fee charged and that which is allowed by BCBS.

Under this contractual agreement, BCBS agrees to

- send payments directly to the provider,
- host periodic staff training seminars,
- offer guides and newsletters at no charge,
- provide assistance with claim problems, and
- publish the practice's information in the BCBS PAR directory.

Providers who are not a part of the aforementioned contractual agreement are referred to as *nonPAR providers*. In this case, providers do not have to file patient claims and can balance bill the difference between their charges and BCBS-allowed charges. The downside is that in many cases BCBS mails payments to the patient rather than the provider, and the health insurance professional must collect the fees directly from the patient unless the patient agrees to assign benefits (in writing). Benefits can be assigned either by having the patient sign Block 13 on the CMS-1500 form or sign a separate assignment of benefits form. Assigning benefits authorizes the third-party carrier to send the payment directly to the provider.

IMAGINE THIS!

Dr. Mueller is nonPAR with Blue Cross and Blue Shield. The medical receptionist neglected to ask new patient Agnes Blank to assign benefits, so Blue Cross and Blue Shield sent the payment for Agnes' medical services directly to her. Agnes cashes the insurance check but fails to pay Dr. Mueller's bill. Statements mailed to Agnes are returned stamped "Moved; no forwarding address."

WHAT DID YOU LEARN?

1. Name two things a Blue Cross and Blue Shield PAR provider must agree to.
2. What special benefits do Blue Cross and Blue Shield extend to PAR providers?

COMPLETING THE CMS-1500 FORM FOR A COMMERCIAL PLAN

Guidelines for completing the CMS-1500 form for commercial claims, as shown in Table 2-1, are basically the same for all carriers with a few subtle differences in certain blocks. Health insurance professionals should be familiar with the guidelines of common carriers that their patients use. These guidelines should be kept handy in a file or portfolio and updated periodically to ensure any changes are noted. When a patient is covered by an insurance company with which the health insurance professional is unfamiliar, the carrier should be called, and guidelines should be requested to facilitate claim submission and to avoid claim delays and rejections.

For an example of how to complete the CMS-1500 claim for a commercial carrier, the Blue Cross and Blue Shield step-by-step guidelines are used in Table 2-1.

WHAT DID YOU LEARN?

1. In what block should the patient's insurance ID number appear?
2. What is the POS code for services rendered in the provider's office?
3. What information might appear in Blocks 17 and 17a and 17b?
4. How do you relate Block 24e with Block 21?

SUBMITTING COMMERCIAL CLAIMS

Blue Cross and Blue Shield member offices publish specialty-specific billing guides to help practitioners code and bill specific services, such as physical medicine, eye care, and home medical equipment. These guides can be viewed online under "Provider Guides" on most member websites. Paper copies also are available on request. Fig. 2-3 shows a CMS-1500 claim form "template" with the shaded blocks indicating those that need to be completed for Iowa Blue Cross and Blue Shield claims. The health insurance professional must keep in mind, however, that claims completion requirements can differ from one commercial carrier to another.

Timely Filing

The time limit for filing claims varies among third-party payers. Providers contracting with BCBS must file claims within 365 days following the last date of service provided to the patient. If a claim is not filed within this timely filing period, BCBS normally does not allow benefits for the claim. If payment on the claim is denied for this reason, the provider cannot collect payment from the patient. Unusual circumstances may allow the provider to request payment past the deadline. Situations such as these are handled on a case-by-case basis.

Filing Commercial Paper and Electronic Claims

Filing CMS-1500 paper claims for commercial carriers is similar to filing claims with all other carriers. If up-to-date guidelines for claims completion for the specific carrier are not on file, the health insurance professional should contact the carrier and request these guidelines. If the provider's office is set up for electronic claims filing, the health insurance professional should contact the carrier before submitting the claims directly to find out what format to use to be compatible. If the provider uses a claims clearinghouse, the clearinghouse manages this process. The Health Insurance Portability and

TABLE 2-1	Step-by-Step Claims Completion Guidelines for Blue Cross and Blue Shield

Block	Block Name	Explanation
1	Type of insurance	Place an "X" in the proper box indicating the type of insurance
1a	Insured's ID number	Enter the patient's ID number as shown on his or her ID card without spaces or dashes
2	Patient's name	Enter patient's full name as it appears on his or her ID card
3	Patient's date of birth	Enter date of birth (MM/DD/YYYY) and sex of the patient
4	Insured's name	Enter the policyholder's name (if the policyholder and the patient are the same, enter "SAME")
5	Patient's address	Enter the patient's complete address and telephone number (do not use PO Box Numbers). Follow OCR formatting rules
6	Patient relationship to insured	Check the appropriate box (most private carriers do not use the box for "Other")
7	Insured's address	Enter the complete address of the policyholder if different from the patient's address reported in Block 5
8	Patient status	Check the applicable box(es)
9	Other insurance information	Required if 11d is marked "yes." If you determine the patient has other health insurance coverage, enter the name of the other insured
9a	Other insured's policy or group number	Enter the other insured's policy or group number
9b	Other insured's date of birth	Enter the other insured's date of birth (MM/DD/YYYY) and sex
9c	Employer's name or school name	Enter the employer's name or school name
9d	Insurance plan	Enter the other insurance plan name or program name
10	Is patient's condition related to	Check the appropriate box if the patient's condition is related to employment, an auto accident, or "other" accident. For auto accident, report the 2-letter state code where the accident occurred
11-11c	Insured's policy group or FECA number	Not required for private payers if there is no secondary private coverage
11d	Another health benefit plan	Request this information from the patient. If the answer is "yes," go back and complete blocks 9a-9d
12	Patient's authorization to release information	Patient (or his/her authorized representative) should sign in this block. If a current release of information is on file, "SIGNATURE ON FILE" or "SOF" is acceptable
13	Assign benefits	Not required if the provider participates in the plan; otherwise, follow the same guidelines as with Block 12
14	Date of current illness/injury/pregnancy	Enter the six- or eight-digit date that applies to accident and medical emergency situations
15	Same or similar illness	Usually not required for private plans; consult specific payer guidelines
16	Dates unable to work	Usually not required for private plans; consult specific payer guidelines
17	Name of referring physician or other source	Enter the name and credentials of the referring physician. For laboratory and x-ray claims, enter the name of physician who ordered the diagnostic services
17a-17b	ID number of referring physician	In Block 17b, enter the NPI of the referring/ordering physician reported in Block 17 (Block 17a is not to be reported after May 23, 2007)
18	Related hospitalization	Enter the dates of any related inpatient hospitalization
19	Reserved for local use	Consult specific payer guidelines

TABLE 2-1	Step-by-Step Claims Completion Guidelines for Blue Cross and Blue Shield—cont'd	

Block	Block Name	Explanation
20	Outside laboratory	Normally not required. Consult specific payer guidelines. "NO" indicates that any reported laboratory tests were performed by the billing entity; "YES" indicates laboratory tests were performed by an outside facility but are being billed on this claim. If "YES," indicate the charges
21	Diagnosis or nature of illness/injury	Enter documented ICD-9-CM code(s). List primary diagnosis code first (if there is more than one diagnosis, indicate in field 24e which diagnosis applies to the procedure being billed on each line item of the claim; narrative descriptions are not acceptable)
22	Medicaid resubmission	Not required by private payers
23	Prior authorization number	Required only for inpatient hospitalization and/or specific diagnostic tests. Consult specific payer guidelines
24	Shaded portion	Some carriers require provider-administered drugs to be reported in the shaded portion of Block 24. In such cases, consult specific payer guidelines
24a	Date of service from/to	For office or hospital outpatient services, list each service on a separate line with the same "from" and "to" dates. The only exceptions in which date spanning is allowed on one line is when billing inpatient services or monthly rental of home medical equipment. For inpatient practitioner visits, date spanning is acceptable as long as the following is true: (1) the service provided is the same procedure code, (2) the dates of service are consecutive, (3) services are submitted within the same month
24b	Place of service	Enter the place of service code by using the applicable two-digit code. If the place of service code does not match the procedure code, or if you leave this field blank, the claim will be returned (these codes can be found in Chapter 1, Table 1-1).
24c	EMG	Enter an "X" or an "E" as appropriate for services performed as a result of a medical emergency; otherwise, leave blank
24d	Procedure codes/modifiers	Enter a CPT or HCPCS code for each line of service. Add a current two-digit CPT or HCPCS modifier when applicable. Consult specific payer guidelines because some payers do not accept all modifiers
24e	Diagnosis code	Link the diagnostic code for the listed service back to Block 21, using numbers 1, 2, 3, or 4, whichever is applicable. Spaces, commas, or dashes are usually not allowed, and some carriers allow only one "pointer" per service. Consult specific carrier guidelines
24f	Total charge	Enter a charge for each service billed on a line. Do not use a $ or decimal point (per OCR instructions)
24g	Days or units	Enter the number of services (in whole numbers) based on the time period or amount designated by the procedure code. To bill anesthesia, submit the actual time in minutes spent administering anesthesia services
24h	EPSDT family plan	Leave blank; not applicable to private insurer claims
24i	ID Qual.	Normally leave blank for private claims. If provider does not have an NPI, consult specific carrier guidelines for appropriate entry
24j	Rendering provider ID number	Enter the rendering provider's NPI in the lower portion of the block. Do not use the shaded portion

Continued

TABLE 2-1   Step-by-Step Claims Completion Guidelines for Blue Cross and Blue Shield—cont'd

Block	Block Name	Explanation
25	Federal tax ID number	Enter the practice's nine-digit federal taxpayer ID number (EIN). Sole proprietors who are not incorporated usually use their Social Security number
26	Patient's account number	Enter the practice's computer-assigned patient number (required for electronic submissions)
27	Accept assignment	Conditionally required; check with carrier in question. When the provider accepts assignment, it indicates that the amount allowed by the insurer will be accepted as payment in full, plus deductible and co-insurance
28	Total charges	Enter the total of all charges from Block 24f (if the number reported in Block 24g is more than 1, multiply that number by the amount reported in Block 24f to arrive at a correct total)
29	Amount paid	Normally leave blank. Consult specific payer guidelines
30	Amount due	Normally leave blank. Consult specific payer guidelines
31	Signature of provider	In addition to the physician/supplier's physical signature, a computer-generated name, a stamp facsimile, or the signature of an authorized person is generally acceptable in this block
32	Service facility location information	Enter the name/address of the facility where services occurred using OCR formatting rules (Some carriers do not require an entry here if the services were performed in the provider's office or in the patient's home. Consult the carrier in question)
32a-32b	Facility information	Enter NPI of service facility in Block 32a. Block 32b is not to be reported after May 23, 2007, unless specifically required by the carrier
33	Billing provider's information and telephone number	Enter the complete billing name, address, and telephone number of the provider
33a-33b		Report the NPI of the billing provider in Block 33a. After May 23, 2007, Block 33b is not to be reported unless specifically required by the carrier

Accountability Act–Administrative Simplification (HIPAA-AS) was passed by Congress in 1996 to set standards for the electronic transmission of health care data and to protect the privacy of individually identifiable health care information.

The step-by-step guidelines for completing a BCBS claim may differ from one state or region to another. Because it is impractical to address every BCBS carrier in the United States, the author has used the guidelines for her state. It is important, however, that you contact your local BCBS office for precise claims completion guidelines.

WHAT DID YOU LEARN?

1. What is the filing deadline for submitting Blue Cross and Blue Shield claims?
2. If the provider's office is set up for electronic claims filing, how can the health insurance professional find out if his or her facility is compatible with the carrier's electronic standards?

COMMERCIAL CLAIMS INVOLVING SECONDARY COVERAGE

It is not unusual for a patient to be covered under a second insurance policy. A typical situation would be when a husband and wife are employed with companies that offer a paid, or partially paid, group insurance plan. Because of the rising costs of health insurance, however, dual coverage is becoming less common. When a situation involving dual coverage arises, it is important to find out which policy is primary and submit the CMS-1500 claim to that carrier first. Usually, the best way to determine primary coverage is to ask the patient. Normally, when a husband and wife are covered under separate policies, primary coverage follows the patient. If the patient is unsure, call his or her employer, or contact the third-party payer directly.

In the case of dual coverage, a CMS-1500 claim should be submitted to the primary carrier first. When the primary carrier has processed the claim

1500

HEALTH INSURANCE CLAIM FORM

APPROVED BY NATIONAL UNIFORM CLAIM COMMITTEE 08/05

PICA ☐☐ | | PICA ☐☐

1. MEDICARE (Medicare #) ☐ MEDICAID (Medicaid #) ☐ TRICARE CHAMPUS (Sponsor's SSN) ☐ CHAMPVA (Member ID#) ☐ GROUP HEALTH PLAN (SSN or ID) ☐ FECA BLK LUNG (SSN) ☐ OTHER (ID) ☐ | 1a. INSURED'S I.D. NUMBER (For Program in Item 1)

2. PATIENT'S NAME (Last Name, First Name, Middle Initial) | 3. PATIENT'S BIRTH DATE MM DD YY SEX M ☐ F ☐ | 4. INSURED'S NAME (Last Name, First Name, Middle Initial)

5. PATIENT'S ADDRESS (No., Street) | 6. PATIENT RELATIONSHIP TO INSURED Self ☐ Spouse ☐ Child ☐ Other ☐ | 7. INSURED'S ADDRESS (No., Street)

CITY | STATE | 8. PATIENT STATUS Single ☐ Married ☐ Other ☐ | CITY | STATE

ZIP CODE | TELEPHONE (Include Area Code) ( ) | Employed ☐ Full-Time Student ☐ Part-Time Student ☐ | ZIP CODE | TELEPHONE (Include Area Code) ( )

9. OTHER INSURED'S NAME (Last Name, First Name, Middle Initial) | 10. IS PATIENT'S CONDITION RELATED TO: | 11. INSURED'S POLICY GROUP OR FECA NUMBER

a. OTHER INSURED'S POLICY OR GROUP NUMBER | a. EMPLOYMENT? (Current or Previous) ☐ YES ☐ NO | a. INSURED'S DATE OF BIRTH MM DD YY SEX M ☐ F ☐

b. OTHER INSURED'S DATE OF BIRTH MM DD YY SEX M ☐ F ☐ | b. AUTO ACCIDENT? PLACE (State) ☐ YES ☐ NO | b. EMPLOYER'S NAME OR SCHOOL NAME

c. EMPLOYER'S NAME OR SCHOOL NAME | c. OTHER ACCIDENT? ☐ YES ☐ NO | c. INSURANCE PLAN NAME OR PROGRAM NAME

d. INSURANCE PLAN NAME OR PROGRAM NAME | 10d. RESERVED FOR LOCAL USE | d. IS THERE ANOTHER HEALTH BENEFIT PLAN? ☐ YES ☐ NO If yes, return to and complete item 9 a-d.

READ BACK OF FORM BEFORE COMPLETING & SIGNING THIS FORM.
12. PATIENT'S OR AUTHORIZED PERSON'S SIGNATURE I authorize the release of any medical or other information necessary to process this claim. I also request payment of government benefits either to myself or to the party who accepts assignment below.

SIGNED _____ DATE _____ | 13. INSURED'S OR AUTHORIZED PERSON'S SIGNATURE I authorize payment of medical benefits to the undersigned physician or supplier for services described below.

SIGNED _____

14. DATE OF CURRENT: MM DD YY ◀ ILLNESS (First symptom) OR INJURY (Accident) OR PREGNANCY(LMP) | 15. IF PATIENT HAS HAD SAME OR SIMILAR ILLNESS. GIVE FIRST DATE MM DD YY | 16. DATES PATIENT UNABLE TO WORK IN CURRENT OCCUPATION MM DD YY MM DD YY FROM TO

17. NAME OF REFERRING PROVIDER OR OTHER SOURCE | 17a. | 17b. NPI | 18. HOSPITALIZATION DATES RELATED TO CURRENT SERVICES MM DD YY MM DD YY FROM TO

19. RESERVED FOR LOCAL USE | 20. OUTSIDE LAB? ☐ YES ☐ NO $ CHARGES

21. DIAGNOSIS OR NATURE OF ILLNESS OR INJURY (Relate Items 1, 2, 3 or 4 to Item 24E by Line)
1. |___.___| 3. |___.___|
2. |___.___| 4. |___.___| | 22. MEDICAID RESUBMISSION CODE ORIGINAL REF. NO.

23. PRIOR AUTHORIZATION NUMBER

24. A. DATE(S) OF SERVICE From MM DD YY To MM DD YY	B. PLACE OF SERVICE	C. EMG	D. PROCEDURES, SERVICES, OR SUPPLIES (Explain Unusual Circumstances) CPT/HCPCS MODIFIER	E. DIAGNOSIS POINTER	F. $ CHARGES	G. DAYS OR UNITS	H. EPSDT Family Plan	I. ID. QUAL.	J. RENDERING PROVIDER ID. #
1									NPI
2									NPI
3									NPI
4									NPI
5									NPI
6									NPI

25. FEDERAL TAX I.D. NUMBER SSN ☐ EIN ☐ | 26. PATIENT'S ACCOUNT NO. | 27. ACCEPT ASSIGNMENT? (For govt. claims, see back) ☐ YES ☐ NO | 28. TOTAL CHARGE $ | 29. AMOUNT PAID $ | 30. BALANCE DUE $

31. SIGNATURE OF PHYSICIAN OR SUPPLIER INCLUDING DEGREES OR CREDENTIALS (I certify that the statements on the reverse apply to this bill and are made a part thereof.)

SIGNED _____ DATE _____ | 32. SERVICE FACILITY LOCATION INFORMATION a. NPI b. | 33. BILLING PROVIDER INFO & PH # ( ) a. NPI b.

NUCC Instruction Manual available at: www.nucc.org | APPROVED OMB-0938-0999 FORM CMS-1500 (08/05)

Fig. 2-3 CMS-1500 "template" with shaded blocks.

CARRIER

PATIENT AND INSURED INFORMATION

PHYSICIAN OR SUPPLIER INFORMATION

and payment is determined, a new claim is sent to the secondary carrier with the original **explanation of benefits (EOB)** from the primary carrier attached. An EOB, also called a remittance notice, is a document prepared by the carrier that gives details of how the claim was adjudicated. It typically includes a comprehensive listing of patient information, dates of service, payments, or reasons for nonpayment (Fig. 2-4).

STOP AND THINK

Carol Bolton is a computer programmer for American Commuter Services (ACS), Inc. She and her dependents are covered under an employer-sponsored group policy, and ACS pays the entire premium. Jim Bolton, her husband, is employed by ESI Repairs and is covered under a similar family plan through his employer. How might it be determined which policy is primary when Carol is seen in the office for her yearly physical?

WHAT DID YOU LEARN?

1. What is the best way to determine primary coverage for a patient who has two insurance policies?
2. What is the purpose of an EOB?

SUMMARY CHECK POINTS

☑ FFS, or indemnity, insurance is a traditional kind of health care policy wherein the insurance company pays fees for the services provided to the insured individuals covered by the policy. This type of health insurance offers the most choices of health care providers.

☑ FFS insurance offers three levels of coverage:
1. *Basic health* includes
   - hospital room and board and inpatient hospital care;
   - some hospital services and supplies, such as x-rays and medicine;
   - surgery, whether performed in or out of the hospital; and
   - some physician visits.
2. *Major medical* includes
   - treatment for long-lasting, high-cost illnesses or injuries and
   - inpatient and outpatient expenses.
3. *Comprehensive* is a combination of the two.

☑ With FFS, the insurance company pays for part of the physician and hospital bills. The patient pays the following:
   - A monthly fee, called a *premium*
   - A certain amount of money each year, known as the *deductible,* before the insurance payments begin (deductible amounts vary with choice, typically from $100 to $5000, and apply to each year of the policy; not all health expenses count toward the deductible)
   - A portion of each charge, called *co-insurance* (after the deductible amount for the year has been met, the patient shares the bill with the insurance company based on certain percentages spelled out in the policy—typically 90/10 or 80/20)

☑ Commercial (or private) health insurance is any kind of health insurance paid for by somebody other than the government.

☑ A self-insured health plan is one for which an employer or other group sponsor, rather than an insurance company, is financially responsible for paying plan expenses, including claims made by group plan members.

☑ TPAs and ASOs are administrative entities that typically perform some or all of the following functions for self-insured plans:
   - General administrative
   - Planning
   - Marketing
   - Human resources management
   - Financing and accounting

☑ The national Blue Cross and Blue Shield Association was formed in the 1982 merger of the Blue Cross Association and the National Association of Blue Shield Plans. BCBS insurers also act as Medicare administrators in many states or regions of the United States. They also provide group coverage to state government employees and the federal government under a nationwide option of the Federal Employees Health Benefit Program established by the Association on their behalf. Plan choices include the following:
   - FFS
   - PPOs
   - POS plans
   - HMOs

☑ More than 80% of health care providers in the United States accept BCBS patients.

**Explanation of
Health Care Benefits
THIS IS NOT A BILL**

Page Number
1

Identification No.:	111-23-4567
Patient Name:	Sarah M. White
Provider Name:	Dean P. Locks, MD

Ildludddllulluudllublulludddllulllulludl
MURRAY L. WHITE
3434 West Covington Place
Somewhere, XY 12345

Benefits Summary

Billed Charges	Provider Savings	Other Insurance Settlement	Blue Cross Blue Shield Settlement	Amount You Owe
136.00				136.00

Claim Details

Place of Service	OFFICE		OFFICE		OFFICE		OFFICE	
Description of Service	MEDICAL CARE		LABORATORY		LABORATORY		LABORATORY	
Service Date: From/To	12/11 12/11/03	Notes	12/11 12/11/03	Notes	12/11 12/11/03	Notes	12/11 12/11/03	Notes
Billed Charge	90.00		18.00		18.00		10.00	
Provider Savings (-)								
Contract Limitations (-)			11.00		11.00		6.25	
Copayment (-)								
Deductible (-)	90.00		7.00		7.00		3.75	
Sub-Total				1		1		1
Coinsurance								

Please see the back of this form for the "Definition of Terms."

Group Number	Claim Number	Account Number	Provider Number	Date Received	Date Processed
000059999–2104	05040190981500	A–0000960	17437	01–19–04	01–20–04

NOTES

1–YOU MAY BE MISSING OUT ON SAVINGS THAT YOU WOULD RECEIVE IF SERVICES HAD BEEN
PERFORMED BY A BLUE CROSS AND BLUE SHIELD PARTICIPATING PROVIDER. (Z183)

$107.75 OF THIS CLAIM HAS BEEN APPLIED TO YOUR BASIC BLUE CROSS AND BLUE SHIELD
DEDUCTIBLE. FOR THE PERIOD BEGINNING ON 10/01/02 THROUGH 12/31/03, THIS PATIENT HAS
SATISFIED $2969.42 OF THE $5000.00 DEDUCTIBLE. (Z551)

530-409 C-5356 (MD) 7/02

Fig. 2-4   Sample explanation of benefits.

Continued

NOTES KEY

A. Your benefit plan covers accidental injury, medical emergency and surgical care. Other medical care received in the hospital's outpatient department or practitioner's office is not covered by your benefit plan.

B. The services identified on this claim do not meet the criteria of a medical emergency as defined in your benefit plan.

C. These services and/or supplies are not a benefit for the diagnosis, symptom or condition given on the claim.

D. These services are not covered by your benefit plan as described in the *Services Not Covered* section.

E. Routine physical exams and related services are not covered by your benefit plan as described in the *Services Not Covered* section.

F. These services were not performed within the time limit for treatment of accidental injury.

G. Routine vision examinations, eyeglasses, or examinations for their prescription or fittings are not covered by your benefit plan as described in the *Services Not Covered* section.

H. The services of this provider are not covered by your benefit plan.

I. These services exceed the maximum allowed by your benefit plan as described in the *Summary of Payment* section.

J. These services were received before you satisfied the waiting period required by your benefit plan as described in *Your Payment Obligations* section.

K. These services were not submitted within timely filing limits. Timely filing requires that we receive claims within 365 days after the end of the calendar year you receive services.

L. Using the identification number provided, we are unable to identify you as a member.

M. These services were performed before your benefit plan became effective.

N. These services were performed after your benefit plan was cancelled.

O. This individual is not covered by your benefit plan.

P. This individual may be eligible for Medicare. File this claim first with Medicare, if the individual has no other group health coverage as primary.

Q. The Plan in the state where these services were received will process this claim. Your claim has been sent to that Plan for processing.

R. These services have been billed to the wrong plan. Please forward your claim to the plan named on your identification card for processing.

S. These services are a duplication of a previously considered claim.

T. All or part of these services were paid by another insurance company or Medicare.

U. We have received no response to our request for additional information. Until this information is received, the claim is denied.

V. Personal convenience items or hospital-billed non-covered services are not covered by your benefit plan as described in the *Services Not Covered* section.

W. Services covered by Workers' Compensation are not covered by your benefit plan as described in the *Services Not Covered* section.

X. These services should be billed to the carrier that provides your hospital or medical coverage.

DEFINITION OF TERMS

Billed Charge: The total amount billed by your provider. *(If your coverage is Select and you receive covered services in the office of a Select provider, your coinsurance is based on this amount).*

Coinsurance: The amount, calculated using a fixed percentage, you pay each time you receive certain covered services.

Copayment: The fixed dollar amount you pay for certain covered services.

Deductible: The fixed dollar amount you pay for covered services before benefits are available.

Sub-Total: The amount reached by subtracting from the billed charge the following applicable amounts: provider savings; contract limitations; copayment and deductible. Your coinsurance is calculated on this amount *(unless your coverage is Select and you receive covered services in the office of a Select provider. In this case, your coinsurance is based on billed charge).*

Settlement: The total amount fulfilled by us as a result of our agreement with the provider; or the amount we pay directly to you.

Other Insurance Settlement: The total amount settled by another carrier (or us) because you are covered by more than one health plan.

Provider Savings: The amount saved because of our contracts with providers. For some inpatient hospital services, this amount may be an estimate. See explanation of payment arrangements in your benefits certificate.

Contract Limitations: Amounts for which you are responsible based on your contractual obligations with us. Examples of contract limitations include all of the following:

- Amounts for services that are not medically necessary.
- Amounts for services that are not covered by this certificate.
- Amounts for services that have reached contract maximums.
- If you receive services from a nonparticipating provider, any difference between the billed charge and usual, customary, and reasonable (UCR) amount.
- Penalty amounts for services that are not properly precertified.
- Penalty amounts for receiving inpatient hospital services from a nonparticipating hospital.

NOTICE OF RIGHT TO APPEAL AND ERISA RIGHTS

If you disagree with the denial, or partial denial of a claim, you are entitled to a full and fair review.

1. Submit a WRITTEN request for a review within 180 days OF THE DATE OF THIS NOTICE. Your request should include:

   - Date of your request;
   - Your printed name and address (and name and address of authorized representative if you have designated one);
   - The identification number and claim number from your Explanation of Health Care Benefits;
   - The date of service in question.

2. Send your request to:

Fig. 2-4, cont'd

BCBS underwrites or administers many plans, including the following:
- BlueCard and BlueCard Worldwide Programs
- FEHB Program
- FEP
- Health care service plans
- Medicare supplement plans

 BCBS claims must be filed within 365 days following the last date of service provided to the patient.

Closing Scenario

Some of the topics in this chapter turned out to be a little more challenging than Emilio and Latisha had anticipated, especially the concept of self-insurance. Both students found the information on Blue Cross and Blue Shield particularly interesting, and they were already aware that it was a large and well-known organization. They had seen TV commercials on "The Blues," but they had not known how the organization got its start. Compared with today's costs, the idea of hospital room and board costing $6 a day was difficult to comprehend.

Emilio recalls changing physicians 2 years ago because the practice from which his family received most of their medical care discontinued their participating provider contract with Blue Cross and Blue Shield. He was unaware at the time, however, of the ramifications of a provider being either PAR or nonPAR. Now, he realizes how this difference can affect the patient directly.

Latisha is focusing her attention on the Blue Cross and Blue Shield guidelines for completing the CMS-1500 claim form. Many of the patients in the health care facility where she previously worked were covered under a Blue Cross and Blue Shield preferred provider plan, and she was familiar with how that plan functioned.

WEBSITES TO EXPLORE

- A wealth of information about Blue Cross and Blue Shield can be found on the following website:

  http://www.bluecares.com

- For more information on HIPAA-AS, log on to

  http://www.hipaadvisory.com

Chapter Review

Assessment

Multiple Choice

Directions: *In the questions/statements presented, choose the response that **best** answers/completes the stem, and circle the letter that precedes it.*

1. The type of health insurance that offers the most choices of providers, in which patients can choose any provider they want and can change providers at any time is a(an) __D__.
   A. managed care plan
   B. indemnity plan
   C. FFS plan
   D. B or C

2. An example of a third-party payer is __D__.
   A. a commercial insurance company
   B. Blue Cross and Blue Shield
   C. Medicare/Medicaid
   D. all of the above

3. Group insurance typically is __C__.
   A. the most expensive kind
   B. paid entirely by the employer
   C. a contract between an insurance company and an employer
   D. mandated by the federal government

4. The type of insurance that comprises a group of providers who share the financial risk of the plan or who have an incentive to deliver cost-effective, but quality, service is a(an) __A__.
   A. managed care plan
   B. indemnity plan
   C. FFS plan
   D. B or C

5. The best type of health care plan is a(an) __D__.
   A. HMO
   B. indemnity plan
   C. PPO
   D. No one type is universally best

6. Most FFS plans include the patient paying a __D__.
   A. periodic payment (premium)
   B. yearly deductible
   C. per-visit coinsurance
   D. all of the above

7. The typical levels of coverage in an FFS plan include __A__.
   A. basic/major medical/comprehensive
   B. basic/preventive care/planned care
   C. outpatient/inpatient/emergency
   D. auto/workers' comp/long-term care

8. With FFS insurance, which of the following is typically true?
   A. Only employers can offer it through a group policy.
   B. The higher the deductible, the lower the premium.
   C. All health care expenses count toward the yearly deductible.
   D. After the yearly deductible is met, the policy covers 100% of services.

9. The amount of money the policyholder has to pay out-of-pocket for any one incident or in any 1 year is limited by __A__.
   A. yearly deductible
   B. per-visit co-insurance
   C. insurance cap
   D. periodic premium

10. When the fee charged by a provider falls within the parameters of the fee commonly charged for that particular service within a specific geographic area, it is said to be __C__.
    A. medically necessary
    B. a participating fee
    C. reasonable and customary
    D. Medicare approved

11. A provider who signs a contractual arrangement with a third-party insurance contractor and agrees to accept the amount paid by the carrier as payment in full is referred to as a __A__.
    A. participating provider (PAR)
    B. nonparticipating provider (nonPAR)
    C. primary care provider (PCP)
    D. principal attending physician (PAP)

12. The government health insurance program that provides coverage for its own civilian employees is called __C__.
    A. Medicare
    B. Medicaid
    C. Federal Employees Health Benefits (FEHB) Program
    D. Blue Cross and Blue Shield

13. When the employer—not an insurance company—is responsible for the cost of its employees' medical services, the employer has a __C__.
    A. workers' compensation program
    B. third-party group plan
    C. self-insured program
    D. disability benefits plan

14. The federal law designed to protect the rights of beneficiaries of employee benefit plans offered by employers and that sets minimum standards for pension plans in private industry is called __C__.
    A. Social Security
    B. Workers' compensation
    C. Employee Retirement Income Security Act (ERISA)
    D. Consolidated Omnibus Budget Reconciliation Act (COBRA)

15. A person or organization that processes claims and performs other contractual administrative services is commonly referred to as a __A__.
    A. third-party administrator (TPA)
    B. management commissioner (MC)
    C. fiscal intermediary
    D. third-party payer

True/False

Directions: *Place a "T" in the blank preceding the statement if it is true; place an "F" if it is false.*

___F___ 1. With managed health care, patients can choose any physician they want and can change physicians any time.

___T___ 2. A third-party payer is any organization that provides payment for specified coverages provided under a health plan.

___F___ 3. Group insurance is generally more expensive because it covers more individuals.

___T___ 4. Traditional FFS insurance is gradually becoming less popular than managed care.

___T___ 5. With FFS insurance, the policyholder controls the choice of physician and facility.

___F___ 6. FFS plans all have the same deductible amount.

___T___ 7. "Reasonable and customary" is a term used to refer to the commonly charged or prevailing fees for health services within a geographic area.

___T___ 8. Commercial health insurance is standard in price and the kinds of benefits that the policy covers.

___T___ 9. Most organizations that are self-insured are large entities, which can draw from hundreds or thousands of enrollees.

___T___ 10. Stop-loss insurance is protection from the devastating effect of exorbitant medical claims.

___T___ 11. Blue Cross policies cover inpatient hospital care; Blue Shield covers physicians' services.

___F___ 12. Blue Cross and Blue Shield offers only indemnity (FFS) plans.

___F___ 13. If an individual belongs to a BlueCard PPO, the initials PPO appear inside a blue globe.

___F___ 14. Blue Cross and Blue Shield organizations are no longer governed at a national level, and each has its own specific guidelines for completing the CMS-1500 claim form.

___T___ 15. It is important to consult all patient insurance plans for their specific guidelines to avoid claim delays and rejections.

___T___ 16. Normally, when husband and wife are covered under separate policies, primary coverage follows the patient.

___T___ 17. An explanation of benefits (EOB) is a document prepared by the carrier that gives details of how the claim was adjudicated.

___F___ 18. The time limit for filing claims is the same for all third-party payers—1 year.

___F___ 19. Filing CMS-1500 paper claims for commercial carriers is much the same as with all other carriers.

___T___ 20. HIPAA mandates that all commercial claims be submitted electronically.

Short Answer/Fill-in-the-Blank

1. Name four basic types of plans.

FFS — FEES FOR SERVICE

PPO — PREFERRED PROVIDER ORGANIZATION

POS PLANS — POINT OF SERVICE

HMO — HEALTH MAINTAINANCE ORGANIZATION

2. List three out-of-pocket costs that are standard for patients to pay with FFS plans.

CO-INSURANCES

DEDUCTIBLE

HEALTH INSURANCE POLICY PREMIUM

3. List four functions commonly performed by TPAs and administrative services organizations.

MARKETING

FINANCING & ACCOUNTING

PLANNING

HUMAN RESOURCE MANAGEMENT

4. Explain what a "carve out" is and give an example.

ELIMINATING ~~ELIMAN~~ A SPECIALTY IN HEALTH COVERAGE

5. Explain (in your own words) the difference between a PAR and a nonPAR provider.

A PAR MEANS IVE ACCEPTED THE PROVIDERS PAYMENT AS FULL

6. What is a fiscal intermediary, and what functions does it perform?

INFRASTRUCTURE FOR TRACKING & PROCESSING CLAIMS

7. Explain what is meant by "timely filing" as it relates to claims.

THEY HAVE 365 DAYS FROM ORGINAL DATE TO FILE CLAIM.

8. Timely filing for Blue Cross and Blue Shield claims is _____365_____ days.

Critical Thinking Activities

A. You are working as a health insurance professional at Silverstone Mental Health Clinic. Patient Philippe Sanchez comes in for an appointment with Dr. Gerald T. Field, a psychiatrist. This is Mr. Sanchez's first visit to the clinic. Fig. 2-5 shows Mr. Sanchez's completed patient information form. There are two insurance companies listed, with Sunset Assurance, a family policy in his wife's name, listed first. The second one is a single policy in the patient's name. Mr. Sanchez explains that the family policy is in Maria's name through her employer, but it does not cover treatment for mental health. "Send my bill to the packing plant," he states. "They will take care of it." Further questions only confuse Mr. Sanchez, and it is apparent that he knows little about the two policies. How can you, the health insurance professional, determine the following?

- Which carrier is actually primary?
- Do both policies cover mental health treatment?
- Should you send a claim to both third-party payers?
- Where would you find out more information about the coverage of the American Indemnity policy and the Sunset Assurance policy?

Registration Data

1. Your Name   Sanchez   Philippe   M   Sex ☒ Male   Date of Birth 06/16/1969
         (Last)   (First)   (Middle)   ☐ Female

2. Social Security #:   111-22-3333   Marital Status: S (M) D Se W

3. Address: 811 46th St.   4. SSS-621-8765
         (Street)   (Phone)

    Wilton   X Y   12345
      (City)   (State)   (Zip)

5. Employer: Southwest Packers Inc   Occupation: Inspector

    Employer Address: Hwy 409 West, Wilton   SSS-621-5432
                             (Work Phone)

    Spouse: Maria   Employer: Wilton Comm. Schools Occupation: Teacher Aide

    Employer Address: 1667 Parkway, Wilton   SSS-621-8864
                             (Work Phone)

6.

Other Household Members	Date of Birth	Relationship
Emilio	05/03/1995	Son
Rita	01/24/1998	daughter
	/ /	
	/ /	
	/ /	

7. Medical Insurance Information

	Ins. Company Name	Policy No.	Policy Holder	Type of Coverage			
				Sgl.	Fmly.	Primary	Sec.
(1)	Sunset Assurance	001-445678	Maria	☐	☒	☐	☐
(2)	American Indemnity	046911FML	Philippe	☒	☐	☐	☐
( )				☐	☐	☐	☐

8. Person to Contact in an Emergency   Maria   Relationship to you   Wife
                                                                DOB 03/18/1972

    Their Work Phone SSS-621-8864   Their Home Phone SSS-621-8765

9. Party with primary responsibility for payment: ☒ Self   ☐ Other

    Name _____   Relationship to you _____

    Address _____   Home Phone _____

For Office Use Only

Date Completed _____   Account No. _____   Patient No. _____

Household Status   ☐ Head of Household

    ☐ Spouse   ☐ Child   ☐ Other: _____

    Head of Household Name _____

Fig. 2-5 Registration data sheet for Philippe Sanchez.

B. Eloise Stout comes to the orthopedic clinic (where you work) for treatment of a Colles' fracture. She informs you that she lives out of state and is here on vacation visiting her daughter. Fig. 2-6 shows a facsimile of her insurance ID card. From the information on the ID card, answer the following questions:

- What Blue Cross and Blue Shield plan does the patient have?
- What does the alpha prefix signify?
- If a "suitcase logo" appeared in the upper right-hand corner of this card (as it normally does with this specific program), what would it indicate?
- Will the patient be able to receive the same benefits as she would at home?
- What form will you use to submit the claim?
- Where will you send the completed claim?

Note: You may have to go to a website for some answers. Use "Blue Card Program" as search words.

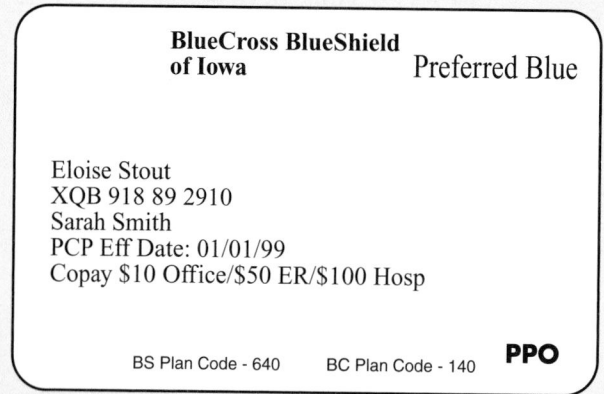

Fig. 2-6   Sample of a Blue Cross and Blue Shield ID card.

Note: Blue Cross and Blue Shield's address is 2604 West 32nd, Des Moines, IA 52230.

C. Many health insurance professional students have difficulty understanding the differences between Blue Cross and Blue Shield's Federal Employee Program (FEP) and the FEHB Program. Write a critical thinking paragraph briefly explaining each program and highlight the differences.

D. Following are two patient scenarios. Using the criteria given, calculate the total amount each patient will have to pay out-of-pocket, including the co-insurance and deductible. Assume in both cases that Blue Cross and Blue Shield's usual, customary, and reasonable fee for this procedure is $4250 and none of the yearly deductible has been met.

Patient No. 1

Steven Barnes	**Provider is PAR**
Cholecystectomy	Charge: $5000
Deductible: $500	Co-insurance 80/20
Total patient responsibility	

Patient No. 2

Sylvia Manley	Provider is nonPAR
Hysterectomy	Charge: $5000
Deductible: $250	Co-insurance 90/10
Total patient responsibility	

Illustrate on the portions of the following ledger cards how these charges and payments would be posted. The amount in the current balance column should reflect the total out-of-pocket amount the patient owes.

Note: When posting services/payments, make sure you include the date the insurance claim was submitted (1 day after service) and the date the claim was paid (3/13/20XX).

Patient No. 1 (Steven Barnes)

Date of Service	Procedure/Service	Amount Charged	Amount Paid	Adjustments	Current Balance
02/13/20XX	Cholecystectomy	5000.00			5000.00

Patient No. 2 (Sylvia Manley)

Date of Service	Procedure/Service	Amount Charged	Amount Paid	Adjustments	Current Balance
02/13/20XX	Hysterectomy	5000.00			5000.00

Case Studies

A. Review the Patient Information Form for Philippe Sanchez (see Fig. 2-5). Assume you have contacted American Indemnity and learned that they are primary and will accept claims submitted on the universal form (CMS-1500). Complete the top portion of the claim form (Fig. 2-7), using the information from his registration data. (American Indemnity's address is 2345 West Palm Avenue, Petaluma, CA, 99001.) (Patient has an up-to-date release of information and assignment of benefits on file.)

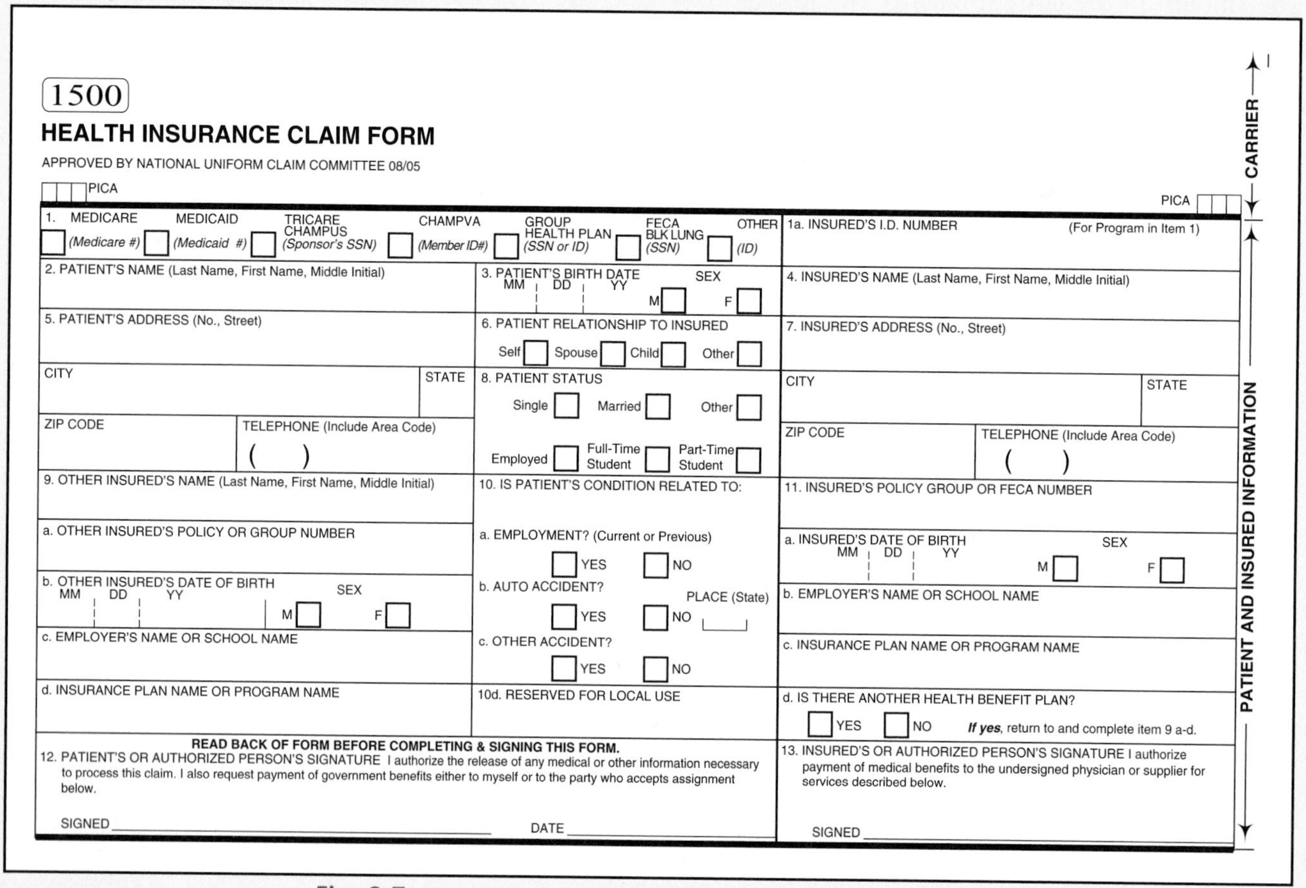

1500

HEALTH INSURANCE CLAIM FORM

APPROVED BY NATIONAL UNIFORM CLAIM COMMITTEE 08/05

PICA — PICA

1. MEDICARE (Medicare #) MEDICAID (Medicaid #) TRICARE CHAMPUS (Sponsor's SSN) CHAMPVA (Member ID#) GROUP HEALTH PLAN (SSN or ID) FECA BLK LUNG (SSN) OTHER (ID)

1a. INSURED'S I.D. NUMBER (For Program in Item 1)

2. PATIENT'S NAME (Last Name, First Name, Middle Initial)

3. PATIENT'S BIRTH DATE MM DD YY SEX M F

4. INSURED'S NAME (Last Name, First Name, Middle Initial)

5. PATIENT'S ADDRESS (No., Street)

6. PATIENT RELATIONSHIP TO INSURED Self Spouse Child Other

7. INSURED'S ADDRESS (No., Street)

CITY STATE

8. PATIENT STATUS Single Married Other

CITY STATE

ZIP CODE TELEPHONE (Include Area Code) ( )

Employed Full-Time Student Part-Time Student

ZIP CODE TELEPHONE (Include Area Code) ( )

9. OTHER INSURED'S NAME (Last Name, First Name, Middle Initial)

10. IS PATIENT'S CONDITION RELATED TO:

11. INSURED'S POLICY GROUP OR FECA NUMBER

a. OTHER INSURED'S POLICY OR GROUP NUMBER

a. EMPLOYMENT? (Current or Previous) YES NO

a. INSURED'S DATE OF BIRTH MM DD YY SEX M F

b. OTHER INSURED'S DATE OF BIRTH MM DD YY SEX M F

b. AUTO ACCIDENT? YES NO PLACE (State)

b. EMPLOYER'S NAME OR SCHOOL NAME

c. EMPLOYER'S NAME OR SCHOOL NAME

c. OTHER ACCIDENT? YES NO

c. INSURANCE PLAN NAME OR PROGRAM NAME

d. INSURANCE PLAN NAME OR PROGRAM NAME

10d. RESERVED FOR LOCAL USE

d. IS THERE ANOTHER HEALTH BENEFIT PLAN? YES NO *If yes*, return to and complete item 9 a-d.

READ BACK OF FORM BEFORE COMPLETING & SIGNING THIS FORM.

12. PATIENT'S OR AUTHORIZED PERSON'S SIGNATURE I authorize the release of any medical or other information necessary to process this claim. I also request payment of government benefits either to myself or to the party who accepts assignment below.

SIGNED ______ DATE ______

13. INSURED'S OR AUTHORIZED PERSON'S SIGNATURE I authorize payment of medical benefits to the undersigned physician or supplier for services described below.

SIGNED ______

CARRIER — PATIENT AND INSURED INFORMATION

Fig. 2-7 Top half of CMS-1500 form (for Philippe Sanchez).

B. The encounter form in Fig. 2-8 documents procedures, services, and a diagnosis for Susan Martin, a 9-year-old girl. Fig. 2-9 shows her completed patient information sheet. Using these two documents, complete the following tasks:

1. Complete the patient ledger card in Fig. 2-10 for this patient.
2. Using the information on the encounter form (see Fig. 2-8) and the completed ledger card (see Fig. 2-10), complete the bottom half (provider/supplier section) of the claim form in Fig. 2-11.

BROADMOOR MEDICAL CLINIC

PRACTICE #
0 4

ACCT. #:	DATE OF SERVICE:	CATEGORY:	DIAGNOSIS:
02 201	12/04/20XX		787.0/780.6

PATIENT'S NAME: Martin, Susan A.

CPT	✔	DESCRIPTION	FEE	CPT	✔	DESCRIPTION	FEE	CPT	✔	DESCRIPTION	FEE
OFFICE VISIT - NEW PATIENT				**IMMUNIZATIONS**				**INJECTIONS (CONT'D.)**			
99201		Focused		90701		DtaP		J3410		Vistaril	
99202		Expanded		90632		Hep A (Adult)		J3420		Vitamin B12	
99203		Detailed		90633		Hep A (Ped)		J2000		Xylocaine	
99204		Comprehensive		90744		Hep B (Ped)		**PROCEDURES**			
99205		Complex		90746		Hep B (Adult)		46600		Anoscopy	
OFFICE VISIT - ESTABLISHED PATIENT				90737		Hib		92551		Audio Screening	
99211		Minimal		90657		Influenza		11730		Avulsion Nail, Partial or	
99212	✔	Focused	80.00	90707		MMR				Complete, Single	
99213		Expanded		90732		Pneumococcal		11200		Rem. of Skin Tags up to 15	
99214		Detailed		90718		Td		11201		Each Additional 10	
				90703		Tetanus Toxoid		10060		I & D Simple Abscess	
				90716		Varicella		10120		Removal FB Skin	
PHYSICAL EXAM - NEW PATIENT								11740		I & D Subung. Hematoma	
99381		Age Under 1 Year		**INJECTIONS**				58310		IUD Removal	
99382		Age 1 - 4 Years		J1200		Benadryl up to 50 mg		94010		Spirometry	
99383		Age 5 - 11 Years		J0540		Bicillin up to 1,200,000 mg		A4570		Splint	
99384		Age 12 - 17 Years		J0690		Cefazolin Sodium 250 mg		99173		Vision Screening	
99385		Age 18 - 39 Years		J0704		Celestone		**LABORATORY**			
99386		Age 40 - 64 Years		J0780		Compazine		82270		Blood Occult	
99387		Age 65+ Years		J1100		Decadron		85680		TB Intradermal	
				J0970		Delestrogen		81000		Urine Dip Stick	
PHYSICAL EXAM - ESTABLISHED PATIENT				J1050		Depo Provera		84703		Serum Pregnancy Test	
99391		Age Under 1 Year		J1510		Gamma Globulin		87082		Strep Screen	
99392		Age 1 - 4 Years		J3301		Kenalog					
99393		Age 5 - 11 Years		J1940		Kasix		36415		Venipuncture	
99394		Age 12 - 17 Years		J2550		Phenergan		99000		Handling	
99395		Age 18 - 39 Years		J3490		Rocephin					
99396		Age 40 - 64 Years		J1070		Testosterone		**MISCELLANEOUS**			
99397		Age 65+ Years		J3250		Tigan					
				J1885		Torodol					

ICD-9 ☐ DIAGNOSIS

CARDIOLOGY
794.31 ☐ Abn Ekg
786.50 ☐ Chest Pain, Nos
780.4 ☐ Dizziness And Giddiness
787.1 ☐ Heartburn
272.0 ☐ Hypercholesterolem
272.4 ☐ Hyperlipidemia Nec/Nos
401.1 ☐ Hypertension Benign
401.9 ☐ Hypertension Nos
401.0 ☐ Hypertension, Malig.
785.1 ☐ Palpitations
ENDOCRINE
250.01 ☐ IDDM Controlled
250.03 ☐ IDDM Uncontrolled
250.02 ☐ NIDDM Uncontrolled
250.00 ☐ NIDDM Controlled
251.2 ☐ Hypoglycemia
244.9 ☐ Hypothyroidism
242.90 ☐ Hyperthyroidism
EAR, NOSE, THROAT
386.30 ☐ Labyrinthitis Nos
382.9 ☐ Otitis Media, Ac./Chr.
462. ☐ Pharyngitis Acute
477.9 ☐ Rhinitis, Allergic
461.9 ☐ Sinusitis, Ac Nos
473.9 ☐ Sinusitis, Chronic
528.0 ☐ Stomatitis
034.0 ☐ Strep Throat

388.30 ☐ Tinnitus Nos
463. ☐ Tonsillitis, Acute
474.0 ☐ Tonsillitis, Chronic
FEMALE / GYNECOLOGY
795.0 ☐ Abn Pap Smear-Cervix
793.8 ☐ Abn Findings-Breast
626.0 ☐ Amenorrhea
611.72 ☐ Breast Mass/Lump
616.0 ☐ Cervicitis
V25.09 ☐ Contracept. Mgmt.
625.3 ☐ Dysmenorrhea
626.4 ☐ Menstruation, Irreg.
625.2 ☐ Menstruation, Excessive
614.9 ☐ Pelvic Inflam Dis
V22.2 ☐ Preg State, Incidental
616.10 ☐ Vaginitis
PHYSICAL EXAM
V20.1 ☐ Well Child
V72.84 ☐ Pre-Op Exam
GASTRO-INTESTINAL
789.06 ☐ Abnormal Pain, Epigastric
794.3 ☐ Abn. Liver Function Study
578.1 ☐ Blood in Stool
564.0 ☐ Constipation
787.91 ☐ Diarrhea
562.11 ☐ Diverticulitis
530.81 ☐ Esophageal Reflux
535.5 ☐ Gastritis/Duodenitis Nos
455.6 ☐ Hemorrhoids

787.0 ☒ Nausea And Vomiting
533.90 ☐ Peptic Ulcer Nos
569.3 ☐ Rectal Bleeding
GENITO-URINARY
585. ☐ Chronic Renal Failure
595.0 ☐ Cystitis Acute
788.1 ☐ Dysuria
599.7 ☐ Hematuria
601. ☐ Prostatitis Acute
599.0 ☐ UTI
HEMATOLOGY
790.6 ☐ Abn Blood Chemistry Nec
285.9 ☐ Anemia Nos
280.1 ☐ Anemia, Iron Def
INFECTIOUS
616.3 ☐ Abcess: Bartholin Gland
682.9 ☐ Abcess: Skin
780.6 ☒ Fever: Unkn. Origin
IMMUNOLOGY - ALLERGIES
995.3 ☐ Allergic Reaction Nos
477.0 ☐ Allergy, Hay Fever
042. ☐ Human ImmunoVirus Dis.
ORTHOPEDICS
716.90 ☐ Arthritis Unspec.
724.5 ☐ Backache Nos
727.3 ☐ Bursitis Nec
354.0 ☐ Carpal Tunnel Syndrome
719.40 ☐ Joint Pain-Unspec.
729.1 ☐ Myalgia And Myositis Nos.

733.00 ☐ Osteoporosis
845.00 ☐ Sprain: Ankle
847.2 ☐ Sprain: Back
847.0 ☐ Sprain: Cervical
840.9 ☐ Sprain: Shoulder
729.81 ☐ Swelling of Limb
726.00 ☐ Tendonitis
NEUROLOGY
784.0 ☐ Headache
346.9 ☐ Migraine Nos
724.3 ☐ Sciatica
307.81 ☐ Tension Headache
780.4 ☐ Vertigo
OPHTHALMOLOGY
373.00 ☐ Blepharitis Nos
372.30 ☐ Conjunctivitis
918.1 ☐ Corneal Abrasion
PULMONARY / RESPIRATORY
493.9 ☐ Asthma Nos
466.0 ☐ Bronchitis Acute
490. ☐ Bronchitis Nos
486. ☐ Pneumonia
786.2 ☐ Cough
786.0 ☐ Dyspnea/Resp Abn
487. ☐ Influenza
786.52 ☐ Painful Respiration
786.09 ☐ SOB
465.9 ☐ URI
079.9 ☐ Viral Syndrome

PSYCH / MENTAL HEALTH
303.9 ☐ Alcoholism
300.00 ☐ Anxiety State Nos
300.00 ☐ Depression
SKIN / DERMATOLOGIC
706.1 ☐ Acne Nec
691. ☐ Dermatitis, Atopic
692. ☐ Dermatitis, Contact
110.1 ☐ Dermatophytosis, Nail
691.0 ☐ Diaper Rash
054.9 ☐ Herpes Simplex Nos
053.9 ☐ Herpes Zoster Nos
054.10 ☐ Herpes Genital Nec
684. ☐ Impetigo
703. ☐ Ingrowing Nail
215.9 ☐ Nevus
110.1 ☐ Onychomycosis
696.1 ☐ Psoriasis
706.2 ☐ Sebaceous Cyst
708.8 ☐ Urticaria Nec
078.1 ☐ Warts, Viral
OTHER - MISC.
780.7 ☐ Malaise and Fatigue
780.2 ☐ Syncope
WRITE - IN

INSTRUCTIONS:
fluids & rest
OTC acetominophen for fever
No RX at this time

RETURN APPOINTMENT:		PAID		
___ Days ___ Weeks ___ Months ☒ PRN		☐ CASH	PREV. BAL.	146.50
		☐ CHECK	TODAY'S FEE	80.00
___ 15 ___ 30 ___ 45		☐ CR. CD.	AMT. REC'D.	10.00

Fig. 2-8 Encounter form (for Susan Martin).

PATIENT INFORMATION SHEET

Today's date: 12/04/20XX

HEAD OF HOUSEHOLD

Head of household: Anna P. Costello

Social Security #: 333-00-1111

Sex: F   Date of birth: 4/2/76

Address: 603 Maplelawn

City, St: Wilton, XY   Zip: 12345

Home phone #: SSS-621-1111

Occupation: seamstress

Employer's name: Apex Mattress Factory

Employer's address: North Ft. Gaslight Rd.

Employer's City, St: Wilton, XY   Zip: 12345

Employer's phone #: SSS-621-2330

PATIENT INFORMATION

Patient's legal name: Susan Ann Martin   Nickname: _____   Relationship to head of household: daughter

Date of birth: 6/1/19XX   Age: 9   Sex: F   Marital Status: _____

Employer name: student   Social Security #: 911-999-0000

Employer address: _____   Employer phone #: _____

City, St: _____   Zip: _____   Worker's Compensation Carrier (If applicable): _____

Referring Physician: _____   Allergies: penicillin

EMERGENCY INFORMATION

Other contact not living with you: Patsy Evans   Home phone#: SSS-654-3210   Work phone#: _____

Address: 26 Fox Ct, #152   City: Wilton   St: XY   Zip: 12345

Patient relationship to other contact: grandmother   If patient is a child, parent name: Anna Costello

INSURANCE INFORMATION

Primary insurance: BCBS   Subscriber: Anna Costello

ID #: XYZ911999000   Relationship to subscriber: daughter

Secondary insurance: _____   Subscriber: _____

ID #: _____   Relationship to subscriber: _____

OTHER FAMILY MEMBERS:

Name _____   Date of birth: _____

Name _____   Date of birth: _____

Name _____   Date of birth: _____

Name _____   Date of birth: _____

I understand that it is my responsibility that any incurred charges are paid.
   To the extent necessary to determine liability for payment to obtain reimbursement, process claim forms, I authorize the release of any medical information necessary to process claims.
   I here by assign all medical and/or surgical benefits, to include major medical benefits to which I am entitled, including Medicare, private insurance, and other health plans to Family Medicine of Mt. Pleasant, P.C.
   This assignment will remain in effect until revoked by me in writing, a photocopy of this assignment is to be considered as valid as an original. I hereby authorize said assignee to release all information necessary to secure the payment.

Signed: Anna P. Costello   Date: 12/04/20XX
If patient is a minor, parent or guardian signature.

Fig. 2-9 Patient information sheet (for Susan Martin).

STATEMENT

BROADMOOR MEDICAL CLINIC
4353 Pine Ridge Drive
Milton, XY 12345-0001
Telephone: 555-656-7890

DATE	PROFESSIONAL SERVICE DESCRIPTION	CHARGE		CREDITS		CURRENT BALANCE	
				PAYMENTS	ADJUSTMENTS		

Due and payable within 10 days.   **Pay last amount in balance column**

Fig. 2-10 Blank patient ledger card (for Susan Martin).

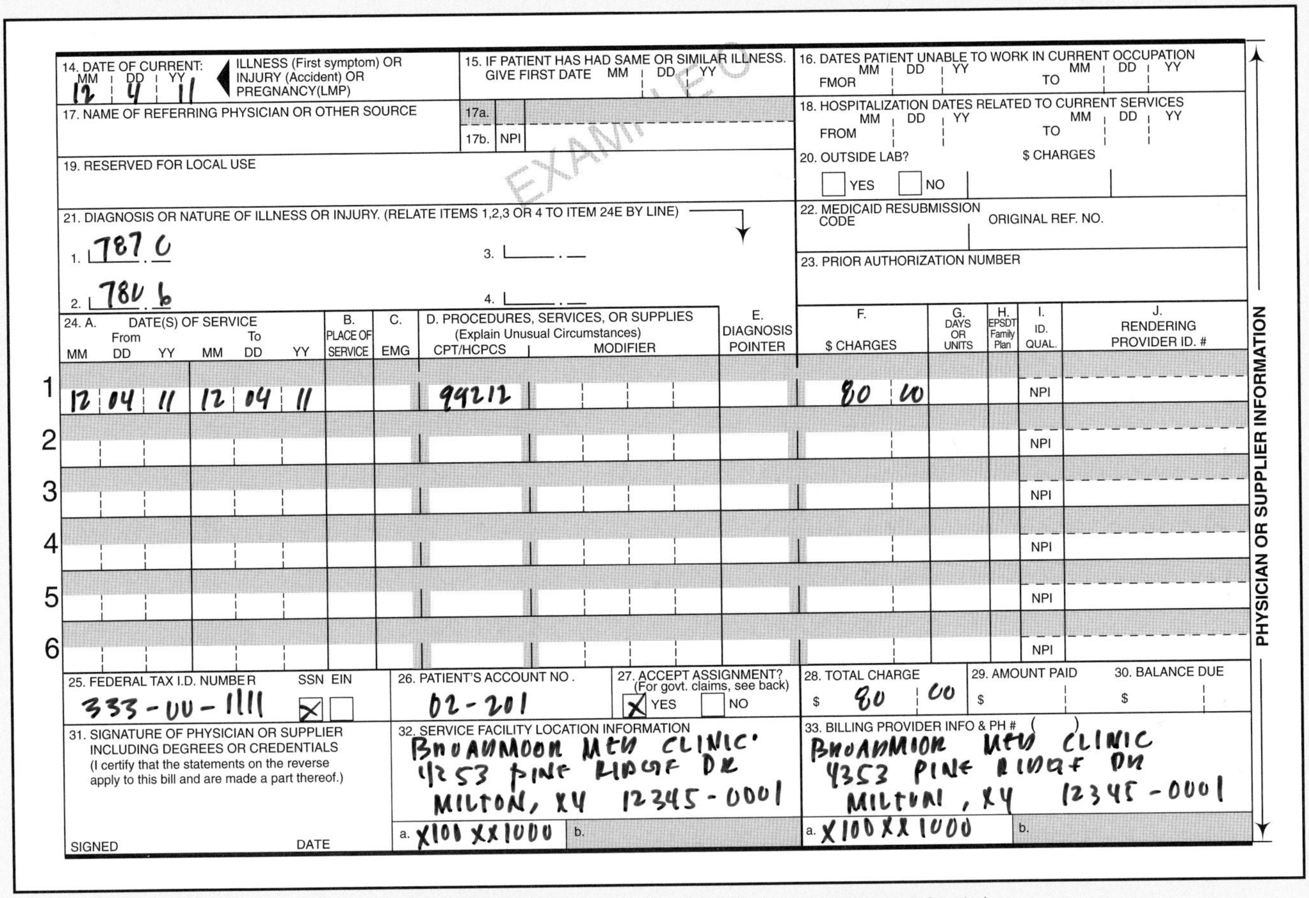

14. DATE OF CURRENT: ILLNESS (First symptom) OR INJURY (Accident) OR PREGNANCY(LMP) — MM DD YY: 12 4 11

15. IF PATIENT HAS HAD SAME OR SIMILAR ILLNESS. GIVE FIRST DATE MM DD YY

16. DATES PATIENT UNABLE TO WORK IN CURRENT OCCUPATION FROM / TO

17. NAME OF REFERRING PHYSICIAN OR OTHER SOURCE — 17a. 17b. NPI

18. HOSPITALIZATION DATES RELATED TO CURRENT SERVICES FROM / TO

19. RESERVED FOR LOCAL USE

20. OUTSIDE LAB? YES NO $ CHARGES

21. DIAGNOSIS OR NATURE OF ILLNESS OR INJURY. (RELATE ITEMS 1,2,3 OR 4 TO ITEM 24E BY LINE)
1. 787.0
2. 780.6
3.
4.

22. MEDICAID RESUBMISSION CODE — ORIGINAL REF. NO.

23. PRIOR AUTHORIZATION NUMBER

24. A. DATE(S) OF SERVICE From MM DD YY	To MM DD YY	B. PLACE OF SERVICE	C. EMG	D. PROCEDURES, SERVICES, OR SUPPLIES CPT/HCPCS	MODIFIER	E. DIAGNOSIS POINTER	F. $ CHARGES	G. DAYS OR UNITS	H. EPSDT Family Plan	I. ID. QUAL.	J. RENDERING PROVIDER ID. #
1 12 04 11	12 04 11			99212			80 00			NPI	
2										NPI	
3										NPI	
4										NPI	
5										NPI	
6										NPI	

25. FEDERAL TAX I.D. NUMBER: 333-00-1111 — SSN [X] EIN [ ]

26. PATIENT'S ACCOUNT NO.: 02-201

27. ACCEPT ASSIGNMENT? (For govt. claims, see back) [X] YES [ ] NO

28. TOTAL CHARGE $ 80 00 — 29. AMOUNT PAID $ — 30. BALANCE DUE $

31. SIGNATURE OF PHYSICIAN OR SUPPLIER INCLUDING DEGREES OR CREDENTIALS (I certify that the statements on the reverse apply to this bill and are made a part thereof.) SIGNED DATE

32. SERVICE FACILITY LOCATION INFORMATION: BROADMOOR MED CLINIC, 4353 PINE RIDGE DR, MILTON, XY 12345-0001 — a. X100XX1000 b.

33. BILLING PROVIDER INFO & PH # ( ): BROADMOOR MED CLINIC, 4353 PINE RIDGE DR, MILTON, XY 12345-0001 — a. X100XX1000 b.

PHYSICIAN OR SUPPLIER INFORMATION

Fig. 2-11 Bottom half of CMS-1500 form (for Susan Martin).

C. Let's assume that in Case Study A, Mr. Sanchez's mental health treatment is covered under both of the policies he listed on his new patient registration form. You have determined that Maria's family policy through Wilton Community Schools is primary. Explain the procedure for filing dual claims when the patient is covered under a secondary policy.

Broadmoor Medical Clinic	Clinic EIN # 42-1898989
4353 Pine Ridge Drive	Dr. R.G. Jones NPI 1234567890
Milton, XY 12345-0001	Dr. Marilou Lucero NPI 2907511822
Clinic NPI X100XX1000	Group # GRW0000
Telephone: 555-656-7890	Date claim 1 day after examination

D. Examine the EOB form shown in Fig. 2-12, then match each column number with the correct written explanation by placing the correct column number in the blank space preceding the written explanation.

___8___ Amount applied to co-insurance

___11___ Amount patient is responsible for paying

___3___ Amount the provider charged for each service

___5___ Amount(s) applied to co-pay, deductible, or not covered

___6___ Balance the insurer will apply to benefits

___9___ Coordination of benefits adjustment

___2___ Date(s) patient received services

___1___ Description of services rendered

___4___ Fee adjustment

___7___ Percentage of coverage

___10___ Total amount paid by insurance plan

EXPLANATION OF BENEFITS

(This is NOT a bill)

July 1, 2002

Group number:	0000123
Member:	Jane M Sample
Member's ID:	123456789 02
Claim number:	8000000001
Provider:	Smith, Robert
Payment Reference ID:	2002062510100013

1	2	3	4	5	6	7	8	9	10	11
Service/product description	Dates you received service/product (m/d/y to m/d/y)	Charges billed by provider	Minus provider's fee adjustment	Minus your copay (C), deductible (D) or amount not covered (*)	Total amount eligible for benefits	%	Minus your co-insurance amount	Plus or (minus) coordination of benefits adjustment	Total paid by your plan	Amount you're responsible for
OFFICE VISIT	06/15/02 06/15/02	75.00	12.00	15.00 C	48.00	100%			48.00	15.00
LAB	06/15/02 06/15/02	89.12	15.36	50.00 D	23.76	100%			23.76	50.00
X-RAY	06/15/02 06/15/02	100.00	20.00		80.00	80%	16.00		64.00	16.00
SURGERY	06/15/02 06/15/02	50.00		50.00 575	0.00	0%			0.00	$0.00
Totals		**$314.12**	**$47.38**	**$115.00**	**$151.76**		**$16.00**		**$135.76**	**$131.00**

Your 2002 medical deductible satisfied so far: $100.00
Your 2002 family medical deductible satisfied so far: $300.00

Amount we paid your provider: $135.76

Amount you're responsible for: $131.00

* **Message Codes:**

575   This procedure is considered cosmetic. Your plan does not cover cosmetic services.

Fig. 2-12 Explanation of benefits form.

Internet Exploration

A. Blue Cross and Blue Shield is one of the most popular insurers in the United States. Log on to their website (http://www.bcbs.com) and research the available information to answer the following questions:

1. Who should the health insurance professional contact when there is a billing question?

2. List the various types of coverage Blue Cross and Blue Shield offers its enrollees.

3. Blue Cross and Blue Shield has _____ member companies and covers approximately

   _____ (number) of people.

4. What is "Blueworks"?

5. What type of coverage would you likely purchase if you were traveling outside of the United States?

6. To submit a claim for medical care overseas, you complete a(an) _____ and send it to

   the _____.

B. Search the Blue Cross and Blue Shield Association website, and locate the current guidelines for completing the new CMS-1500 form in your particular area.

C. Log on to the Blue Cross and Blue Shield website. Under "Media Resources," there is an informational item titled "Guidelines for the Role of Participating Physicians in Health Plans." Read and study this article and be prepared for an in-class discussion.
http://www.bcbs.com/bluefinder

D. Using search words "PAR versus nonPAR providers," search the Internet for advantages and disadvantages of each. Then prepare for a debate/in-class discussion on this topic.

E. Log on to http://www.bcbs.com and click on "Blueworks." Surf the topics under the caption "What the Blues Are Doing Now." Do any of these items relate to your state? If so, research the topic(s) and prepare a 3- to 5-minute oral presentation to the class highlighting new Blue Cross and Blue Shield programs/initiatives to improve health care. If your state is not among the topics listed, choose one that you find of particular interest to present.
http://www.bcbs.com/blueworks/index.html

OBJECTIVES

After completion of this chapter, the student should be able to:

1. Explain the concept of managed care.
2. Discuss the structure of the two major types of managed care organizations.
3. List and explain briefly the various health maintenance organization models.
4. Evaluate the advantages and disadvantages of managed care.
5. Identify and explain the role of the two managed care accrediting organizations.
6. Discuss the utilization review process.
7. Explain the function of pre-authorization, precertification, and referral forms.
8. Analyze the future predictions of managed care.

UNRAVELING THE MYSTERIES OF MANAGED CARE

KEY TERMS

capitation
closed panel HMO
consultation
co-payment
direct contract model
enrollees
grievance
group model
health maintenance organization (HMO)

iatrogenic effects
individual practice association (IPA)
managed care
network
network model
open panel plan
point of service (POS)
pre-authorization

precertification
predetermination
preferred provider organization (PPO)
primary care physician (PCP)
referral
specialist
staff model
utilization review

Opening Scenario

Emilio and Latisha had heard a lot about managed care before they enrolled in the course, but they did not think they fully understood the term and its effect on health care in general. Both students remember hearing stories on the news of medical cases gone wrong because of an HMO's refusal to pay for certain services; however, they are determined to remain open-minded regarding these controversial issues. They are prepared to learn the pros and cons of all facets of medical insurance and realize that there is a lot to learn in this particular area of health care.

Latisha has gotten a part-time job at Isis Health Care. She is certain her new job will offer a great deal of insight into managed care because many of the patients visiting the facility are enrolled in a preferred provider organization. She admits that she does not fully understand the ramifications of this type of managed care.

Emilio has decided to volunteer at the free clinic in his neighborhood, which he hopes will foster his understanding of health insurance and what it means to be a health insurance professional. His mentor at the clinic has explained how their HMO functions. Similar to Latisha, Emilio still has a lot of unanswered questions. Both students are anticipating the information this chapter offers and are confident their questions will be answered and their uncertainty put to rest.

WHAT IS MANAGED CARE?

No doubt you have heard the term "managed care." Managed care is on television news broadcasts nearly every day; it's in the papers; it's everywhere you go! But exactly what is managed care? We learned what traditional fee-for-service (indemnity) insurance was in Chapter 2. In this chapter, we attempt to unravel the mysteries of managed care.

The cost of health care is increasing rapidly. In the 1970s, there was a growing concern within the general population with how much individuals in the United States had to pay for health care. Experts developed some ideas for controlling, or "managing," these costs. Managed care has changed the face of health care in the United States today, and it is no doubt here to stay. **Managed care** is a complex health care system in which physicians, hospitals, and other health care professionals organize an interrelated system of people and facilities that communicate with one another and work together as a unit, commonly referred to as a **network**. This network coordinates and arranges health care services and benefits for a specific group of individuals, referred to as **enrollees**, for the purpose of managing cost, quality, and access to health care. A managed care organization (MCO) typically performs three main functions (Fig. 3-1):

- MCOs set up the contracts and organizations of the health care providers who furnish medical care to the enrollees.
- MCOs establish the list of covered benefits tied to managed care rules.
- MCOs oversee the health care they provide.

Managed care has strongly influenced the practice of medicine. The principles of managed health care shown in Fig. 3-1 represent key components in promoting effective managed care techniques that are fair and equitable to physicians in ensuring that high-quality health care services are delivered to patients. MCOs and third-party payers are strongly encouraged to use these guidelines in developing their own policies and procedures. In addition, any public or private entities that evaluate MCOs or their contracted entities for purposes of certification or accreditation are encouraged to use these principles in conducting their evaluations.

IMAGINE THIS!

Managed care is not a new idea or even a recent one. Its origins can be traced back to the 1880s, when German Chancellor Otto Van Bismarck developed a form of prepaid health insurance for his

1. Managed care organizations should encourage access to health coverage—including those individuals with the greatest health risk.
2. Managed care organizations must recognize physicians' principal role in making medical decisions and guarantee strong physician leadership.
3. Managed care organizations should promote members' health by ascertaining that health plans and providers have incentives to provide high-quality medical care.
4. Managed care organizations should be accountable for the health of members by preventing, as well as managing, diseases and illnesses.
5. Managed care organizations are ultimately accountable for the health of the enrollees and for the outcomes of the treatment they receive.
6. Managed care organizations should communicate the outcomes of their services based on valid measures of medical quality.
7. To fulfill their responsibility to society and the communities they serve, managed care organizations should work together with public sector agencies to resolve gaps between commercial insurance and "safety net" programs.
8. Managed care organizations can help the government fulfill its responsibility to ensure health care for all through the provision of a more cost-effective and comprehensive system of care.

Fig. 3-1 Principles of managed health care.

workers as a means of warding off plans for a government-run insurance program in Germany. In the United States, the original form of managed care dates back to 1933, when a young California surgeon accepted the invitation of Henry Kaiser to provide his workers health care on a prepaid basis, and the Permanente Foundation Hospital was established. The hospital was named after the Permanente River, which never ran dry. (*Permanente* means "everlasting" in Spanish.) Today, Kaiser Permanente is the largest HMO in the United States.

WHAT DID YOU LEARN?

1. Explain the concept of managed care.
2. How did managed health care get started in the United States?
3. What main functions do MCOs perform?

COMMON TYPES OF MANAGED CARE ORGANIZATIONS

Although there are many forms of managed health care (Fig. 3-2), we concentrate on the two most common types:

- Preferred provider organization (PPO)
- **Health maintenance organization (HMO)**

Preferred Provider Organization

Preferred provider organizations (PPOs) are popular throughout the United States. PPOs typically provide a high level of health care and a variety of medical facilities to everyone who chooses to participate in the PPO.

A PPO functions as follows: A group of health care providers works under one umbrella—the PPO—to provide medical services at a discount to the individuals who participate in the PPO. The PPO contracts with this network of providers, who agree to offer medical services to the PPO members at lower rates (smaller **co-payments** and co-insurance limits) in exchange for being part of the network. This agreement allows the PPO to reduce overall health care costs. Two things about PPOs make them popular:

- PPO members do not have to choose a **primary care physician (PCP)**, which is a specific provider who oversees the member's total health care treatment.
- Participants do not need authorization from the PCP, commonly referred to as a **referral**, to visit any physician, hospital, or other health care provider who belongs to the network.

Plan members also can visit physicians and hospitals outside of the network. Visits to health care providers who do not belong to the PPO network do not have the same coverage, however, as visits to providers within the network, and the amount of money the patient has to pay out of his or her own pocket, the co-payment, is higher. The deductible normally does not change if a PPO member sees a provider outside the network.

Other advantages of PPOs include the following:

- PPO networks are not as tightly controlled by laws and regulations as HMOs.
- Many PPOs offer a wider choice of treatments to members with fewer restrictions than HMOs.

Disadvantages include the following:

- Loosely controlled PPOs often are not much better at controlling costs than traditional fee-for-service (indemnity) health insurance, which results in higher premiums over time.
- More tightly controlled PPOs come at the expense of the patients' ability to manage their own health care treatments.
- The fact that an individual belongs to a PPO may lead the individual to believe that he or she is paying lower premiums than he or she

PLAN COST	PROVIDER SELECTION	CONSULTS/SPECIALIST	MEMBER OUT-OF-POCKET COSTS
Traditional Insurance	Patient can select any physician, hospital, or health care provider (HCP).	Patient can use any specialist. However, some plans require pre-approval for certain procedures performed by specialists.	Patients may have to pay an annual deductible-usually ranging from $250 to $1000 (depending on what they choose). Patients may also be responsible for co-insurance payments (typically 20%). Coverage for routine care and drugs varies with the policy.
PPO	Patients may select any HCP in the network. If they use a provider outside of the network, they pay a larger portion (up to 50%) of the fee.	Patients may use any specialist in the network, but if they use a provider outside of the network, they will pay a larger portion of the fee.	Patients may have to pay co-payments for network doctor visits and drugs. When using a provider outside the network, there may be a deductible and then the plan will reimburse at 70% of the costs.
HMO	Patients may select only providers in the network. If they select a provider outside the network without the HMO approval, they will pay the entire bill.	The PCP determines the need for a specialist—if approval is not received the patient is responsible for the entire bill.	Patients may have to pay co-payments for doctor visits and drugs. May be charged co-payments for hospital stays and emergency room visits. Usually there are no deductibles.

Fig. 3-2 Comparison of types of health care plans, providers, consultants, and costs.

would for traditional health care, when this may not be the case at all.

STOP AND THINK

Ellen Comstock's health insurance carrier is a PPO. Soon after her second child was born, Ellen learned that Dr. Wallingford, her obstetrician, severed her contractual affiliation with the PPO network. Ellen wants to continue seeing Dr. Wallingford. What ramifications should Ellen consider in seeing a provider outside of her PPO network?

Health Maintenance Organization

Under the federal HMO Act, an entity must have three characteristics to call itself an HMO, as follows:

- An organized system for providing health care or otherwise ensuring health care delivery in a geographic area
- An agreed-on set of basic and supplemental health maintenance and treatment services
- A voluntarily enrolled group of people

HMOs provide members with basic health care services for a fixed price and for a given period of time. In return, the participant receives medical services, including physician visits, hospitalization, and surgery, at no additional cost other than a small per-encounter co-payment—typically less than $25 per visit and sometimes only $5.

Each HMO has a network of physicians who participate in the HMO system. When an individual first enrolls in the HMO, he or she chooses a PCP from the HMO network. This PCP serves as caretaker for the enrollee's future medical needs and is the first person the patient calls when he or she needs medical care. PCPs are usually physicians who practice family medicine, internal medicine, or pediatrics. The PCP determines whether or not the patient's problem warrants a referral to a **specialist**, a physician who is trained in a certain area of medicine (e.g., a cardiologist, who specializes in diseases and conditions of the heart). If an enrollee sees a specialist without the PCP's approval, the HMO normally does not pay specialist's fees, even if the specialist practices within the network. Fig. 3-2 is a comparison of three common types of health care plans.

HMOs are more tightly controlled by government regulations than PPOs. Members must use the HMO's health care providers and facilities, and medical care outside the system usually is not covered except in emergencies. HMOs typically have no deductibles or plan limits. As mentioned earlier, the member pays only a small fee, called a co-payment, for each visit, or sometimes nothing at all. Because the HMO provides all of a member's health care for one set monthly premium, it is considered in everyone's best interest to emphasize preventive health care.

Some HMOs operate their own facilities, staffed with salaried physicians; others contract with individual physicians and hospitals to be part of the HMO. A few do both. An HMO can be a good choice for some individuals; however, there are many restrictions. If its facilities are convenient, and the individual wants to avoid most out-of-pocket expenses and paperwork, an HMO might be a good health care option. One problem exists, however: some states, especially states that are predominantly rural, offer few HMO choices. Iowa, for instance, had only four functioning HMOs in 2002 compared with 27 in New York.

Several types of managed care come under the HMO umbrella. We look at some of the more common types in the following paragraphs.

Staff Model

A **staff model** HMO is a multispecialty group practice in which all health care services are provided within the buildings owned by the HMO. The staff model is a **closed panel HMO**, meaning other health care providers in the community generally cannot participate. Participating providers are salaried employees of the HMO who spend their time providing services only to the HMO enrollees. All routine medical care is furnished, or authorized, by the member's PCP. Pre-authorization is necessary for referrals to specialists. In a staff model HMO, the HMO bears the financial risk for the entire cost of health care services furnished to the HMO's members.

Group Model

In a **group model**, the HMO contracts with independent, multispecialty physician groups who provide all health care services to its members. Physician groups usually share the same facility, support staff, medical records, and equipment. Group physicians receive reimbursement in the form of **capitation**, a reimbursement system in which health care providers receive a fixed fee for every patient enrolled in the plan, regardless of how many or few services the patient uses. (The word "capitation" comes from the Latin phrase *per capita,* meaning "each head.") The managed care insurer negotiates with the provider and agrees to pay him or her $100 a month to care for each of its subscribers, regardless of the amount of services each subscriber uses. Generally, the financial risk (whether or not the capitation amount is enough for the HMO to make a profit) falls on the shoulders of the group practice.

Individual Practice Association

In an **individual practice association (IPA)**, services are provided by outpatient networks composed of individual health care providers (the IPA) who provide all the needed health care services for the HMO. The providers maintain their own offices and identities and see patients who belong to the HMO and non-HMO patients. This is an **open panel plan** because health care providers in the community may participate, if they meet certain HMO/IPA standards. IPA reimbursement methods vary from plan to plan.

Network Model

The **network model** HMO has multiple provider arrangements, including staff, group, or IPA structures. This model usually allows the health care provider to be paid on a fee-for-service basis, whereas the group practices in the network might receive a capitation payment by the health care plan.

Direct Contract Model

The **direct contract model** HMO is similar to an IPA except the HMO contracts directly with the individual physicians. The HMO recruits a variety of community health care providers, including PCPs and specialists.

Point of Service

The **point of service (POS)** model is a "hybrid" type of managed care (also referred to as an open-ended HMO) that allows patients to use the HMO provider or go outside the plan and use any provider they choose. When individuals enroll in a POS plan, they are required to choose a PCP to monitor their health care. This PCP must be chosen from within the health care network and becomes the individual's "point of service." The primary POS physician may make referrals outside the network, but this is discouraged because co-payments and deductibles are higher when patients go outside the plan.

WHAT DID YOU LEARN?

1. Name the two most common types of managed care.
2. Explain how a PPO works.
3. List the main differences between PPOs and HMOs.
4. What is the function of a PCP?
5. List four types of managed care.

ADVANTAGES AND DISADVANTAGES OF MANAGED CARE

There are advantages and disadvantages to managed care.

Advantages

- *Preventive care*—HMOs pay for programs aimed at keeping their members healthy (e.g., yearly wellness checkups) to avoid paying for more costly services if the members get sick.

- *Lower premiums*—Because they limit which physicians their members can see and when they can see them, HMOs are able to charge lower premiums.
- *Prescriptions*—As part of their preventive approach, HMOs typically cover most prescriptions for a low co-payment (e.g., $2).
- *Fewer unnecessary procedures*—HMOs give physicians financial incentives to provide only necessary care, so physicians are less likely to order tests or operations their patients might not need.
- *Limited paperwork*—Although physicians and hospitals have more paperwork under some types of managed care, HMO members usually only have to show their membership card and pay a small co-payment.

Disadvantages

- *Limited provider pool*—To keep costs down, many HMO models tell their members which physicians they can see, including specialists.
- *Restricted coverage*—Often, members cannot expect treatment on demand because the PCP first must justify the need based on what benefits the plan covers.
- *Prior approval needed*—If a member wants to see a specialist, authorization is needed from the PCP.
- *Possibility of undertreatment*—Because HMOs typically give physicians financial incentives to limit care, some physicians have been known to hold back on the treatment they give their patients.
- *Compromised privacy*—HMOs use patient records to monitor physicians performance and efficiency, so details of members' medical histories are seen by other people, which may breach their right to privacy.

STOP AND THINK

Imagine you are employed as a health insurance professional with a multispecialty medical group. Mr. Washburn, a new patient, says to you, "I hear a lot of bad things about HMOs. Are they all true?" What would you tell him?

WHAT DID YOU LEARN?

1. List and explain the advantages of managed care.
2. List and explain the disadvantages of managed care.

MANAGED CARE CERTIFICATION AND REGULATION

HMOs receive their accreditation from two organizations: the National Committee on Quality Assurance (NCQA) and The Joint Commission.

National Committee on Quality Assurance

NCQA, a private, nonprofit organization, accredits health care plans based on careful evaluation of the quality of care members receive and member satisfaction rates. Its membership includes about 90% of all MCOs nationwide. NCQA is committed to improving the quality of health care throughout the United States. NCQA provides health care information through the World Wide Web and the media to help consumers and employers make more informed health care choices.

In addition to accrediting and certifying a wide range of health care organizations, NCQA manages the development of the Health Plan Employer Data and Information Set (HEDIS), the performance measurement tool used by most health plans in the United States. MCOs must collect and report HEDIS data to earn NCQA accreditation.

For a particular managed health care plan to become accredited by NCQA, it first must undergo a survey and meet certain standards designed to evaluate the facility's clinical and administrative systems. These standards fall into five broad categories, as follows:

- Access and service
- Qualified providers
- Staying healthy
- Getting better
- Living with illness

To evaluate these five categories, NCQA reviews health plan records and providers' credentials, conducts surveys, and interviews health plan staff. A national committee of physicians assigns one of five possible accreditation levels (excellent, commendable, accredited, provisional, or denied) based on the plan's level of compliance with NCQA standards.

Access and Service

NCQA evaluates how well a health plan provides its members with access to needed care and with good customer service. Evaluative questions might include the following: Are there enough PCPs and specialists to serve the number of people in the plan? What kind of problems do patients report in getting needed care? Does the health plan follow up effectively on grievances?

Qualified Providers

NCQA evaluates health plan activities that ensure each physician is licensed and trained to practice medicine, and that the health plan's members are satisfied with their physicians' performance. Questions NCQA might ask include the following: Does the health plan check whether physicians have had sanctions or lawsuits against them? How do health plan members rate their personal physicians or nurses?

Staying Healthy

NCQA evaluates health plan activities that help people maintain good health and avoid illness. NCQA might ask the following questions: Does the health plan give its practitioners guidelines about how to provide appropriate preventive health care? Are members receiving appropriate tests and screenings?

Getting Better

To make an appraisal in this category, NCQA looks at health plan activities that help individuals recover from illness. NCQA might ask the following questions: How does the health plan evaluate new medical procedures, drugs, and devices to ensure that patients have access to the most up-to-date care? Do physicians in the health plan advise smokers to quit?

Living with Illness

NCQA evaluates health plan activities that help people manage chronic illness. NCQA might ask the following questions: Does the plan have programs in place to assist patients in managing chronic conditions such as asthma? Do diabetics, who are at risk for blindness, receive eye examinations as needed?

National Committee on Quality Assurance and Health Insurance Portability and Accountability Act

The 2003 standards also make NCQA's privacy and confidentiality requirements reflect key elements of the Health Insurance Portability and Accountability Act (HIPAA). In particular, NCQA has strengthened standards requiring members to be notified at the time of enrollment of their MCO's policies on the use of their personal health information (e.g., treatment records, claims data). Since the new standards went into effect in July 2003, an organization must inform members about its privacy policies, along with the members' rights and options for accessing their own medical information. The 2003 Standards and Guidelines for the Accreditation of Managed Care Organizations that went into effect in July 2003 have been made available as printed or electronic publications.

The Joint Commission

The Joint Commission is the second entity that evaluates and accredits health care organizations. Similar to NCQA, The Joint Commission is an independent, not-for-profit organization and is considered the predominant standards-setting and accrediting body in health care in the United States. The Joint Commission is governed by a 29-member Board of Commissioners that includes nurses, physicians, consumers, medical directors, administrators, providers, employers, a labor representative, health plan leaders, quality experts, ethicists, a health insurance administrator, and educators.

Since 1951, The Joint Commission's standards have been used to evaluate the compliance of health care organizations. Their evaluation and accreditation services are provided for all types of health care organizations, including the following:

- Hospitals
- Managed care plans
- Home care organizations
- Nursing homes and other long-term care facilities
- Assisted living facilities
- Behavioral health care organizations
- Ambulatory care providers
- Clinical laboratories

Joint Commission accreditation is nationally recognized as a symbol of quality that reflects an organization's commitment to meeting quality performance standards. To earn and maintain accreditation, an organization must undergo an on-site survey by a Joint Commission survey team every 2 to 3 years, depending on the type of facility.

The Joint Commission developed its standards in consultation with health care experts, providers, measurement experts, purchasers, and consumers. The standards address an organization's level of performance in key functional areas, such as patient rights, patient treatment, and infection control. The standards focus not only on an organization's ability to provide safe, high-quality care but also on its actual performance. The Joint Commission's standards outline performance expectations for activities that affect the safety and quality of patient care. These standards include the following:

- The rights of patients
- The assessment and treatment of patients
- A safe environment for patients and health care employees
- The quality of patient care
- The management of patients' records
- The organizational responsibilities of leadership and staff

The Joint Commission and NCQA have incorporated the HIPAA standards into their own accreditation criteria.

Utilization Review

Utilization review, sometimes referred to as *utilization management*, is a system designed to determine the medical necessity and appropriateness of a requested medical service, procedure, or hospital admission prior, concurrent, or retrospective to the event. A utilization review may include ambulatory review, case management, certification, concurrent review, discharge planning, prospective review, retrospective review, or second opinions. The utilization review generally is accomplished by the third-party payer's professional staff (nurses and physicians) using standardized medical research data from across the United States and reviewing patient health records in an attempt to make fair and reasonable decisions on behalf of the patients and the third-party payers. Deciding whether a service, procedure, or hospital admission is "appropriate" also can be influenced by what is covered in the individual's health insurance plan.

Utilization review is used in managed care plans to reduce unnecessary medical inpatient or outpatient services. An individual within the plan or a separate organization on behalf of the insurer reviews the necessity, use, appropriateness, efficacy, or efficiency of health care services, procedures, providers, or facilities.

Complaint Management

If a particular medical service or procedure is determined not to be medically necessary by the payer or by an independent utilization review organization, it is not paid for by the insurer. If the patient disagrees, he or she may file a grievance protesting the decision. A **grievance** is a written complaint submitted by an individual covered by the plan concerning any of the following:

1. An insurer's decisions, policies, or actions related to availability, delivery, or quality of health care services
2. Claims payment or handling or reimbursement for services
3. The contractual relationship between a covered individual and an insurer
4. The outcome of an appeal

Some states have enacted laws that allow residents to air their complaints to the state insurance commissioner's office when certain medical payments are denied by their health insurer. If a

A Review of Michigan's Insurance Complaint System, May 2002

Michigan's Office of Financial and Insurance Services (OFIS) contracted with two organizations to act as independent review organizations to review residents' complaints. The system was put into effect in May of 2002. The external review process followed strict policies and procedures; the independent review organizations had 14 days to process the review request. The independent review panel was staffed with qualified, trained, and licensed clinicians as well as other health professionals who are experts in the treatment of the medical condition that is the subject of the external review.

Findings: During the first 16 months of the insurance complaint program, 418 requests for claim reviews were filed with Michigan's OFIS. From the initial 418 requests, there were 309 cases that went to internal review organizations for adjudication. Of these 309 cases, 143 cases were resolved in favor of the patient. A total of 36 cases were dismissed, resulted in a split decision, or have yet to be decided. The OFIS staff resolved the remaining 72 cases internally, thus avoiding the need for external review. One request for external review was withdrawn.

Fig. 3-3 A review of Michigan's insurance complaint system, May 2002.

complaint is accepted, an independent review organization (IRO) looks into the situation and determines whether the claim should have been paid under the guidelines of the medical policy. The IRO decision is generally final, and if the IRO sides with the insurer, the individual's only remaining alternative is to pursue remediation through the court system. Fig. 3-3 shows an example of one state's insurance complaint system.

IMAGINE THIS!

Texas is the first state to post information about complaints filed against HMOs and other insurers on the Internet. The Internet Complaint Information System, launched by the state's Department of Insurance, also includes complaints against auto and property insurers. The information is updated quarterly, and only complaints that have been investigated and resolved are included. The most common complaints from concerned members were prescription coverage, reimbursement, and denial or nonpayment for emergency care. Most provider complaints were related to denial or delay of payment.

WHAT DID YOU LEARN?

1. MCOs receive their accreditation from what two organizations?
2. List NCQA's five evaluative categories.
3. What types of health care facilities does The Joint Commission evaluate?
4. What is a utilization review?

PRE-AUTHORIZATION, PRECERTIFICATION, PREDETERMINATION, AND REFERRALS

A common method many health care payers use to monitor and control health care costs is by evaluating the need for a medical service before it is performed. Most commercial health care organizations and MCOs now request that they be made aware of and consent to certain procedures and services before their enrollees acquire them. Pre-authorization and precertification are two cost-containment features whereby the insured must contact the insurer before a hospitalization or surgery and receive prior approval for the service.

Pre-Authorization

Pre-Authorization is a procedure required by most managed health care and indemnity plans before a provider carries out specific procedures or treatments for a patient—typically inpatient hospitalization and certain diagnostic tests. Pre-authorization typically works as follows: The health care provider or a member of his or her staff contacts the health care plan by phone, by fax, or in writing and requests permission to perform the treatment or service proposed. The plan's representative authorizes the service or procedure or not, depending on what the plan covers and whether the procedure or service is considered medically necessary and appropriate. Often, when a procedure or service is authorized, the MCO or carrier assigns a specific identifying number or code.

HIPAA TIP

Before faxing any patient information, make sure that the individual on the receiving end of the transmission has a "medical right to know" and that the destination location has a security system in place. HIPAA requires a "confidentiality statement" at the bottom of each fax cover sheet.

Pre-authorization pertains to medical necessity and appropriateness only and does not, in all instances, guarantee payment. It is not a treatment recommendation or a guarantee that the patient will be insured or eligible for benefits when services are performed.

Pre-authorization also is used to identify members for case management or disease management programs. Approval or denial of requests for services is determined by review of all available related medical information and possibly a discussion with the requesting physician (Fig. 3-4).

STOP AND THINK

You overhear a patient telling another that she is going to be admitted to the hospital for an operation. "They have to get permission from my HMO before I can be admitted," the woman says. "If my HMO says it's okay," she continues, "they'll pay all of my hospital bills." Should you, as a health insurance professional, interrupt the conversation to clarify what impact a pre-authorization has on her hospitalization? If so, what would you say?

Precertification

Precertification is a process used by health insurance companies to control health care costs and is similar to pre-authorization. One definition of precertification is "a formal assessment of the medical necessity, efficiency, or appropriateness of a medical provider's treatment plan for a specific illness or injury." The treatment plan needs to be consistent with the diagnosis or condition; rendered in a cost-effective manner; and in line with national medical practice guidelines regarding type, frequency, and duration of treatment.

Precertification involves collecting information before inpatient admissions or performance of selected ambulatory procedures and services (Fig. 3-5). The process permits advance eligibility verification, determination of coverage, and communication with the physician or plan member or both. The precertification process also allows the insurance company to coordinate the patient's transition from the inpatient setting to the next level of care (discharge planning) or to register patients for specialized programs, such as disease management, case management, or a prenatal program.

In some instances, precertification is used to inform physicians, members, and other health care providers about cost-effective programs and alternative therapies and treatments. Typically, the things the plan's representative takes into consideration when precertifying a service or procedure include the following:

- Verifying the member's eligibility and benefits in accordance with applicable plan documents
- Determining coverage for inpatient admissions and selected ambulatory services
- Assessing appropriateness of the proposed site of service
- Identifying alternatives to proposed care or site of service when appropriate
- Identifying and referring to case management programs when appropriate

Tri-State Medical Group

PRE-AUTHORIZATION REQUEST FORM

PATIENT INFORMATION

Last Name: _____ First Name: _____

DOB: _____ Member #: **R**_____ Group #: _____

PRE-AUTHORIZATION REQUEST INFORMATION

Please list *both* procedure/product code <u>and</u> narrative description:

CPT / HCPCS Code(s): _____ Durable Medical Equipment: ☐ Rental ☐ Purchase

Description: _____

_____

Date of Service: _____ Length of Stay (if applicable): _____

Place of Service or Vendor Name: _____

Assistant Surgeon Requested? ☐ Yes ☐ No **Please list *both* diagnosis(es) code <u>and</u> narrative description:**

1. ICD-9 Code: _____

   Description: _____

2. ICD-9 Code: _____

   Description: _____

Ordering Physician/Provider: _____ Office Location: _____
FIRST <u>AND</u> LAST NAMES PLEASE

Referring Physician/Provider: _____
FIRST <u>AND</u> LAST NAMES PLEASE; REQUIRED FOR PRIME PLANS

Date: _____ Contact Person: _____ Phone: _____

> *Please Note: Incomplete forms will delay the pre-authorization process.*
> *Requests received after 3:00 PM are processed the next working day.*
>
> **PacificSource responds to pre-authorization requests within 2 working days.**
> **A determination notice will be mailed to the requesting provider, facility, and patient.**
>
> **Please attach pertinent chart notes as appropriate.**

FOR INTERNAL OFFICE USE ONLY:

STATUS: APPROVED / DENIED / PENDING / EXPLANATION

DATE: _____ ACUITY: _____ INITIALS: _____

Reason/Status _____

_____

Field 11 Notes _____ LOS Approved _____

☐ Chart notes filed with pre-authorization

Notes _____

Field 10 Facility Copy _____

PO Box 5555 • Somewhere OR 00908 • (541) 555-5584 • (800) 555-6052 x 2584

MEDICAL AFFAIRS DEPARTMENT CONFIDENTIAL FAX: (541) 555-2051

9/8/2003

Fig. 3-4 Generic pre-authorization form.

Tri-State Medical Group

FAX Request Form for Precertification Review

To:_____Date:_____

(Area Code) Fax:_____

(Area Code) Phone:_____

Attn:_____

From:_____Fax:_____

Number of Pages (Including Cover Sheet):_____
If there is a problem with the receipt of this fax, please call _____.Thank you.

Recipient/Patient Name:_____
Complete Recipient
Address _____

_____

ID Number:_____CAMA ☐ Yes ☐ No

Requested Admit Date:_____Diagnosis Code(s):_____

Procedure Date(s): _____

Days Requested: _____ Procedure Code(s):_____

New Admit? ( ) Transfer ( )

Recertification Review? Y( ) If So, Par/Reference #_____

Setting: ☐ Inpatient   ☐ Physician Office
                 ☐ Outpatient   ☐ Out of State

Admit Type: ☐ Non-urgent/Emergent   ☐ Urgent/Emergent

Physician Name:_____Phone:_____
                                           Fax:_____

Facility:_____Phone:_____
                                           Fax:_____

Clinical Information:_____
_____
_____
_____
_____
_____

Fig. 3-5 Generic precertification form.

- Identifying any quality-of-care issues and referring for review
- Identifying and documenting potential coordination of benefits, subrogation, or workers' compensation information

Predetermination

Predetermination is when the provider notifies the insurance company of the recommended treatment before it begins. The insurance company estimates the benefit amount that is normally paid for this, or similar, treatment; however, as with preauthorization, it is not a guarantee of payment.

Referrals

A **referral** is a request by a health care provider for a patient under his or her care to be evaluated or treated by another provider, usually a specialist. The purpose of a referral by a PCP to a specialist is to

- inform a specialist that the patient needs to be seen for care (or second opinion) in his or her field of specialty and
- inform the insurance company that the PCP has approved the visit to a specialist because most managed care companies would not pay for care that has not been authorized with a referral.

How a Patient Obtains a Referral

A patient obtains a referral as follows: The patient schedules a visit with the PCP, who evaluates the problem. If the PCP decides that the patient's condition or symptoms warrant a specialist's opinion, a referral form is completed (Fig. 3-6). In most managed care situations, for the insurance company to recognize the referral, it must come from the patient's designated PCP or a provider who is covering for the PCP. If an orthopedic physician refers a patient to a physical therapist, the patient also must obtain a referral from his or her PCP to process through the insurance company.

IMAGINE THIS!

Velda Smith, a 34-year-old HMO enrollee, injured her knee in an ice skating accident. Dr. Mazzio, Velda's PCP, referred her to an orthopedist for evaluation, who subsequently performed arthroscopy of the knee. After the surgical procedure, the orthopedist recommended physical therapy four times a week for 6 weeks. Velda was instructed by her HMO that she must return to Dr. Mazzio for proper authorization procedures before beginning physical therapy.

Referrals Versus Consultations

There is a significant difference between a referral and a consultation. A **consultation** is when the PCP sends a patient to another health care provider, usually a specialist, for the purpose of the consulting physician rendering his or her expert opinion regarding the patient's condition. The intent of a consultation usually is for the purpose of an expert opinion only, and the PCP does not relinquish the care of the patient to the consulting provider. In the case of a referral, the PCP typically relinquishes care of the patient—at least a specific portion of care—to the specialist. The insurance professional must determine whether the visit is a consultation or a referral because this affects accurate CPT code selection for the visit.

IMAGINE THIS!

Daniel Bowers visited Dr. Adler, his PCP, with complaints of back pain and numbness in his left leg radiating down to his left foot. Dr. Adler x-rayed Daniel's spinal column and discovered a degenerative disc condition and subsequently referred him to Dr. Langford, who specialized in degenerative disc disease.

Susan Lane, another patient of Dr. Bowers, complained of heart palpitations during an office visit for treatment of a severe case of poison ivy. After performing an electrocardiogram, Dr. Bowers informed Susan that he was sending her to Dr. Woodley for a stress electrocardiogram and an echocardiogram to determine if her palpitations represented a serious cardiac problem.

While in the hospital for a hip replacement, Evelyn Conner was diagnosed with diabetes. Dr. Blake, her surgeon, asked Dr. Martin, a specialist in endocrinology, to manage Mrs. Conner's diabetic condition.

STOP AND THINK

Study the three cases in Imagine This! Decide whether each one is a consultation or a referral.

WHAT DID YOU LEARN?

1. Explain the difference between pre-authorization and precertification.
2. List some typical things that a plan's representative takes into consideration when precertifying a procedure or service.
3. What is a referral?

Florida WIC Program Medical Referral Form

Shaded areas <u>must</u> be completed.   See instructions for completing this form on the reverse side.

Is this client eligible for Healthy Start? ☐ Yes ☐ No   <u>For WIC Office Use Only</u>:
Date of WIC Certification Appointment _____

Client's Name _____   Birth Date _____   **Sex** M F

Address _____   Phone Number (_____) _____-_____

City _____ Zip Code _____   Social Security # _____-_____-_____

Parent's/Guardian's Name _____ (for infants and children only)

☐ *For Pregnant Women*

Height _____ Weight _____ Date Taken _____ (no older than 60 days)

Hemoglobin _____ OR Hematocrit _____ Date Taken_____ (must be taken during current pregnancy)

Expected Date of Delivery _____ Date of First Prenatal Visit _____ Prepregnancy Weight _____

☐ *For Breastfeeding and Postpartum (Non-Breastfeeding) Women*

Height _____ Weight _____ Date Taken _____ (no older than 60 days)

Hemoglobin _____ OR Hematocrit _____ Date Taken_____ (must be taken in postpartum period)

Date of Delivery _____ Date of First Prenatal Visit _____ Weight at Last Prenatal Visit _____

☐ *For Infants and Children less than 24 months of age*

Birth Weight _____ lb _____ oz   Birth Length _____ inches

Current Height _____ Current Weight _____ Date Taken _____ (no older than 60 days)

Hemoglobin _____ OR Hematocrit _____ Date Taken_____ (required once between 6 to 12 months
                                                                         AND once between 12 to 24 months)

☐ *For Children 2 to 5 years of age*

Current Height _____ Current Weight _____ Date Taken _____ (no older than 60 days)

Hemoglobin _____ OR Hematocrit _____ Date Taken_____ (once a year unless value < 11.1 Hgb or
                                                                         < 33% Hct, then required in 6 months)

✓ **Check all that apply. Please refer your client to WIC, even if nothing is checked below.** This information
assists the WIC nutritionist in determining eligibility, developing a nutrition care plan, and providing nutrition counseling. WIC staff may
need to contact you or your staff to obtain more detailed medical information prior to providing WIC services.

☐ Medical condition (specify)
_____

☐ High venous lead level (10 µg/dl or more)
Lead level _____ Date taken _____

☐ Recent major surgery, trauma, burns (specify)
_____

☐ Food allergy (specify) _____

☐ Current or potential breastfeeding complications
(specify) _____

☐ Failure to Thrive

☐ **Special Formula Needed** (diagnosis/signature required)
Type of formula _____
Number of months _____ (not to exceed 6 months)
Diagnosis _____
Signature of physician, PA, or ARNP required for
special formula _____

☐ Other (specify) _____

☐ **Nutrition Counseling Requested** – specify diet prescription/order _____

WIC Local Agency Address:

I refer this client for WIC eligibility determination:

Signature/Title of Health Professional _____

Date _____   **PLEASE PLACE <u>OFFICE STAMP</u> BELOW:**

Address:

Phone Number:

Parent or Guardian: Please bring a copy of your baby's/child's shot record to the WIC office.

DH Form 3075, 12/03 (Stock Number: 5744-000-3075-5) (Replaces 1/01 edition, which may be used.)   *WIC is an equal opportunity provider.*

Fig. 3-6   Referral form. *(Courtesy Florida Department of Health.)*

Continued

Instructions for Completing the Florida WIC Program Medical Referral Form
All shaded areas must be completed in order for the form to be processed.

1. Check (✓) YES if the client has been screened and is eligible for Healthy Start. Check (✓) NO if the client is not eligible for Healthy Start. Leave blank if the client has not been screened. <u>Note</u>: Eligibility for Healthy Start does <u>not</u> affect a client's eligibility for WIC.

2. Complete the **client's name and birth date.**

3. Optional Information: the client's sex, mailing address, phone number, city, zip code, social security number, and the parent's or guardian's name for infants and children.

4. Complete the appropriate shaded section for the client.

   Pregnant Women: Complete the height and weight measurements and the date they were taken. These measurements are to be taken no more than 60 days before the client's WIC appointment. (The WIC appointment may be recorded at the top of the form.) Complete the hemoglobin or hematocrit value and the date the value was taken. There is no limit on how old the bloodwork data can be, as long as the measurement was taken during the current pregnancy. Complete the expected date of delivery, the date of the client's first prenatal visit, and the prepregnancy weight.

   Breastfeeding Women (eligible up to one year after delivery) **and Postpartum Women—Non-Breastfeeding** (eligible up to 6 months after delivery/termination of pregnancy): Complete the height and weight measurements and the date they were taken. These measurements are to be taken no more than 60 days before the client's WIC appointment. (The WIC appointment may be recorded at the top of the form.) Complete the hemoglobin or hematocrit value and the date the value was taken. There is no limit on how old the bloodwork data can be, as long as the bloodwork is taken after delivery of the most recent pregnancy. Complete the actual date of delivery, the date of the first prenatal visit, and the weight measurement at the last prenatal visit.

   Infants and Children less than 24 months of age: Complete the infant's birth weight and birth length. Complete the current height and weight measurements and the date they were taken. These measurements are to be taken no more than 60 days before the client's WIC appointment. (The WIC appointment may be recorded at the top of the form.) Complete the hemoglobin or hematocrit value and the date the value was taken. <u>A bloodwork value is required once during infancy between 6 to 12 months of age (preferably between 9 to 12 months of age) and once between 1 to 2 years of age (preferably 6 months from the infant bloodwork value).</u>

   Children 2 to 5 years of age: Complete the current height and weight measurements and the date they were taken. These measurements are to be taken no more than 60 days before the client's WIC appointment. (The WIC appointment may be recorded at the top of the form.) Complete the hemoglobin or hematocrit value and the date the value was taken. A bloodwork value is required once a year unless the value is abnormal (< 11.1 hemoglobin or < 33% hematocrit), then a bloodwork value is required in 6 months.

5. Check (✓) any health problem that you have identified. **Even if you have not identified a health problem, refer the client to the WIC program.**

6. **Special Formula Needed:** This form may be used to order special formula as long as the type of formula, number of months that the special formula is needed, and the diagnosis are completed. Also, the signature of a physician, PA, or ARNP is required in order to accept the prescription.

7. If you would like a nutritionist to counsel your client on a specific diet, check the box and specify the diet prescription or diet order requested.

8. If possible, please provide a copy of the immunization record for infant and child clients.

9. Complete the shaded area at the bottom of the form with the **signature** of the health professional taking the measurement or his/her designee and the office address and phone number. **Stamp** the form with the office stamp or the health professional's stamp.

10. Give this completed form to the client or parent/guardian to bring to the WIC certification appointment or mail/fax the form to the local WIC agency address shown in the bottom left corner of the form.

Fig. 3-6, cont'd

≋ HEALTH INSURANCE PORTABILITY AND ACCOUNTABILITY ACT AND MANAGED CARE

HIPAA was intended to improve the efficiency of health care delivery, reduce administrative costs, and protect patient privacy. Generally, the law required covered entities (most health plans, health care clearinghouses, and health care providers who engage in certain electronic transactions) to come into compliance with each set of HIPAA standards within 2 years following adoption except for small health plans, which have 3 years to come into compliance. For the electronic transaction and code sets rule only, Congress in 2001 enacted legislation extending the deadline to October 16, 2003, for all covered entities, including small health plans. The legislative extension did not affect the compliance dates for the health information privacy rule, which was April 14, 2003, for most covered entities (April 14, 2004, for small health plans).

Previously, we discussed the fact that if an insured person lost insurance coverage for some reason (e.g., losing a job), he or she could be required to prove insurability before obtaining new coverage. For most individuals, this was not a problem; however, for individuals with chronic or preexisting health problems or whose health deteriorated while they were covered, it was a serious problem. Such individuals frequently lived in fear of losing their jobs or stayed in "dead end" jobs so that they would not lose their health care coverage. Now, under HIPAA regulations, if an individual has been insured for the past 12 months, a new insurance company cannot refuse to cover the individual and cannot impose preexisting conditions or a waiting period before providing coverage.

HIPAA regulations affect other areas of health care, too, including the following:

- Maintaining patient confidentiality
- Implementing standards for electronic transmission of transactions and code sets
- Establishing national provider and employer identifiers
- Resolving security and privacy issues arising from the storage and transmission of health care data

How do these regulations affect managed health care? Some experts claim the cost of complying with HIPAA would exceed the $9 billion cost of Y2K preparations. The repercussions of this added cost likely would affect all health care, not just managed care.

Large medical facilities for the most part were able to shoulder the expense of becoming HIPAA compliant; however, many small one- or two-physician practices found it very difficult. HIPAA zeros in on electronic health information. Even if a solo practitioner has all paper records, as soon as he or she starts dealing electronically with billing of third-party payers, the practitioner encounters HIPAA's strict regulations.

IMAGINE THIS!

Elliot Larson was the sole proprietor of a small podiatry practice in south-central Iowa. He employed two full-time staff members—a receptionist and an assistant who was a licensed practical nurse. When the HIPAA law was enacted, his office was already computerized and submitting claims electronically to a certain major carrier. Dr. Larson's financial advisor calculated that it would cost approximately $50,000 to upgrade his office to HIPAA compliancy. Dr. Larson did not want to revert to a manual accounting system, plus he was under contract to submit claims electronically to the major carrier under whom most of his patients had coverage. To justify the cost to upgrade to HIPAA's regulations, he would have to raise his fees. The socio-economic area where he practiced was predominantly agricultural-related—farmers and rural people—who could not afford increased charges. Dr. Larson closed his practice in the small, rural town where he'd been practicing for 10 years and joined a multispecialty group in Des Moines.

The consequences of noncompliance are the legal penalties HIPAA exacts for failure to adopt its standards. Fines range from $100 for violating a general requirement to $50,000 or more for more serious offenses, such as wrongful disclosure of individually identifiable health information.

HIPAA TIP

HIPAA impact on MCOs is the same as that for fee-for-service structures. HIPAA does not have a separate set of rules and regulations for MCOs.

WHAT DID YOU LEARN?

1. List four areas of health care affected by HIPAA regulations.
2. What are the consequences of HIPAA noncompliance?

≋ IMPACT OF MANAGED CARE

Since the 1990s, the United States has witnessed a transformation in all phases of the health care system, from financing to the way health care services are organized and delivered. The driving force in this transformation, experts say, is the shift from traditional fee-for-service systems to managed care networks. These changes in the U.S. health care system are in response to market forces for cost control, to regulatory initiatives on cost and quality, and to consumer demands for quality care and greater flexibility in provider choice. Because these changes occurred so rapidly and extensively, little is known about the long-term effects of managed care on access to care, cost, and quality of care.

The Agency for Health Care Policy and Research (AHCPR) is the leading federal agency charged with supporting and conducting health services research. Their studies are designed to produce information that ultimately will improve consumer choice, improve the quality and value of health care services, and support and improve the health care marketplace. Most research on managed care has been conducted in HMOs.

Impact of Managed Care on the Physician-Patient Relationship

Managed care can affect relationships between physicians and patients in a variety of ways. First, it may change the way in which such relationships begin and end. The typical HMO pays only for care provided by its own physicians. Preferred provider groups restrict access to physicians by paying a smaller percentage of the cost of care when patients go outside the network. These restrictions can limit patients' ability to establish a relationship with the physician of their choice. Termination of physician-patient relationships also can occur without patients' choosing. When employers shift managed care health plans that mandate the determination of PCPs, employees may have no choice but to sever ties with the PCP of the previous plan and establish a relationship with a new one.

IMAGINE THIS!

Arnold Talbott is a fabrication specialist with Jones Implement. Employees were covered under a group health insurance contract with Superior Healthcare Systems, an HMO, when Arnold first started working for Jones Implement in 1993. Over the years, Arnold and his family established a mutually satisfying patient-provider relationship with Dr. VanHorn, their PCP. In 2004, Jones changed carriers and switched their group coverage to Ideal Health Maintenance Group. Because Dr. VanHorn was not a part of Ideal's network, Arnold and his family had to choose a new PCP and have all of their health records transferred.

Some forms of managed care create a financial incentive for physicians to spend less time with each patient. Under preferred provider arrangements, physicians may compensate for reduced fees for services by seeing more patients. This compensation ultimately reduces the time available to discuss patients' problems, explore alternative treatment options, and maintain a meaningful relationship with established patients.

Managed care arrangements often control patients' access to medical specialists, restricting patients' freedom to choose providers and obtain the medical services they desire. In HMOs, PCPs function as "gatekeepers" who authorize patient referrals to medical specialists. Critics of managed care claim that this gatekeeping reduces the quality of care, whereas supporters believe that gatekeeping yields benefits such as reducing **iatrogenic effects** (a symptom or illness brought on unintentionally by something that a physician does or says); promoting rigorous review of standards of care; and emphasizing low-technology, care-oriented services.

The physician—and the practice as a whole—is the main experience of their plan for most patients. If that experience is difficult or substandard, the patient is likely to blame the practice. Whatever help a practice can give its patients in navigating the waters of managed care can reduce problems for everybody.

Impact of Managed Care on Health Care Providers

Most health care providers believe that the shift within the health care industry from fee-for-service toward managed care is requiring providers to do the following:

1. Become participants in larger provider practice structures (e.g., single-specialty or, preferably, multispecialty group practices, or independent practice associations)
2. Become participants in integrated delivery systems, which may include acquisition of physician practices by a hospital system
3. Become employees and service providers for large insurance organizations or HMOs or both

With the advent of managed care, such acquisitions are being considered necessary more often by smaller scale health care providers (e.g., sole practitioners and small partnerships and group practices) to satisfy the increasing demands of managed care contracting. Large employers, insurance organizations, and HMOs view as appealing—and seek to contract with—health care providers who can offer a complete package of "seamless" health care services, which satisfies most medical needs within a single integrated delivery system. Providers within these more integrated medical organizations are likely to experience increasing economic viability as managed care continues to transform the medical environment.

The PCP is considered by most within the medical sector of the health care industry to be the future controller of patient flow and revenue-generating potential of fellow practitioners. Functioning in the role of gatekeeper, the PCP is likely to be required to perform an increased level of services—services that formerly were referred to specialists—to control health care costs in capitation model health care plans.

On a more positive note, in a study of 20,000 subjects that examined variations in health care delivery systems, AHCPR-supported research indicated the following:

- *HMO physicians spent more time* with their patients than fee-for-service physicians, and their patients received more preventive care, asked more questions, and were more involved in treatment planning.
- *Managed care patients spent 2 fewer days* in an intensive care unit (ICU) than patients with fee-for-service health insurance, with the average stay for managed care patients costing less. (There was no difference, however, in mortality or ICU readmission between the two groups.)
- *HMO patients were hospitalized 40% less often* than patients with fee-for-service plans and treated in solo practices. Group practice outpatient clinic patients had shorter stays and incurred lower costs at a hospital in the study but received the same quality of care as traditional clinic patients at the hospital.
- *Chronically ill patients in managed care plans had better access to care* than patients in fee-for-service plans, but (in a study of 1200 patients in three cities) their care was not as comprehensive, they waited longer for care, and physician-patient continuity was less.

Most patients and health care providers agree the theory of managed care is a good one: Patients receive care through a single, "seamless" system as they move from wellness to sickness back to wellness again. Continuity of care, prevention, and early intervention are stressed.

FUTURE OF MANAGED CARE

Many people think that managed care is more a principle than a structure. This principle says that a health care system should work to keep people healthy, and when they are sick or injured, a well-run system should work to ensure the right treatment in the right setting by the right people. At its core, managed care places health care providers as the individuals responsible for the health of the community. Managed care exists in different forms, with different benefit structures, financing mechanisms, and provider configurations. Managed care is still evolving and is very much a work in progress.

The future of managed care is not clear-cut. Statistics show that the public and private sector movement from fee-for-service systems to managed care has slowed in recent years. Surveys have indicated that there also is a shift from staff model HMOs toward less centralized systems, such as PPOs and POS plans. Public concerns about managed care have influenced many health care providers and integrated delivery systems to back away from strongly capitated plans in favor of discounted fee-for-service structures.

Experts predict, however, that despite the alleged problems and negative implications voiced in regard to managed health care, it will continue to be a popular choice for the delivery of health care in the United States. As stated earlier, managed care for the most part focuses on quality, choice, and access—not just cost cutting. It is predicted that future cost cutting will come from innovation, especially in the area of information technology. Computers will help MCOs do exactly what their name implies—*manage care* and costs. Huge databases of information on patients' and providers' use of health care delivery and outcomes will help to determine optimal treatment programs. With an aging population and increasingly sophisticated and expensive medical technology, health care costs no doubt will continue to increase, and managed care will play an important role in helping curb these rising costs. It already has shown progress in the area of preventive health.

WHAT DID YOU LEARN?

1. What is AHCPR, and how does it relate to managed care?
2. How does managed care affect the patient-physician relationship?
3. List ways that managed care affects health care providers.

WHAT DID YOU LEARN?

1. What is the principle behind managed health care?
2. What effect will managed care have on the future of health care in general?
3. In what ways will information technology affect the future of health care?

SUMMARY CHECK POINTS

☑ Managed care is a health care system wherein insurance companies attempt to control the cost, quality, and access of medical care to individuals enrolled in their plan by limiting the reimbursement levels paid to providers, by reducing utilization, or both.

☑ A PPO is a group of hospitals and physicians that agree to render particular services to a group of people, generally under contract with a private insurer. These services may be furnished at discounted rates if the members receive their health care from member providers. Services received from providers outside the organization may result in larger out-of-pocket expenses.

☑ In HMOs, enrollees receive comprehensive preventive and hospital and medical care from specific medical providers who receive a prepaid fee. Members select a PCP or medical group from the HMO's list of affiliated physicians. PCPs coordinate the patient's total care, which is normally free from hassles involving deductibles or claim forms. When using medical services, members pay a small co-payment, usually between $5 and $25. There are several types of plans under the HMO umbrella, as follows:
- *Staff model*—a closed panel HMO in which a multispecialty group of physicians is contracted to provide health care to HMO members and is compensated by the contractor via salary and incentive programs.
- *Group model*—a managed health care model involving contracts with physicians organized as a partnership, professional corporation, or other association. The health plan compensates the medical group for contracted services at a negotiated rate, and that group is responsible for compensating its physicians and contracting with hospitals for care of their patients.
- *IPA*—a type of HMO in which enrollees' health care is arranged through contracting physicians in the community, who practice in their own offices and who also may see patients from other HMOs or non-HMO patients on a fee-for-service basis. Physicians may be paid on a capitated or discounted fee-for-service basis.
- *Network model*—a type of HMO that contracts with two or more independent group practices to care for their members. Compensation is specific to the contract between the medical groups and the physicians. Participating groups maintain their independent practices and serve their own patients and HMO patients.
- *Direct contract model*—similar to an IPA except the HMO contracts directly with individual physicians.
- *POS*—a managed care plan (also called an open-ended model HMO) that allows enrollees to use the HMO providers or to go outside the plan and use a provider of their choice; however, when non-HMO providers are used, enrollees typically pay larger out-of-pocket expenses.

☑ Advantages of managed care include the following:
- Preventive care
- Lower premiums
- Prescription coverage
- Fewer unnecessary procedures
- Limited paperwork

☑ Disadvantages of managed care include the following:
- Limited physician pool
- Restricted coverage
- Prior approval needed for specialists
- Possibility of undertreatment
- Compromised privacy

☑ MCOs receive their accreditation from two organizations: NCQA and The Joint Commission.

☑ NCQA is a private, not-for-profit organization dedicated to improving health care quality and frequently is referred to as a watchdog for the managed care industry. NCQA has been accrediting MCOs since 1991 in response to the need for standardized, objective information about the quality of these organizations. Although the MCO accreditation program is voluntary, it has been well received by the managed care industry. For an organization to become accredited by NCQA, it must undergo a rigorous survey and meet certain standards designed to evaluate the health plan's clinical and administrative systems. In particular, NCQA evaluates health plans in the areas of patient safety, confidentiality, consumer protection, access, service, and continuous improvement.

☑ The Joint Commission is a private, independent, nonprofit organization that evaluates medical facility compliance based on a focused set of standards that are long known as essen-

tial to the delivery of good patient care. Joint Commission standards are guidelines for achieving "quality" patient care. These standards include the following:
- The rights of patients
- The assessment and treatment of patients
- A safe environment for patients and health care employees
- The quality of patient care
- The management of patients' records
- The organizational responsibilities of leadership and staff

☑ The *utilization review* process is a method of tracking, reviewing, and giving opinions regarding care provided to patients. Utilization review evaluates the necessity, appropriateness, and efficiency of the use of health care services, procedures, and facilities to control costs and manage care. Utilization review is one of the primary tools used by MCOs and other health plans.

☑ *Pre-authorization* is the process whereby certain tests, procedures, or inpatient hospitalization is ascertained as "medically necessary" before the service or procedure is performed. Pre-authorization does not guarantee payment.

☑ *Precertification* is a process whereby the provider (or a member of his or her staff) contacts the patient's managed care plan before inpatient admissions and performance of certain procedures and services to verify the patient's eligibility and coverage for the planned service.

☑ A *referral* is when the PCP requests another provider (usually a specialist) to render a second opinion or to perform a more extensive evaluation or treatment of a patient's problem.

☑ The future of managed care is not clear-cut, but the movement from fee-for-service systems to managed care has slowed, and managed care choices tend to be moving away from the tighter controlled staff model HMOs toward less centralized systems, such as PPOs and POS plans. Experts predict, however, that managed health care will overcome its problems and will have a prominent place in the future of health care.

Closing Scenario

There was a lot of information to assimilate in this chapter regarding managed care, especially because Emilio and Latisha knew so little about it before they began the course. They now think they understand the concepts much better, however. Latisha was surprised to learn that there were so many different types of HMOs—she thought an HMO was an HMO. She and Emilio, similar to so many others, had heard a lot of negative reports regarding managed care, and they assumed it was inferior health care. They now realize that not all MCOs are bad; there are many good ones and a few inferior ones—as is true for fee-for-service carriers.

At the free health clinic where Emilio volunteers, he has developed an information sheet for patients explaining managed care in simple terms, comparing it with the more familiar fee-for-service structure and including the pros and cons of both. Equipped now with a better understanding of the various structures of health insurance, he is beginning to feel more comfortable in his volunteer work at the free clinic. Being a health insurance professional has taken on a new meaning: It's not just knowing how to complete an insurance form and submitting it; it's also knowing how to build positive relationships with all members of the health care team and the patients. Realizing that everyone's job at the clinic is interrelated and that everyone has to work together for the entire system to work efficiently was an important learning experience for Emilio. An appreciation and understanding of the profession is growing as the students continue their lifelong learning experiences in class and in the workplace.

WEBSITES TO EXPLORE

- To learn more about managed care, visit the websites of the two groups that evaluate MCOs in the United States, the National Committee for Quality Assurance (NCQA) at http://www.ncqa.org and The Joint Commission at http://www.jointcommission.org

Chapter Review

Assessment

Multiple Choice

*Directions: In the questions/statements presented, choose the response that **best** answers/completes the stem, and circle the letter that precedes it.*

1. An organized, interrelated system of people and facilities that communicate with one another and work together as a unit is commonly referred to as a(an) __A__.
   A. network
   B. community
   C. demograph
   D. organizational unit

2. Individuals belonging to a managed health care plan are referred to as __B__.
   A. beneficiaries
   B. enrollees
   C. receivers
   D. entities

3. The two most common types of MCOs are __C__.
   A. PPOs and individual practice associations (IPAs)
   B. IPAs and HMOs
   C. HMOs and PPOs
   D. PPOs and POSs

4. A specific provider who oversees an HMO member's total health care treatment is called a(an) __D__.
   A. specific provider
   B. attending physician
   C. complete care provider
   D. primary care physician (PCP)

5. The amount of money a patient has to pay out-of-pocket per visit is referred to as a(an) __A__.
   A. co-payment
   B. deductible
   C. premium
   D. allowable fee

6. When an individual first enrolls in an HMO, he or she chooses a(an) __D__.
   A. specialist
   B. insurance carrier
   C. fiscal intermediary
   D. PCP

7. Most managed health care plans emphasize _____.
   A. small co-payments
   B. frequent physician visits
   C. preventive health care
   D. paying premiums on time

8. A multispecialty group practice in which all health care services are provided within the building(s) owned by the HMO is called a __A__.
   A. staff model
   B. group model
   C. network model
   D. direct contact model

9. An HMO that contracts with independent, multispecialty physician groups that provide all health care services to its members and usually share the same facility, support staff, medical records, and equipment is called a __B__.
   A. staff model
   B. group model
   C. network model
   D. direct contact model

10. A reimbursement system in which health care providers receive a fixed fee for every patient enrolled in the plan, regardless of how many or few services the patient uses, is called a(an) __B__.
    A. usual, customary, and reasonable
    B. capitation
    C. misallocation
    D. allowed fee system

11. A managed care system composed of individual health care providers who offer health care services for HMO and non-HMO patients but maintain their own offices and identities is called a(an) __B__.
    A. network model
    B. open-panel IPA
    C. direct-contact model
    D. POS plan

12. A plan that allows patients to use the HMO provider or go outside the plan and pay a higher co-payment and deductible is a(an) __D__.
    A. network model
    B. open-end HMO
    C. direct-contact model
    D. POS plan

13. A system designed to determine the medical necessity and appropriateness of a requested medical service, procedure, or hospital admission prior, concurrent, or retrospective to the event is called __C__.
    A. accreditation
    B. certification
    C. utilization
    D. endorsement determination

14. If a particular medical service or procedure is determined not to be "medically necessary," a patient may file a(an) __A__.
    A. grievance
    B. objection
    C. lawsuit
    D. appeal

15. A procedure required by third-party payers that requires permission before a provider can carry out specific procedures and treatments is __D__.
    A. referral
    B. certification
    C. adjudication
    D. pre-authorization

True/False

Directions: Place a "T" in the blank preceding the sentence if it is true; place an "F" if it is false.

__T__ 1. An HMO provides its members with basic health care services for a fixed price and for a given period of time.

__T__ 2. PPOs typically do not require authorization from a PCP for a referral to a specialist.

_____ 3. PPOs are more tightly controlled by government regulations than HMOs.

_____ 4. HMOs typically have no deductibles or plan limits.

_____ 5. The federal government requires that HMOs operate their own facilities, staffed with salaried physicians.

_____ 6. HMOs are neither accredited nor certified.

__T__ 7. Pre-authorization pertains to medical necessity and appropriateness and guarantees payment.

_____ 8. Precertification involves collecting information before inpatient admissions or performance of selected ambulatory procedures and services.

_____ 9. A referral is a request by a health care provider for a patient under his or her care to be evaluated or treated or both by another provider.

_____ 10. In all managed care situations, for the health care plan to recognize the referral, it must come from the patient's designated PCP.

Fill-in-the-Blank

*Directions: Select the word or word groups from the box on the next page to complete the following statements correctly. (**Note:** Some word or word groups can be used more than once.)*

1. _____ describes types of health insurance that control the use of health services by their members so that they can contain health care costs, the quality of care, or both.

2. An interrelated system wherein people and facilities communicate with one another and work together as a unit is referred to as a(an) __NETWORK__.

3. Individuals who are eligible for health care services and benefits under a specific managed care plan are called _____.

4. The two most common types of MCOs are __HMO__ and __PPO__.

5. _____ are groups of health care providers who work under one umbrella to provide medical services at a discount to individuals who participate in the managed care plan.

6. A(an) __PCP__ is a specific provider who oversees an HMO member's total health care treatment.

7. When a patient's problem exceeds the expertise of his or her PCP, the PCP can arrange a(an) __PCP__ to a specialist to take over the patient's care.

8. _____ typically have no deductibles or plan limits.

9. Managed care plans emphasize _____ health care.

10. A(an) _____ HMO is a multispecialty group practice wherein all health care services are provided within the building(s) owned by the HMO.

11. In a(an) _____, the HMO contracts with independent, multispecialty physician groups who provide all health care services to its members.

12. _____ is a fixed fee per member per specified time period (usually monthly).

13. The staff model is a(an) _CLOSED PANEL_ HMO.

14. The _CONTRACT MODEL_ HMO is similar to an IPA except the HMO contracts directly with the
  DIRECT
individual physicians.

15. An IPA is a(an) _OPEN PANEL PLAN_

16. The _GROUP MODEL_ HMO is one that has multiple provider arrangements, including staff, group, or IPA structures.

17. The _POS MODEL_ is a "hybrid" type of managed care (also referred to as an *open-ended HMO*) that allows patients to use the HMO provider or go outside the plan and use any provider they choose.

18. _____ is a system designed to determine the medical necessity and appropriateness of a medical service, procedure, or hospital admission.

19. _____ is a procedure required by most managed health care and indemnity plans before a provider is able to carry out specific procedures or treatments for a patient.

20. A(an) _____ is when the PCP requests another physician to provide his or her expert opinion regarding the patient's condition.

---

capitation
consultation
enrollees
health maintenance organizations (HMOs)
managed care
network model
point of service (POS) model
preferred provider organizations (PPOs)
primary care physician (PCP)
staff model

closed panel
direct contract model
group model
open-panel plan
pre-authorization
preventive
referral
utilization review
network

Short Answer

1. An MCO typically performs three main functions, which are as follows:

   _____

   _____

   _____

2. Explain briefly in your own words each of the following types of managed care systems:

   PPO: _____

   HMO: _____

   IPA: _____

   POS: _____

3. Under the Federal HMO Act, an entity must have three characteristics to call itself an HMO. List them.

   _____

   _____

   _____

4. List three advantages and three disadvantages of HMOs.

   _____

   _____

   _____

   _____

   _____

5. For a particular managed health care plan to become accredited by the National Committee for Quality Assurance (NCQA), it first must undergo a survey and meet certain standards designed to evaluate the facility's clinical and administrative systems. These standards fall into five broad categories. List them.

   _____

   _____

   _____

   _____

6. The Joint Commission's standards outline performance expectations for activities that affect the safety and quality of patient care. List the six categories these standards include.

_____

_____

_____

_____

_____

_____

7. List four types of actions against which a patient can file a grievance.

_____

_____

_____

_____

8. Explain the difference between a referral and a consultation.

_____

9. How do the Health Insurance Portability and Accountability Act's (HIPAA's) regulations affect managed care?

_____

10. In your own opinion, what is the future of managed care?

_____

Critical Thinking Activities

A. New patient Dorothy Scoval comes to the medical facility with a knee injury. She informs you that she is a current enrollee of Envision, a local HMO. Would the procedure for gathering demographic and insurance information differ with this patient compared with one who is insured under a traditional commercial plan? Explain why or why not.

B. Examine the ID card shown in Fig. 3-7, then answer the following questions from the information printed on the card.

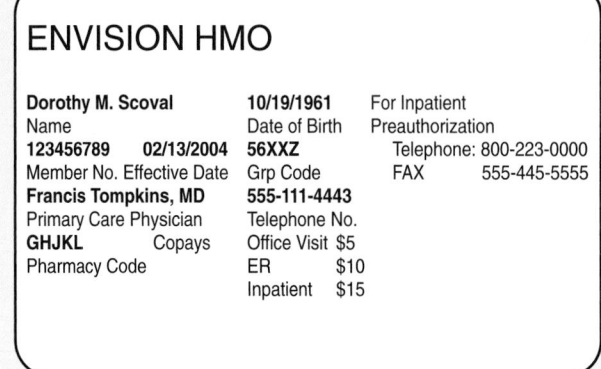

ENVISION HMO

Dorothy M. Scoval	10/19/1961	For Inpatient
Name	Date of Birth	Preauthorization
123456789 02/13/2004	**56XXZ**	Telephone: 800-223-0000
Member No. Effective Date	Grp Code	FAX 555-445-5555
Francis Tompkins, MD	**555-111-4443**	
Primary Care Physician	Telephone No.	
GHJKL Copays	Office Visit $5	
Pharmacy Code	ER $10	
	Inpatient $15	

Fig. 3-7   Health maintenance organization ID card for Scoval.

1. What is the name of the insured individual?
2. What is the name of the patient's PCP?
3. What dollar amount should you collect from the patient for an office visit?
4. What type of HMO is this?
5. If the patient was seen on February 2, 2004, would the HMO pay for the visit?

C. Established patient Dorothy Scoval telephones 1 week after her initial encounter complaining of chest pain and shortness of breath. She asks if she can schedule an appointment with an Envision cardiologist. The scheduling receptionist refers the call to you, the health insurance professional. How should this request be handled?

D. The medical facility in which you work as a health insurance professional is part of Envision, a staff model HMO. The health care providers are employees of the HMO and see patients on a "capitated" (per patient) basis. How does this payment structure affect claims submission for the plan's enrollees?

E. Health care reform has been a popular topic in the United States for many years; however, not everyone has a clear picture of exactly what managed care is and how it functions. Following are several statements regarding managed care, particularly HMOs. Place a "T" in the blank preceding all true statements; place an "F" in the blank if the statement is false.

_____ 1. Most HMOs typically offer substandard health care to keep costs under control.

_____ 2. MCOs encourage members to take a proactive or "preventive" role in their own health care.

_____ 3. All HMOs are the same.

_____ 4. The primary differences among managed care plans are found in the type of plan, what benefits it covers, and the out-of-pocket costs members will pay for services.

_____ 5. The NCQA has developed standards to evaluate the medical and quality systems in HMOs.

_____ 6. The main role of the PCP in HMOs is to serve as a "gatekeeper," rationing treatment options simply to contain costs.

_____ 7. The best physicians do not participate in HMO networks; members cannot be sure they are getting quality medical care.

_____ 8. Most health care providers participate in some type of managed care plan.

_____ 9. Most HMO members are dissatisfied with their plans.

_____ 10. Managed care plans are able to keep costs low because of an emphasis on disease prevention and wellness.

Case Studies

A. Eric Thomas has health care coverage with a PPO. His deductible is $500, which he has met for the current year. According to his policy, if he is treated by a PPO member physician, his co-insurance ratio is 90/10. If he is treated by a non-PPO physician, the co-insurance ratio is 80/20. Calculate the amount Eric would have to pay either of the two following physicians.

PPO Member Physician	Non-PPO Physician
Benjamin P. Moore, M.D.	Lydia R. Davis, M.D.
Est. Pt. Level II OV = $90	Est. Pt. Level II OV = $65
Eric's payment: _____	Eric's payment: _____

B. The following case study is for patient Judith Kelley. Read it thoroughly and complete the referral authorization form in Fig. 3-8.

Patient Name: Judith A. Kelley
DOB: 03/14/1955
Med. Record No.: 10445
Health Insurance: Zenith HMO
Member No.: 444661112

Judith Kelley visited Kayla Parsons, her PCP, on 08/22/20XX, complaining of nausea, loss of appetite, and unexplained weight loss, which began about 2 months before this visit after a bout of the flu. After taking a detailed history and performing a complete examination, including a urinalysis and complete blood count, Dr. Parsons suspects that Mrs. Kelley's symptoms point to a serious underlying condition and warrants a referral to a specialist for evaluation and treatment. Dr. Marvel Sutton is an endocrinologist and practices within the patient's HMO system. Initially, Dr. Parsons has authorized two visits with Dr. Sutton, and the first appointment date is 08/30/20XX.

Diagnoses: (1) Loss of weight—783.21; (2) Nausea—787.02
Referral No.: 032425
Provider ID No.: 6544355
Dr. Parson's phone number: 555-876-2123; fax: 555-876-2110

Note: Students should use their own name as a contact person.

HEALTH Referral Authorization Form

This facsimile transmission is private, confidential, and intended only of the recipient named hereon. If you receive this transmission in error, please contact Iowa Health's Medical Management Dept. at (555) 333-XXXX or (800) 222-XXXX.
FAX THIS COMPLETED FORM TO: (555) 333-XXXX or (800) 222-XXXX

Referral #: _____   **ALL REFERRALS EXPIRE IN 60 DAYS**

Patient Information

Member Name	Member #	DOB	Refer to Provider	Specialty

Please check the requested services: ☐ Evaluation and recommendation   ☐ Evaluate and treat
☐ OPS   ☐ One follow-up visit   ☐ Send report to PCP

Number of Visits:	Appointment Date:

Medical Information

Diagnosis:	ICD-9 Code:

Symptoms: _____
_____
_____

Previous Treatment (if pertinent for referral): _____
_____

Lab/X-Ray Finding (if pertinent for referral): _____
_____

Medical Record #:

Authorization

PCP Name	Phone # (Include Area Code)
Contact Name	Fax #

For Office use only

PCP Provider #		Refer to Provider	
Member Effective Date	Auth Type		Extent of Care
Auth Start Date	Auth End Date		# of Visits Approved
Approved by:		Date:	
Entered by:		Date:	

This referral does not constitute a payment agreement. Coverage is based on the eligibility of the member at the time of service is rendered.

Fig. 3-8   Referral authorization form (Kelley).

C. The following case study is for patient Fredric Basquez. From this information, complete the prior authorization request form in Fig. 3-9.

Patient Name: Fredric M. Basquez
DOB: 09/26/1972
Health Insurance Plan: OutReach Plus
Subscriber ID No.: QST99442
Med. Record No.: BA092662
Social Security No.: 222-00-9999

Fredric Basquez comes to see Dr. Eric Woods, an orthopedic surgeon, for complaints of head and neck pain accompanied by numbness and tingling in his right arm after an all-terrain vehicle (ATV) accident. The patient reports he was riding on the back of his brother's ATV, when the vehicle came into contact with a concealed tree stump. He was subsequently thrown from the vehicle, landing on the right side of his head. A 2-cm laceration of the right cheek was sutured in the emergency department yesterday, and debridement of minor abrasions and contusions of the face and shoulder was performed. X-rays of the head and neck, done at the time of the emergency department visit, were inconclusive. He was given prescriptions for naproxen. An emergency department staff member scheduled an appointment with this office for follow-up. A detailed history was taken, and a complete physical examination was done. Suspected herniated disk with progressive objective neurological deficits.

Diagnosis: Neck injury—959.09
Provider ID No.: 6577890113
Dr. Woods' phone number: 555-232-0987; fax: 555-232-0980

Dr. Woods asks you to arrange an MRI for Mr. Basquez. You note from the patient's insurance ID card that prior authorization must be obtained for any outside diagnostic testing. From the information above, complete the Prior Authorization Request form for Mr. Basquez's MRI. (*Note:* You will be attaching a copy of the initial history and physical examination [H & P] with this form.)

Note: Do not complete the area below the heavy black line.

Prior Authorization Request for MRI/CT Scan of the Neck and Spine

To Be Completed By Ordering Provider / *Date:*

Patient Name:	Patient Subscriber ID:	Patient Date of Birth:
Provider Name:	Provider ID Number:	Provider Phone: Provider Fax:

Please Indicate the Study Ordered:	☐ MRI	☐ Neck ☐ Spine	☐ CT	☐ Neck ☐ Spine

Diagnosis (ICD-9 Code):   Scheduled Date:

MRI Indications		CT Indications
☐ Myelopathy	☐ Congenital anomalies of spine	☐ Spinal fracture
☐ Infection of spine/cord/disk	☐ Spinal stenosis	
☐ Spinal trauma	☐ Post-op spinal surgery w/residua	
☐ Grossly abnormal plain films	☐ Where contrast is required	
☐ Co-existing systemic illness	☐ Known malignancy/suspected mets	

Conditional Indications

Suspected herniated disk with one or more of the following:	☐ Progressive objective neurological deficits (sensory/motor loss, reflex change, fasciculations, wasting) ☐ Cauda equina syndrome	☐ Serious systemic illness (malignancy, TB, etc.) ☐ Spinal cord compression
Uncomplicated back pain or sciatica only after 4–6 weeks of the conservative treatment with:	☐ Home self-care ☐ Analgesics ☐ PT or chiropractic care ☐ Spinal exercises	
If none of the above, rationale for exception (all exceptions must have supporting documentation):		

Supporting Documentation: ☐ Initial Evaluation (H & P)   ☐ Treatment Plan   ☐ Office Notes

To Be Completed By   ☐ Approved   ☐ Denied

Comments: _____

_____

This notice is not a guarantee payment will be provided and only approves the medical necessity and appropriateness of the medical services requested and authorized. The determination on payment of claims will be made when the claim is received. The claim will be subject to the terms and limitations of the member's benefit plan, including applicable deductibles and co-payments. Additionally, prior authorization will be honored only if the member is a covered member and dues are paid at the time the services are provided. Payment will not be allowed if the member is not covered at the time of service.

Reviewed by: _____   Date: _____

Fig. 3-9 Prior authorization request (Basquez).

Internet Exploration

A. Log on to the Internet, and using the search words "managed health care," locate a website that provides current information regarding new managed health care issues. Prepare a 1-page essay or a 3-minute oral presentation entitled "What's New in Managed Health Care." Your instructor will provide specific guidelines for this activity.

B. Research The Joint Commission website (**http://www.jointcommission.org**) and identify current updates regarding HIPAA compliance standards. At The Joint Commission home page, enter HIPAA in the search box located in the top right corner.

C. Explore the Kaiser Permanente website (**http://www.kaiserpermanente.org**). Note the various informational areas. Click on "a prospective member," choose a region of interest to you, and check out the various plan options.

Application Exercises

Generate a Document for a Nonroutine HMO Patient

Morris Bennett comes to Broadmoor Medical Clinic, where you are employed as a health insurance professional, complaining of severe pain in the right lower quadrant accompanied by cramping, mild fever, and constipation of 4 days' duration. Morris is employed by John Deere Health, an HMO in Illinois, and became ill while visiting relatives over the Thanksgiving holiday in the city where your office is located. You contact his insurance carrier, and they fax Mr. Bennett the following instruction sheet for claims purposes:

If you need to pay for care because of an emergency or urgent (nonroutine) situation when traveling outside of our network, or on vacation, send an itemized bill including the following information:

1. Member's name and member ID
2. Date of service or supplies provided
3. State or country in which services were rendered or supplies obtained
4. Description of services/supplies
5. The provider's name, address, and tax identification number
6. An interpretation of the claim, if in a foreign language (any information provided will assist in making the proper payment determination and prevent delays)
7. Accident details (if applicable)

The chart notes indicate that Mr. Bennett has been under the care of Dr. Edgar Billingham for treatment of diverticulosis for quite some time. Today, he was prescribed ampicillin, 500 mg t.i.d. #30, and was instructed to drink only clear fluids for 2 to 3 days for bowel rest. He was given instructions regarding prevention and control of this disorder and told to see his family physician on returning home.

The claim address is: John Deere Health, 4000 16th Avenue, Moline, XY, 61265.

Include patient name, patient ID, and a daytime phone number where the patient can be reached. Payment is subject to the terms and conditions of the Plan Administrator's benefit plan.

From the information on Mr. Bennett's registration and encounter forms (Figs. 3-10 and 3-11), (1) generate an itemized bill (using the blank ledger card in Fig. 3-12), and (2) compose a brief explanatory cover letter to accompany the bill.

Registration Data

1. Your Name __Bennett Morris T.__   Sex ☒ Male   Date of Birth __10-21-46__
   (Last)   (First)   (Middle)   ☐ Female

2. Social Security #: __333-44-SSSS__   Marital Status: S Ⓜ D Se W

3. Address: __2900 Sunnylawn__   4. __SSS-343-2222__
   (Street)   (Phone)
   __Moline__   __IL__   __SSS66__
   (City)   (State)   (Zip)

5. Employer: __John Deere Enterprises__   Occupation: __Inspector__

   Employer Address: __4910 John Deere Blvd. Moline, IL SSS66__   __SSS-343-8762__
                                                                  (Work Phone)
   Spouse: __Frieda__   Employer: __N/A__   Occupation: __Housewife__

   Employer Address: _____   _____
                                                                  (Work Phone)

6. | Other Household Members | Date of Birth | Relationship |
   |---|---|---|
   | | / / | |
   | | / / | |
   | | / / | |
   | | / / | |
   | | / / | |

7. Medical Insurance Information

	Ins. Company Name	Policy No.	Policy Holder	Sgl.	Type of Coverage Fmly.	Primary	Sec.
( )	John Deere Health	333XLM	Morris Bennett	☐	☒	☐	☐
( )				☐	☐	☐	☐
( )				☐	☐	☐	☐

8. Person to Contact in an Emergency __Frieda Bennett__ Relationship to you __spouse__

   Their Work Phone _____   Their Home Phone __SSS-343-2229__

9. Party with primary responsibility for payment: ☒ Self   ☐ Other

   Name _____   Relationship to you _____

   Address _____   Home Phone _____

For Office Use Only

Date Completed _____   Account No. _____   Patient No. _____

Household Status   ☐ Head of Household

☐ Spouse   ☐ Child   ☐ Other: _____

Head of Household Name _____

Fig. 3-10   Registration data sheet (Bennett).

BROADMOOR MEDICAL CLINIC

PRACTICE # 0 4

ACCT. #: 32100	DATE OF SERVICE: 11-26-20XX	CATEGORY: GA	DIAGNOSIS: diverticulitis

PATIENT'S NAME: Morris T. Bennett   Rec #11336

CPT	✔	DESCRIPTION	FEE	CPT	✔	DESCRIPTION	FEE	CPT	✔	DESCRIPTION	FEE
OFFICEVISIT - NEW PATIENT				**IMMUNIZATIONS**				**INJECTIONS (CONT'D.)**			
99201		Focused		90701		DtaP		J3410		Vistaril	
99202		Expanded		90632		Hep A (Adult)		J3420		Vitamin B12	
99203	✔	Detailed	185.00	90633		Hep A (Ped)		J2000		Xylocaine	
99204		Comprehensive		90744		Hep B (Ped)		**PROCEDURES**			
99205		Complex		90746		Hep B (Adult)		46600		Anoscopy	
OFFICEVISIT - ESTABLISHED PATIENT				90737		Hib		92551		Audio Screening	
99211		Minimal		90657		Influenza		11730		Avulsion Nail, Partial or	
99212		Focused		90707		MMR				Complete, Single	
99213		Expanded		90732		Pneumococcal		11200		Rem. of Skin Tags up to 15	
99214		Detailed		90718		Td		11201		Each Additional 10	
99215		Comprehensive		90703		Tetanus Toxoid		10060		I & D Simple Abscess	
				90716		Varicella		10120		Removal FB Skin	
PHYSICAL EXAM - NEW PATIENT								11740		I & D Subung. Hematoma	
99381		Age Under 1 Year		**INJECTIONS**				58310		IUD Removal	
99382		Age 1 - 4 Years		J1200		Benadryl up to 50 mg		94010		Spirometry	
99383		Age 5 - 11 Years		J0540		Bicillin up to 1,200,000 mg		A4570		Splint	
99384		Age 12 - 17 Years		J0690		Cefazolin Sodium 250 mg		99173		Vision Screening	
99385		Age 18 - 39 Years		J0704		Celestone		**LABORATORY**			
99386		Age 40 - 64 Years		J0780		Compazine		82270	✔	Blood Occult	30.00
99387		Age 65+ Years		J1100		Decadron		85680		TB Intradermal	
				J0970		Delestrogen		81000	✔	Urine Dip Stick	15.00
PHYSICAL EXAM - ESTABLISHED PATIENT				J1050		Depo Provera		84703		Serum Pregnancy Test	
99391		Age Under 1 Year		J1510		Gamma Globulin		87082		Strep Screen	
99392		Age 1 - 4 Years		J3301		Kenalog					
99393		Age 5 - 11 Years		J1940		Kasix		36415	✔	Venipuncture	25.00
99394		Age 12 - 17 Years		J2550		Phenergan		99000	✔	Handling	10.00
99395		Age 18 - 39 Years		J3490		Rocephin					
99396		Age 40 - 64 Years		J1070		Testosterone		**MISCELLANEOUS**			
99397		Age 65+ Years		J3250		Tigan					
				J1885		Torodol					

ICD-9 ☐ **DIAGNOSIS**

CARDIOLOGY
794.31 ☐ Abn Ekg
786.50 ☐ Chest Pain, Nos
780.4 ☐ Dizziness And Giddiness
787.1 ☐ Heartburn
272.0 ☐ Hypercholesterolem
272.4 ☐ Hyperlipidemia Nec/Nos
401.1 ☐ Hyptertension Benign
401.9 ☐ Hypertension Nos
401.0 ☐ Hypertension, Malig.
785.1 ☐ Palpitations
ENDOCRINE
250.01 ☐ IDDM Controlled
250.03 ☐ IDDM Uncontrolled
250.02 ☐ NIDDM Uncontrolled
250.00 ☐ NIDDM Controlled
251.2 ☐ Hypoglycemia
244.9 ☐ Hypothyroidism
242.90 ☐ Hyperthyroidism
EAR, NOSE, THROAT
386.30 ☐ Labyrinthitis Nos
382.9 ☐ Otitis Media, Ac./Chr.
462. ☐ Pharyngitis Acute
477.9 ☐ Rhinitis, Allergic
461.9 ☐ Sinusitis, Ac Nos
473.9 ☐ Sinusitis, Chronic
528.0 ☐ Stomatitis
034.0 ☐ Strep Throat

388.30 ☐ Tinnitus Nos
463. ☐ Tonsillitis, Acute
474.0 ☐ Tonsillitis, Chronic
FEMALE / GYNECOLOGY
795.0 ☐ Abn Pap Smear-Cervix
793.8 ☐ Abn Findings-Breast
626.0 ☐ Amenorrhea
611.72 ☐ Breast Mass/Lump
616.0 ☐ Cervicitis
V25.09 ☐ Contracep. Mgmt.
625.3 ☐ Dysmenorrhea
626.4 ☐ Menstruation, Irreg.
625.2 ☐ Menstruation, Excessive
614.9 ☐ Pelvic Inflam Dis
V22.2 ☐ Preg State, Incidental
616.10 ☐ Vaginitis
PHYSICAL EXAM
V20.1 ☐ Well Child
V72.84 ☐ Pre-Op Exam
GASTRO-INTESTINAL
789.06 ☐ Abnormal Pain, Epigastric
794.3 ☐ Abn. Liver Function Study
578.1 ☐ Blood in Stool
564.0 ☐ Constipation
787.91 ☐ Diarrhea
562.11 ☒ Diverticulitis
530.81 ☐ Esophageal Reflux
535.5 ☐ Gastritis/Duodenitis Nos
455.6 ☐ Hemorrhoids

787.0 ☐ Nausea And Vomiting
533.90 ☐ Peptic Ulcer Nos
569.3 ☐ Rectal Bleeding
GENITO-URINARY
585. ☐ Chronic Renal Failure
595.0 ☐ Cystitis Acute
788.1 ☐ Dysuria
599.7 ☐ Hematuria
601.0 ☐ Prostatitis Acute
599.0 ☐ UTI
HEMATOLOGY
790.6 ☐ Abn Blood Chemistry Nec
285.9 ☐ Anemia Nos
280.1 ☐ Anemia, Iron Def
INFECTIOUS
616.3 ☐ Abcess: Bartholin Gland
682.9 ☐ Abcess: Skin
780.6 ☐ Fever: Unkn. Origin
IMMUNOLOGY - ALLERGIES
995.3 ☐ Allergic Reaction Nos
477.0 ☐ Allergy, Hay Fever
042. ☐ Human ImmunoVirus Dis.
ORTHOPEDICS
716.90 ☐ Arthritis Unspec.
724.5 ☐ Backache Nos
727.3 ☐ Bursitis Nec
354.0 ☐ Carpal Tunnel Syndrome
719.40 ☐ Joint Pain-Unspec.
729.1 ☐ Myalgia And Myositis Nos.

733.00 ☐ Osteoporosis
845.00 ☐ Sprain: Ankle
847.2 ☐ Sprain: Back
847.0 ☐ Sprain: Cervical
840.9 ☐ Sprain: Shoulder
729.81 ☐ Swelling of Limb
726.00 ☐ Tendonitis
NEUROLOGY
784.0 ☐ Headache
346.9 ☐ Migraine Nos
724.3 ☐ Sciatica
307.81 ☐ Tension Headache
780.4 ☐ Vertigo
OPHTHALMOLOGY
373.00 ☐ Blepharitis Nos
372.30 ☐ Conjunctivitis
918.1 ☐ Corneal Abrasion
PULMONARY / RESPIRATORY
493.9 ☐ Asthma Nos
466.0 ☐ Bronchitis Acute
490. ☐ Bronchitis Nos
486. ☐ Pneumonia
786.2 ☐ Cough
786.0 ☐ Dyspnea/Resp Abn
487. ☐ Influenza
786.52 ☐ Painful Respiration
786.09 ☐ S O B
465.9 ☐ URI
079.9 ☐ Viral Syndrome

PSYCH / MENTAL HEALTH
303.9 ☐ Alcoholism
300.00 ☐ Anxiety State Nos
300.00 ☐ Depression
SKIN / DERMATOLOGIC
706.1 ☐ Acne Nec
691. ☐ Dermatitis, Atopic
692. ☐ Dermatitis, Contact
110.1 ☐ Dermatophytosis, Nail
691.0 ☐ Diaper Rash
054.9 ☐ Herpes Simplex Nos
053.9 ☐ Herpes Zoster Nos
054.10 ☐ Herpes Genital Nec
684. ☐ Impetigo
703.0 ☐ Ingrowing Nail
215.9 ☐ Nevus
110.1 ☐ Onychomycosis
696.1 ☐ Psoriasis
706.2 ☐ Sebaceous Cyst
708.8 ☐ Urticaria Nec
078.1 ☐ Warts, Viral
OTHER - MISC.
780.7 ☐ Malaise and Fatigue
780.2 ☐ Syncope
WRITE - IN

INSTRUCTIONS: Make appt w/PCP upon returning home	RETURN APPOINTMENT: ___ Days ___ Weeks ___ Months ___ PRN ___ 15 ___ 30 ___ 45	**PAID** ☒ CASH ☐ CHECK ☐ CR. CD.	PREV. BAL. — 0 — TODAY'S FEE 265.00 AMT. REC'D. 5.00

Fig. 3-11 Encounter form (Bennett).

Insurance:
   John Deere Health HMO
   ID# 333XLM
   DOB: 10/21/1946
   A/C#32100

STATEMENT

BROADMOOR MEDICAL CLINIC
4353 Pine Ridge Drive
Milton, XY 12345-0001
Telephone: 555-656-7890

Spouse: Frieda

MORRIS T. BENNETT
2900 SUNNYLAWN
MOLINE, IL 55566

DATE 20XX	PROFESSIONAL SERVICE DESCRIPTION	CHARGE	CREDITS		CURRENT BALANCE
			PAYMENTS	ADJUSTMENTS	

Due and payable within 10 days.   Pay last amount in balance column

Fig. 3-12 Ledger card (Bennett).

Enrichment Activities

A. Contact an HMO or other managed care plan health insurance professional in your area. Interview the health insurance professional to determine (1) what benefits are offered and (2) how claims are handled. Request information brochures or fact sheets.

B. Visit a local medical facility that is a member of an HMO or other managed care plan. Interview the health insurance professional there to determine the differences in handling managed care cases compared with cases with traditional insurance. Request copies of any applicable office brochures and pre-authorization/referral forms.

C. Generate a bulletin board collage of the various brochures, fact sheets, and forms you acquired from A and B.

OBJECTIVES

After completion of this chapter, the student should be able to:

1. Explain Medicaid.
2. Define the federal government's role in Medicaid.
3. Outline how individual states can modify Medicaid coverage.
4. Name the two major groups that qualify for Medicaid, and explain both.
5. List the services typically covered by Medicaid.
6. Explain the various methods for verifying Medicaid eligibility.
7. Interpret third-party liability as it relates to Medicaid.
8. List common Medicaid billing errors.
9. Explain the Medicaid standard remittance advice.
10. Discuss fraud and abuse in the Medicaid system.

UNDERSTANDING MEDICAID

KEY TERMS

balance billing
budget period
categorically needy
cost avoid(ance)
cost sharing
countable income
disproportionate share hospitals
dual coverage (Medi-Medi)
dual eligibles
Early and Periodic Screening, Diagnosis,
 and Treatment (EPSDT) program
federal poverty level (FPL)
fiscal intermediary (FI) (fiscal agent)
mandated services

Medicaid
Medicaid "simple" claim
medically necessary
medically needy
Medicare hospital insurance (Medicare HI)
Medicare-Medicaid crossover claims
optional services
pay and chase claims
payer of last resort
Program of All-Inclusive Care for the
 Elderly (PACE)
Qualified Disabled and Working
 Individuals

Qualified Medicare Beneficiaries
reciprocity
remittance advice (RA)
Specified Low-Income Medicare
 Beneficiaries
spend down
State Children's Health Insurance Program
 (SCHIP)
Supplemental Security Income (SSI)
supplementary medical insurance (SMI)
Temporary Assistance for Needy Families
 (TANF)
third-party liability

Opening Scenario

Nela Karnama has been employed as a medical receptionist in a multispecialty medical practice for 9 years. She heard that there was soon going to be an opening in the billing department, which would be a promotion for Nela if she qualified for the position. She had always wanted to specialize in this area but did not feel qualified, so she enrolled in an evening course at a community college satellite center in a nearby town. Nela thought she knew quite a lot about Medicaid because after her husband was killed in an automobile accident, she and her children became eligible for benefits. After perusing the contents of Chapter 4, it was obvious to her, however, that what she did know about it was limited to the program she and her children were on and that there was a lot more to learn.

Nela carpooled with Berta Kazinski, a neighbor who also had enrolled in the course. Berta, a nontraditional student, was basically unfamiliar with the program. She recalled that Medicaid had begun paying for part of her mother-in-law's expenses after she had been in a nursing home for several years, but Berta was unaware of the financial implications that led to her mother-in-law's eligibility for this care.

The discussion concerning Medicaid broadened during their commute to the class, and it was obvious that there was more to the Medicaid program than either of the women realized. Using a time study schedule they created in Chapter 2, they laid out their study plans for the next learning phase of their health insurance career.

WHAT IS MEDICAID?

Medicaid is a combination federal and state medical assistance program designed to provide comprehensive and quality medical care for low-income families with special emphasis on children, pregnant women, the elderly, the disabled, and parents with dependent children who have no other way to pay for health care. Congress established the Medicaid program under Title XIX (19) of the Social Security Act of 1965. Under the federal Medicaid guidelines, federal and state governments must contribute a specified percentage of total health care expenditures. The federal contribution is approximately 50%. The states pay the remaining costs, after which they are free to choose whom to cover and what benefits to provide. There is usually a single state agency in charge of the program in each state, but many states have the program administered by county and city governments.

Although Medicaid benefits vary from state to state, all states have Medicaid programs. As a result, there are essentially 56 different Medicaid programs—one for each state, territory, and the District of Columbia. The individual state programs cover a variety of health care services, and each state sets its own guidelines regarding eligibility standards, services, benefits package, payment rates, and program administration within the broader federal guidelines.

WHAT DID YOU LEARN?

1. What is Medicaid?
2. When was the Medicaid program established?
3. Under what major act does the Medicaid program fall?

EVOLUTION OF MEDICAID

Medicaid originally was created to give low-income Americans access to health care. Since its inception, Medicaid has evolved from a narrowly defined program available only to individuals eligible for cash assistance (welfare) into a large insurance program with complex eligibility rules. Today, Medicaid is a major social welfare program and is administered by the Centers for Medicare and Medicaid Services (CMS), formerly called the Healthcare Financing Administration (HCFA).

The Medicaid program that was formerly referred to as *Aid to Families with Dependent Children* is now called **Temporary Assistance for Needy Families (TANF)**. TANF is the federal-state cash assistance program for poor families, typically headed by a single parent. Each state sets its own income eligibility guidelines for TANF, and individuals who are eligible for TANF automatically qualify for Medicaid. Not all states refer to this program as TANF. Many states have coined their own name for this program. Vermont calls it ANFC/RU (Aid to Needy Families with Children/Reach Up); New York calls it simply the Family Assistance (FA) Program; and Kentucky's program is called K-TAP (Kentucky Transitional Assistance Program). For a listing of what all states call their TANF programs, consult the Websites to Explore section at the end of this chapter.

In 1972, federal law established the **Supplemental Security Income (SSI)** program, which provides federally funded cash assistance to qualifying elderly and disabled poor. Under the SSI program, the Social Security Administration determines eligibility criteria and sets the cash benefit amounts for SSI. SSI is a cash benefit program controlled by the Social Security Administration; however, it is not related to the Social Security Program.

States may choose to supplement federal SSI payments with state funds. To be eligible for SSI, an individual must be at least 65 years old or blind or disabled and have limited assets (or resources). Income is determined by the standards set forth in the **federal poverty level (FPL)** guidelines (Table 4-1). The figures in Table 4-1 represent the income of the individual or family. The U.S. Department of Health and Human Services issues new FPL guidelines in January or February each year. These guidelines serve as one of the indicators for determining eligibility in a wide variety of federal and state programs. Eligibility for SSI benefits is not based on work record. The income benefits limit is $623 per month for an individual and $934 for a couple (2007 figures). Eligible recipients also qualify for SSI Medicaid assistance for health care (for updates, see Websites to Explore at the end of this chapter).

The amount of the SSI payment is the difference between the individual's countable income and the Federal Benefit Rate. Income is anything a person receives during a calendar month and uses to meet needs for food, clothing, or shelter. It may be in cash income or "in-kind" income. In-kind income is not cash; it is food, clothing, shelter, or something one can use to obtain food (e.g., food stamps), clothing, or shelter. **Countable income** is the amount left over after

1. eliminating all items that are not considered income (e.g., child support or student loans) and
2. applying all appropriate exclusions (earned or unearned income exclusions) to the items that are considered income.

During the late 1980s and early 1990s, Congress expanded Medicaid eligibility to include more categories of people—the poor elderly, individuals with disabilities, children, and certain categories of pregnant women. In addition to expanding eligibility parameters, Medicaid programs were broadened as a result of federal mandates. These program expansions include the following:

- Payments to hospitals that serve large numbers of poor, uninsured, or Medicaid recipients

TABLE 4-1	2007 Department of Health and Human Services Poverty Guidelines		
Size of Family Unit	**48 Contiguous States and D.C.**	**Alaska**	**Hawaii**
1	$10,210	$12,770	$11,750
2	13,690	17,120	15,750
3	17,170	21,470	19,750
4	20,650	25,820	23,750
5	24,130	30,170	27,750
6	27,610	34,520	31,750
7	31,090	38,870	35,750
8	34,570	43,220	39,750
For each additional person, add	3,480	4,350	4,000

From *Fed Reg* 72:3147-3148, 2007.

- Coverage of prenatal and delivery services for qualifying pregnant women and their infants who have no other insurance
- Expansion of services to many children in low-income families who do not receive cash assistance (TANF)
- Expansion of Medicaid to fill gaps in Medicare services to the poor elderly or disabled individuals
- Coverage of the full range of federally allowable Medicaid services as medically necessary and appropriate for all children on Medicaid

As a result of these and other federal law changes, the eligibility determination process is more intricate today than in the past. Computer systems designed for a smaller and simpler program now manage information for millions of people in dozens of different eligibility groups.

HIPAA TIP

Medicaid HIPAA Compliant Concept Model (MHCCM)
MHCCM shows how HIPAA affects the Medicaid enterprise and provides practical tools to help a state determine the best course of action for analyzing the HIPAA impact, determine implementation strategies, determine best practices, and validate what a state has accomplished.

The website for MHCCM is at http://www.cms.hhs.gov/medicaid/hipaa/adminsimp.

WHAT DID YOU LEARN?

1. As it was originally created, what was the only group Medicaid covered?
2. What is TANF?
3. What does SSI provide?
4. What additional group was added to the Medicaid program in 1972?
5. Who administers Medicaid?
6. Why is it difficult to determine Medicaid eligibility in today's health care?

STRUCTURE OF MEDICAID

Medicaid is a combination federal and state public assistance program, which pays for certain health care costs of individuals who qualify. The program is administered by CMS under the general direction of the Department of Health and Human Services. Eligibility is based on need by meeting certain income and resource limits. The federal govern-

ment has established broad requirements for eligibility, and the individual states refine eligibility requirements and coverage to the needs of its population.

Federal Government's Role

The federal government establishes broad national guidelines for Medicaid eligibility. Within the federal guidelines, each state establishes its own eligibility standards; determines the type, amount, duration, and scope of services; sets the rate of payment for services; and administers its own program. Under the broadest provisions of the federal statute, individuals, no matter what their financial status, must fall into a designated group before they are eligible for Medicaid. These groups are shown in Fig. 4-1.

States' Options

States generally are allowed wide parameters in determining which groups their Medicaid programs cover and the financial criteria for Medicaid eligibility within each particular program. To be eligible for federal funds, however, states are required to provide Medicaid coverage for certain individuals

CATEGORICALLY NEEDY

Families, pregnant women, and children
- Persons meeting Family Medical criteria (including TANF recipients)
- Children under the age of 1 and pregnant women whose countable income does not exceed 150% of the FPL
- Children ages 1-5 whose countable income does not exceed 133% of the FPL
- Children ages 6-18 whose countable income does not exceed 100% of the FPL

Aged and Disabled Individuals
- SSI recipients
- Qualified Medicare Beneficiaries (QMBs)
- Individuals residing in intermediate or long-term care facilities
- Medicaid beneficiaries
- Dual coverage (Medi-Medi) beneficiaries

MEDICALLY NEEDY

Individuals who do not qualify for Medicaid benefits under the categorically needy programs because of income or resources exceeding the level of qualifying criteria but are medically indigent

- Pregnant women
- Children up to age 18 (or age 18 working toward a high school diploma or its equivalent)
- Persons 65 years of age and older
- Persons who are disabled or blind under Social Security Administration standards

Fig. 4-1   Who is eligible for Medicaid?

who receive federally assisted income-maintenance payments and for related groups not receiving cash payments. In addition to their Medicaid programs, most states have other, "state-only" programs to provide medical assistance for specified poor individuals who do not qualify for Medicaid. Federal funds are not provided for state-only programs.

States must cover **categorically needy** individuals, but they have options as to how to define "categorically needy." Categorically needy individuals typically include the following:

- Low-income families with children
- Individuals receiving SSI
- Pregnant women, infants, and children with incomes less than a specified percent of the FPL
- Qualified Medicare Beneficiaries

Who qualifies for Medicaid benefits in a particular state varies depending on the options that state has elected to include in the program. States that include the SSI program cover everyone who qualifies for the SSI (aged, blind, and disabled). These states cannot have rules, however, that are more restrictive than the federal government rules for SSI.

In addition to the categorically needy, a state may elect to cover other optional categorical groups, such as the following:

- Individuals who have large medical expenses and might qualify for Medicaid categorically, but their income and resources are too high (referred to as **medically needy**) and aged, blind, or disabled individuals
- Members of families with dependent children who have too much income or resources or both to be eligible for cash assistance, but not enough for needed medical care
- Aged and disabled individuals with incomes less than 100% of the FPL
- Institutionalized individuals with incomes no greater than 300% of the SSI federal benefit rate

Mandated Services

Title XIX of the Social Security Act requires that for a state to receive federal matching funds, certain basic services (referred to as **mandated services**) must be offered to the categorically needy population in any state program. These services include the following:

- Inpatient hospital services
- Outpatient hospital services
- Prenatal care
- Vaccines for children

- Physician services
- Nursing facility services for individuals 21 years old or older
- Family planning services and supplies
- Rural health clinic services
- Home health care for individuals eligible for skilled-nursing services
- Laboratory and x-ray services
- Pediatric and family nurse practitioner services
- Nurse-midwife services
- Federally qualified health center services, and ambulatory services of a federally qualified health center that would be available in other settings
- Early and Periodic Screening, Diagnosis, and Treatment (EPSDT) program services for children younger than age 21

To see a timeline of Medicaid's mandated services, log on to the CMS website and type "Medicaid mandated services" into the search box at the top of the page.

Optional Services

Federal funding also is available for federally approved **optional services**. They are called optional services because states can provide as many or as few as they choose. Also, individual states can provide optional services to their categorically needy population, which they do not provide to other groups. Following are the most common of the 34 currently approved optional Medicaid services:

- Diagnostic services
- Clinic services
- Intermediate care facilities for the mentally retarded
- Prescribed drugs and prosthetic devices
- Optometrist services and eyeglasses
- Nursing facility services for children younger than 21 years old
- Transportation services
- Rehabilitation and physical therapy services
- Home and community-based care to certain individuals with chronic impairments

The resource limits for medically needy individuals are higher than the limits for other categories of eligibility. These individuals can **"spend down"** their assets to the Medicaid eligibility level by deducting incurred medical expenses. A spend down occurs when private or family finances are depleted to the point where the individual family becomes eligible for Medicaid assistance. Almost any medical bills the applicant or the applicant's family still owes or that were paid in the months for which Medicaid is sought (called the **budget period**) can be used to meet the spend down requirement.

The medically needy spend down process is normally a voluntary process and frequently is done to allow an elderly individual eligible for Medicaid to help pay for nursing home care that he or she otherwise could not afford. It also is used in certain family situations when an unexpected illness or injury occurs that results in large medical bills the family does not have the funds to pay.

States may provide home and community-based care waiver services to certain individuals who are eligible for Medicaid. The services to be provided to these individuals may include case management, personal care services, respite care services, adult day health services, homemaker/home health aide, habilitation, and other services requested by the state and approved by CMS.

In addition to the assistance Medicaid provides in its federally mandated programs, states have more freedom of choice in the services they may provide for the medically needy category. States also have the option to provide additional services or may cover non–Medicaid-eligible individuals for which the federal government will not provide matching funds. There are many different programs in various states, and the rules and regulations vary from program to program and state to state. This can be a confusing situation when one looks at the Medicaid picture as a whole. The health insurance professional must learn the specific guidelines for the programs offered in the state in which he or she is employed to perform his or her job judiciously. The health insurance professional should contact the Medicaid **fiscal intermediary (FI)**, a commercial insurer contracted by the Department of Health and Human Services for the purpose of processing and administering claims, in his or her state to obtain a guide as to what programs are available and what each one covers in that state. An alternative resource for this information is listed in Websites to Explore at the end of this chapter. For a more in-depth discussion of Medicaid, visit the following website: http://www.cms.hhs.gov/MedicaidGenInfo/03_TechnicalSummary.asp.

State Children's Health Insurance Program

States also can participate in Title XXI (21) of the Social Security Act, which is the **State Children's Health Insurance Program (SCHIP)**. The SCHIP program allows states to expand their Medicaid eligibility guidelines to cover more categories of children. Many states also have programs that assist others not eligible for Medicaid but who have difficulty paying for medical care. Additionally, most states have programs that provide rehabilitative assistance to the disabled—especially children—and provide medically needy coverage to relatives who care for dependent children. These state programs do not receive matching federal funds, however.

IMAGINE THIS!

Inez Burke, a widow, resides in a nursing home and has complications of diabetes and cellulitis. Six years ago, Inez's husband died, leaving her with a modest savings account. The homestead on which she and her husband raised their family had earlier been divided into parcels for the three children, with the arrangement that Inez would receive life estate in the property. In just a few years, the bills generated as a result of her medical condition depleted her savings account. Realizing that she could no longer live alone, Inez's son arranged for her care at the Sunset Care Center. Because Inez's savings were used up paying her medical bills, Inez qualified for Medicaid. Her monthly Social Security check is applied toward her care at Sunset; other than that, Medicaid pays her room and board plus any medical care she receives from the staff that Medicare does not pay.

STOP AND THINK

Referring back to the Inez Burke scenario in Imagine This!, what Medicaid category does this individual fall into?

IMAGINE THIS!

Jim Norton has monthly income of $723. If the Medicaid income limit is $623, Jim is over the limit by $100. If Jim has monthly medical expenses of more than $100, he can be eligible for Medicaid with a spend down of $100. (He must spend $100 per month on his medical expenses before Medicaid will begin paying.)

Fiscal Intermediaries

Medicaid does not, as a rule, process claims. Instead, individual states contract with an organization specializing in administering government health care programs, an FI, sometimes referred to as a **fiscal agent**. This organization processes all health care claims on behalf of the Medicaid program. Some states have more than one FI—one FI for fee-for-service Medicaid claims and a second one for managed care claims. Before an FI is selected by the state, there is a bidding process, similar to when contractors bid for the job of constructing a bridge or building a road. FIs typically contract 1 year at a time and must bid again for subsequent years.

Responsibilities of the FI may differ from state to state; however, more common responsibilities are as follows:

- Process claims
- Provide information for health care providers for the particular government program involved
- Generate guidelines for providers to facilitate the claims process
- Answer beneficiary questions about benefits, claims processing, appeals, and the explanation of benefits (remittance advice [RA]) document

The health insurance professional should know the name and telephone number of his or her state Medicaid FI and keep it handy because the FI can offer a wealth of information regarding health care claims and administration of the Medicaid program. Additionally, if and when questions arise regarding claims, the FI is there to answer them.

HIPAA TIP

Every health insurance professional who files insurance claims, including Medicaid claims, should be trained in HIPAA policies, procedures, and processes.

WHAT DID YOU LEARN?

1. What is the federal government's role in Medicaid?
2. Explain the state's role in Medicaid.
3. Name the major category of Medicaid eligibles that states must cover under federal mandates.
4. Identify the major categorical group a state might "elect" to cover.
5. Define the term *mandated service.*

WHO QUALIFIES FOR MEDICAID COVERAGE?

We already have learned that the Medicaid program is divided into two major groups: the categorically needy and the medically needy. To understand fully who qualifies for inclusion in these two groups, let's examine them more closely.

Categorically Needy

Individuals in the categorically needy group receive medical assistance because their income falls within the poverty or Family Medical income guidelines or as a result of SSI eligibility. Coverage of the categorically needy is largely mandated by federal law with some limited options. The following list explains the mandatory Medicaid "categorically needy" eligibility groups for which Federal matching funds are provided:

- Individuals are generally eligible for Medicaid if they meet the requirements for the Aid to Families with Dependent Children (AFDC) program that were in effect in their state on July 16, 1996.
- Children younger than 6 years old whose family income is at or below 133% of the FPL are eligible.
- Pregnant women whose family income is below 133% of the FPL are eligible (services to these women are limited to those related to pregnancy, complications of pregnancy, delivery, and postpartum care).
- SSI recipients are eligible in most states (some states use more restrictive Medicaid eligibility requirements that predate SSI).
- Recipients of adoption or foster care assistance under Title IV of the Social Security Act are eligible.
- Special protected groups are eligible—typically individuals who lose their cash assistance because of earnings from work or from increased Social Security benefits, but who may keep Medicaid for a period of time.
- All children born after September 30, 1983, who are younger than age 19, in families with incomes at or below the FPL are eligible.
- Certain qualifying Medicare beneficiaries are eligible.

Medically Needy

The medically needy segment comprises individuals who, although they meet the nonfinancial criteria of one of the categorically needy programs (e.g., age or disability), do not qualify for Medicaid benefits because of excess income or resources or, in the case of pregnant women and children, because they have income that exceeds the FPL guidelines. Most individuals in the medically needy group must pay a share of their medical costs through the spend down process. Coverage of this group is optional under federal law. If a state chooses this option, it must provide coverage for individuals who meet the eligibility standards for one of the following groups:

- Pregnant women
- Certain children younger than age 18 or age 18 and working toward a high school diploma (or its equivalent)
- Individuals 65 years old and older
- Individuals who are disabled or blind under Social Security Administration standards
- Certain relatives of children deprived of parental support and care
- Certain other financially eligible children age 21 or younger

Approximately two thirds of the states have medically needy programs. This option allows states to provide Medicaid coverage to individuals who have extensive or costly medical needs and would be eligible for Medicaid if they met the income or resources tests within their category. Depending on how the state structures its program, individuals may qualify categorically or spend down to a certain income or financial level.

Early and Periodic Screening, Diagnosis, and Treatment Program

Medicaid's child health component, known as the **Early and Periodic Screening, Diagnosis, and Treatment (EPSDT) program**, was developed to fit the standards of pediatric care and to meet the special physical, emotional, and developmental needs of low-income children. Federal law—including statutes, regulations, and guidelines—requires that Medicaid cover a comprehensive set of benefits and services for children, different from adult benefits. EPSDT offers an important way to ensure that young children receive appropriate health, mental health, and developmental services.

Program of All-Inclusive Care for the Elderly

In addition to mandatory and optional services, there are other program options, such as the **Program of All-Inclusive Care for the Elderly (PACE)**. This program provides comprehensive alternative care for noninstitutionalized elderly who otherwise would be in a nursing home. PACE is centered on the belief that it is better for the well-being of elderly with long-term care needs and their families to be served in the community where they live whenever possible. PACE serves individuals who are age 55 or older, certified by their state to need nursing home care, able to live safely in the community at the time of enrollment, and live in

a PACE service area. Although all PACE participants must be certified to need nursing home care to enroll in PACE, only a small percentage of PACE participants reside in a nursing home nationally. If a PACE enrollee does need nursing home care, the PACE program pays for it and continues to coordinate the individual's care.

WHAT DID YOU LEARN?

1. Name the categorically needy groups that are mandated by federal law.
2. What groups make up the "medically needy" classification?
3. What does the PACE program provide?

PAYMENT FOR MEDICAID SERVICES

Medicaid payments are made directly to the health care provider. Providers participating in Medicaid must accept the Medicaid reimbursement as payment in full. Each state is free to determine (within certain federal restrictions) how reimbursements are calculated and the resulting rates for services, with three exceptions:

1. For institutional services, payment may not exceed amounts that would be paid under Medicare payment rates.
2. For disproportionate share hospitals, different limits apply. **Disproportionate share hospitals** are facilities that receive additional payments to ensure that communities have access to certain high-cost services, such as trauma and emergency care and burn services.
3. For hospice care.

States may impose nominal deductibles, co-insurance, or co-payments on some Medicaid recipients for certain services, such as dental and podiatry care. Emergency services and family planning services must be exempt from such co-payments. Certain Medicaid recipients must be excluded from this **cost sharing**, including pregnant women, children younger than age 18, hospital or nursing home patients who are expected to contribute most of their income to institutional care, and categorically needy health maintenance organization enrollees. Cost sharing is a situation in which covered individuals pay a portion of the health costs, such as deductibles, co-insurance, or co-payment amounts.

Medically Necessary

As a general rule, Medicaid pays only for services that are determined to be **medically necessary**. For a procedure or service to be considered medically necessary, it typically must be consistent with the diagnosis and in accordance with the standards of good medical practice, performed at the proper level, and provided in the most appropriate setting. If the health insurance professional questions whether a service or procedure is medically necessary, he or she should consult the current Medicaid provider handbook of the state in which he or she is employed or telephone the FI that administers local Medicaid claims. This should be done before the service or procedure is performed to avoid problems with collecting payment from Medicaid or the patient after the fact.

Prescription Drug Coverage

Recognizing that prescription drugs are an increasingly important element of comprehensive health care, all states have chosen the option of providing prescription drug coverage for their categorically needy populations, and most cover some or all of the other groups. Prescription drug coverage is currently a volatile issue, subject to continual modifications. To find out what prescription drugs are covered for the categorically needy group in a particular state, the health insurance professional should contact the local FI or consult the provider's manual for that state.

Medicaid previously provided drug coverage for more than 6 million Medicare beneficiaries, known as **dual eligibles**. Dual eligibles have Medicare and Medicaid coverage. Beginning January 1, 2006, full benefit, dual eligible individuals began receiving drug coverage through the Medicare Prescription Drug Benefit (Part D) of the Medicare Prescription Drug, Improvement, and Modernization Act of 2003, rather than through their state Medicaid programs. Certain drugs are excluded from coverage under the new Medicare Prescription Drug Benefit, however. The Department of Health and Human Services Secretary is responsible for automatically enrolling dual eligible individuals into Part D plans if they do not sign up on their own.

To the extent that state Medicaid programs cover the excluded drugs for Medicaid recipients who are not full benefit dual eligibles, states are required to cover the excluded drugs for full benefit dual eligibles with federal financial participation. More information on the new Medicare Prescription Drug Plan can be found in Chapter 5.

Accepting Medicaid Patients

Physicians can choose whether or not to accept Medicaid patients. This refers to a patient with Medicaid only or any combination of Medicaid and another insurance company, whether it is a primary or secondary payer. In an emergency, or if it cannot be determined if the patient has Medicaid at the time of treatment, the patient must be informed as soon as possible after identifying Medicaid coverage whether the practice will accept him or her as a Medicaid patient.

Physicians can limit the number of Medicaid patients they accept, as long as there is no discrimination by age, sex, race, or religious preference or national origin, in addition to the limits of their scope of practice. If a practice sees only children, refusing to accept adult patients is not considered discrimination. If a patient has Medicare and Medicaid coverage, however, and the practice does not accept the Medicaid coverage, the health insurance professional must make sure the patient understands this before treatment. The patient then has the opportunity to seek a physician who would accept the patient's Medicaid coverage. If a Medicaid recipient insists on being treated by a nonparticipating health care provider (one who does not accept Medicaid), it is recommended that the health insurance professional ask the patient to sign a form verifying his or her understanding that the practice does not accept Medicaid, and the patient will be responsible for paying the deductible and coinsurance amounts.

Participating Providers

The health care provider can elect to accept or refuse Medicaid patients; however, many state regulations say if a Medicaid participating provider elects to treat one Medicaid patient, all Medicaid patients must be accepted—the provider cannot single out which ones to treat. Providers can put a cap, however, on the total number of new patients, including Medicaid patients, that they will accept. Additionally, providers must agree to accept what Medicaid pays as payment in full for covered services and are prohibited by law to balance bill Medicaid patients for these services. The health care professional should know beforehand whether a particular service or procedure is covered by Medicaid. If the patient insists on being treated for a particular noncovered service, it is recommended that the patient sign a waiver that spells out the fact that the service is not covered by Medicaid and that the patient acknowledges responsibility for payment. Some practices ask the patient to pay for noncovered services in advance.

VERIFYING MEDICAID ELIGIBILITY

Medicaid providers always should ensure that Medicaid will pay for patients' medical care before providing services to determine eligibility for the current date and to discover any limitations to the recipient's coverage. Because most states grant eligibility a month at a time, for most Medicaid-eligible patients, eligibility should be verified every month. If a patient is being seen more often (e.g., a patient who receives weekly allergy injections or frequent monitoring for some other condition), verifying eligibility on a monthly basis is probably often enough; however, you might want to check with your local Medicaid FI. Several methods are available in most states that the health insurance professional can use to verify eligibility, as follows:

- The patient's Medicaid identification (ID) card
- An automated voice response (AVR) system
- Electronic data interchange (EDI)
- A point-of-sale device
- A computer software program

Medicaid Identification Card

A common method for verifying the patient's Medicaid eligibility is the ID card. This card provides important information regarding eligibility date and type. The following steps are suggested for eligibility verification when using the ID card:

- Ensure that the patient's name is on the ID card. (Typically, the patient's birth date and sex also are listed.)
- Unless you know the patient personally, ask to see another form of identification to confirm his or her identity.
- Check the eligibility period. There should be "from" and "through" dates that tell you the time period in which the patient is Medicaid-eligible. Medicaid pays only for dates of service during this eligibility period.
- Look for insurance information. In the example shown in Fig. 4-2, there is a "1" under the "Ins. No." column. The "Insurance Data" block shows details of the patient's insurance coverage.
- Ask the patient if there is any other insurance coverage.
- Photocopy the Medicaid ID card and enter any new information in the patient's record.

Many states color code the ID cards, which tells the health insurance professional which type of Medicaid program the recipient is enrolled in. Also, the card should be examined closely to see if the patient is in a special program or has special coverage. It is important for the health insurance professional to obtain a provider's guide from the Medicaid FI in his or her state for assistance in interpreting the codes on the Medicaid ID card.

Automated Voice Response System

A touch-tone phone can be used to call an AVR system for eligibility information. For this method of verification, the health insurance professional needs to know the patient's Medicaid ID number or Social Security number and date of birth. The AVR system can provide the following eligibility information:

- Eligibility for specific dates of service
- The type of coverage or special programs in which the patient is enrolled
- If the patient is covered under Medicare Part A and Medicare Part B
- Information known by Medicaid concerning other insurance coverage

If the health insurance professional has access to this type of eligibility verification, he or she should know how to use it correctly and keep current by requesting and reading periodic updates.

Electronic Data Interchange

Providers may obtain Medicaid eligibility information electronically. Online, interactive eligibility

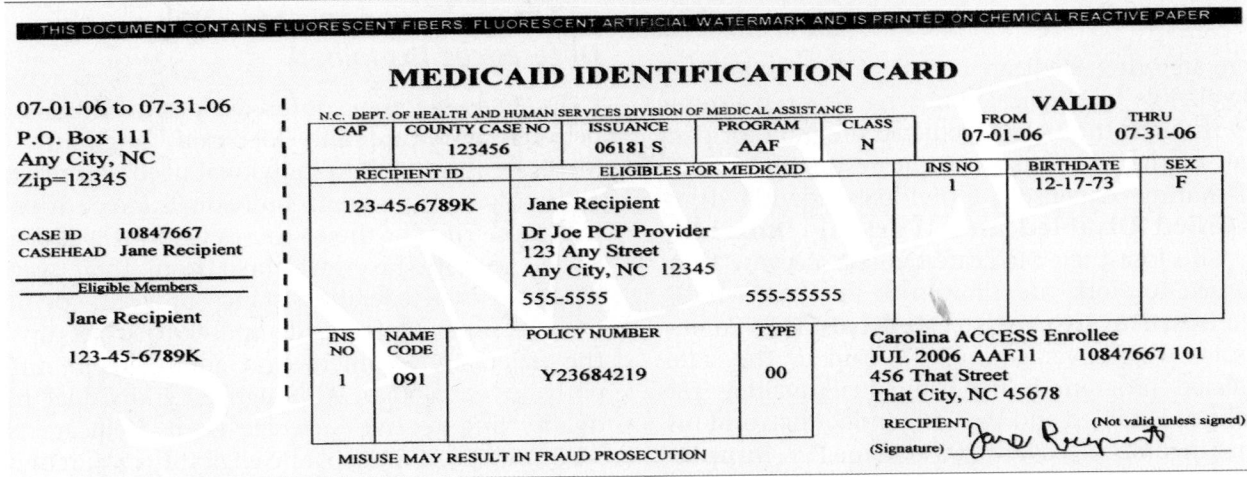

Fig. 4-2 Medicaid ID card. *(Source: North Carolina Department of Health and Human Services.)*

verification is available from EDI vendors (sometimes referred to as *clearinghouses*). Use of an EDI vendor is voluntary to providers. EDI vendors interface directly with the Medicaid recipient database maintained by Electronic Data Services for claims processing. The database is updated every day from the state's master eligibility file. This service is available 24 hours a day, 7 days a week, except for periods when it is down for system maintenance. EDI vendors normally charge a fee for their services, and providers might be required to pay a transaction fee to the state's Medicaid FI.

Point-of-Sale Device

With a point-of-sale device, the patient is issued an ID card that is similar in size and design to a credit card. The provider can swipe the card and, through the information on the magnetic strip, receive an accurate return of eligibility information within a matter of seconds.

Computer Software Program

With this method of eligibility verification, the provider can key the patient's information into a computer software program and in a short time have an accurate return of eligibility information.

Benefits of Eligibility Verification System

By using one of these eligibility verification system methods, providers can reduce the number of denied claims by verifying recipient eligibility and insurance information before services are provided. Up-front verification using the eligibility verification system results in the submission of more accurate claims and decreases eligibility-related claims denials.

HIPAA TIP

Medicaid providers and their vendors who bill electronically need to verify that their systems accept HIPAA-compliant Medicaid transactions.

WHAT DID YOU LEARN?

1. Why is it important for the health insurance professional to verify eligibility?
2. What should the health insurance professional do if a patient insists on receiving non–Medicaid-covered services?
3. What are the benefits of the eligibility verification system?

MEDICARE/MEDICAID RELATIONSHIP

Most elderly or disabled individuals who are very poor are covered under Medicaid and Medicare, commonly referred to as **dual coverage**, dual eligibility, or **Medi-Medi**. These individuals may receive Medicare services for which they are entitled and other services available under that state's Medicaid program. As each state sets up its Medicaid plan, certain services typically not covered by Medicare (e.g., hearing aids, eyeglasses, and nursing facility care beyond the 100 days covered by Medicare) may be provided to these individuals by the Medicaid program. In addition, the Medicaid program pays all of the cost-sharing portions (deductibles and co-insurance) of Medicare Part A and B for these dually eligible beneficiaries.

Special Medicare/Medicaid Programs

There are other Medicare beneficiaries who are not fully eligible for Medicaid but who do receive some help through the state's Medicaid program for part or all of the individual's Medicare premiums and cost-sharing expenses. Individuals identified as **Qualified Disabled and Working Individuals**, who lose their Medicare benefits because they returned to work, are allowed to purchase **Medicare hospital insurance (Medicare HI)**. Premiums for such coverage must be paid by the state Medicaid program if the individual qualifies for Qualified Disabled and Working Individuals and his or her income falls below 200% of the FPL. **Supplementary medical insurance (SMI)** coverage also is available to qualifying beneficiaries; however, premiums for SMI coverage are not paid by Medicaid.

Other Medicare beneficiaries who may receive some Medicaid assistance are referred to as **Qualified Medicare Beneficiaries**. These Medicare beneficiaries qualify only if they have incomes below the FPL and resources at or below twice the standard allowed under the SSI program. In this case, the state pays all the Medicare cost-sharing expenses and premiums for Medicare HI and SMI.

The Medicaid program pays SMI premiums of another classification, known as **Specified Low-Income Medicare Beneficiaries**, which are beneficiaries with resources similar to Qualified Medicare Beneficiaries but with slightly higher incomes. Medicaid does not pay for the Medicare HI premium for this group. The Qualified Individuals Program, which also is known as Additional Low-Income Medicare Beneficiaries, is a limited expansion of Specified Low-Income Medicare Beneficiaries. The Qualified Individuals Program requires state Medicaid programs to pay the Medicare Part B premium for individuals who are not otherwise eligible for Medicaid and who have incomes between 120% and 135% of FPL and limited resources. There is currently no asset limit. Applications and information about these programs are available at the individual's local Department of Social Services office.

In all cases, Medicaid is always the **payer of last resort**, meaning that all other available third-party resources must meet their legal obligation to pay claims before the Medicaid program pays for the care of an individual eligible for Medicaid. If an individual is a Medicare beneficiary, payments for any services covered by Medicare are made by the Medicare program before any payments are made by the Medicaid program. In short, Medicaid pays last.

Medicare and Medicaid Differences Explained

Individuals are often confused about the differences between Medicare and Medicaid. Eligibility for Medicare is not tied to individual need. Rather, it is an entitlement program. Individuals are entitled to it because they or their spouses paid for it through Social Security taxes withheld from their wages. Medicaid is a federal assistance program for low-income, financially needy individuals, set up by the federal government and administered differently in each state. Although an individual may qualify and receive coverage from Medicare and Medicaid, there are separate eligibility requirements for each program, and being eligible for one program does not mean an individual is eligible for the other.

The following lists describe the differences between the two programs:

Medicare

- Provides health care insurance for disabled individuals, individuals 65 years old and older, and any age individual with end-stage renal disease
- Must have contributed to Medicare system (deductions from wages) to be eligible
- Pays for primary hospital care and related medically necessary services
- May have a co-pay provision depending on the services received
- Federally controlled, uniform application across the United States

Medicaid

- Needs-based health care program
- Pays for long-term care for qualifying individuals
- Must meet income and financial limitations to be eligible for certain programs
- Must be 65 years old or older, or disabled, or blind to qualify for coverage
- Requires mandatory contribution of *all* recipient's income in certain programs
- Individual state-by-state plan options create a different program in each state (generally similar but may be different in specific application)

Table 4-2 briefly summarizes the major differences between the two programs.

TABLE 4-2	Medicare and Medicaid: Two Different Programs

Medicare	Medicaid
Title 18	Title 19
Federal administration	State administration with federal oversight
Work history affects eligibility	Eligibility based on need
Public insurance	Public assistance
For aged, blind, disabled	For aged, blind, disabled, pregnant women, children, and caretaker relatives
Funded by Social Security and Medicare payroll tax deductions	Funded by federal general fund appropriations combined with individual state funds

WHAT DID YOU LEARN?

1. If an individual has dual coverage under Medicaid and Medicare, which claim is filed first?
2. Name two other categories of Medicare beneficiaries who are eligible for partial Medicaid coverage.
3. What are the major differences between Medicaid and Medicare?

Medicaid Managed Care

Managed care organizations are designed to improve access and reduce costs by eliminating inappropriate and unnecessary services and relying more heavily on primary care and coordination of care. States have had the option to enroll Medicaid beneficiaries voluntarily in managed care plans since the 1960s but now have broader authority to *mandate* enrollment. Most states currently use "waivers" to implement statewide mandatory managed care enrollment for certain categories of beneficiaries as part of comprehensive health care reform demonstrations. The Balanced Budget Act (BBA) of 1997 gave states authority to mandate enrollment in managed care organizations without obtaining a federal waiver (except for special needs children, Medicare beneficiaries, and Native Americans). Currently, nearly every state has enrolled some portion of its Medicaid population in managed care. The future success of Medicaid managed care depends on the adequacy of the capitation rates and the ability of state and federal governments to monitor access and quality.

MEDICAID CLAIM

The universal CMS-1500 claim is accepted by Medicaid FIs in most states. Some states have their own form that must be used for submitting claims for Medicaid recipients. The health insurance professional must check with the local Medicaid FI to ensure the correct claim form is used. For the exercises in this text and accompanying student workbook, the CMS-1500 form is used.

Completing the CMS-1500 Form Using Medicaid Guidelines

Table 4-3 provides guidelines on completing the CMS-1500 form for a Medicaid claim. The name and address of the FI is keyed in the upper-right-hand corner. The guidelines used in the form in Table 4-3 are generic and may differ from the guidelines used in your state. This example is for a **Medicaid "simple" claim**—that is, the patient has Medicaid coverage only and no secondary insurance. The health insurance professional must follow the exact guidelines for completing the CMS-1500 form issued by the FI in his or her state. A template for a Medicaid simple claim form is shown in Appendix B.

Resubmission of Medicaid Claims

When errors or omissions are detected on a Medicaid claim, it is typically rejected and returned to the provider for correction and resubmission. Although every Medicaid FI may have differing guidelines for correcting and resubmitting claims, most require a resubmission code or reference number or both, which is reported in Block 22 of the CMS-1500 claim form. In some states, Medicaid FIs offer online, real-time claims processing and resubmission capabilities. The health insurance professional should be aware of the Medicaid resubmission rules applicable in his or her state.

TABLE 4-3   Step-by-Step Medicaid Claims Instructions

Block 1	Enter an "X" in the Medicaid box
Block 1a	Enter the Medicaid recipient's ID number
Block 2	Enter the name of the Medicaid recipient exactly as it appears on the ID card, keying the last name first, followed by the first name and middle initial (if one is listed). Remember to use the correct OCR guidelines
Block 3	Enter the patient's birth date (using the MM DD YYYY format with spaces), and enter an "X" in the appropriate gender box
Block 4	This block is left blank
Block 5	Enter the patient's complete mailing address as indicated on lines 1 and 2 in this block. When keying the telephone number, use spaces rather than dashes or parentheses
Blocks 6-9d	These blocks are typically left blank on Medicaid "simple" claims
Blocks 10a-c	Key an "X" in the appropriate boxes to indicate whether or not the claim is a result of an auto or other accident or was related to employment. In the case of an auto accident, key the 2-letter state code to indicate the state in which the accident happened
Block 10d	Usually left blank. Check with your fiscal intermediary (FI) for special situations
Blocks 11-11d	Leave blank
Blocks 12-13	Leave blank (signatures are normally not required on Medicaid claims)
Blocks 14-16	Leave blank
Block 17	Enter the full name and credentials of the referring or ordering provider when applicable
Block 17a Block 17b	Leave blank; enter the national provider identifier (NPI) of the referring/ordering provider if one is reported in Block 17
Block 18	If the claim is for inpatient hospital services, enter the admission and discharge dates using either the mm cc yy or the MM DD YYYY format. If the patient is still hospitalized, leave the "To" block blank. If no hospitalization, leave blank
Block 19	Check the guidelines of your Medicaid FI
Block 20	Enter an "X" in the "NO" block. Outside laboratory facilities must bill Medicaid directly
Block 21	Enter the patient's diagnosis(es) using ICD-9-CM codes, listing the primary diagnosis first. There is space for 4 codes, which should be listed in priority order
Block 22	If this is a resubmission, enter the applicable Medicaid code
Block 23	If pre-authorization was required, enter this number (consult the specific Medicaid guidelines for your state)
Block 24a	Enter each date of service on a separate line. Enter the month, day, and year in the MMDDYY or the MMDDYYYY (no spaces) format for each service. Medicaid does not allow "date ranging for consecutive services"
Block 24b	Enter the applicable Place of Service (POS) code
Block 24c	The block is conditionally required; enter this number. Enter an "X" or an "E" as appropriate for services performed as a result of a medical emergency
Block 24d	Enter the code number using appropriate five-digit CPT/HCPCS procedure code and a two-digit modifier, when applicable. If using an unlisted procedure code (ending in "-99"), a complete description of the procedure must be provided as a separate attachment
Block 24e	Link the procedure code back to the appropriate diagnosis code in Block 21 by indicating the applicable number assigned to the diagnosis (1, 2, 3, or 4)
Block 24f	Enter the amount charged for the service. Do not use dollar signs or decimal points
Block 24g	Enter the number of days or units for each single visit
Block 24h	Consult your local Medicaid guidelines. Enter an "E" if the service was performed under the Early and Periodic Screening Diagnosis and Treatment (EPSDT) program. Enter an "F" for Family Planning services
Block 24i	Usually not reported after May 23, 2007. Consult your Medicaid FI for specific guidelines
Block 24j	Leave blank
Block 25	Enter the nine-digit federal tax employer identification number (EIN) assigned to that provider (or group) with a space instead of a hyphen after the first two digits, and check the appropriate box in this field. In the case of an unincorporated practice or a sole practitioner, the provider's Social Security number is typically used
Block 26	Enter the patient's account number as assigned by the provider's computerized accounting system

TABLE 4-3	Step-by-Step Medicaid Claims Instructions—cont'd
Block 27	Place an "X" in the "YES" box
Block 28	Enter the total charges for all services listed in column 24f
Blocks 29-30	Leave blank
Block 31	Enter the signature of the provider, or his or her representative and initials, and the date the form was signed. The signature may be typed, stamped, or handwritten. Make sure no part of the signature falls outside of the block
Block 32	Key the name and address of the location where services were provided, and enter the Medicaid provider number on the last line of this block. Check for updated changes with your Medicaid FI (some Medicaid FIs do not require this block to be reported if services were provided in the provider's office [which appears in Block 33] or in the patient's home)
Block 32a	Enter the NPI of the service facility in Block 32
Block 32b	This block is usually not to be reported after May 23, 2007; however, you should consult the specific guidelines of the Medicaid FI in your state to be sure
Block 33	Enter the name, address, Zip Code, and telephone number of the facility providing services. Do not include a hyphen or a space in the telephone number
Block 33a	Effective May 23, 2007, the NPI of the billing provider or group must be reported here
Block 33b	Block 33b is normally not to be reported after May 23, 2007; however, consult the guidelines of your state Medicaid FI to be sure

Reciprocity

A simple dictionary definition of *reciprocity* is the occurrence of a situation in which individuals or entities offer certain rights to each other in return for the rights being given to them. When one state allows Medicaid beneficiaries from other states (usually states that are adjacent) to be treated in its medical facilities, this exchange of privileges is referred to as **reciprocity**. Health insurance professionals should be aware of which states, if any, offer reciprocity for Medicaid claims in their states.

WHAT DID YOU LEARN?

1. What is a Medicaid "simple" claim?
2. Explain what is meant by "reciprocity."

IMAGINE THIS!

Ellen Statler is a single mother of two dependent children living in a small Illinois town along the Mississippi River. Ellen is covered under Illinois Medicaid; however, because the nearest Illinois town where there is a health care provider who accepts Medicaid patients is 35 miles away, Ellen travels across the bridge into Iowa and receives care from a family practice clinic there, 2 miles from her home. This arrangement works out much more favorably for Ellen because both of her children have acute asthma, and periodic emergency visits are common.

MEDICAID AND THIRD-PARTY LIABILITY

Third-party liability refers to the legal obligation of third parties to pay all or part of the expenditures for medical assistance furnished under a state plan. Earlier in this chapter, we discussed the fact that the Medicaid program, by law, is intended to be the payer of last resort. Examples of third parties that may be liable to pay for services before Medicaid include the following:

- Employment-related health insurance
- Court-ordered health insurance by noncustodial parent
- Workers' compensation
- Long-term care insurance
- Other state and federal programs (unless specifically excluded by federal statute)

Medicaid pays the bills when due and does not put the burden of collection from a third party on the Medicaid client. Individuals eligible for Medicaid assign their rights to third-party payments to the state Medicaid agency. States are required to take all reasonable measures to ensure that the legal liability of third parties to pay for care and services is met before funds are made available under the state Medicaid plan. Health care providers are obligated to inform Medicaid of any known third parties who might have liability. When states have determined that a potentially liable third party exists, the state is required to **cost avoid** or **pay and chase claims**. Cost avoidance is where the health care provider bills and collects from liable third parties before sending the claim to Medicaid. Pay and chase is used when the state Medicaid agency pays the medical bills and then attempts to recover these paid funds from liable third parties. States generally are required to cost avoid claims unless they have a waiver approved by CMS that allows them to use the pay and chase method. To learn more about third-party liability, cost avoidance, and collection, refer to Websites to Explore at the end of this chapter.

In the case of third-party liability, certain blocks of the CMS-1500 form are filled out differently (Table 4-4). This information is generic, and the health insurance professional must follow the specific Medicaid guidelines in his or her state.

As mentioned previously, in a case in which the patient has dual eligibility for Medicaid and Medicare (Medi-Medi), Medicare is primary. The claim is submitted first to Medicare, which pays its share and then "crosses it over" to Medicaid. Chapter 5 contains more information on **Medicare-Medicaid crossover claims**.

WHAT DID YOU LEARN?

1. What is "third-party liability"?
2. List some examples of third-party entities that would be primary to Medicaid.
3. Explain the difference between "cost avoid" and "pay and chase" in reference to Medicaid claims.

COMMON MEDICAID BILLING ERRORS

The primary goal of the health insurance professional is to create and submit insurance claims in a manner in which the maximum benefits the medical record supports are received in the minimal amount of time. This is a learned process, however, and it takes an experienced individual to avoid making common errors that cause a claim to be delayed or rejected. Fig. 4-3 lists some of these common billing errors.

WHAT DID YOU LEARN?

1. What is the first goal of the health insurance professional?
2. How can the health insurance professional avoid common billing errors?

MEDICAID REMITTANCE ADVICE

Every time a claim is sent to Medicaid, a document is generated explaining how the claim was adjudicated, or how the payment was determined. In the past, this document was referred to as the *explanation of benefits*; however, Medicaid now calls it the **remittance advice (RA)**. The RA can be in paper or electronic form (if the medical facility is set up to accept the standard electronic version) and contains information from one or several claims (Fig. 4-4). The RA typically contains several "remark codes" and "reason codes"; the importance of understanding the codes and interpreting this document cannot be stressed enough. Many states generate an RA periodically (e.g., weekly), and the current status of all claims (including adjustments and voids) that have been processed during the past week is indicated. The RA format may differ from state to state; however, they all furnish basically the same information. It is the health insurance

TABLE 4-4 CMS-1500 Guidelines for Medicaid Secondary Claims

Block 4	Enter the primary policyholder's complete name (last, first, middle initial) as it appears on the ID card. Remember to use optical character recognition formatting rules
Block 9	Enter the primary policyholder's complete name (last, first, middle initial) as it appears on the ID card. If it is the same as the patient, key "SAME"
Block 9a	Enter the primary insurer's policy and group numbers as indicated on the ID card
Block 9b	If the primary policyholder is other than the patient, enter his or her date of birth using the MM DD YYYY format
Block 9d	Enter the primary policy name
Block 11	Conditionally required. If the primary payer rejected the claim, enter the rejection code
Block 11d	"X" the "YES" box
Block 29	Enter the amount (if any) paid by the primary insurer. If nothing was paid by the primary policy, indicate so using zeroes
Block 30	If an amount was entered in Block 29, subtract it from Block 28, and enter the balance here

All claims submitted to Medicaid must pass screening criteria before they can be processed. If one or more of the following conditions are not met, the claim will be returned to the provider.

Patient ID (Field 1a) There must always be an 11-digit patient number assigned by Medicaid. If this field is blank, has less than or more than 11 digits, or is invalid, the claim will be returned.

Diagnosis Code (Field 21 and 24-E) There must be a diagnosis code listed in Field 21 and/or Field 24-E. A claim with a written description without a corresponding diagnosis code is often held until staff is available to code them. If the description is not specific enough to code, the claim will be returned. (**Note:** Diagnosis codes beginning with an E or M are not accepted as a primary diagnosis code in some states.)

Dates of Service (Field 24-A) There must be a "From" date. If you are billing a date range, both the "From" and "To" date fields must be completed. Future service dates may not be billed.

Place of Service Code (Field 24-B) This must be a two-digit code. If the Place of Service Code is blank, less or more than two digits, or an invalid code, the claim will be returned.

Procedure Code (Field 24-D) This must be a five- or six-digit code. If the minimum criteria are not met, the claim is returned.

Charges (Field 24-F) There must be a charge for each line billed. (**Note:** Only EPSDT claims will be accepted with a zero line submitted amount.)

Days or Units (Field 24-G) There must be a whole number in this field (no decimals).

Signature (Field 31) There must be a handwritten signature or a computer-generated name. The name may not be the provider office name; it needs to be an actual person's name who is responsible for the information submitted on the claim. Initials only are also not accepted.

Billing Date (Field 31) The date billed must be on the claim form in Field 31. If the bill date in Field 31 or the claim received date is before the latest date of service on the claim, the claim will be returned.

Total Charge (Field 28) There must be a correct total charge. Claims will be returned for no total charge or for an incorrect total charge. Each claim form must have a total.

Date Received The date received must be no earlier than the latest date of service on the claim. Do not bill for future dates. Claims received before the latest date of service on the claim will be returned to the provider.

Fig. 4-3 CMS-1500 common billing errors.

professional's responsibility to interpret and reconcile this document with patient records. All Medicaid claims and RAs should be maintained for 6 years or longer if mandated by state statutes of limitation.

SPECIAL BILLING NOTES

The health insurance professional must keep several things in mind when filing Medicaid claims, as follows.

Time Limit for Filing Medicaid Claims

The time limit for filing Medicaid claims varies from state to state. The health insurance professional should check with the Medicaid FI or carrier in his or her state for the filing deadline. It is good practice to file all claims in a timely manner—typically right after the service has been performed, unless additional services are anticipated within the same month or eligibility period.

Co-Payments

Services rendered by some types of health care providers (e.g., podiatrists, dentists, chiropractors) often require that the Medicaid recipient make a co-payment. If the health insurance professional is employed by one of these types of health care providers, he or she should contact the Medicaid FI in his or her state or consult the Medicaid provider manual for information. This information usually is indicated on the Medicaid recipient's ID card. Experienced health insurance professionals suggest that if a co-payment is required, it should be collected before services are rendered.

Accepting Assignment

As mentioned previously, Medicaid payments are made directly to the health care provider. FIs in most states point out, however, that it is still important that assignment is accepted on all Medicaid claims; if Block 27 on the CMS-1500 form is not checked "yes," the claim may be denied. Providers participating in Medicaid must accept the Medicaid reimbursement as payment in full. **Balance billing**, or billing the recipient for any amount not paid by Medicaid, is not allowed. Additionally, according to federal law, a provider who accepts Medicaid payment for services furnished to an ill or injured individual has no right to additional payment from a liable third party even if Medicaid has been reimbursed.

Services Requiring Prior Approval

Prior approval may be required for some Medicaid services, products, and procedures to verify medical necessity, with the exception of some emergency situations. If prior approval is required, the provider must request and obtain prior approval before rendering the service, product, or procedure to seek Medicaid payment. Obtaining prior approval *does not* guarantee payment or ensure recipient eligibility on the date of service. The recipient must be Medicaid eligible on the date the service, product, or procedure is provided. Requests for prior approval must be submitted as specified by the local Health and Human Services office or the Medicaid FI in the particular state in which the services are rendered.

```
PERF PROV  SERV DATE   POS NOS  PROC   MODS   BILLED   ALLOWED   DEDUCT   COINS      GRP /RC-AMT      PROV  PD

NAME  ALPHA, ALBERT        HIC 699777777A  ACNT 1111111111         ICN 1402065330030  ASG Y  MOA  MA01
W88888888  1215 121501  11   1 92547        98.00    27.22     0.00    5.44  CO-42      70.78          21.78
W88888888  1215 121501  11   1 92541        45.00    39.89     0.00    7.98  CO-42       5.11          31.91
PT RESP    13.42             CLAIM TOTALS  143.00    67.11     0.00   13.42             75.89          53.69
                                                                                                      53.69 NET


NAME  BAKER, LEEANN         HIC 699123123A  ACNT 0009              ICN 1102025001590  ASG Y  MOA  MA01  MA18
W88888888  0113 011302  11   1 J9202 GACC  600.00   446.49     0.00   89.30  CO-42     153.51         357.19
           (J9217)
W88888888  0121 012102  11   1 J9202 CC    600.00   446.49     0.00   89.30  CO-42     153.51         357.19
                   (J9217)
PT RESP   178.60             CLAIM TOTALS 1200.00   892.98     0.00  178.60            307.02         714.38
                                                                                                     714.38 NET

CLAIM INFORMATION FORWARDED TO:  BCBS OF MINNESOTA   ❹


NAME  CHARLIE, CINDY        HIC 699222222A  ACNT 22222222          ICN 1402008151040  ASG Y  MOA  MA01
W88888888  0106 010602  11   1 76091  26    80.00    43.76     0.00    8.75  CO-42      36.24          35.01
W88888888  0106 010602  11   1 G0236  26    50.00     0.00     0.00    0.00  CO-B5      50.00          00.00
REM: M58
PT RESP     8.75             CLAIM TOTALS  130.00    43.76     0.00    8.75             86.24          35.01

ADJS: PREV PD    0.00  INT    0.17  LATE FILING CHARGE     0.00     ❷                                  35.18 NET


NAME  BETA, BOB             HIC 699111111A  ACNT 12345678901234567890 ICN 1402063333010 ASG Y  MOA  MA01  MA72
W88888888  0304 030402  11   1 99214       180.00    81.99    47.65    6.87  CO-42      98.01          00.00
W88888888  0304 030402  11   1 82010        30.00     0.00     0.00    0.00  CO-B7      30.00          00.00
W88888888  0304 030402  11   1 J1040        10.00     9.39     0.00    1.88  CO-42      00.61          00.00
PT RESP    56.40             CLAIM TOTALS  220.00    91.38    47.65    8.75            128.62          00.00
                                                                                                      00.00 NET


NAME  BUMAN, JAMES          HIC 699555555A  ACNT 55555555          ICN 1402065200070  ASG Y  MOA  MA01
W88888888  0304 030402  11   1 99214        75.00     0.00     0.00    0.00  PR-B7      75.00          00.00
                                                                            OA-71      20.00
                                                                            PR-A3     -20.00
PT RESP    55.00             CLAIM TOTALS   75.00     0.00     0.00    0.00             75.00          00.00
                                                                                                      00.00 NET


TOTALS:  # OF       BILLED      ALLOWED      DEDUCT       COINS       TOTAL       PROV PD       PROV    ❸
         CLAIMS      AMT          AMT          AMT         AMT       RC-AMT        AMT        ADJ AMT        CHECK
                                                                                                            AMT
            5       1768.00     1095.23       47.65      209.52      672.77       803.08      108.50        749.56


PROVIDER ADJ DETAILS:  PLB REASON CODE    FCN              HIC            AMOUNT   ❶
                           CS        1402063333010   699111111A      34.98
                           CS        1402065200070   699555555A      20.00
                           WO        7101347082956                   53.69
                           L6                                        -0.17
```

GLOSSARY: Group, Reason, MOA, Remark and Adjustment Codes:

CO	Contractual Obligation. Amount for which the provider is financially liable. The patient may not be billed for this amount.
PR	Patient Responsibility. Amount that may be billed to a patient or another payee.
OA	Other Adjustment.
A3	Medicare Secondary Payer liability met.
B5	Claim/Service denied/reduced because coverage guidelines were not met or were exceeded.
B7	This provider was not certified for this procedure/service on this date of service.
42	Charges exceed our fee schedule or maximum allowable amount.
71	Primary Payer amount.
M58	Please resubmit the claim with the missing/correct information so that it may be processed.
MA01	If you do not agree with what we approved for these services, you may appeal our decision. To make sure that we are fair to you, we require another individual that did not process your initial claim to conduct the review. However, in order to be eligible for a review, you must write to us within 6 months of the date of this notice, unless you have a good reason for being late.
MA119	Provider level adjustment for late claim filing applies to this claim.
MA18	The claim information is also being forwarded to the patient's supplemental insurer. Send any questions regarding supplemental benefits to them.
MA72	The beneficiary overpaid you for these assigned services. You must issue the beneficiary a refund within 30 days for the difference between his/her payment to you and the total of the amount shown as patient responsibility and as paid to the beneficiary on this notice.
CS	Adjustment
WO	Withholding
L6	Interest

3/25/02

Fig. 4-4 Standard paper remittance advice notices, revised format.

Pre-Authorization

Pre-authorization is needed for all inpatient hospitalizations, unless the hospitalization was due to an emergency. In the case of an emergency, most Medicaid FIs require 24-hour notification. Normally, a pre-admission or preprocedure review is performed by the provider before the patient is admitted to the hospital and the procedure or service is performed. The areas of required review are not paid unless the claim indicates that review has been performed, the admission is medically necessary, and the setting is appropriate. The Medicaid FI provides a pre-authorization number, which should be entered in Block 23 of the CMS-1500 form. The health insurance professional should review and be aware of what procedures and services require a pre-admission/preprocedure review and pre-authorization. This information usually can be found in the Medicaid provider manual, or the health insurance professional can contact his or her local Medicaid FI.

HIPAA TIP

Paper claim and Prior Authorization Request Form (PA/RF) instructions must be consistent with the Administrative Simplification provisions of HIPAA.

Retention, Storage, and Disposal of Records

The question "How long should a practice keep medical records?" often generates a challenging discussion. According to HIPAA's proposed privacy regulation, medical records must be maintained for 6 years. According to federal statute, the government can take criminal or civil action up to 7 years. To make it more confusing, the Department of Health and Human Services Privacy Act of 1974 established a new system of records, called the National Provider System. The National Provider System states that "records are retained indefinitely, except in the instance of an individual provider's death, in which case HCFA [now CMS] would retain such records for a 10-year period following the provider's death." In addition, there may be state laws and regulations giving specific time frames for medical record retention. Some practices archive paper records permanently using a photoduplicating process, such as microfilm or microfiche.

Storage of medical records also is important. The health care staff needs to be able to find the records they are looking for easily. If dozens of boxes must be searched to find specific medical records, it would cost the practice time and money; records must be stored where they can be located quickly and easily.

Computerized records can be stored on electronic media, such as disks, magnetic tape, or CD-ROM. Use of magnetic storage media does not guarantee permanency, however. Computer experts suggest using a permanent-type CD-ROM.

When it has been determined that a medical record has met all requirements (state and federal) for disposal, this process should be done according to state statute. Typically, the rule of thumb for paper record disposal is a shredding process. It is unacceptable merely to discard paper records in a trash bin because of security violations. Records kept on magnetic media can be erased or deleted.

WHAT DID YOU LEARN?

1. What is the time limit for filing Medicaid claims?
2. Name the types of providers that might require a co-payment.
3. Pre-authorization is always needed for what types of Medicaid services?

FRAUD AND ABUSE IN THE MEDICAID SYSTEM

Fraud is an intentional misrepresentation or deception that could result in an unauthorized benefit to an individual or individuals and usually comes in the form of a false statement requesting payment under the Medicaid program. Abuse typically involves payment for items or services in which there was no intent to deceive or misrepresent, but the outcome of poor and inefficient methods results in unnecessary costs to the Medicaid program.

What Is Medicaid Fraud?

Medicaid fraud occurs when a health care provider, such as a physician, dentist, pharmacist, hospital, nursing home, or other health care service, engages in one or more of the following practices:

- Billing for medical services not actually performed
- Billing for a more expensive service than was rendered
- Billing separately for several services that should be combined into one billing
- Billing twice for the same medical service
- Dispensing generic drugs and billing for brand-name drugs
- Giving or accepting something in return for medical services (kickbacks)
- Bribery

- Providing unnecessary services
- False cost reports
- Billing for ambulance runs when no medical service is provided
- Transporting multiple passengers in an ambulance and billing a run for each passenger

Medicaid fraud and abuse increase health care costs for everyone. The health insurance professional should contact the Attorney General's Medicaid Fraud Control Unit if he or she has evidence of or suspects a health care provider (or patient) is committing Medicaid fraud.

Patient Abuse and Neglect

Frequent unexplained injuries or complaints of pain without obvious injury can be indicators of patient abuse and neglect, such as the following:

- Burns or bruises suggesting the use of instruments or cigarettes
- Passive, withdrawn, and emotionless behavior
- Lack of reaction to pain
- Sexually transmitted diseases or injury to the genital area
- Difficulty in sitting or walking
- Fear of being alone with caretakers
- Obvious malnutrition
- Lack of personal cleanliness
- Habitually dressed in torn or dirty clothes
- Obvious fatigue and listlessness
- Begs for food or water
- In need of medical or dental care
- Left unattended for long periods
- Bedsores and skin lesions

IMAGINE THIS!

Superior Ambulance Company transports patients from the Coast View Convalescent Home to a nearby medical center. The vehicles are equipped to carry four patients at a time. Shirley Holmes, whose father (a Medicaid recipient) resides at Coast View, received a bill for $800 for an emergency transport. She was with her father at the time of transport and noted that two other residents were occupants of the ambulance at the same time her father was taken to the medical center. Mrs. Holmes discussed the charge with Coast View's administrator, and it was discovered that the ambulance company, rather than splitting the cost of the transport among the three patients who were transported on that run, charged each patient the entire $800 fee.

STOP AND THINK

Martin Roble received a prescription for a medication that was to be filled using a generic product. The pharmacist filled the prescription with generic drugs, according to Medicaid rules, but charged Medicaid for the more expensive brand-name medication. Would this be considered fraud or abuse?

The health insurance professional should learn how to recognize fraud and abuse and do everything possible to prevent it. There is a Medicaid Fraud Control Unit in every state, which is a federally funded state law enforcement entity located in the State Attorney General's office. In addition to investigating fraud committed by health care providers, the Medicaid Fraud Control Unit investigates the abuse, neglect, and exploitation of elderly, ill, and disabled residents of long-term care facilities, such as nursing homes, facilities for the mentally and physically disabled, and assisted living facilities. The investigation of corruption in the administration of the Medicaid program is another important responsibility of the Medicaid Fraud Control Unit. To report fraud or abuse, health insurance professionals may use the state's hotline number or contact the Medicaid Fraud Control Unit nearest them.

Extensive information on Medicaid fraud and abuse can be found on the CMS website. At the CMS home page, click on "Medicaid" under the heading "CMS Programs and Information." Under the topic "Medicaid Fraud and Abuse" (on the next screen), click on "Fraud and Abuse for Professionals." Here you will find a related link for state contacts, which will give you information on to how to contact individual state Medicaid Fraud Control Units.

WHAT DID YOU LEARN?

1. What is the difference between fraud and abuse?
2. What should the health insurance professional do when fraud or abuse is suspected?

SUMMARY CHECK POINTS

 Medicaid is a combination federal and state medical assistance program designed to provide medical care for low-income individuals and families, specifically children, pregnant women, the elderly, the disabled, and parents with dependent children.

☑ The federal government establishes broad national guidelines for Medicaid eligibility and contributes approximately 50% of the Medicaid cost to the individual states.

☑ Each state can set its own guidelines regarding Medicaid eligibility standards, services, benefits packages, payment rates, and program administration within the broader federal guidelines. To be eligible for federal funds, however, states are required to provide Medicaid coverage for certain individuals who receive federally assisted income-maintenance payments and for related groups not receiving cash payments. In addition to the federally mandated programs, states can have additional "state-only" programs, but these programs do not receive federal funds.

☑ The two major groups that qualify for Medicaid are the categorically needy and the medically needy. The categorically needy group includes individuals who are eligible for a cash benefit under the SSI program or who meet Family Medical guidelines. Children and pregnant women who have incomes that fall below certain poverty level guidelines also are classified within this group. The medically needy group includes individuals who do not qualify in the categorically needy program (because of excess income or resources) but need help to pay for excessive medical expenses. To qualify for the medically needy group, individuals must spend down their financial assets.

☑ As a general rule, Medicaid pays only for services that are determined to be medically necessary. For a procedure or service to be considered medically necessary, it typically must be consistent with the diagnosis and in accordance with the standards of good medical practice, performed at the proper level, and provided in the most appropriate setting.

☑ Medicaid eligibility can be verified in the following ways:
- Patient's Medicaid ID card
- AVR system, which uses a touch-tone phone process
- EDI, an electronic method that involves online interactive clearinghouses
- Point-of-sale device, in which eligibility information is contained on a magnetic strip similar to a credit card
- Computer software programs, which involves keying patient information into a computer

☑ In insurance terms, a third party is an individual, entity, or a program that, although not directly involved in the implied contract between patient and provider, plays a role in the health insurance claim process—typically paying for a portion of the medical expenses incurred. Medicaid, by law, is the "payer of last resort." Claims must be sent to any third parties involved, and the third parties must meet their legal obligation to pay the claims before Medicaid is billed. Third parties in this case typically would include the following
- Employment-related health insurance
- Court-ordered health insurance by noncustodial parents
- Workers' compensation
- Long-term care insurance
- Other state and federal programs, such as Medicare

☑ Some common Medicaid billing errors include
- Incorrect patient ID numbers
- Incorrect diagnosis/procedure codes
- Incorrect dates of service format
- Omitting a charge (there must be one for each line of service)
- Incorrect billing date
- Incorrect signature

☑ Every time a claim is sent to Medicaid, a document is generated explaining how the claim was adjudicated, or how the payment was determined. In the past, this document was referred to as the *explanation of benefits*; however, Medicaid now calls it the RA. The RA can be in paper or electronic form (if the medical facility is set up to accept the standard electronic version) and contains information from one or several claims. The RA typically contains "remark codes" and "reason codes," which the health insurance professional must be able to understand to interpret and reconcile this document with patient records.

☑ Medicaid fraud occurs when a health care provider, such as a physician, dentist, pharmacist, hospital, nursing home, or other health care service, deliberately engages in illegal or deceptive practices. Abuse, although not as serious as fraud, also is a growing problem in Medicaid programs. There are countless ways that Medicaid fraud and abuse can occur, and the health insurance professional should learn to recognize fraud perpetrated by the provider and the patient. To report fraud or abuse, the health insurance professional should use the state's hotline number or contact the Medicaid Fraud Control Unit.

Closing Scenario

When they first began the chapter, Nela and Berta felt as if they were on a ship heading into uncharted waters. Looking over the chapter objectives and terms left them feeling more than slightly apprehensive. There was so much to learn; however, the study plan they laid out before starting Chapter 4 was to "bite off one chunk at a time," which worked well for them in understanding the concepts presented. In addition to what was in the chapter, they frequently visited the CMS website for more detailed information. Additionally, they consulted the Medicaid website in their state to become knowledgeable about their individual state's regulations.

Berta, because her mother-in-law was currently in a nursing home, was particularly interested in learning about the "spend down" process, which apparently her mother-in-law went through to become eligible for Medicaid. Nela's interest was in the area of programs for women and children because of her own situation. By now, the women have had enough experience with completing the CMS-1500 claim that they had few problems filling out the blocks for typical Medicaid cases. Understanding the Medicaid remittance advice proved to be more of a challenge, however, and the women admitted that it might take additional experience before they acquired the necessary skill to become efficient. Their instructor assured them that this skill would come with time. It was becoming apparent that a career as a health insurance professional was going to be interesting and rewarding, albeit challenging.

WEBSITES TO EXPLORE

- To learn about the Medicaid program, visit the website for the Centers of Medicare and Medicaid Services at
  http://www.cms.hhs.gov

- To learn about the Medicaid program in your state, log on to
  http://cms.hhs.gov/medicaid/consumer.asp
  and select the applicable state site

- To find out what the TANF program is called in your state, log on to
  http://www.acf.hhs.gov/programs/ofa/tnfnames.htm

- For state-by-state Medicaid descriptions and plans, research the following website:
  http://64.82.65.67/medicaid/states.html

- To learn the specific guidelines for the Medicaid programs offered in a particular state, log on to
  http://www.cms.hhs.gov/medicaid/consumer.asp
  and insert the name of the state in the "select state" box.

- For complete information on the Medicare Prescription Drug, Improvement, and Modernization Act of 2003, log on to
  http://www.cms.hhs.gov/MMAUpdate

- The CMS website provides extensive information on third-party liability, cost avoidance, and collection, at
  http://www.cms.hhs.gov/ThirdPartyLiability

- To learn more about SSI benefits, countable income, and exclusions for the SSI program, log on to
  www.socialsecurity.gov

- For updates on SSI benefits, log on to
  www.socialsecurity.gov/pubs/10003.pdf

Chapter Review

Assessment

Multiple Choice

Directions: *In the questions/statements presented, choose the response that **best** answers/completes the stem, and circle the letter that precedes it.*

1. Title XIX of the Social Security Act of 1965 established ____.
   A. Social Security benefits to people older than 65
   B. Workers' compensation
   C. Medicare
   D. Medicaid

2. Medicaid is administered by ____.
   A. Congress
   B. CMS
   C. the Social Security Administration
   D. the Federal Insurance Advisory Board

3. Supplemental Security Income (SSI) is a cash benefit program controlled by ____.
   A. the Social Security Administration
   B. CMS
   C. individual state governments
   D. the Federal Insurance Advisory Board

4. Categorically needy individuals typically include ____.
   A. low-income families with children
   B. individuals receiving SSI
   C. pregnant women, infants, and children with incomes less than a specified percent of the federal poverty level (FPL)
   D. qualified Medicare Beneficiaries (QMBs)
   E. all of the above

5. The term used for the process of depleting private or family finances to the point where the individual/family becomes eligible for Medicaid assistance is ____.
   A. cataloging
   B. spend down
   C. asset reduction
   D. diminution

6. The program that provides comprehensive alternative care for noninstitutionalized elderly who otherwise would be in a nursing home is known as ____.
   A. SSI
   B. Social Security Disability Insurance
   C. Program of All-Inclusive Care for the Elderly
   D. long-term care

7. Medicaid coverage should be verified ____.
   A. every time a patient comes to the office
   B. no less than once a month
   C. at least annually
   D. biannually

8. Aged or disabled individuals who are very poor are covered under the Medicaid and Medicare programs, which are commonly referred to as _____.
   A. dual eligibles
   B. Medi-Medi
   C. supplemental coverage
   D. A and B

9. Medicare beneficiaries who qualify for certain Medicaid benefits if they have incomes below the FPL and resources at or below twice the standard allowed under the SSI program are known as _____.
   A. QDWIs
   B. QMBs
   C. SLMBs
   D. SMIs

10. When one state allows Medicaid beneficiaries from other states to be treated in its medical facilities, this exchange of privileges is referred to as _____.
    A. reciprocity
    B. Medi-Medi
    C. co-insurance
    D. dual coverage

True/False

Directions: *Place a "T" on the blank preceding the statement if it is true; place an "F" if the statement is false.*

_____ 1. Medicaid benefits are the same from state to state.

_____ 2. All states have a Medicaid program.

_____ 3. In 1972, federal law established the SSI program, which provides federally funded cash assistance to unmarried pregnant women with dependent children.

_____ 4. To be eligible for SSI, an individual must be at least 65 years old, blind, or disabled and have limited resources.

_____ 5. Eligibility for SSI benefits is based on an individual's employment record.

_____ 6. All states must cover the cost of prescription drugs for all categories of Medicaid recipients.

_____ 7. All providers must accept and treat all categories of Medicaid patients.

_____ 8. Providers must agree to accept what Medicaid pays as payment in full for covered services and are prohibited by law to "balance bill."

_____ 9. Medicaid, by law, is intended to be the "payer of last resort."

_____ 10. The time limit for filing Medicaid claims in all states is 1 year.

_____ 11. Providers are never allowed to ask a Medicaid-eligible patient to make a co-payment.

_____ 12. Assignment should be accepted on all Medicaid claims.

Short Answer/Fill-in-the-Blank

Directions: *Read the statements, and then, using the textbook for review, insert the correct word or words that complete the sentence or answer the question.*

1. Medicaid originally was created to give _____ access to health care.

2. The Medicaid program, formerly referred to as *Aid to Families with Dependent Children*, is now called

   _____ in many states.

3. Under Medicaid guidelines, families, pregnant women, and children fall under the _____ classification.

4. Persons receiving institutional or other long-term care in nursing and intermediate care facilities fall

   under the _____ classification.

5. _____ classification includes low-income individuals who lose employer health care coverage.

6. List the services that categorically needy individuals must be provided with according to federal standards.

   _____

   _____

   _____

7. List some of the optional coverage that individual states can provide.

   _____

   _____

   _____

8. Define and explain the function of a fiscal intermediary (FI).

   _____

9. List common responsibilities of an FI.

   _____

   _____

   _____

10. List the federally mandated services specified by law that Medicaid must cover.

_____

_____

_____

_____

_____

11. List four optional services commonly covered by states to their categorically needy population not provided to other groups.

_____

_____

_____

_____

_____

_____

_____

12. Explain the basic differences between Medicare and Medicaid.

_____

_____

_____

_____

13. List four examples of third-party liability.

_____

_____

_____

_____

Critical Thinking Activities

A. Explain the difference between "categorically needy" and "medically needy" and give examples of individuals who fall into each group.

B. You are a health insurance professional employed by Generic Family Practice. On September 7, 20XX, Emily Carson brought her 4-year-old son, Cory, to the office. Cory, complaining of ear pain and a sore throat, is new to the practice. Ms. Carson, a single mother, states that she and Cory are on Medicaid. After greeting Ms. Carson, what is the first thing you should do?

C. Brice Samuels, a 9-year-old girl, comes to Generic Family Practice on a monthly basis for follow-up treatment for a severe case of asthma. Gina Peters, a temp who is filling in for you during an absence, notes that Brice was eligible for Medicaid every month for the last 2 years. Assuming that Brice also is eligible for Medicaid benefits on this visit, Gina neglects to verify current eligibility.
  1. What, if any, possible problems could result from Gina's failure to follow proper procedures?
  2. If Brice's visits have been covered by Medicaid for the past 2 years, what possible reasons might there be for Medicaid to discontinue benefits?

D. Lamont Frasier, the senior physician at Generic Family Practice and a Medicaid participating provider, tells you that because he is getting close to retirement, he does not want you to accept any more Medicaid patients. "I have a total of 50 Medicaid patients, and that's enough," he tells you. What might be an appropriate response to Dr. Frazier's statement?

E. Dr. Frasier has several patients (age 65 or older) whom he sees periodically at the Sunshine Nursing Home. You do not see these patients, but you are responsible for the billing. Two of them are on Medicaid. How do you process Dr. Frasier's fees for these two Medicaid patients?

F. Dr. Alexandra Parsons, a psychiatrist, charges $250 for 1 hour of psychotherapy and $175 for a 30-minute session. She knows that Medicaid's allowable charge is $200 and $150, so she cuts the time she spends with her patients accordingly. When she counsels Wayne Gerber, she spends 40 minutes with him and charges Medicaid the full hour. She sees Tabitha Enrich for 20 minutes and charges Medicaid for the full 30 minutes. Dr. Parsons rationalizes that, by doing this, she does not lose so much money and really does not cheat the patient. You are Dr. Parsons's health insurance professional. Is this fraud? If so, what should you do?

Case Studies

Complete a CMS-1500 for each of the following case studies using the patient record, the Medicaid ID card, and the ledger card. Use a blank CMS-1500 form. Post the charge(s) on the ledger card. (Date claim form submissions 1 day after encounter.) Use the information in the Broadmoor Medical Clinic provider box for claims completion.

Provider Box	
Broadmoor Medical Clinic	Clinic EIN No. 42-1898989
4353 Pine Ridge Drive	Dr. R. L. Jones NPI 1234567890
Milton, XY 12345-0001	Dr. Marilou Lucero NPI 2907511822
Clinic NPI X100XX1000	Group # GRW0000
Telephone: 555-656-7890	Date claims 1 day after examination

A. Medicaid patient Pricilla Atkins—Record No. 052541 (Figs. 4-5, 4-6, and 4-7).

B. Medicaid patient Hattie Lawrence—Record No. 052544 (Figs. 4-8, 4-9, and 4-10).
Note: This patient has Medicare and Medicaid.

C. Using the Medicare/medical insurance record tracking form (Fig. 4-11), post the two Medicaid claims generated in Case Studies A and B.
Note: Remember to post the Medicaid claim filing notation on the ledger card.

Patient Record No. 052541

Name: Pricilla Atkins   Birth Date: 06/15/99   Sex: F

Address: 456 Summer Street   City/State/Zip: Middletown, XT 12345

Employer/Occupation: _____

Employer Address/Phone No.: _____

Responsible Party (Spouse/Parent/Guardian): Sherril Atkins

Relationship to Patient: mother

Occupation/Employer: custodian Silver Creek Shopping Center

Employer Address/Phone No.: 4500 Highway 406 W., Middletown, XT 12345

Primary Insurance: _____ Subscriber: _____

Policy No.: _____ Group No.: _____ Effective Date: _____

Other Insurance: _____ Subscriber: _____

Policy No.: _____ Group No.: _____ Effective Date: _____

Medicare No.: _____ Medicaid No.: 169426G SSN: _____

Name/NPI of Referring Provider: _____

Referring Provider's Address/Phone No.: _____

PROGRESS NOTES

02/13/20XX   Pricilla returns to the office today for destruction of two flat warts on her left hand. The lesion that was removed from her right hand two weeks ago is healing nicely. RTN 2 wks.

DIAGNOSIS   Juvenile warts (078.19)

R. L. Jones, M.D.

CHARGES: 17110 Ex Les. x 2 (L) $ 80.00

Fig. 4-5 Patient record (Atkins).

XTRA DEPARTMENT OF HUMAN SERVICES
MEDICAL ASSISTANCE ELIGIBILITY CARD

| FEBRUARY Month Valid | | | 20XX Year |
| 30-8   Aid-Type | J35982000 | | 29 County |

PERSON ID	NAME	BIRTHDATE	OTHER
169426G	PRICILLA ATKINS	06/15/1999	0000
2899123B	JACOB ATKINS	11/22/2002	0000

Client Address: 456 Summer Street
Middletown, XT 12345   PH 555 666 7377

Fig. 4-6 Medicaid ID card (Atkins).

Ins: Medicaid
Ph # 555-666-7377

STATEMENT

169426G Pricilla 6/15/99
2899123B Jacob 11/22/02

BROADMOOR MEDICAL CLINIC
4353 Pine Ridge Drive
Milton, XY 12345-0001
Telephone: 555-656-7890

Mrs. Sherrill Atkins
456 Summer Street
Middletown, XT 12345

DATE 20XX	PROFESSIONAL SERVICE DESCRIPTION	CHARGE	CREDITS PAYMENTS	CREDITS ADJUSTMENTS	CURRENT BALANCE
1/31	99212 OV EST (Pricilla)	65 00			65 00
1/31	17000 EX LES (RT)	45 00			110 00
2/3	Medicaid Claim	—			
2/10	Medicaid Ck#0317004		110 00		— 0 —

Due and payable within 10 days.   Pay last amount in balance column ⇧

Fig. 4-7 Ledger card (Atkins).

Patient Record No. 052544

Name: Hattie Lawrence   Birth Date: 06/02/1939   Sex: F

Address: 2925 Aspen Road   City/State/Zip: Milton, XT 12345

Employer/Occupation: unemployed

Employer Address/Phone No.:

Responsible Party (Spouse/Parent/Guardian): self

Relationship to Patient:

Occupation/Employer:

Employer Address/Phone No.:

Primary Insurance: _____ Subscriber: _____

Policy No.: _____ Group No.: _____ Effective Date: _____

Other Insurance: _____ Subscriber: _____

Policy No.: _____ Group No.: _____ Effective Date: _____

Medicare No.: 111223333A Medicaid No.: 788244F SSN: 111-22-3333

Name/NPI of Referring Provider: Everett Barclay, MD 0045557111

Referring Provider's Address/Phone No.: 19 Royal Circle, Ste 440, Milton, XY 23456

PROGRESS NOTES

10/03/20XX	This elderly woman is in the office today complaining of mild pain in the R ear. This has been bothering her for about a week now. She has tried home remedies, which help some, but do not relieve the pain for more than a few hours. Today, she is having some associated dizziness. See H&P in health record.
	Patient was given a prescription for E-Mycin and Benadryl OTC.
PLAN:	Patient is to return in one week for recheck. If not improved, we will do a head CT scan and arrange for hearing test.
DX	Labyrinthitis (386.30) M. Lucero
CHARGES:	99212 OV EST PT $60.00

Fig. 4-8 Patient record (Lawrence).

XTRA DEPARTMENT OF HUMAN SERVICES
MEDICAL ASSISTANCE ELIGIBILITY CARD

OCTOBER Month Valid			20XX Year
31-6	MM-Type	J35982000	29 County

PERSON ID	NAME	BIRTHDATE	OTHER
788244F	HATTIE LAWRENCE	06/02/1939	0003

Client Address: 2925 Aspen Road   PH 555 666 2244
Middletown, XT 12345

Fig. 4-9 Medicaid ID card (Lawrence).

Medicaid 788244F
Medicare 111223333A
Ph # 555-666-2244

STATEMENT

BROADMOOR MEDICAL CLINIC
4353 Pine Ridge Drive
Milton, XY 12345-0001
Telephone: 555-656-7890

Ms. Hattie Lawrence
2925 Aspen Road
Middletown, XT 12345

DATE 20XX	PROFESSIONAL SERVICE DESCRIPTION	CHARGE	CREDITS		CURRENT BALANCE
			PAYMENTS	ADJUSTMENTS	

Due and payable within 10 days.   Pay last amount in balance column ⇧

Fig. 4-10 Ledger card (Lawrence).

Name: Broadmoor Med. Clinic
Year: 20XX   **Page:** 122

**Medical Insurance
Record Tracking Form**

Service Provided			Medicare/Medicaid						Private Insurance			Patient Responsibility	
Date of Service	Patient Name & ID Number	CPT Service Codes	Assigned Y or N	Amount Billed	Amount Approved	Applied To Deductible	Amount Paid Provider	Amount Paid Patient	Date Sent	Amount Paid Provider	Amount Paid Patient	Amount Patient Paid	Date Paid Check #

Fig. 4-11   Insurance tracking form.

Internet Exploration

A. Using the website **http://cms.hhs.gov/medicaid/consumer.asp,** locate the Medicaid office in your state. Determine the following:

- Current FI
- Optional covered benefits for your state
- Required claim form

B. Some states provide a choice of Medicaid plans—fee-for-service and managed care. Log on to **http://www.cms.hhs.gov/home/medicaid.asp** to see if your state offers a managed care choice. If so, generate a chart comparing the two plans. If your state does not have a managed care plan, choose one that does.

C. Log on to the CMS fraud website at **http://www.cms.hhs.gov/FraudAbuseforProfs** (in addition, students should also research the "Related Links" at the bottom of the page). Create a page for the Office Procedures Manual giving step-by-step instructions for reporting suspected fraud and abuse in your state. Include a list of pertinent names, addresses, and telephone numbers.

D. Log on to the CMS website at **http://www.cms.hhs.gov,** and click on SCHIP. Under the SCHIP Summary, choose the SCHIP Resource Index. Next, under State Information, click on Fact Sheets. Locate the fact sheet for your state. Study and compare how children qualify for coverage and the cost sharing of your SCHIP with that of other states.

OBJECTIVES

After completion of this chapter, the student should be able to:

1. Describe the Medicare program and its structure.
2. Explain Medicare Parts A, B, C, and D.
3. List and discuss Medicare Combination Coverages (Medi-Medi, Medigap, and Medicare Secondary Policy).
4. List the advantages and disadvantages of Medicare health maintenance organizations.
5. Explain how Medicare determines "medically necessary" services.
6. Discuss the purpose of the advance beneficiary notice and determine when it should be used.
7. Discuss how to determine correct charges based on the Medicare fee schedule.
8. Explain the Medicare "Crossover" Program and how it affects claims submission.
9. Define *small providers* and their exemption from filing claims electronically.
10. Define the Medicare Summary Notice and discuss what information it contains.
11. Explain a Medicare remittance advice and how the health insurance professional uses the information it contains.
12. Define electronic remittance advice and explain who can use it and how it works.
13. Explain the function and purpose of electronic funds transfer.
14. Explain the purpose of quality review studies.
15. Define CLIA and explain its function.

CONQUERING MEDICARE'S CHALLENGES

KEY TERMS

adjudicated
advance beneficiary notice (ABN)
allowable charges
beneficiary
benefit period
biologicals
claims adjustment reason codes
Clinical Laboratory Improvement
    Act (CLIA)
coordination of benefits contractor
coverage requirements
credible coverage
crosswalks
demand bills
denial notice
downcoding
dual eligibles
electronic funds transfer (EFT)
electronic Medicare Summary Notice
electronic remittance advice (ERA)
end-stage renal disease (ESRD)
Federal Insurance Contributions Act
Health Care Quality Improvement
    Program

health insurance claim number (HICN)
HMO with point-of-service (POS) option
initial claims
lifetime (one-time) release of information
    form
local coverage determinations (LCDs)
local medical review policies (LMRPs)
mandated Medigap transfer
medically necessary
Medicare
Medicare Beneficiary Protection Program
Medicare gaps
Medicare HMOs
Medicare limiting charge
Medicare managed care plan
Medicare nonparticipating provider
    (nonPAR)
Medicare Part A
Medicare Part A fiscal intermediary (FI)
Medicare Part B
Medicare Part B carrier
Medicare Part B Crossover Program
Medicare Part C (Medicare Advantage
    plans)

Medicare Part D (Prescription Drug
    Plan)
Medicare participating provider (PAR)
Medicare Secondary Payer (MSP)
Medicare Summary Notice (MSN)
Medicare supplement policy
Medigap insurance
Medi-Medi
network
noncovered services
open enrollment period
peer review organization (PRO)
Program of All-Inclusive Care for
    the Elderly (PACE)
prospective payment system (PPS)
provider sponsored organization (PSO)
quality improvement organization (QIO)
quality review study
remittance remark codes
resource-based relative value system
self-referring
standard paper remittance advice
    (SPRA)
trading partner agreement

Opening Scenario

Rita Thomas, a high school dropout, attended an alternative high school to earn her general education diploma (GED). A single mother of a 3-year-old son, Rita lives with her grandmother and works as a waitress in a neighborhood bar and grill. Grandma Nan, as Rita calls her, encourages her granddaughter to enroll in night classes at the local community college. The evening schedule works well because Rita can keep her day job, and Grandma Nan is available to babysit for her. Rita signs up for a health insurance course.

"Learn as much as you can about Medicare, and then you can explain it all to me," Grandma Nan implores. "It's all so confusing." Encouraged by her grandmother's request, Rita enthusiastically begins her pursuit of "conquering Medicare's challenges." Up to now, Medicare was just a word to Rita without much meaning. She had heard Grandma Nan and her elderly friends discussing it many times, but Rita paid little attention. She was aware, however, that these women did not understand Medicare's whole picture. Now Rita has an opportunity to do something not only for herself but also for her grandmother, who has done so much for her.

MEDICARE PROGRAM

Medicare, a comprehensive federal insurance program, was established by Congress in 1966 to provide individuals age 65 and older financial assistance with medical expenses. In 1972, the Medicare program was expanded to include certain categories of disabled individuals younger than age 65 and individuals of any age who have **end-stage renal disease (ESRD)**, permanent kidney disorders requiring dialysis or transplant (Fig. 5-1). Medicare is administered by the Center for Medicare and Medicaid Services (CMS), formerly called Healthcare Financing Administration (HCFA). CMS is a division of the Department of Health and Human Services and is based on laws enacted by Congress.

The **Federal Insurance Contributions Act** provides for a federal system of old age, survivors, disability, and hospital insurance. Social Security taxes finance the old age, survivors, and disability insurance part. The hospital insurance part of Medicare is funded through taxes withheld from employees' wages matched by employer contributions. In 2007, the individual Medicare contribution rate (amount withheld from wages) was 1.45%. Employers must contribute a matching percentage for a total contribution of 2.9%. All wages are subject to the Medicare tax; there is no wage base limit.

Medicare is not provided free of charge. Medicare requires cost sharing in the form of premiums, deductibles, and co-insurance, all of which are discussed in this chapter.

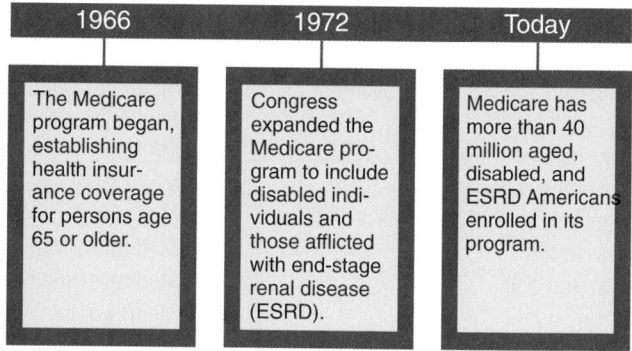

Fig. 5-1 The Medicare program. *(Modified from Centers for Medicare and Medicaid: World of Medicare. 2005. Available at http://cms.meridianksi.com/kc/ilc/scorm_course_launch_frm.asp.)*

Medicare Program Structure

Medicare is composed of the following four parts:

- **Medicare Part A**—hospital insurance
- **Medicare Part B**—medical (physicians' care) insurance (original Medicare)
- **Medicare Part C (Medicare Advantage plans)**—managed care–type plans (formerly Medicare+Choice)
- **Medicare Part D (Prescription Drug Plan)**—prescription drug program

Medicare Part A

Medicare Part A (hospital insurance) helps pay for services for the following types of health care (Table 5-1):

TABLE 5-1	2007 Medicare Hospital Insurance (Part A) Covered Services		
Services	**Benefit**	**Medicare Pays**	**You Pay**
Hospitalization Semiprivate room and board, general nursing, and other hospital services and supplies (Medicare payments based on benefit periods) (see comments 1 and 2)	First 60 days 61st-90th day 91st-150th day (60 reserve days may be used only once) Beyond 150 days	All but $992 All but $248/day All but $496/day Nothing	$992 $248/day $496/day All costs
Skilled Nursing Facility Care Semiprivate room and board, skilled nursing and rehabilitative services, and other services and supplies (Medicare payments based on benefit periods) (see comments 1 and 2)	First 20 days Additional 80 days Beyond 100 days	100% of approved amount All but $124/day Nothing	Nothing Up to $124/day All costs
Home Health Care Part-time or intermittent skilled care, home health aide services, durable medical equipment and supplies, and other services	Unlimited as long as Medicare requirements for home health care benefits are met	100% of approved amount; 80% of approved amount for durable medical equipment	Nothing for services; 20% of approved amount for durable medical equipment
Hospice Care Pain relief, symptom management, and support services for the terminally ill	For as long as physician certifies need	All but limited costs for outpatient drugs and inpatient respite care	Limited cost sharing for outpatient drugs and inpatient respite care
Blood (See Part B) When furnished by a hospital or skilled nursing facility during a covered stay	Unlimited during a benefit period if medically necessary	All but first 3 pints per calendar year	For first 3 pints

Modified from http://www.insurance.wa.gov/publications/consumer/Medicare_Chart_A_B.pdf.
Comments:
1. Neither Medicare nor Medigap insurance will pay for most nursing home care.
2. A benefit period begins the first day an individual receives a Medicare-covered service in a qualified hospital. It ends when the individual has been out of a hospital (or other facility that primarily provides skilled nursing or rehabilitation services) for 60 days in a row. It also ends if the individual remains in a facility (other than a hospital) that primarily provides skilled nursing or rehabilitation services, but does not receive any skilled care there for 60 days in a row. If the individual enters a hospital again after 60 days, a new benefit period begins.
3. Premium for Part A: If an individual has less than 30 quarters of coverage—$410/mo. For 30-39 quarters of coverage—$226/mo.

- Inpatient hospital care (including critical access hospitals)
- Inpatient care in a skilled nursing facility (SNF)
- Home health care
- Hospice care
- Blood

Medicare Part A does not cover custodial or long-term care.

Coverage requirements under Medicare state that for a service to be covered, it must be considered **medically necessary**—reasonable and necessary for the diagnosis or treatment of an illness or injury or to improve the functioning of a malformed body part.

Noncovered services are situations in which an item or service is not covered under Medicare and include, but are not limited to, the following:

- Program exclusions as designated by CMS
- Medical devices or **biologicals** (drugs or medicinal preparations obtained from animal tissue or other organic sources) that have not been approved by the Food and Drug Administration
- Items and services that are determined to be investigational in nature

Medicare Part A is free to any individual age 65 or older who is

- eligible to receive monthly Social Security benefits or
- eligible based on wages on which sufficient Medicare payroll taxes were paid.

Medicare Part A also is free to any disabled individual younger than age 65 who has

- received Social Security disability benefits for 24 months as a worker, surviving spouse, or adult child of a retired, disabled, or deceased worker or
- accumulated a sufficient number of Social Security credits to be insured for Medicare and meets the requirements of the Social Security disability program.

A **beneficiary** (an individual who has health insurance through the Medicare or Medicaid program) automatically qualifies for Part A if he or she was a federal employee on January 1, 1983. Application for Medicare Part A is automatic when an individual applies for Social Security benefits. A husband or wife also may qualify for Part A coverage at age 65, based on the spouse's eligibility for Social Security. If an individual is not eligible for free Part A, he or she may purchase this coverage. The **Medicare Part A fiscal intermediary (FI)**, a private organization that contracts with Medicare to pay Part A and some Part B bills, determines payment to Part A facilities for covered items and services provided by the facility.

IMAGINE THIS!

Eloise Graham went to the Argyle County Mental Health Center (ACMHC) for psychiatric counseling. Under Medicare, this is a covered service, but the adult day care services Eloise receives that are provided at ACMHC are not considered reasonable and necessary. A claim submitted to Medicare for the adult day care services was denied.

Medicare Part B

Medicare Part B is medical insurance financed by a combination of federal government funds and beneficiary premiums, which helps pay for the following:

- Medically necessary physicians' services
- Outpatient hospital services
- Clinical laboratory services
- Durable medical equipment (DME) (to qualify as DME, it must be ordered by a physician for use in the home, and items must be reusable, e.g., walkers, wheelchairs, or hospital beds)
- Blood (received as an outpatient)

If a beneficiary became eligible for Medicare on or after January 1, 2005, Medicare covers a "Welcome to Medicare" one-time physical examination if it is performed within the first 6 months of coverage, if that individual has Part B. Part B also can help pay for many other medical services and supplies that are not covered by Part A and home health care if the beneficiary is not enrolled in Medicare Part A. Medicare now covers some preventive health care services, such as the following:

- Bone mass measurements
- Colorectal cancer screening
- Diabetes services
- Glaucoma testing
- Pap tests, pelvic examinations, and clinical breast examinations
- Prostate cancer screening
- Screening mammograms
- Certain vaccinations

Table 5-2 lists additional services and supplies that Medicare Part B helps pay for and services not covered by Part B.

All Medicare Part B beneficiaries pay for Part B coverage. In 2007, the Part B monthly premium was $93.50. This premium is deducted from the beneficiary's monthly Social Security benefits check. This monthly premium is subject to an increase every year.

TABLE 5-2	Services and Supplies Medicare Part B Helps Pay for and Services Not Covered by Part B

Items Medicare Part B Helps Pay For*	Services Not Covered By Medicare Part B[†]
Ambulance services	Acupuncture
Certain chiropractic services	Cosmetic surgery
Clinical trials	Custodial care
Diabetic self-management training	Deductibles, co-insurance and co-payments
Diabetic supplies (except syringes and insulin)	Dental care and dentures
Diagnostic tests	Eye refractions
Durable medical equipment	Health care received outside of the United States
Emergency department services	Hearing aids and hearing examinations (for the
Eyeglasses (limited coverage)	purpose of fitting a hearing aid)
Foot examinations and treatment	Hearing tests (other than for fitting a hearing aid)
Hearing and balance examinations	Long-term care (custodial care in a nursing home)
Kidney dialysis services	Orthopedic shoes
Long-term care (skilled care)	Prescription drugs
Medical nutrition therapy	Routine foot care
Mental health care	Routine eye care and most eyeglasses
Practitioner services	Routine physical examinations (Medicare covers a
Prescription drugs (limited, such as injectable cancer drugs)	one-time examination for new enrollees)
Prosthetic and orthotic items	Screen tests
Second surgical opinions	Shots and vaccinations (except flu shots)
Smoking cessation counseling	Some diabetic supplies
Surgical dressings	
Telemedicine (in some areas)	
Transplant services	
Travel (limited to specific travel situations outside the United States)	
Urgently needed care	

* With certain limitations.
[†] With certain exceptions.

The health insurance professional should become familiar with Medicare's guidelines to determine if a specific procedure or service is covered. The Websites to Explore at the end of this chapter provide several Internet links to follow for additional help and information.

Similar to a Medicare FI, the **Medicare Part B carrier** determines payment of Part B—covered items and services. A Medicare Part B carrier is a private company that contracts with CMS to provide claims processing and payment for Medicare Part B services. The local Medicare carrier also has the ability and authority to designate an item or service as noncovered for its service area or jurisdiction. For a complete list of all noncovered items or services for your state, contact your local Medicare carrier.

Enrollment

Before an individual reaches age 65, he or she must decide whether to enroll in Medicare Part A or Part B or both. If eligible beneficiaries want Medicare coverage to start the month they reach age 65, they should contact their local Social Security office 3 months before their 65th birthday. If they decide not to sign up for Medicare until after their 65th birthday, the Medicare Part B effective date is delayed.

If individuals do not sign up for Medicare Part B when first becoming eligible and later decide to enroll, the monthly premiums are 10% higher than the basic premium for each 12-month period they were eligible to enroll but did not. An eligible beneficiary may delay enrollment without a penalty or a waiting period, however, if the individual was still employed and covered by an employer's group health plan at the time he or she first became eligible for Medicare benefits. Individuals who do not enroll within the 3-month period before becoming age 65 must wait and enroll during the general enrollment period, which is January 1 through March 31 of each year. Medicare Part B coverage becomes effective on July 1 of the year of enrollment.

Premiums and Cost-Sharing Requirements

Medicare Part B (medical insurance) cost-sharing requirements include a monthly premium ($93.50 in 2007). This premium, which is automatically deducted from the beneficiary's monthly Social Security check, is subject to change every year. The second cost-sharing requirement in Medicare Part B is an annual deductible ($131 in 2007). After the deductible is met, Medicare pays 80% of **allowable charges**. Allowable charges are the fees Medicare permits for a particular service or supply. Table 5-3 summarizes the Medicare Part B cost-sharing amounts for various types of services.

A **benefit period** is the duration of time during which a Medicare beneficiary is eligible for Part A benefits for services incurred in a hospital or SNF or both. A benefit period begins the day an individual is admitted to a hospital or SNF. The benefit period ends when the beneficiary has not received care in a hospital or SNF for 60 days in a row. If the beneficiary is readmitted to the hospital or SNF before the 60 days elapse, it is considered to be in the same benefit period. If the beneficiary is admitted to a hospital or SNF after the initial 60-day benefit period has ended, a new benefit period begins. The inpatient hospital deductible must be paid for each benefit period, but there is no limit to the number of benefit periods allowed.

As mentioned previously, Part A is free for individuals who have worked enough quarters to qualify (40 or more). For 30 to 39 quarters of Social Security work credit, the monthly premium is $226 (2007), and for less than 30 quarters of Social Security work credit, the monthly premium is $410 (2007). Penalties may be assessed for failing to enroll at appropriate times. For Part A, the penalty applies only to beneficiaries who pay for Part A coverage. An example of a beneficiary who must pay for Part A is someone not eligible for Social Security benefits at age 65. This individual is eligible for Medicare, but not for free Part A. The penalty is a flat 10% of the Part A premium, and it is paid for twice the number of years enrollment was delayed. These amounts are subject to change every year. A premium penalty is imposed when an individual fails to enroll in Medicare Part B during the Initial Enrollment Period or Special Enrollment Period. Each year delay results in a penalty of 10% of the current monthly premium: a 2-year delay would be 20%; a 3-year delay would be a 30% penalty. This penalty is paid for the remainder of the individual's life.

Medicare Part C (Medicare Advantage Plans)

The Balanced Budget Act of 1997, which went into effect in January 1999, expanded the role of private plans under Medicare+Choice to include managed care plans, such as preferred provider organizations (PPOs), provider sponsored organizations (PSOs), private fee-for-service plans, and medical savings accounts (MSAs) coupled with high-deductible insurance plans. The Medicare Prescription Drug, Improvement, and Modernization Act of 2003 renamed the program "Medicare Advantage" and created another option: regional PPOs.

Medicare Advantage plans (formerly Medicare+Choice) are prepaid health care plans that offer regular Medicare Parts A and B coverage in addition to *coverage* for other services. Under Medicare Part C, individuals who are eligible for Medicare Parts A and B can choose to get their Medicare benefits through a variety of plans (see previously), with the exception of individuals with ESRD. The primary Medicare Part C plans include the following:

- *Medicare managed care plans,* such as health maintenance organizations (HMOs), provider sponsored organizations (PSOs), preferred provider organizations (PPOs), and other certified public or private coordinated care plans that meet the standards under the Medicare law.
- *Medicare private, unrestricted fee-for-service plans* that allow beneficiaries to select certain private providers. These providers must accept the plan's payment terms and conditions.
- *MSA plans* that allow beneficiaries to enroll in a plan with a high deductible. After the deductible is met, the MSA plan pays providers. Money remaining in the MSA can be used to pay for future medical care, including some services not usually covered by Medicare Part A and Part B, such as dentures.

Medicare Part C coverage not only includes Part A and Part B coverage but also pays for services not covered under the original Medicare plan, such as the following:

- Preventive care
- Prescription drugs
- Eyeglasses
- Dental care
- Hearing aids

For a Medicare beneficiary to qualify for one of these Medicare Advantage options, he or she must be eligible for Medicare Parts A and B and live in the service area of the plan. Generally, an individual

TABLE 5-3	2007 Medicare Medical Insurance (Part B) Covered Services		
Services	**Benefit**	**Medicare Pays**	**You Pay**
Medical Expenses Physician's services, inpatient and outpatient medical and surgical services and supplies, physical and speech therapy, diagnostic tests, durable medical equipment, and other services	Unlimited if medically necessary	80% of approved amount (after $131 deductible); 50% of approved amount for most outpatient mental health services	$131 deductible,* plus 20% of approved amount and limited charges above approved amount[†]; 50% for most outpatient mental health services
Clinical Laboratory Services Blood test, urinalysis, and more	Unlimited if medically necessary	Generally 100% of approved amount	Nothing for services
Home Health Care[‡] Part-time or intermittent skilled care, home health aide services, durable medical equipment and supplies, and other services	Unlimited as long as Medicare requirements are met	100% of approved amount; 80% of approved amount for durable medical equipment	Nothing for services; 20% of approved amount for durable medical equipment
Outpatient Hospital Treatment Services for the diagnosis or treatment of an illness or injury	Unlimited if medically necessary	Medicare payment to hospital based on hospital costs	20% of billed amount (after $131 deductible)*
Blood[§]	Unlimited if medically necessary	80% of approved amount (after $131 deductible and starting with 4th pint)	First 3 pints plus 20% of approved amount for additional pints (after $131 deductible)[¶]

Modified from http://www.insurance.wa.gov/publications/consumer/Medicare_Chart_A_B.pdf.

We attempt to provide the most current information possible. Because of frequent changes, always check with the company for the latest premiums. The appearance of a company on this list does not constitute endorsement of a company or its policies by the Washington State Office of the Insurance Commissioner, the SHIBA HelpLine, or its volunteers.

* Once an individual has had $131 of expense for covered services, the Part B deductible does not apply to any other covered services received for the rest of the year.

[†] Federal law limits charges for physician services.

[‡] Part B for home health care only if an individual does not have Part A of Medicare.

[§] The 3-pint blood deductible (donated or paid for) can be met via inpatient (Part A) or outpatient (Part B) and is required only once in a calendar year.

[¶] Monthly Part B premium—$93.50. Depending on income level, some clients pay $106, $124.70, $143.40, or $162.10.

is not eligible to elect a Medicare Advantage plan if he or she has been diagnosed with ESRD. There are exceptions to this eligibility rule, however, such as individuals who are already members of a Medicare Advantage plan when they develop ESRD and individuals who received a kidney transplant and no longer require regular dialysis treatments.

Medicare Part D (Medicare Prescription Drug Benefit Plan)

The Medicare Prescription Drug Improvement and Modernization Act of 2003, signed into law in December 2003, introduced significant changes to the Medicare program. Included in the Act is the

TABLE 5-4	Medicare Basic Benefits under Part D (2007)			

Beneficiary Drug Costs	Beneficiary Pays	Medicare Pays	Total Beneficiary Out-of-Pocket Costs Per Year*
$0-$265	100% ($265)	$0	$265
$266-$2400	25% ($533.75)	75% ($1601.25)	$798.75
$2401-$5451.25	100% ($3051.25)	$0	$3850
Greater than $5451.25	5%	95%	$3850 + 5% of costs greater than $5451.25

* Does not include premium costs.

new Medicare Part D coverage for prescription drugs. On January 1, 2006, this revised Medicare plan went into effect.

The main change in this plan is that all Medicare beneficiaries are asked to choose a prescription drug plan to help offset the increasing cost of prescription drugs. If they enroll in Medicare Part D, they pay an additional premium (which can be deducted from their monthly Social Security check). Premiums range from $2 to $100, depending on the plan, with a national average of approximately $35. Individual plans offer varying benefits; however, each must offer no less than the basic Medicare coverage, referred to as **"credible coverage."** Table 5-4 shows Medicare's basic benefits under Part D. These figures are subject to change every year. Many plans offer more comprehensive coverage than Medicare's basic coverage.

Individuals qualifying for Medicare and Medicaid benefits (**dual eligibles**, sometimes referred to as **Medi-Medi**) who receive the full Medicaid benefits package lose their prescription drug coverage under Medicaid but can enroll in the Medicare Part D Prescription Drug Benefit Plan. Medicare pays the Part D deductible for all dual eligibles and their monthly premiums, if they enroll in an average or low-cost Part D plan. These subsidies eliminate the gap in coverage for dual eligibles that Medicare beneficiaries who do not qualify for Medicare and Medicaid face. Dual eligibles are responsible, however, for small co-pays ranging from $2 to $5. Dual eligibles residing in nursing homes or other institutions are exempt from co-pays because they already are contributing all but a small portion of their income to the cost of their nursing home care.

Although the new law shifts drug coverage for dual eligibles from Medicaid to Medicare, there is no provision for providing full financial assistance to states. States are required to pay for most of the cost of providing the Medicare Part D prescription drug benefit to dual eligibles through payments to the federal government. Under the new bill, states are not allowed to use federal Medicaid matching funds to supplement prescription drug coverage for dual eligibles under Part D plans. A state can choose, however, to use state-only funds to offset the cost of the prescription drug benefit.

Program of All-Inclusive Care for the Elderly

The **Program of All-Inclusive Care for the Elderly (PACE)** provides community-based acute and long-term care services. A multidisciplinary team composed of a physician, nurse, therapists (physical, occupational, or recreational), dietitian, social worker, home care coordinator, and transportation supervisor completes an initial and semi-annual assessment of each participant with a documented plan of treatment. Most services are provided at a licensed day activity center. Participants must accept the PACE organization and its contractors as their only service provider for all Medicaid and Medicare services. PACE is available only in areas where a PACE organization is under contract to deliver services.

To be eligible for the PACE program, an individual must meet the following criteria:

- Age 55 or older
- Meet the nursing facility medical need criteria
- Live in an area serviced by a PACE organization
- Be safely served in the community according to the PACE organization

To be eligible for PACE Medicaid, the following criteria must be met:

- Be eligible for Supplemental Security Income benefits
- Have been eligible for Medicaid as a result of protective coverage mandated by federal law
- Be eligible for Medicaid benefits if institutionalized

MEDICARE COMBINATION COVERAGES

Because Medicare does not cover some services, and there are deductibles and co-payments that patients must pay out-of-pocket for most services, beneficiaries often have added health insurance coverage to help with the gaps in Medicare's coverage. This extra coverage can be one of the following:

- Medicare/Medicaid dual eligibility
- Medicare supplement policies
- Medicare Secondary Payer (MSP)

The following sections explain each of these supplemental types of health care coverage.

Medicare/Medicaid Dual Eligibility

Dual eligibility, as stated earlier, refers to individuals who qualify for benefits under the Medicare and Medicaid programs. Most dual eligibles are low-income elderly and individuals younger than 65 with disabilities. Medicare does not pay for all health services, just basic physician and hospital care. In addition, Medicare beneficiaries have to meet a yearly deductible and pay a monthly premium and a 20% co-payment (cost sharing) for all covered services. Dual eligibles rely on Medicaid to pay Medicare premiums and cost-sharing expenses and to pay for the needed benefits Medicare does not cover, such as long-term care.

Medicare Supplement Policies

The traditional Medicare program provides valuable coverage of health care needs, but it leaves uninsured areas with which elderly and disabled Americans need additional help. To ensure that they are adequately protected, many seniors purchase a **Medicare supplement policy** (also referred to as a *Medigap policy*). A Medicare supplement policy is a health insurance plan sold by private insurance companies to help pay for health care expenses not covered by Medicare and Medicare's deductibles and co-insurance. An individual may qualify for supplemental insurance through an employer-sponsored retirement plan or, more commonly, through a Medigap plan.

Medigap Insurance

Sometimes Medicare supplement policies are referred to as **Medigap insurance**. Medigap insurance is designed specifically to supplement Medicare benefits and is regulated by federal and state law. A Medigap policy must be clearly identified as Medicare supplemental insurance, and it must provide specific benefits that help fill the gaps in Medicare coverage. Other kinds of insurance may help with out-of-pocket health care costs, but they do not qualify as Medigap plans.

There are 12 standard Medicare supplement plans called "A" through "L." Each plan has a different set of benefits. Plan "A" is the basic plan, and it has the least amount of benefits. Plan "J" is the most comprehensive. Table 5-5 shows Medigap plans A through L and what each covers.

When an individual buys a Medicare supplement policy, he or she pays a premium to the private insurance company. This premium is above and beyond the Medicare Part B premium. If the individual has a Medicare Advantage plan, it is unnecessary to have a Medicare supplement policy because these plans typically include much of the same coverage as Medigap. *Note*: Since the new Medicare D plan became effective in January 2006, insurance companies are no longer allowed to sell Medicare supplement policies H, I, and J with prescription drug coverage.

STANDARD MEDIGAP POLICIES. The 12 standard Medigap policies were developed by the National Association of Insurance Commissioners and incorporated into state and federal law. The plans cover specific expenses not covered or not fully covered by Medicare. Insurance companies are not permitted to change the combination of benefits or the letter designations of any of the plans.

All states must allow the sale of plan A, and all Medigap insurers must make plan A available if they are going to sell any Medigap plans in their state. Although not required to offer any of the other plans, most insurers do offer several of these alternative plans to pick from; some offer all 12. Insurers can decide which of the optional plans they sell as long as the state in which the plans are sold approves. Although insurers must offer the same coverage in each plan, they do not have to charge the same premium rates; it is strongly suggested that individuals shop around and compare prices before purchasing a Medigap policy.

TABLE 5-5 Twelve Standard Medicare Supplemental Plans

Basic Benefits	A	B	C	D	E	F	G	H	I	J	K	L
Part A Hospital												
Day 61-90 co-insurance	X	X	X	X	X	X	X	X	X	X	X	X
Day 91-150 co-insurance	X	X	X	X	X	X	X	X	X	X	X	X
365 more days—100%	X	X	X	X	X	X	X	X	X	X	X	X
Part B Co-insurance or Co-pay	X	X	X	X	X	X	X	X	X	X	50%*	75%*
Parts A and B Blood	X	X	X	X	X	X	X	X	X	X	50%	75%

Additional Benefits	A	B	C	D	E	F	G	H	I	J	K	L
Skilled Nursing Facility Co-insurance Day 21-100			X	X	X	X	X	X	X	X	50%	75%
Part A Deductible		X	X	X	X	X	X	X	X	X	50%	75%
Part B Deductible			X			X				X		
Part B Excess						100%	80%		100%	100%		
Foreign Travel Emergency			X	X	X	X	X	X	X	X		
At-Home Recovery				X			X		X	X		
Preventive Medical Care					X					X		
Out-of-Pocket Annual Limit											$4140	$2070

From Iowa Medicare Supplemental Premium Comparison Guide, Iowa Insurance Division, 2008.
* Plans K and L pay 100% of Part B co-insurance for preventive services.

WHERE THE GAPS ARE. Box 5-1 describes the **Medicare gaps** in various types of care.

WHAT MEDIGAP PLANS COVER. Medigap policies pay most, if not all, of the Medicare co-insurance amounts and may provide coverage for Medicare's deductibles. Some standard plans pay for services not covered by Medicare, such as at-home recovery, preventive screening, and emergency medical care while traveling outside the United States. Coverage also is provided in some plans for health care provider charges in excess of Medicare's approved amount and for some care in the home.

ELIGIBILITY. If an individual enrolls in Medicare Part B when he or she becomes 65, federal law forbids insurance companies from denying eligibility for Medigap policies for 6 months. This 6-month period is called the **open enrollment period**. If the individual did not enroll in Medicare Part B when turning 65, he or she can sign up for it later during the yearly general enrollment period—January to March. The individual has a 6-month open enrollment period for Medigap policies beginning July 1 of that year. Individuals who were covered by a group health insurance plan when they turned 65 have a 6-month open enrollment period for Medigap

policies beginning the date their Part B coverage begins, regardless of when they sign up for it.

Medicare Secondary Payer

Medicare Secondary Payer (MSP) is the term used when Medicare is not responsible for paying first because the beneficiary is covered under another insurance policy. The MSP program, enacted in 1980, was created to preserve Medicare funds and to ensure that funds would be available for future generations. Since the program's beginning, a series of federal laws have changed the coordination of benefits provision between Medicare and other insurance carriers. These federal laws take precedence over individual state law and private insurance contracts. For certain categories of individuals, Medicare is the secondary payer regardless of state law or plan provisions. Medicare most likely would be the secondary payer in any of the following situations:

- Workers' compensation (injury or illness that occurred at work)
- Working aged (older than 65 years) who are covered by a group health plan through their own or their spouse's current employment

---

BOX 5-1   Medicare Gaps by Care Type

During a hospital stay, Medicare Part A does not pay
- yearly deductible;
- co-insurance amount for each day of hospitalization more than 60 days and up to 90 days for any one benefit period;
- co-insurance amount for each day of hospitalization more than 90 days and up to 150 days, for any one benefit period past a 150-day hospitalization;
- anything past a 150-day hospitalization;
- the cost of 3 pints of blood, unless replaced; or
- medical expenses during foreign travel.

During a stay in a skilled nursing facility, Medicare Part A does not pay
- co-insurance amount for each day in the facility more than 20 days and up to 100 days for any one benefit period or
- anything for a stay of more than 100 days.

For home health care, Medicare Part A does not pay
- 20% of the approved cost of durable medical equipment or approved nonskilled care or

- anything for nonmedical personal care services.

For physicians, clinics, laboratories, therapies, medical supplies, and equipment, Medicare Part B does not pay
- yearly deductible,
- 20% of the Medicare-approved amount,
- 15% above the Medicare-approved amount if provider does not accept assignment,
- preventive or routine examinations and testing except for the "Welcome to Medicare" examination if received within the first 6 months of eligibility,
- treatment that is not considered medically necessary,
- prescription medication that can be self-administered,
- general dental work,
- routine eye and hearing examinations, or
- glasses or hearing aids.

- Disabled individuals age 64 and younger who are covered by a large group health plan (more than 100 employees) through their own or a family member's current employment
- Medicare beneficiaries with permanent kidney failure covered under a group health plan
- Individuals with black lung disease covered under the Federal Black Lung Program
- Veterans Administration benefits
- Federal Research Grant Program

It is often the responsibility of the health insurance professional to determine, in cases in which the Medicare beneficiary has other insurance coverage, to which third-party payer the CMS-1500 claim is submitted first. Many medical practices use a structured form, such as an MSP questionnaire, to simplify this process. An example of an MSP questionnaire is shown in Fig. 5-2.

In 2001, the CMS created a separate entity called the **coordination of benefits contractor**. This individual assumes responsibility for nearly all initial MSP development activities formerly performed by Medicare intermediaries and carriers. The main job of the coordination of benefits contractor is to ensure that the information on Medicare's eligibility database regarding other health insurance primary to Medicare is up to date and accurate. The coordination of benefits contractor also handles MSP-related inquiries other than those related to specific claims or recoveries.

The goal of these MSP information-gathering activities is to identify MSP situations quickly, ensuring correct primary and secondary payments by the responsible party. Health care providers and other suppliers benefit from this activity because the total payments received for services provided to Medicare beneficiaries are greater when Medicare is a secondary payer to a group health plan than when Medicare is the primary payer. Table 5-6 summarizes the role of the coordination of benefits contractor in various processes.

Medicare and Managed Care

Medicare-eligible individuals have a choice of whether they receive Medicare benefits through traditional Medicare or through a managed care plan. A **Medicare managed care plan** is an HMO or PPO that uses Medicare to pay for part of its services for eligible beneficiaries. Medicare managed care plans fill the gaps in basic Medicare similar to Medigap policies; however, Medicare managed care plans and Medigap policies function differently. Medigap policies work along with Medicare to pay for medical expenses. Medical claims are sent to Medicare and then to a Medigap insurer, and each pays a portion of the approved charges. Medicare managed care plans provide all basic Medicare benefits, plus some additional coverages (depending on the plan) to fill the gaps Medicare does not pay. The extent of coverage beyond Medicare, the size of

Medicare Secondary Payer Questionnaire

Patient Name: _____   Date: _____

HICN: _____

Medicare law requires that we determine if your medical services might be covered by another insurer. In order to assist us in the correct billing of these services, please answer the following questions:

1. Is your injury/illness due to:

   A. Work-related accident/condition?
   - [ ] No
   - [ ] Yes, name and address of workers' compensation plan: _____
   _____
   _____
     Policy or ID#: _____
     Accident date: _____

   B. A condition covered under the Federal Black Lung Program?
   - [ ] No
   - [ ] Yes

   C. An automobile accident?
   - [ ] No
   - [ ] Yes, name and address of auto insurance: _____
   _____
     Name of insured: _____
     Policy or ID#: _____
     Accident date: _____ Accident location: _____

   D. An accident <u>other</u> <u>than</u> an automobile accident?
   - [ ] No
   - [ ] Yes, name and address of no-fault insurer: _____
   _____
     Name of insured: _____
     Policy or ID#: _____
     Accident date: _____ Accident location: _____

   E. The fault of another party?
   - [ ] No
   - [ ] Yes, name and address of no-fault insurer: _____
   _____
     Name of insured: _____
     Policy or ID#: _____
     Accident date: _____ Accident location: _____

DMERC Region D Supplier Manual   *(Rev. 1/2001) Exhibit 1*

Fig. 5-2 Medicare Secondary Payer questionnaire. *(Source: U.S. Department of Health and Human Services, Centers for Medicare and Medicaid Services.)*

Medicare Secondary Payer Questionnaire (cont'd)

2. Are you eligible for coverage under the Veterans' Administration?
   - ☐ No
   - ☐ Yes

3. Are you employed?
   - ☐ No. Date of retirement:
   - ☐ Yes, employer name and address: _____
   _____

   Do you have employer group health plan coverage?
   - ☐ No
   - ☐ Yes, insurer name and address: _____
   _____

      Policy #: _____
      Group #: _____

4. Is your spouse employed?
   - ☐ No. Date of retirement, if applicable:
   - ☐ Yes, spouse's name: _____
   Employer name and address: _____

   Are you covered under your spouse's employer group health plan?
   - ☐ No
   - ☐ Yes, insurer name and address: _____
   _____

      Policy #: _____
      Group #: _____

5. Are you a dependent covered under a parent's/guardian's employer group health plan?
   - ☐ No
   - ☐ Yes, employer name and address: _____
   _____

   Insurer name and address: _____
   _____

   Name of insured: _____
   Policy #: _____
   Group #: _____

Thank you for your cooperation in ensuring that your medical services will be billed to the proper insurer(s).

Exhibit 1 (Rev. 1/2001)   *DMERC Region D Supplier Manual*

Fig. 5-2, cont'd

TABLE 5-6	Role of the Coordination of Benefits Contractor
Process	**Description**
First claim development	When a Medicare intermediary or carrier receives the first claim for a Medicare beneficiary, the claim is processed, and a questionnaire is sent to the provider to collect information on the existence of other insurance that may be primary to Medicare
Secondary claim development	When a claim is submitted with an explanation of benefits attached from an insurer other than Medicare, a questionnaire is sent to the beneficiary to collect information on the existence of other insurance that may be primary to Medicare
Trauma code development	When a diagnosis appears on a claim that indicates a traumatic accident, injury, or illness, which might form the basis of MSP, a questionnaire is sent to the beneficiary to collect information on the existence of other insurance that may be primary to Medicare
Self-report development	A self-report covers the full spectrum of MSP situations. Any source that contacts the coordination of benefits contractor initiates this type of development process to address these inquiries and to ensure that the information provided is accurate
CFR 411.25	This process confirms MSP information received from a third-party payer

premiums and co-payments, and decisions about paying for treatment all are controlled by the managed care plan itself, not by Medicare.

The basic premise of managed care is that the patient/enrollee agrees to receive care only from an approved list of physicians, hospitals, and other providers—called a **network**—in exchange for reduced overall health care costs. Several types of Medicare managed care plans exist. Some have tight restrictions concerning members visiting specialists or seeing providers outside the network. Others give members more freedom to choose when they see providers and which providers they may consult for treatment.

Medicare Health Maintenance Organizations

Similar to the structure of the HMOs we learned about in Chapter 3, **Medicare HMOs** maintain a network of physicians and other health care providers. The HMO member/enrollee must receive care only from the providers in the network except in emergencies. If a member sees a provider outside the network, the HMO usually pays nothing toward the bill. Because an HMO plan member has technically withdrawn from traditional Medicare by opting to join the managed care organization, Medicare also pays nothing. The result in this case: the plan member must pay the entire bill out-of-pocket.

The HMO is the least expensive and most restrictive Medicare managed care plan; it has four main restrictions:

- Care from network providers only
- All care coordinated through primary care physician
- Prior HMO approval of certain services
- Limited rights to appeal the plan's decisions (typically limited to appeals outside the HMO or to Medicare)

Health Maintenance Organization with Point-of-Service Option

One type of HMO has a significant modification that makes it more popular, albeit more costly, than the standard HMO plan. This plan offers what is referred to as an **HMO with point-of-service (POS) option**. A member is allowed to see providers who are not in the HMO network and receive services from specialists without first going through a primary care physician. This method is called **self-referring**. When a member goes outside the network or sees a specialist directly, however, the plan pays a smaller portion of the bill than if the member had followed regular HMO procedures. The member pays a higher premium for this plan than for a standard HMO plan and a higher co-payment each time the option is used.

Preferred Provider Organization

A PPO works much the same as an HMO with POS option. If a member receives a service from a PPO's network of providers, the cost to the member is lower than if the member sees a provider outside the network. In contrast to an HMO with POS option, a member does not have to go through a primary care physician for referrals to specialists. PPO patients usually are allowed to self-refer to specialists. PPOs tend to be more expensive than standard HMOs, charging a monthly premium and a higher co-payment for non-network services. For many individuals, this extra flexibility in selecting the provider of their choice is an important reassurance to them, however, and worth the extra money.

Provider Sponsored Organization

A **provider sponsored organization (PSO)** is a group of medical providers—physicians, clinics, and hospitals—that skips the insurance company middleman and contracts directly with patients. As with an HMO, members pay a premium and a co-payment each time a service is rendered. Some PSOs in urban areas are large conglomerations of physicians and hospitals that offer a wide choice of providers. Some PSOs are small networks of providers that contract through a particular employer or other large organization or that serve a rural area where no HMO is available.

Advantages and Disadvantages of Medicare Health Maintenance Organizations

As with most areas of health care insurance, there are advantages and disadvantages of enrolling in a Medicare HMO.

ADVANTAGES
- HMOs often do not health screen; enrollment may not be denied because of health status.
- HMOs may cover services that traditional Medicare does not cover, such as routine physical examinations, eyeglasses, hearing aids, prescriptions, and dental coverage.
- Enrollees do not need Medigap insurance.
- Paperwork is limited or nonexistent, in contrast to traditional Medicare coverage.
- Enrollees do not have to pay the Medicare deductibles and co-insurance.

DISADVANTAGES
- Choice of health care providers and medical facilities is limited.
- Members/enrollees are covered only for health care services received through the HMO except in emergency and urgent care situations.
- Prior approval usually is needed from a primary care physician for a specialist's services, surgical procedures, medical equipment, and other health care services.
- Enrollees who travel out of the HMO's service area do not receive coverage except in emergency and urgent care situations.

- If an enrollee decides to switch from the HMO to the traditional Medicare plan, coverage does not begin until the first day of the month after the disenrollment request.

Why This Information Is Important to the Health Insurance Professional

As a health insurance professional, you will be doing more than sitting at a desk entering data into a computer or at a typewriter filling in the blocks of CMS-1500 forms. In your job, you no doubt will become a liaison between many third-party payers and the entire health care team. Additionally, you must be able to answer patients' questions about Medicare accurately. The Medicare program and all its various parts and choices can be very confusing to people, especially the elderly. Although it is important that the health insurance professional learn all of the intricacies of the Medicare program from the provider standpoint, he or she also must become an expert from the beneficiaries' perspective. Just the fact alone that the fee-for-service (called *original* or *traditional* Medicare) plan covers 80% of *allowed charges* is enough to create confusion. When you present an elderly patient with an advance beneficiary notice (ABN) or begin discussing Medicare's lifetime release of information form, you must be prepared to answer questions in layman's language.

IMAGINE THIS!

Clara Thornton visited her family practice provider for a yearly wellness examination 8 months after becoming eligible for Medicare. When she received the MSN from Medicare, she noticed that Medicare did not pay for the service. Disturbed, she called her daughter, saying, "Medicare is supposed to pay for a Welcome to Medicare exam. Why didn't they pay this?" Together they read through the beneficiary booklet "Medicare & You" that Medicare had sent to Clara when she enrolled. Only then did she learn that Medicare pays for a one-time physical examination, but it must be within 6 months of becoming eligible for Part B.

WHAT DID YOU LEARN?

1. What categories of people make up the "dual eligible" classification?
2. How does Medicaid assist Medicare beneficiaries?
3. List two types of Medicare supplement policies.
4. What do most Medigap plans cover?
5. Name four payers that typically would be primary to Medicare.

PREPARING FOR THE MEDICARE PATIENT

When a Medicare beneficiary comes to the office for an appointment, the procedure for handling the encounter is basically the same as with non-Medicare patients with a few exceptions.

Medicare's Lifetime Release of Information Form

The medical facility should maintain a current release of information form for every patient. Among other things, this form allows the health insurance professional to complete and submit the insurance form legally. Typically, a release of information is valid for only 1 year; however, with Medicare, a **lifetime (one-time) release of information form** may be signed by the beneficiary, eliminating the necessity of annual updates. Fig. 5-3 is an example of a lifetime release of information.

Determining Medical Necessity

Before Medicare pays for a service or procedure, it must be determined if it is medically necessary. To meet Medicare's definition of medical necessity, the service or procedure must meet the following criteria:

LIFETIME AUTHORIZATION AND REQUEST FOR MEDICAL INFORMATION

I hereby release Charles H. Shaw, M.D., P.A. DBA Gainesville Orthopaedic Group to release my records to the physician individual I direct verbally or in writing.

RELEASE OF MEDICAL INFORMATION
I, the below named patient, hereby authorize Charles H. Shaw, M.D./D. Troy Trimble, D.O., Gainesville Orthopaedic Group to release to my referring physician and/or family physician and any third party payer (such as an insurance company or government agency, e.g., Blue Cross or Medicare) any medical information and records concerning my treatment when requested or by such third party payer or other entity for use in connection with making or determining claim payment for such treatment and/or diagnosis.

ASSIGNMENT OF BENEFITS AND GUARANTEE OF PAYMENT
I, the below named patient/subscriber, hereby absolutely assign payments directly to Charles H. Shaw, M.D./D. Troy Trimble, D.O., Gainesville Orthopaedic Group and any group and/or individual surgical and/or major medical benefits herein specified and otherwise payable to me for their services as described.

Medicare/Medicaid: I certify that the information given me in applying for payment under title XVIIIVXIX of the Social Security Administration or its intermediaries or carriers any information needed for this or a related Medicare claim. I request that payment of authorized benefits be made on my behalf. I assign the benefits payable for physician's services to Charles H. Shaw, M.D./D. Troy Trimble, D.O., Gainesville Orthopaedic Group.

I/We hereby guarantee payment of all charges incurred for the below named patient from the date of the first treatment until discharged from care by Charles H. Shaw, M.D./D. Troy Trimble, D.O., Gainesville Orthopaedic Group. I/We agree that should the amount of insurance benefit to be insufficient to cover the expenses, I/We will be responsible for the entire amount due for services rendered. I/We understand that statements are due when received unless other arrangements have been made with Charles H. Shaw, M.D./D. Troy Trimble, D.O. DBA Gainesville Orthopaedic Group. I/We understand that if there is no response or payment from the insurance company within 60 days of billing, I/we will be responsible for the balance due on account.

_____   _____
Subscriber (insured person) Signature   Date

                                                ☐ Checking this box indicates a digital signature.

_____
Subscriber Printed Name

_____   _____
Patient Signature (if different from the subscriber)   Date

_____
Patient Printed Name

Fig. 5-3   CMS lifetime (one-time) release authorization for Medicare beneficiaries.

- Consistent with the symptoms or diagnosis of the illness or injury being treated
- Necessary and consistent with generally accepted professional medical standards
- Not furnished primarily for the convenience of the patient or physician
- Furnished at the most appropriate level that can be provided safely to the patient

CMS has the power under the Social Security Act to determine if the method of treating a patient in a particular case is reasonable and necessary on a case-by-case basis. Even if a service is reasonable and necessary, coverage may be limited if the service is provided more frequently than allowed under a national coverage policy, a local medical policy, or a clinically accepted standard of practice.

IMAGINE THIS!

Arlene Sorensen had been told by her gynecologist when she was younger that it was important to receive a Pap smear every year. After she became eligible for Medicare, she told her family practice provider that she wanted to continue this practice. The first Pap smear was covered by Medicare; however, a subsequent Pap smear 1 year later was not. When she questioned her physician, he referred her to the health insurance professional, who informed Mrs. Sorensen that Medicare only considers Pap smears "medically necessary" every 2 years, unless the patient is considered high risk.

Claims for services that are not medically necessary are denied, but not getting paid is not the only risk. If Medicare or other payers determine that services were medically unnecessary *after* payment already has been made, it is treated as an *overpayment,* and the beneficiary is asked to refund the money, with interest. If a pattern of such claims is evident, and the provider knows or should have known that the services were not medically necessary, the provider may face large monetary penalties, exclusion from the Medicare program, and possibly criminal prosecution.

One of the most common reasons for denial of Medicare claims is that the provider did not know the services provided were not medically necessary. Lack of knowledge is not a defense, however, because a general notice to the medical community from CMS or a carrier (including a Medicare report or special bulletin) that a certain service is not covered is considered sufficient notice. If a provider was on Medicare's mailing list as of the publication date, CMS considers it sufficient evidence to establish that the provider received the notice. Courts have

concluded that it is reasonable to expect providers to comply with the published policies or regulations they receive, and no other evidence of knowledge may be necessary. This is one reason why it is important for the health insurance professional to attend periodic educational seminars, read all Medicare/Medicaid-related publications, and make every conceivable effort to keep up with these changes. Something else to be aware of is that if a provider fails to read Medicare's publications but delegates that responsibility to others, the physician or the professional corporation still may be held liable for what the physician should have known.

Health insurance professionals can protect the physicians they work for by obtaining up-to-date information on services covered by Medicare from several sources. CMS publishes a periodical called *The CMS Quarterly Provider Update*. These quarterly updates include all changes to Medicare instructions that affect physicians, provide a single source for national Medicare provider information, and give physicians advance notice on upcoming instructions and regulations (see Websites to Explore).

IMAGINE THIS!

Shelly Jennings, a health insurance professional employed by Medical Specialties, Inc., asked all Medicare patients receiving a "screening" colonoscopy to sign an ABN because when she first started working at the facility, Medicare did not cover this procedure unless there were symptoms indicating a problem. After several patients complained, Medicare made an inquiry. Shelly's excuse was that she did not have time to read all the publications Medicare sent or attend periodic educational seminars and did not realize that Medicare now paid for a colonoscopy screening every 10 years, unless the patient is considered high risk.

Local Medical Review Policies and Local Coverage Determinations

Most of Medicare's policies are established at the local level, giving Medicare FIs and carriers a great deal of authority over payment policy in a given state. Through development of local Medicare policy, carriers determine whether a procedure is considered reasonable, medically necessary, and appropriate in an attempt to clarify specific coverage guidelines, particularly in instances when a carrier has identified overuse of a procedure. This policy includes the listing of indications and ICD-9-CM codes that support medical necessity. These policies, formerly called **local medical review** policies (LMRPs), are now referred to as **local coverage determinations (LCDs)**.

There are subtle differences between LMRPs and LCDs. An LCD is defined as "a decision by a fiscal intermediary (FI) or carrier whether to cover a particular service on an intermediary-wide or carrier-wide basis." An LCD consists only of information pertaining to when a procedure is considered medically reasonable and necessary (e.g., indications and ICD-9-CM codes), whereas LMRPs are comprehensive documents, which list the tests and procedures that are considered medically necessary and are covered by Medicare for a specific diagnosis. LMRPs pair the ICD-9 and CPT codes that trigger Medicare reimbursement and comprise coding guidelines, reasons for denial, and detailed descriptions of the procedure. Because LCDs do not include this information, carriers now communicate such information to physicians through a separate publication, which typically can be viewed on the carrier's website. LMRPs contain more than information regarding medical necessity. LMRPs contain

1. frequency limits (e.g., only one mammogram is covered each year);
2. statutory exclusions (Medicare does not cover preventive care except for certain initial screenings, e.g., colonoscopies);
3. national coverage decisions (e.g., Medicare does not pay for removal of benign keratosis, unless there is a medical, noncosmetic reason, such as interference with vision); and
4. various other rules (e.g., Medicare will not pay for a complex procedure for a certain diagnosis, unless other measures are taken first).

In December 2003, CMS began a transition of LMRPs to LCDs. This transition is significant because it changes the process for deciding whether Medicare will pay for a particular service considering the patient's diagnosis. By December 2005, all Medicare FIs and carriers were to have completed the shift from LMRPs to LCDs. Although LMRPs are to be retired, there may be an active LCD version of the policy.

Advance Beneficiary Notice

In addition to ascertaining that a valid release of information form is on file for a Medicare patient, the health insurance professional should ensure that the service requested is eligible for Medicare coverage. Medicare pays only for services that it considers medically necessary.

The health insurance professional must have the essential current publication on hand to consult if a question arises as to whether a particular service

is included on the Medicare-eligible list. After checking the coverage rules, if the health insurance professional believes that it is likely that Medicare *would not* pay for a test or procedure the provider orders, the patient should be asked to sign an **advance beneficiary notice (ABN)**. An ABN also should be provided to a Medicare patient before rendering a service that Medicare might otherwise cover but is likely to be denied on this particular occasion. When the health insurance professional has good reason to expect that the procedure will be denied on the basis of other Medicare denials or local medical review policies, or because the patient's diagnosis or procedure does not meet the Medicare program standards for medical necessity, the patient should be asked to sign an ABN.

The ABN is intended to provide the patient advanced notice that it is likely the procedure will be denied and allows the patient to make an informed decision whether to receive the service for which he or she may be personally responsible. Claims for such services may be submitted with the HCPCS modifier "GA" to indicate that a "waiver of liability" is on file. If the service is denied and a signed ABN is not on file, the physician may not hold the patient responsible for payment. Fig. 5-4 is an example of a typical ABN.

When patients are asked to sign an ABN, they have two options:

- They may choose to receive the test or procedure, agree to be responsible for payment, and sign the ABN.
- They may choose not to receive the test or procedure, refuse to be responsible for payment, and sign the ABN.

When patients are given an ABN, the health insurance professional should be able to answer questions about financial responsibility and payment options so that patients can make informed decisions about their health care. If the patient refuses to sign the ABN and still demands the service, it should be made clear that he or she will be held personally and fully responsible for payment. In such cases, some practices ask for payment for the service in advance.

Supplemental insurance policies may pay for some services not paid for by Medicare, depending on the particular coverage. If the patient thinks that his or her secondary insurance may pay for the service not covered by Medicare, the health insurance professional can bill Medicare for a **denial notice,** an explanation that an LCD does not cover a certain item or service. After it has been established that Medicare will not pay the claim, the secondary insurer can be billed.

(A) **Notifier(s):**
(B) **Patient Name:**   *(C)* **Identification Number:**

ADVANCE BENEFICIARY NOTICE OF NONCOVERAGE (ABN)

NOTE: If Medicare doesn't pay for *(D)*_____ below, you may have to pay.

Medicare does not pay for everything, even some care that you or your health care provider have good reason to think you need. We expect Medicare may not pay for the *(D)*_____ below.

*(D)*_____	*(E)* **Reason Medicare May Not Pay:**	*(F)* **Estimated Cost:**

WHAT YOU NEED TO DO NOW:

- Read this notice, so you can make an informed decision about your care.
- Ask us any questions that you may have after you finish reading.
- Choose an option below about whether to receive the *(D)*_____listed above.
  Note: If you choose Option 1 or 2, we may help you to use any other insurance that you might have, but Medicare cannot require us to do this.

(G) OPTIONS: Check only one box. We cannot choose a box for you.

❑ **OPTION 1.** I want the *(D)*_____ listed above. You may ask to be paid now, but I also want Medicare billed for an official decision on payment, which is sent to me on a Medicare Summary Notice (MSN). I understand that if Medicare doesn't pay, I am responsible for payment, but **I can appeal to Medicare** by following the directions on the MSN**.** If Medicare does pay, you will refund any payments I made to you, less co-pays or deductibles.

❑ **OPTION 2.** I want the *(D)*_____ listed above, but do not bill Medicare. You may ask to be paid now as I am responsible for payment. **I cannot appeal if Medicare is not billed**.

❑ **OPTION 3.** I don't want the *(D)*_____listed above. I understand with this choice I am **not** responsible for payment, and **I cannot appeal to see if Medicare would pay.**

(H) **Additional Information:**

This notice gives our opinion, not an official Medicare decision. If you have other questions on this notice or Medicare billing, call **1-800-MEDICARE** (1-800-633-4227/**TTY:** 1-877-486-2048). Signing below means that you have received and understand this notice. You also receive a copy.

(I) **Signature:**	*(J)* **Date:**

Form CMS-R-131 (03/08)   Form Approved OMB No. 0938-0566

Fig. 5-4 Example of an advance beneficiary notice.

Health Insurance Claim Number and Identification Card

The Medicare beneficiary's **health insurance claim number (HICN)** is in the format of nine numerical characters, usually the beneficiary's Social Security number, followed by one alpha character. It also might be a six-digit or nine-digit number with one or two letter prefixes or suffixes. This type of coding allows the health insurance professional to look at the patient's identification (ID) card and immediately determine what the coverage is. When the status of a beneficiary changes, the prefix or suffix of his or her claim number may change. Fig. 5-5 shows an example of a Medicare ID card. Table 5-7 lists alpha codes for HICNs and what they stand for. Patients belonging to a Medicare Advantage plan do not have the traditional ID card, but instead use the ID card of the plan in which they are enrolled.

≋ MEDICARE BILLING

Billing for services rendered to Medicare beneficiaries is slightly different than that of non-Medicare patients. The health insurance professional must divert from the regular physician's fee schedule and use Medicare's special fee schedule. The fees contained in this schedule for the service performed by the physician are dictated by a complex formula worked out by the federal government and printed periodically in the Medicare Physician Fee Schedule.

Physician Fee Schedule

Health care providers must use the Medicare fee schedule when billing Medicare for beneficiary services. CMS publishes an updated Medicare

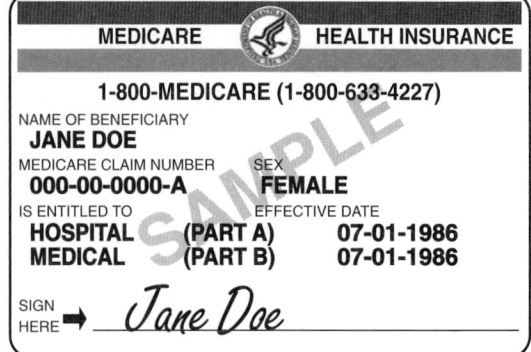

Fig. 5-5 Sample Medicare ID card.

TABLE 5-7	Traditional Medicare Health Insurance Claim Number Alpha Code Types
A	Wage earner (retirement)
B	Wife
B1	Husband
B2	Young wife
C1-C9	Child (includes disabled or student)
D	Aged widow
D1	Widower
D6	Surviving divorced wife benefits
E	Widowed mother
E1	Surviving divorced mother
E4	Widowed father
E5	Surviving divorced father
F1	Father
F2	Mother
F3	Stepfather
F4	Stepmother
F5	Adopting father
F6	Adopting mother
G	Claimant of lump-sum death benefits
HA	Wage earner (disability)
HB	Wife of disabled wage earner
HB1	Husband of disabled wage earner
HC	Child of disabled wage earner
M	Uninsured—premium HIB (Part A)
M1	Uninsured—qualified for but refused HIB (Part A)
T	Uninsured—entitled to HIB (Part A) under deemed or renal provisions
W	Disabled widow
W1	Disabled widower
W6	Disabled surviving divorced wife

HIB, Health insurance benefits.

TABLE 5-8	2007 Medicare Fee Schedule						
PROC	S	PAR	NONPAR	LIMITING CHARGE	GLB	INTR	P/T
97001	A	61.40	58.33	67.08	XXX	0.00	7
97002	A	37.66	35.78	41.15	XXX	0.00	7
97002*	A	30.75	29.21	33.59	XXX	0.00	7
97003	A	75.76	71.97	82.77	XXX	0.00	7
97003*	A	59.97	56.97	65.52	XXX	0.00	7
97004	A	45.22	42.96	49.40	XXX	0.00	7

Data from U.S. Department of Health and Human Services, Centers for Medicare and Medicaid Services.
* These amounts apply when service is performed in a facility setting.

Physician Fee Schedule every year. In the last decade, the Medicare fee schedule was changed from fee-for-service to a **resource-based relative value system**. This means that each of the payment values is found within a range of payments. Table 5-8 is a portion of a sample page from the 2007 Medicare Physician Fee Schedule.

Payment for each service in the fee schedule is based on the following three factors:

1. A nationally uniform relative value for the specific service. This relative value is based on calculations for each service based on components of work, practice overhead, and professional liability, and is referred to as a *relative value unit*.
2. A geographically specific modifier that considers variation in different areas of the United States. Each different area of the United States has its own geographic practice cost indices for each of the relative value factors of work, practice overhead, and professional liability.
3. A nationally uniform conversion factor that is updated annually.

Medicare Participating and Nonparticipating Providers

In its simplest explanation, a **Medicare participating provider (PAR)** or supplier is one who has signed a contract with Medicare; a **Medicare nonparticipating (nonPAR)** provider or supplier has not signed a contract. Medicare PARs agree to accept Medicare's allowed amount as payment in full. Medicare typically pays 80% of the *allowed* fee for medically necessary procedures and services after the annual deductible has been met. Medicare nonPARs and suppliers may choose whether to accept Medicare's approved amount as payment on a case-by-case basis. If they do not accept the approved amount, the beneficiary pays the full

billed amount. The "full billed" amount cannot exceed **Medicare limiting charge**, however, which is 115% of Medicare's allowed amount.

Medicare PARs agree to accept Medicare fee schedule amounts as full payment for Medicare services. Medicare pays 80% of the fee schedule amount for a physician's service, and the beneficiary is responsible for 20% of the fee schedule amount. Medicare PARs benefit from the following advantages:

- Their Medicare fee schedule is 5% higher than that of nonPARs.
- They are provided with toll-free lines if they submit claims electronically.
- Their names are listed in the Medicare Participating Physician/Supplier Directory, which is furnished to senior citizen groups.

NonPARs not accepting assignments are advised that they can charge beneficiaries no more than 115% of the Medicare allowance. All Medicare providers, regardless of whether they accept assignment, must submit Medicare claims for the patient. Medicare providers generally are required to submit claims for beneficiaries whether they are PAR or nonPAR. Problems with claims processing occur when a service has been rendered by a provider who is not enrolled with the Medicare program. The most common service rendered by a nonenrolled provider is a flu shot. In such cases, beneficiaries typically must submit claims to Medicare on their own behalf. Some nonenrolled providers submit claims for beneficiaries, however.

Determining What Fee to Charge

The health insurance professional needs to know how to interpret the Medicare fee schedule so that he or she can determine the correct fee to charge the patient. Using the example fee schedule shown in Table 5-8, and choosing CPT code 97001 (a physical therapy evaluation), the amount Medicare allows a PAR to charge the patient is the amount shown in column 3 under the heading "PAR," or $61.40. A Medicare nonPAR accepting assignment can charge the amount in the next column under the heading "NON-PAR," or $58.33. The limiting charge for providers *not accepting* assignment is the amount in the next column under the heading "LIMITING," or $67.08—15% more than the nonPAR amount.

What Did You Learn?

1. Who uses Medicare's "limiting charge"?
2. List three advantages of becoming a Medicare PAR.
3. How does a health insurance professional determine what fee to charge for a Medicare-eligible service?

COMPLETING THE CMS-1500 FORM FOR MEDICARE CLAIMS

To ensure accurate and quick claim processing, the following guidelines should be followed for paper claims:

- Do not staple, clip, or tape anything to the CMS-1500 claim form.
- Place all necessary documentation in the envelope with the CMS-1500 claim form.
- Include the patient's name and Medicare number on each piece of documentation submitted.
- Use dark ink.
- Use only uppercase (CAPITAL) letters.
- Use 10 or 12 pitch (pica) characters and standard dot-matrix fonts.
- Do not mix character fonts on the same form.
- Do not use italics or script.
- Avoid using old or worn print bands or ribbons.
- Do not use dollar signs, decimals, or punctuation.
- Enter all information on the same horizontal plane within the designated field.
- Do not print, hand-write, or stamp any extraneous data on the form.
- Ensure data are in the appropriate fields, and do not overlap into other fields.
- Remove pin-fed edges at side perforations.
- Use only an original red-ink-on-white-paper CMS-1500 claim form.

Submission of paper claims that do not meet the carrier's requirements may delay payments.

The process of completing the CMS-1500 form for Medicare claims is similar to that of a commercial claim with a few exceptions. Table 5-9 provides complete Medicare claims filing instructions, which are effectively the same as those provided on the NUCC website.

HIPAA Tip

The determining factor for the correct place of service (POS) for Medicare beneficiaries is determined by the status of the patient. When a patient is registered as an inpatient (POS 21) or outpatient (POS 22), one of these POS codes must be used to bill Medicare.

Completing a Medigap Claim

Completion of Blocks 9 through 9d is conditional for insurance information related to Medigap. Only PARs are required to complete Block 9 and its subdivisions, and only when the patient wishes to assign his or her benefits under a Medigap policy to the PAR. PARs of service and suppliers must enter information required in Block 9 and its subdivisions if requested by the beneficiary. (PARs sign an agreement with Medicare to accept assignment of Medicare benefits for *all* Medicare patients. NonPARs can accept assignment on a case-by-case basis.)

A claim for which a beneficiary elects to assign his or her benefits under a Medigap policy to a PAR is called a **mandated Medigap transfer**. If a PAR and the patient want Medicare payment data forwarded to a Medigap insurer under a mandated Medigap transfer, all of the information in Blocks 9, 9a, 9b, and 9d must be complete and accurate. Otherwise, Medicare cannot forward the claim information to the Medigap insurer.

If the health insurance professional wishes to use the statement "Signature on File" in Block 13 in lieu of the patient's actual signature, a statement must be signed and dated by the patient and maintained in the practice's records (Fig. 5-6). Table 5-10 contains instructions for completion of blocks that are affected by Medigap policies.

Medicare Secondary Policy

When Medicare is the secondary payer, the claim must be submitted first to the primary insurer. The primary insurer processes the claim in accordance with the coverage provisions in the contract. If the primary insurer does not pay in full for the services after processing the claim, the claim may be submitted to Medicare electronically or via a paper claim for consideration of secondary benefits. It is the

Text continued on p. 171

TABLE 5-9 CMS-1500 Claim Form Instructions for Medicare

Throughout these instructions, the following formats are used to report dates:

MM|DD|YY or MM|DD|CCYY—indicates that a space must be reported between month, day, and year. This space is delineated by a dotted vertical line on the CMS-1500 claim form.

MMDDYY or MMDDCCYY—indicates that no space must be reported between month, day, and year. The date must be reported as one continuous number. Guidelines for completing Medicare claims may vary somewhat from one Medicare carrier to another. Obtain and follow the specific guidelines provided by your local Medicare carrier.

Block 1	Show the type of health insurance coverage applicable to this claim by checking the appropriate box (e.g., if a Medicare claim is being filed, check the Medicare box)
Block 1a	Enter the patient's Medicare health insurance claim number whether Medicare is the primary or secondary payer (do not include spaces or hyphens)
Block 2	Enter the patient's last name, first name, and middle initial, if any, exactly as shown on the patient's Medicare card. Remember to use OCR formatting rules
Block 3	Enter the patient's eight-digit birth date (MM|DD|CCYY) and sex
Block 4	When the insured and the patient are the same, enter the word "SAME." If the patient has insurance primary to Medicare, through the patient's or spouse's employment or any other source, list the name of the insured here. If Medicare is primary, leave blank
Block 5	On the first line, enter the patient's street address; the second line, the city and two-letter state code; the third line, the Zip Code and phone number. Do not use a hyphen in the phone number
Block 6	Check the appropriate box for the patient's relationship to the insured when Block 4 is completed. If Medicare is the primary insurance, leave this block blank
Block 7	Complete this block only when Blocks 4 and 11 are completed. Enter the insured's address and telephone number. When the address is the same as the patient's, enter the word "SAME"
Block 8	Check the appropriate box for the patient's marital status, and whether employed or a student
Block 9	Enter the last name, first name, and middle initial of the enrollee in a Medigap policy, if it is different from that shown in Block 2. Otherwise, enter the word "SAME." If no Medigap benefits are assigned, leave blank. This field may be used in the future for supplemental insurance plans*
Block 9a	Enter the policy or group number of the Medigap insured preceded by MEDIGAP, MG, or MGAP. Block 9d must be completed if you enter a policy or group number in Block 9a
Block 9b	Enter the Medigap insured's eight-digit birth date (MMDDCCYY) and sex
Block 9c	Leave blank if a Medigap PAYERID is entered in Block 9d. Otherwise, enter the claims processing address of the Medigap insurer. Use an abbreviated street address, two-letter postal code, and Zip Code copied from the Medigap insured's Medigap ID card. For example: 1257 Anywhere Street, Baltimore, MD 21204 is shown as "1257 Anywhere St MD 21204"
Block 9d	Enter the nine-digit (alpha-numerical and up to 9 digits) PAYERID number of the Medigap insurer. If no PAYERID number exists, enter the Medigap insurance program or plan name. If you are a PAR facility and the beneficiary wants Medicare payment data forwarded to a Medigap insurer under a mandated Medigap transfer, all of the information in Blocks 9-9d must be complete and accurate. Otherwise, the Medicare carrier cannot forward the claim information to the Medigap insurer

Modified from http://www.cms.hhs.gov/transmittals/downloads/R735CP.pdf.

* Only PARs are to complete Block 9 and its subdivisions, and only when the beneficiary wishes to assign his or her benefits under a Medigap policy to the participating physician or supplier. PARs must enter information required in Block 9 and its subdivisions if requested by the patient. PARs sign an agreement with Medicare to accept assignment of benefits for all Medicare patients. A claim for which a beneficiary elects to assign his or her benefits under a Medigap policy to a participating physician or supplier is called a mandated Medigap transfer. Do not list other supplemental coverage in Block 9 and its subdivisions at the time a Medicare claim is filed. Other supplemental claims are forwarded automatically to the private insurer if the private insurer contracts with the carrier to send Medicare claim information electronically. If there is no such contract, the beneficiary must file his or her own supplemental claim.

Continued

TABLE 5-9 CMS-1500 Claim Form Instructions for Medicare—cont'd

Blocks 10a-10c	Check "YES" or "NO" to indicate whether employment, auto liability, or other accident involvement applies to one or more of the services described in Block 24. For auto accidents, enter the two-letter state code in which the accident occurred. Any block checked "YES" indicates that there may be other insurance primary to Medicare. If any items in this block are checked "YES," identify primary insurance information in Block 11
Block 10d	Use this block exclusively for Medicaid (MCD) information. If the patient is entitled to Medicaid, enter the patient's Medicaid number preceded by MCD. Consult your Medicare carrier for specific guidelines
Block 11	This block must be completed on Medicare claims. By doing so, the provider acknowledges having made a good faith effort to determine whether Medicare is the primary or secondary payer. If there is insurance primary to Medicare for the service date on the claim, enter the insured's policy or group number and proceed to Blocks 11a-11c. Note: Enter the appropriate information in Block 11c if insurance primary to Medicare is indicated in Block 11. If there is no insurance primary to Medicare, enter the word "NONE," and proceed to Block 12.[†] If the insured reports a terminating event with regard to insurance that had been primary to Medicare (e.g., insured retired), enter the word "NONE," and proceed to Block 12. Circumstances under which Medicare payment may be secondary to other insurance include Group Health Plan Coverage, Working Aged, Disability (Large Group Health Plan), End Stage Renal Disease, No Fault and/or Other Liability, Work-Related Illness/Injury, Workers' Compensation, Black Lung, and Veterans Benefits. If Medicare is secondary, enter the insured's policy or group number within the box, or if there is no insurance primary to Medicare, enter the word "NONE"
Block 11a	Enter the insured's eight-digit birth date (MM|DD|CCYY) and sex if different from that in Block 3. If entered as a six-digit date, use hyphens or other punctuation, called "delimiters." If entered as an eight-digit date, do not use delimiters. This item is mandatory if a policy or group number is submitted in Block 11 and is different from the date in Block 3
Block 11b	Enter employer's name, if applicable. If there is a change in the insured's insurance status (e.g., retired), enter either a six-digit (MM|DD|YY) or eight-digit (MM|DD|CCYY) retirement date preceded by the word "RETIRED." Add employer's address and phone number to attached copy of explanation of benefits (EOB). This item is mandatory if a policy or group number is submitted in Block 11
Block 11c	Enter the nine-digit PAYERID number of the primary insurer. If no PAYERID number exists, enter the complete primary payer's program or plan name. If the primary payer's EOB does not contain the claims processing address, record the primary payer's claims processing address directly on the EOB. Include the telephone number of the primary payer. This item is mandatory if a policy or group number appears in Block 11
Block 11d	Leave blank. Not required by Medicare
Block 12	The patient or authorized representative must sign and enter a six-digit date (MM|DD|YY), eight-digit date (MM|DD|CCYY), or an alphanumerical date (e.g., January 1, 1998) unless a signature is on file.[‡] If entered as a six-digit date, use delimiters. If entered as an eight-digit date, do not use delimiters. "Signature on file" indicators (SOF) should be on the signature line, immediately following the word "signed." If the signature is not in the correct area, the information may be missed, and the claim could be denied

[†] For a paper claim to be considered for Medicare Secondary Payer benefits, a copy of the primary payer's EOB notice must be attached to the claim form. If a policy or group number is entered, an EOB MUST be attached.

[‡] In lieu of signing the claim, the patient may sign a release of information statement to be retained in the provider's file. If the patient is physically or mentally unable to sign, a representative may sign on the patient's behalf. In this case, the statement's signature line must indicate the patient's name followed by "by;" the representative's name, address, and relationship to the patient; and the reason the patient cannot sign. The authorization is effective indefinitely, unless the patient or the patient's representative revokes this arrangement. The patient's signature authorizes release of medical information necessary to process the claim. It also authorizes payment of benefits to the provider of service or supplier, when the provider of service or supplier accepts assignment on the claim. When an illiterate or physically handicapped enrollee signs by mark, a witness must enter his or her name and address next to the mark.

TABLE 5-9	CMS-1500 Claim Form Instructions for Medicare—cont'd
Block 13	A signature in this block authorizes payment of mandated Medigap benefits to the PAR if required Medigap information is included in Block 9 and its subdivisions. The patient or his or her authorized representative signs this item, or the signature must be on file as a separate Medigap authorization. The Medigap assignment on file in the PAR of service/supplier's office must be insurer specific. It may state that the authorization applies to all occasions of service until it is revoked. "Signature on file" indicators (SOF) should be on the signature line, immediately following the word "signed." If the signature is not in the correct area, the information may be missed, and the claim would not be crossed over to the Medigap insurance company. Block 13 is mandatory when the provider is PAR, and Medigap information is submitted in Blocks 9-9d
Block 14	Enter either a six-digit (MM|DD|YY) or eight-digit (MM|DD|CCYY) date of current illness, injury, or pregnancy, if applicable
Block 15	Leave blank. Not required by Medicare
Block 16	If the patient is employed and is unable to work in current occupation, enter six-digit (MM|DD|YY) or eight-digit (MM|DD|CCYY) date when patient became unable to work. An entry in this field may indicate employment-related insurance coverage. Refer back to Blocks 10a and 11c. Block 16 is mandatory if Blocks 10a and 11c are completed
Block 17	Enter the name of the referring or ordering physician if the service or item was ordered or referred by a physician. Referring physician is a physician who requests an item or service for the beneficiary for which payment may be made under the Medicare program. Ordering physician is a physician or, when appropriate, a nonphysician practitioner, who orders nonphysician services for the patient. Examples of services that might be ordered include diagnostic laboratory tests, clinical laboratory tests, pharmaceutical services, durable medical equipment, and services incident to that physician's or nonphysician practitioner's service
Blocks 17a-b	Block 17b is required when a service listed on the form was ordered or referred and by a physician. When a claim involves multiple referring or ordering physicians, or both, a separate CMS-1500 form must be used for each referring or ordering physician. Effective May 23, 2007, the UPIN in 17a is *not* to be reported. Instead, the NPI must be reported in 17b when a service was ordered or referred by a physician
Block 18	Enter a six-digit (MM|DD|YY) or eight-digit (MM|DD|CCYY) date when a medical service is furnished as a result of, or subsequent to, a related hospitalization
Block 19	Enter either a six-digit or eight-digit date when the patient was last seen, and the NPI of his or her attending physician when an independent physical or occupational therapist submits claims or a physician providing routine foot care submits claims
Block 20	Complete this block when billing for diagnostic tests subject to purchase price limitations. Enter the purchase price under charges if the "YES" block is checked. A "YES" check indicates that an entity other than the one billing for the service performed the diagnostic test. A "NO" check indicates that "no purchased tests are included on the claim." When "YES" is checked, Block 32 must be completed
Block 21	Enter the patient's diagnosis or condition. All providers must use an ICD-9-CM code number and code to the highest level of specificity. Enter four codes in priority order (primary, secondary condition)
Block 22	Leave blank. Not required by Medicare
Block 23	Enter the Quality Improvement Organization (QIO) prior authorization number for procedures requiring QIO prior approval or the Investigational Device Exemption (IDE) number when an investigational device is used in a Food and Drug Administration (FDA)–approved clinical trial. Enter the ten-digit Clinical Laboratory Improvement Act (CLIA) certification number for laboratory services billed by an entity performing CLIA-covered procedures. When a physician provides services to a beneficiary residing in a skilled nursing facility and the services were rendered to a skilled nursing facility beneficiary outside of the skilled nursing facility, the physician enters the Medicare facility provider number of the skilled nursing facility in Block 23 *Note*: Item 23 can contain only one condition. Any additional conditions should be reported on a separate CMS-1500 form

Continued

TABLE 5-9 | **CMS-1500 Claim Form Instructions for Medicare—cont'd**

Block 24a	Enter a six-digit or eight-digit (MMDDCCYY) date for each procedure, service, or supply. When "from" and "to" dates are shown for a series of identical services, enter the number of days or units in column G. This is a required field. Claim will be returned as unprocessable if a date of service extends more than 1 day and a valid "to" date is not present
Block 24b	Enter the appropriate place of service code for each item used or service performed. This is a required field
	Note: When a service is rendered to a hospital inpatient, use the "inpatient hospital" code
Block 24c	Medicare providers are not required to complete this item
Block 24d	Enter the procedures, services, or supplies using the appropriate five-digit CPT or CMS Healthcare Common Procedure Coding System (HCPCS) code. When applicable, show HCPCS code modifiers. When reporting an "unlisted procedure code" or a "not otherwise classified" code, include a narrative description in Block 19 if a coherent description can be given within the confines of that box. Otherwise, an attachment should be submitted with the claim. This is a required field
Block 24e	Enter the diagnosis code reference number as shown in item 21 to relate the date of service and the procedures performed to the primary diagnosis. Enter only one reference number per line item. When multiple services are performed, enter the primary reference number for each service—1, 2, 3, or 4. This is a required field. If a situation arises where two or more diagnoses are required for a procedure code (e.g., Pap smears), the provider shall reference only one of the diagnoses in item 21
Block 24f	Enter the charge for each listed service. Do not use decimals, dashes, or lines
Block 24g	Enter the number of days or units. This field is most commonly used for multiple visits, units of supplies, anesthesia minutes, or oxygen volume. If only one service is performed, enter the number 1
Block 24h	Leave blank. Not required by Medicare
Block 24i	Enter the ID qualifier 1C in the shaded portion for Medicare claims if required by the Medicare carrier
Block 24j	After May 23, 2007, enter the rendering provider's NPI number in the lower portion. In the case of a service provided incident to the service of a physician or nonphysician practitioner, when the person who ordered the service is not supervising, enter the PIN of the supervisor in the shaded portion. Check with your Medicare carrier for specific guidelines in this block
Block 25	Enter the provider of service or supplier Federal Tax ID (Employer Identification Number) or Social Security number. The participating provider of service or supplier Federal Tax ID number is required for a mandated Medigap transfer
Block 26	Enter the patient's account number assigned by the provider's accounting system. This field is optional to assist the provider in patient identification
Block 27	Check the appropriate block to indicate whether the provider accepts assignment of Medicare benefits. If Medigap is indicated in item 9, and Medigap payment authorization is given in item 13, the provider of service or supplier also shall be a Medicare PAR service or supplier and accept assignment of Medicare benefits for all covered charges for all patients
Block 28	Enter total of all charges in Block 24f. Do not use decimals, dashes, or lines
Block 29	Enter the total amount the patient paid on the covered services only. Leave blank if no payment has been made
Block 30	Leave blank. Not required by Medicare
Block 31	Enter the provider's signature or his or her representative, and the six-digit or eight-digit or alphanumerical date (e.g., January 1, 2007) the form was signed. Computer-generated signatures are acceptable
Block 32	Medicare requires name, address, and Zip Code of the facility where services were performed other than those furnished in POS 12 (Home). Medicare does not allow "SAME" to be entered in this block. Purchased tests must have supplier name, address, Zip Code, and PIN. For a certified mammography screening center, enter six-digit FDA-approved number
Block 32a	Enter the NPI of the service facility
Block 32b	After May 23, 2007, this block is not to be reported
	Note: Some Medicare carriers require providers of service (i.e., physicians) to enter the supplier's PIN when billing for purchased diagnostic tests. Check with the Medicare carrier in your area for specific instructions
Block 33	Enter the provider's billing name, address, Zip Code, and telephone number
Block 33a	Effective May 23, 2007, the NPI of the billing provider or group must be reported here
Block 33b	Effective May 23, 2007, this block is not to be reported

(Name of Beneficiary) (Health Insurance Claim Number) (Medigap Policy Number)

I request that payment of authorized Medigap benefits be made either to me or on my behalf to the provider of service and (or) supplier for any services furnished to me by the provider of service and (or) supplier. I authorize any holder of Medicare information about me to release to (Name of Medigap Insurer) any information needed to determine these benefits payable for related services.

(Signature) (Date)

Fig. 5-6 Example of "signature on file" statement.

TABLE 5-10	**Modifications to the CMS-1500 Form for a Medigap Claim**
Block 9	Enter the last name, first name, and middle initial of the Medigap enrollee if it is different from that shown in Block 2. Otherwise, enter the word "SAME"
Block 9a	Enter the policy or group number of the Medigap insured preceded by MEDIGAP, MG, or MGAP *Note*: Block 9d must be completed if a policy or group number is in Block 9a
Block 9b	Enter the Medigap enrollee's birth date (MMDDCCYY) and sex
Block 9c	Disregard "employer's name or school name," which is printed on the form. Enter the claims processing address for the Medigap insurer. Use an abbreviated street address, two-letter state postal code, and ZIP code copied from the Medigap insured's Medigap ID card. For example: 1257 Anywhere Street, Baltimore, MD 21204 is shown as "1257 Anywhere St MD 21204." *Note*: If a carrier-assigned unique identifier of a Medigap insurer appears in Block 9d, Block 9c may be left blank
Block 9d	Enter the name of the Medigap insured's insurance company or the Medigap insurer's unique identifier provided by the local Medicare carrier. If you are a participating provider of service or supplier, and the beneficiary wants Medicare payment data forwarded to a Medigap insurer under a mandated Medigap transfer, all of the information in Block 9 and its subdivisions must be complete and correct. Otherwise, the claim information cannot be forwarded to the Medigap insurer
Block 12	All Medicare/Medigap claims must have Block 12 completed. Failure to include an appropriate signature and six-digit date or a "signature on file" statement results in claim rejection. A Medigap authorization signature in Block 13 does not satisfy the Block 12 signature requirement
Block 13	Completion of this block is conditional for Medigap. The signature in Block 13 authorizes payment of mandated Medigap benefits to the PAR of service or supplier if required Medigap information is included in Block 9 and its subdivisions. The patient or his or her authorized representative signs this block, or the signature must be on file as a separate Medigap authorization. The Medigap assignment on file in the participating physician or supplier's office must list the name of the specific Medigap insurer. It may state that the authorization applies to all occasions of service until it is revoked

provider's responsibility to obtain primary insurance information from the beneficiary and bill Medicare appropriately. Claim filing extensions are not granted because of incorrect insurance information.

Insurance Primary to Medicare

Circumstances under which Medicare payment may be secondary to other insurance, include the following:

- Group health plan coverage—working aged, disability (large group health plan), and ESRD
- No fault or other liability

Work-related illness/injury—workers' compensation, black lung, and veterans benefits.

For a paper claim to be considered for MSP benefits, a copy of the primary payer's explanation of benefits (EOB) notice must be forwarded along with the claim form.

STOP AND THINK

Franklin Elmore is a new patient in your office. When he filled out the patient information form, he indicated that he was born February 26, 1939, and is employed full-time at Alamo Distributing Company. Under the insurance section, Mr. Elmore lists Medicare as his primary insurer and group coverage with Amax Quality Assurance through his employer as his secondary insurance. Is Mr. Elmore's information form correct? Which insurer should receive the CMS-1500 claim first?

Completing Medicare Secondary Policy Claims

When Medicare is the secondary payer, the health insurance professional must include a copy of the primary insurer's EOB with the claim. The EOB should include the following information:

- Name and address of the primary insurer
- Name of subscriber and policy number
- Name of the provider of services
- Itemized charges for all procedure codes reported
- Detailed explanation of any denials or payment codes
- Date of service

A detailed explanation of any primary insurer's denial or payment codes must be submitted with the claim to Medicare. If the denial/payment code descriptions or any of the above-listed data are not included with the claim, it may result in a delay in processing or denial of the claim. If the beneficiary is covered by more than one insurer primary to Medicare (e.g., a working aged beneficiary who was in an automobile accident), the EOB statement from all plans must be submitted with the claim.

To submit MSP claims electronically, the health insurance professional should refer to the American National Standards Institute ASC X12N Implementation Guide or the National Standard Format Specifications for reporting requirements. When submitting a paper claim to Medicare as the secondary payer, the following instructions apply:

- The CMS-1500 form must indicate the name and policy number of the beneficiary's primary insurance in Blocks 11 through 11c.
- Providers, whether they are PAR or nonPAR, must submit a claim to Medicare if a beneficiary provides a copy of the primary EOB.
- The claim must be submitted to Medicare for secondary payment consideration with a copy of the EOB. If the beneficiary is not cooperative

in supplying the EOB, the beneficiary may be billed for the amount Medicare would pay as the secondary payer.

- Providers must bill the primary insurer and Medicare the same charge for rendered services. If the primary insurer is billed $50.00 for an office visit, and the insurer pays $35.00, Medicare should not be billed the remaining $15.00. Medicare also must be billed for the $50.00 charge, and a copy of the primary insurer's EOB must be attached to the completed claim form.

It was stated previously that when submitting paper or electronic claims for Medicare, Block 11 must be completed. By completing this block, the physician/supplier acknowledges having made a good faith effort to determine whether Medicare is the primary or secondary payer. A claim without this information would be returned.

When there is insurance primary to Medicare, as in the MSP situation, the health insurance professional should enter the insured's policy or group number in Block 11 and proceed to Blocks 11a through 11c. (When there is no insurance primary to Medicare, enter the word "NONE" in Block 11, and proceed to Block 12.) Completion of Blocks 11b and 11c is conditional for insurance information primary to Medicare. Table 5-11 gives instructions for how Blocks 11a through 11d should be completed for MSP claims.

Medicare Secondary Policy Conditional Payment

Medicare may make a conditional payment if they have knowledge that another insurer is primary to Medicare, but the primary payer does not make prompt payment (within 120 days) or has denied the claim for a reason Medicare considers acceptable. (This conditional payment is applicable, however, only for black lung, workers' compensation, and accidents.) From a reimbursement standpoint, a claim paid conditionally pays the same as if there were no insurance other than Medicare.

Medicare Part B Crossover Program

The **Medicare Part B Crossover program** is a fee-per-claim service that Medicare Part B offers to private insurers and retirement plans. Medicare Part B and a supplemental insurer enter into a formal contract called a **trading partner agreement** for the electronic data interchange of claim information. Trading partners are Medigap insurers, supplemental retirement plans, or other health care payers.

The crossover process, in contrast to Medigap, does not require input from the provider. After a

TABLE 5-11	Modifications to the CMS-1500 for Medicare Secondary Payer Claims
Block 11a	Enter the insured's birth date (MMDDCCYY) and sex, if different from Block 3
Block 11b	Enter the employer's name, if applicable. If there is a change in the insured's insurance status, such as retired, enter the six-digit retirement date (MMDDYY) preceded by the word "RETIRED"
Block 11c	Enter the complete insurance plan or program name (e.g., Blue Shield of [State]). If the primary payer's explanation of benefits does not contain the claims processing address, record the primary payer's claims processing address directly on the explanation of benefits
Block 11d	Can be left blank. Not required by Medicare

trading agreement is signed, the insurer sends an eligibility file to Medicare, and Medicare sends corresponding claim information back to the health care payer. The eligibility file contains the beneficiary's name, Medicare HICN, and policy effective dates. Medicare matches the trading partner's HICN against its own Medicare files. Any resulting claims are automatically sent to the payer for additional payment considerations. This process results in numerous claims sent to each supplemental payer.

Some private insurers may choose to be Medigap and Crossover participants. When private insurance companies send a list of their insureds to Medicare, any resulting claims are handled as Crossover claims. If a Medicare beneficiary's file does not show a private insurer, but a claim from a PAR shows Medigap information, Medicare forwards the information to the supplemental payer.

The Health Insurance Portability and Accountability Act of 1996 (HIPAA) has made Medicare Crossover systems easier to develop and maintain. Examples of benefits through HIPAA are as follows:

- The uniform provider number eliminates the need for **crosswalks** (the process of matching one set of data elements or category of codes to their equivalents within a new set of elements or codes) between the Medicare and Medicaid provider numbering systems.
- With a uniform insurer/payer number, crossover systems are able to forward claims to Medicare carriers if the claim is billed to the state Medicaid agency because the claims can be forwarded easily between payers. In addition, if the beneficiary has a Medicare supplemental policy, the state Medicaid agency can forward the Medicare adjudicated invoice directly to the supplemental insurer, simply by using the uniform payer ID number.
- The transaction sets allow the state Medicaid agency to have all required data on claims crossed over from the carrier or intermediary. Eligibility verification between the Medicaid

agency and the carrier or intermediary can be accomplished online through the use of the eligibility inquiry and response transactions. These transactions also can be used to verify Medicare supplemental insurance.
- Because all payers use the same remittance transactions and coding, providers may be able to use a single program to post the payments to their accounts receivable systems. Direct deposit of provider payments also is beneficial because the cost of printing and mailing checks is eliminated.

Medicare/Medicaid Crossover Claims

Modifications must be made on the CMS-1500 form for dual-eligible beneficiaries. The claim is sent to Medicare first, which determines its liability portion of the charges. Then the claim is automatically crossed over to Medicaid directly from the Medicare carrier. The following blocks are affected:

Block 1: The Medicare and Medicaid boxes should be checked.
Block 10d: Enter the abbreviation MCD followed by the beneficiary's Medicaid ID number.
Block 27: PARs and nonPARS should place an "X" in the "YES" box because assignment must be accepted on Medicare/Medicaid crossover claims.

Filing Medicare Claims Electronically
The Administrative Simplification Compliance Act (ASCA) requires that all **initial claims** for reimbursement under Medicare be submitted electronically as of October 16, 2003. Initial claims are as follows:

- Claims submitted to a Medicare fee-for-service carrier or FI for the first time, including resubmitted previously rejected claims
- Claims with paper attachments
- **Demand bills**. Under Medicare rules, a beneficiary, on receiving notification of

noncoverage, has the right to request that a FI review that determination. Such a request is known as a demand bill (Fig. 5-7). Before using a demand bill, the beneficiary must sign an ABN and agree to pay for the services in full if Medicare coverage is denied. It is up to the medical facility to ensure that this request is filed

• Claims for which Medicare is the secondary payer and there is only one primary payer
• Nonpayment claims

Initial claims do not include
• adjustments,
• previously submitted claims, or
• appeal requests.

This requirement does not apply to claims submitted by
• beneficiaries,
• providers that furnish services only outside the United States, or
• managed care plans or health plans other than Medicare.

HIPAA TIP

With the implementation of HIPAA, it is possible to submit an electronic claim and submit a separate paper attachment for that claim. When an electronic claim is filed, an attachment control number is assigned. The paper attachment is sent with a cover page containing the attachment control number.

HIPAA TIP

As of October 16, 2003, electronically submitted claims must comply with the appropriate claim standards adopted for national use under HIPAA or with standards supported under the Medicare HIPAA contingency plan during the period the plan is in effect.

Exceptions

The guidelines that were issued by CMS that went into effect January 20, 2004, state that, "In some cases, it has been determined that due to limitations in the claims transaction formats adopted for national use under HIPAA, it would not be reasonable or possible to submit certain claims to Medicare electronically. Providers are to self-assess to determine if they meet these exceptions." There are limited exceptions to the government mandate that all Medicare claims be filed electronically. Earlier, we talked about the small provider exception. To

meet this "small provider" exception, the provider must be defined as either

• a provider of services (as that term is defined in section 1861(u) of the Social Security Act) with fewer than 25 full-time equivalent (FTE) employees or
• a physician, practitioner, facility, or supplier that is not otherwise a provider under section 1861(u) with fewer than 10 FTE employees.

To simplify implementation, Medicare considers all providers falling into either of the aforementioned two categories, and that are required to bill a Medicare intermediary, to be small and qualify for the exception to the rule. These regulations do not modify preexisting laws or employer policies defining full-time employment.

Although small providers who meet the exception ruling are exempt from the mandatory electronic claim requirement, they are encouraged to file Medicare claims electronically, if possible. The small provider exception does not apply to health care claim clearinghouses that are agents for small providers. The CMS website furnishes a list of other claim types that are considered to meet the exemption criteria (see Websites to Explore).

STOP AND THINK

You are employed by a two-physician practice. In addition to you, the health insurance professional, there is a medical receptionist, two medical assistants, and a registered nurse. You have just completed transferring all patient accounts to a computerized patient accounting system. Are you now required to submit all Medicare claims electronically?

HIPAA TIP

HIPAA defines a clearinghouse as an entity that translates data to or from a standard format for electronic transmission. HIPAA requires that clearinghouses submit claims electronically effective October 16, 2003, without exception.

Deadline for Filing Medicare Claims

Medicare's fiscal year begins October 1 and ends September 30. Claims typically must be filed no later than the end of the calendar year (December 31) following the fiscal year in which services were provided. Assigned claims can take longer (27 months, depending on the date the service was

DEPARTMENT OF HEALTH AND HUMAN SERVICES
CENTERS FOR MEDICARE & MEDICAID SERVICES

MEDICARE RECONSIDERATION REQUEST FORM

1. Beneficiary's Name:_____

2. Medicare Number:_____

3. Description of Item or Service in Question: _____

4. Date the Service or Item was Received: _____

5. I do not agree with the determination of my claim. MY REASONS ARE:

_____

_____

_____

6. Date of the redetermination notice: _____

(If you received your redetermination more than 180 days ago, include your reason for not making this request earlier.)

_____

_____

_____

7. Additional Information Medicare Should Consider: _____

_____

_____

_____

8. Requester's Name:_____

9. Requester's Relationship to the Beneficiary: _____

10. Requester's Address: _____

_____

11. Requester's Telephone Number: _____

12. Requester's Signature: _____

13. Date Signed: _____

14. ❏ I have evidence to submit. (Attach such evidence to this form.)
❏ I do not have evidence to submit.

15. Name of the Medicare Contractor that Made the Redetermination:_____

NOTICE: Anyone who misrepresents or falsifies essential information requested by this form may upon conviction be subject to fine or imprisonment under Federal Law.

Form CMS-20033 (05/05) EF (05/2005)

Fig. 5-7   Sample demand bill.

performed) if the provider has good reason for delaying claims submission. If not, a 10% reimbursement penalty is assessed to the claim. The health insurance professional always should file claims in a timely manner, if for no other reason than out of courtesy to the patient and for the financial benefit of the provider.

WHAT DID YOU LEARN?

1. What blocks on the CMS-1500 form are typically affected by Medigap claims?
2. What is the significance of a signature in Block 13 on a Medigap claim?
3. Name three circumstances under which Medicare may be the secondary insurer.
4. What must accompany a Medicare secondary payer paper claim?
5. What blocks on the CMS-1500 form are typically affected by MSP claims?

The following chart* provides the filing deadline for the date of service ranges indicated:

DATE OF SERVICE			FILE CLAIM BY
October 1, 2005	through	September 30, 2006	December 31, 2007
October 1, 2006	through	September 30, 2007	December 31, 2008
October 1, 2007	through	September 30, 2008	December 31, 2009
October 1, 2008	through	September 30, 2009	December 31, 2010

*Information adapted from http://www.cms.hhs.gov. *Note*: Assigned claims submitted more than 12 months from the date of service are subject to a 10% late filing deduction. This fee cannot be charged to the beneficiary.

MEDICARE SUMMARY NOTICE

When a Medicare claim is filed, the beneficiary receives a document called the **Medicare Summary Notice (MSN)**. The MSN (Fig. 5-8) replaced the Explanation of Medicare Benefits form in 2001. The MSN form is an easy-to-read monthly statement that lists Part A and Part B claims information, including the patient's deductible status. The health insurance professional should make it clear to the patient that the MSN is not a bill, and he or she should not send any money to the provider or supplier until a statement is received.

Medicare began testing a new service in 2004— the **electronic Medicare Summary Notice**. The electronic MSN allows beneficiaries to look at their MSN on the World Wide Web and print copies from their home computers. The electronic MSN does not replace the paper MSN, which is still mailed each month when a claim is processed, but it is a quick and convenient way for beneficiaries to track their claims.

Information Contained on the Medicare Summary Notice

The MSN gives a breakdown of Medicare claims billed on the patient's behalf and processed by the FI or carrier. In addition to listing the services received along with the name of the provider, the MSN lists

- the total amount billed by providers,
- Medicare's approved payment amount for services,
- amount paid to the beneficiary or his or her provider,
- costs the beneficiary is responsible for, and
- deductible information.

If there is a supplemental insurance policy or Medigap, these insurers also may need a copy of the MSN to process their share of the bill.

The health insurance professional should know how to read the MSN so that he or she can answer any questions beneficiaries might have. Detailed instructions on how to read the MSN can be found on the CMS website.

Medicare Remittance Advice

When a claim has gone through the processing stage, Medicare notifies the provider as to how the claim was **adjudicated** (how the decision was made regarding the payment). This notification is referred to as a *remittance advice (RA)*. The RA is notification Medicare sends to the provider and includes a list of all claims paid and claims rejected or denied during a particular payment period. A paper RA is generated for all providers whether they file paper or electronic claims. The only exception is when the provider has been approved to receive the RA electronically.

Each RA contains a list of claims that Medicare has cleared for payment since the last RA was generated. Also included in the RA are any claims that have moved to a "deny status" since the last RA was sent. RAs are generated in a weekly cycle. Each claim listed on the RA contains detailed processing information. A reimbursement amount, **claims**

Medicare Summary Notice

BENEFICIARY NAME
STREET ADDRESS
CITY, STATE   ZIP CODE

CUSTOMER SERVICE INFORMATION

Your Medicare Number: 111-11-1111A

If you have questions, write or call:
Medicare
555 Medicare Blvd., Suite 200
Medicare Building
Medicare, US XXXXX-XXXX

Local: (XXX) XXX-XXXX
Toll-free: 1-800-XXX-XXXX
TTY for Hearing Impaired: 1-800-XXX-XXXX

BE INFORMED: Beware of telemarketers
offering free or discounted medicare items
or services.

This is a summary of claims processed from 05/10/2004 through 06/10/2004.

PART B MEDICAL INSURANCE – ASSIGNED CLAIMS

Dates of Service	Services Provided	Amount Charged	Medicare Approved	Medicare Paid Provider	You May Be Billed	See Notes Section
Claim Number: 12435-84956-84556						
Paul Jones, M.D., 123 West Street,						a
Jacksonville, FL 33231-0024						
Referred by: Scott Wilson, M.D.						
04/19/04	1 Influenza immunization (90724)	$5.00	$3.88	$3.88	$0.00	b
04/19/04	1 Admin. flu vac (G0008)	5.00	3.43	3.43	0.00	b
	Claim Total	**$10.00**	**$7.31**	**$7.31**	**$0.00**	
Claim Number: 12435-84956-84557						
ABC Ambulance, P.O. Box 2149,						a
Jacksonville, FL 33231						
04/25/04	1 Ambulance, base rate (A0020)	$289.00	$249.78	$199.82	$49.96	
04/25/04	1 Ambulance, per mile (A0021)	21.00	16.96	13.57	3.39	
	Claim Total	**$310.00**	**$266.74**	**$213.39**	**$53.35**	

PART B MEDICAL INSURANCE – UNASSIGNED CLAIMS

Dates of Service	Services Provided	Amount Charged	Medicare Approved	Medicare Paid You	You May Be Billed	See Notes Section
Claim Number: 12435-84956-84558						
William Newman, M.D., 362 North Street						a
Jacksonville, FL 33231-0024						
03/10/04	1 Office/Outpatient Visit, ES (99213)	$47.00	$33.93	$27.15	$39.02	c

THIS IS NOT A BILL – Keep this notice for your records.

Fig. 5-8   Example of Medicare Summary Notice Part B. *(Source: U.S. Department of Health and Human Services, Centers for Medicare and Medicaid Services.)*

adjustment reason codes, and **remittance remark codes** are included for each claim. Claim adjustment reason codes and remittance remark codes are used in the **electronic remittance advice (ERA)** and the **standard paper remittance advice (SPRA)** to relay information relevant to the adjudication of Medicare Part B claims. Reason codes detail the reason that an adjustment was made to a health care claim payment by the payer, and remark codes represent nonfinancial information crucial to understanding the adjudication of the claim.

Standard Paper Remittance Advice

The SPRA is the product of standardization by CMS of the provider payment notification. The form was created to (1) provide a document that is uniform in content and format and (2) ease the transition to the electronic remittance format. The SPRA displays the same reason codes, remark codes, messages, and other data as the ERA for Medicare Part A providers.

Fig. 5-9 shows the SPRA along with a list of the various fields depicted on the SPRA and their definitions. One claim is listed in each block of the remittance and is separated from other claims with a line. The claims on the remittance are organized in alphabetical order, by beneficiary name within each type of claim (i.e., Inpatient, Part A). At the end of each type of claim, there is a subtotal of the information included on the remittance. At the end of the remittance is a total summation.

Electronic Remittance Advice

An ERA is one of several different types of electronic formats that is generated rather than a paper document. Information contained in an ERA furnishes the same information as that contained on the SPRA. An ERA allows automatic posting of claims payment information directly into the facility's practice management system. ERAs eliminate the need for manual posting of Medicare payment information, which saves the provider time and money. Automatic ERA information transfer also eliminates errors made by manual posting of information from the SPRA to the ledger accounts.

WHO CAN RECEIVE ELECTRONIC REMITTANCE?   Any provider or supplier enrolled in the Medicare program who submits claims electronically may receive ERAs. It is not required that a provider be Medicare PAR to receive ERAs. Additionally, providers may allow a billing agent (billing service or clearinghouse) to receive ERAs on their behalf.

HOW DOES IT WORK?   The provider receives a paper Medicare check and SPRA just as before. The Medicare check number appears on paper and electronic versions of the RA. Production of paper remittance notices may be discontinued at the discretion of the provider or CMS or both after a reasonable phase-in period.

STEPS FOR ENROLLING IN ELECTRONIC REMITTANCE   Receiving ERAs is not automatic. The provider must go through an enrollment process, which typically includes several steps, as follows:

Step 1. Providers must contact their software vendor to determine if ERA capability is available for the facility's practice management system. Special programming usually is required to extract the information from the electronic remittance file and automatically post this information to the patient accounts. (An example of an ERA is shown in Fig. 5-10.)

Step 2. The provider must complete an ERA enrollment form (Fig. 5-11).

Electronic Funds Transfer

Payments from Medicare may be automatically deposited to a provider's designated bank account using **electronic funds transfer (EFT)**. Each EFT transaction is assigned a unique number, which functions the same way as a Medicare check number. The EFT number appears on the RA (paper or electronic) in the same field/location as the Medicare check number. EFT is available to all providers who bill Medicare. Providers must request an EFT enrollment form from their Medicare carrier. A request for EFT authorization form is shown in Fig. 5-12.

WHAT DID YOU LEARN?

1. What is an MSN?
2. Explain the difference between the MSN and the Medicare RA.
3. Who is eligible to receive an ERA?
4. What is an EFT?

MEDICARE AUDITS AND APPEALS

Audits

Medicare audits fall into two broad categories: prepayment audits, which, as the name suggests, review claims before Medicare pays the provider, and postpayment audits, which analyze claims after Medicare reimbursement. Some medical facilities believe they can avoid audits because they choose to report lower level Evaluation and Management Medicare codes on the claims; this is referred to as

Standard Paper Remittance (SPR) Advice Notices - Revised Format

The Centers for Medicare & Medicaid Services (CMS) has revised the format of the Standard Paper Remittance (SPR) Advice Notices to correspond with the changes made to the X12 835 as a result of HIPAA. These changes are effective with SPRs printed on and after **April 1, 2002.** Following is a summary of the SPR changes and an example of the revised SPR highlighting these changes.

SPR Changes:

- The "TOTAL PD TO BENE" and "TOTAL MSP" amount fields used in computing provider payment will now be reported as reason code adjustments, rather than in separate fields at the provider summary level. Please refer to Reference ❶ in the attached example.
- The "OFFSET DETAILS" section has been replaced with the "PLB REASON CODE". Please refer to Reference ❶ in the attached example. Some of the offset codes have been replaced and some new offset codes were added. The following is a crosswalk of the codes used in Medicare processing:

Current ADJ/ Offset Reason Code	New Code	Description	Comments
AP	AP	Acceleration of Benefits	Advance Payments
RF	B2	Rebate	Refund, HPSA
RI	CS	Adjustment	Used for multiple reasons
BF	FB	Forwarding Balance	
AJ, J1	J1	Adjustment	Nonreimbursable
IN	L6	Interest	Interest applied on the claim.
OF	WO	Withholding	Offset as a result of a previous overpayment
LF	50	Late Filing Reduction	

- Any adjustment to the submitted charge and/or units will continue to be reported next to the claim line with the appropriate group, reason and remark codes explaining the adjustment. Every provider level adjustment will now be reported in the provider level adjustment section of the SPR as well. Please refer to Reference ❶ in the attached example.
- The "TOTAL PD TO BENE" has been deleted from the provider summary level. The "PD TO BENE" has also been deleted from the claim level field. Amounts paid to the beneficiary will now be reported as a "CS" adjustment reason code in the "PLB REASON CODE" section. Please refer to Reference ❶ in the attached example.
- The "TOTAL INT" has been deleted from the provider summary level but the "INT" remains on the claim level field. Please refer to Reference ❷ in the attached example. Interest amounts will also be reported as a "L6" adjustment reason code in the "PLB REASON CODE" section. Please refer to Reference ❶ in the attached example. The interest amount reported in this section will be displayed as a negative amount if the amount has been included in the "NET" field at the claim level.
- A new claim level field, "LATE FILING CHARGE" has been added for the reporting of late filing reductions. Please refer to Reference ❷ in the attached example. This amount will be reported in the "PLB REASON CODE" section with a "50" adjustment reason code.
- The "TOTAL PREV PD" has been deleted from the provider summary level. This amount will now be reported only in the claim level field "PREV PD". Please refer to Reference ❷ in the attached example.
- The "TOTAL OFFSET" field at the provider summary level has been renamed as "TOTAL PROV ADJ AMT". Please refer to Reference ❸ in the attached example.
- Only the first crossover carrier name will be reported on the SPR, even if COB information is sent to more than one payer. Please refer to Reference ❹ in the attached example.

Note for MSP Claims : The amount of the payment for an MSP claim will not be reflected on the remittance under "NET". This amount is the amount of payment from the primary payer, plus the amount allowed from Medicare. To determine the amount that Medicare paid as their portion, you must deduct the amount in the "PROV ADJ DETAILS" for that claim from the "NET" in the claim detail. In the example shown, the NET was $20.00. The ADJ detail for that claim was also $20.00. The difference is $0, so Medicare did not pay anything on this particular claim. See Reference ❶ and ❺.

Fig. 5-9 Example of standard paper remittance advice. *(Source: U.S. Department of Health and Human Services, Centers for Medicare and Medicaid Services.)*

Continued

Standard Paper Remittance (SPR) Advice Notices - Revised Format (continued)

EXAMPLE OF REVISED SPR

PERF PROV	SERV DATE	POS	NOS	PROC	MODS	BILLED	ALLOWED	DEDUCT	COINS	GRP /RC-AMT	PROV PD
NAME ALPHA, ALBERT			HIC 699777777A	ACNT 1111111111				ICN 1402065330030	ASG Y MOA MA01		
W88888888	1215 121501	11	1	92547		98.00	27.22	0.00	5.44	CO-42 70.78	21.78
W88888888	1215 121501	11	1	92541		45.00	39.89	0.00	7.98	CO-42 5.11	31.91
PT RESP 13.42				CLAIM TOTALS		143.00	67.11	0.00	13.42	75.89	53.69
											53.69 NET

NAME BAKER, LEEANN			HIC 699123123A	ACNT 0009				ICN 1102025001590	ASG Y MOA MA01 MA18		
W88888888	0113 011302	11	1	J9202	GACC	600.00	446.49	0.00	89.30	CO-42 153.51	357.19
				(J9217)							
W88888888	0121 012102	11	1	J9202	CC	600.00	446.49	0.00	89.30	CO-42 153.51	357.19
				(J9217)							
PT RESP 178.60				CLAIM TOTALS		1200.00	892.98	0.00	178.60	307.02	714.38
											714.38 NET

CLAIM INFORMATION FORWARDED TO: BCBS OF MINNESOTA **❹**

NAME CHARLIE, CINDY			HIC 699222222A	ACNT 22222222				ICN 1402008151040	ASG Y MOA MA01		
W88888888	0106 010602	11	1	76091	26	80.00	43.76	0.00	8.75	CO-42 36.24	35.01
W88888888	0106 010602	11	1	G0236	26	50.00	0.00	0.00	0.00	CO-B5 50.00	00.00
REM: M58											
PT RESP 8.75				CLAIM TOTALS		130.00	43.76	0.00	8.75	86.24	35.01
											35.18 NET

ADJS: PREV PD   0.00 INT   0.17 LATE FILING CHARGE   0.00   **❷**

NAME BETA, BOB			HIC 699111111A	ACNT 12345678901234567890				ICN 1402063333010	ASG Y MOA MA01 MA72		
W88888888	0304 030402	11	1	99214		180.00	81.99	47.65	6.87	CO-42 98.01	27.47
W88888888	0304 030402	11	1	82010		30.00	0.00	0.00	0.00	CO-B7 30.00	00.00
W88888888	0304 030402	11	1	J1040		10.00	9.39	0.00	1.88	CO-42 00.61	7.51
PT RESP 56.40				CLAIM TOTALS		220.00	91.38	47.65	8.75	128.62	34.98
											34.98 NET

NAME BUMAN, JAMES			HIC 699555555A	ACNT 55555555				ICN 1402065200070	ASG Y MOA MA01		
W88888888	0304 030402	11	1	99214		75.00	0.00	0.00	0.00	PR-B7 75.00	20.00
										OA-71 20.00	
										PR-A3 -20.00	
PT RESP 55.00				CLAIM TOTALS		75.00	0.00	0.00	0.00	75.00	20.00 **❺**
											20.00 NET

TOTALS:	# OF CLAIMS	BILLED AMT	ALLOWED AMT	DEDUCT AMT	COINS AMT	TOTAL RC-AMT	PROV PD AMT	PROV ADJ AMT **❸**	CHECK AMT
	5	1768.00	1095.23	47.65	209.52	672.77	858.06	108.50	749.56

PROVIDER ADJ DETAILS:	PLB REASON CODE	FCN	HIC	AMOUNT **❶**
	CS	1402063333010	699111111A	34.98
	CS	1402065200070	699555555A	20.00
	WO	7101347082956		53.69
	L6			-0.17

GLOSSARY: Group, Reason, MOA, Remark and Adjustment Codes:

CO	Contractual Obligation. Amount for which the provider is financially liable. The patient may not be billed for this amount.
PR	Patient Responsibility. Amount that may be billed to a patient or another payee.
OA	Other Adjustment.
A3	Medicare Secondary Payer liability met.
B5	Claim/Service denied/reduced because coverage guidelines were not met or were exceeded.
B7	This provider was not certified for this procedure/service on this date of service.
42	Charges exceed our fee schedule or maximum allowable amount.
71	Primary Payer amount.
M58	Please resubmit the claim with the missing/correct information so that it may be processed.
MA01	If you do not agree with what we approved for these services, you may appeal our decision. To make sure that we are fair to you, we require another individual that did not process your initial claim to conduct the review. However, in order to be eligible for a review, you must write to us within 6 months of the date of this notice, unless you have a good reason for being late.
MA119	Provider level adjustment for late claim filing applies to this claim.
MA18	The claim information is also being forwarded to the patient's supplemental insurer. Send any questions regarding supplemental benefits to them.
MA72	The beneficiary overpaid you for these assigned services. You must issue the beneficiary a refund within 30 days for the difference between his/her payment to you and the total of the amount shown as patient responsibility and as paid to the beneficiary on this notice.
CS	Adjustment
WO	Withholding
L6	Interest

Fig. 5-9, cont'd

Provider Name	Provider #:	
Address	Page #:	1 of 2
City State Zip	Date:	08/27/03
	Check/EFT #:	

```
************************************************************************************
*                                                                                  *
*   Effective Monday, September 15, 2003, the phone numbers to contact Noridian    *
*   Administrative Services' Phone Appeals and Provider Enrollment teams will be    *
*   changing. The Phone Appeals number will be 1-800-279-5331 and the Provider      *
*   Enrollment number will be 1-888-608-8816.                                       *
*                                                                                  *
************************************************************************************
```

PERF PROV	SERV DATE	POS NOS	PROC	MODS	BILLED	ALLOWED	DEDUCT	COINS		GRP/RC-AMT	PROV PD
NAME		HIC		ACNT				ICN 1703219015000		ASG Y MOA	MAO1 MA18
	0701 070103 11	1	99213		180.00	44.16	0.00	8.83	CO-42	135.84	35.33
PT RESP	8.83		CLAIM TOTALS		180.00	44.16	0.00	8.83		135.84	35.33
CLAIM INFORMATION FORWARDED TO: BCMNX/BC/BC MINNESOTA											35.33 **NET**

PERF PROV	SERV DATE	POS NOS	PROC	MODS	BILLED	ALLOWED	DEDUCT	COINS		GRP/RC-AMT	PROV PD
NAME		HIC		ACNT				ICN 1803171001050		ASG Y MOA	MAO1
	0402 040203 11	1	76091		150.00	0.00	0.00	0.00	CO-50	150.00	0.00
REM: M25											
PT RESP	0.00		CLAIM TOTALS		150.00	0.00	0.00	0.00		150.00	0.00
											0.00 **NET**

PERF PROV	SERV DATE	POS NOS	PROC	MODS	BILLED	ALLOWED	DEDUCT	COINS		GRP/RC-AMT	PROV PD
NAME		HIC		ACNT				ICN 0102247015010		ASG Y MOA	MAO1 N154
	0510 051002 11	1	99213		150.00	45.79	0.00	9.16	CO-42	104.21	36.63
PT RESP	9.16		CLAIM TOTALS		150.00	45.79	0.00	9.16		104.21	36.63
ADJS: PREV PD	0.00	INT	0.02	LATE FILING CHARGE		0.00					36.65 **NET**

TOTALS:	# OF CLAIMS	BILLED AMT	ALLOWED AMT	DEDUCT AMT	COINS AMT	TOTAL RC-AMT	PROV PD AMT	PROV ADJ AMT	CHECK AMT

PROVIDER ADJ DETAILS:	PLB REASON CODE	FCN	HIC	AMOUNT
	WO	7102352195000		35.33

SUMMARY OF NON-ASSIGNED CLAIMS

PERF PROV	SERV DATE	POS NOS	PROC	MODS	BILLED	ALLOWED	DEDUCT	COINS		GRP/RC-AMT	PROV PD
NAME		HIC		ACNT				ICN 1703219015010		ASG N MOA	MA28
	0704 070403 11	1	99214		200.00	69.11	0.00	13.82	PR-42	10.37	0.00
									CO-45	120.52	
									PR-100	55.29	
PT RESP	79.48		CLAIM TOTALS		200.00	69.11	0.00	13.82		186.18	0.00
											0.00 **NET**

Glossary: Group, Reason, MOA, Remark and Adjustment Codes

CO   Contractual Obligation. Amount for which the provider is financially liable. The patient may not be billed for this amount.

PR   Patient Responsibility. Amount that may be billed to a patient or another payer.

100   Payment made to patient/insured/responsible party.

42   Charges exceed our fee schedule or maximum allowable amount.

45   Charges exceed your contracted/legislated fee arrangement.

MAO1   If you do not agree with what we approved for these services, you may appeal our decision. To make sure that we are fair to you, we require another individual that did not process your initial claim to conduct the review. However, in order to be eligible for a review, you must write to us within 120 days of the date of this notice, unless you have a good reason for being late. An institutional provider, e.g., hospital, SNF, HHA or a hospice may appeal only if the claim involves a reasonable and necessary denial, a SNF non-certified bed denial, or a home health denial because the patient was not homebound or was not in need of intermittent skilled nursing services, or a hospice care denial because the patient was not terminally ill, and either the patient or the provider is liable under Section 1879 of the Social Security Act, and the patient chooses not to appeal. If your carrier issues telephone review decisions, a professional provider should phone the carrier's office for a telephone review if the criteria for a telephone review are met.

MA18   The claim information is also being forwarded to the patient's supplemental insurer. Send any questions regarding supplemental benefits to them.

Fig. 5-10   Electronic remittance advice. (*Source: U.S. Department of Health and Human Services, Centers for Medicare and Medicaid Services.*)

Submitter Name: _____	Submitter ID: _____
Contact Person: _____	Phone Number: _____

Remittance Format and version:

ANSI X12 835, version 4010 A1	_____	ANSI X12 835, version 3030	_____
National Standard Format, version 1.04	_____	ANSI X12 835, version 3051,3B.00	_____
National Standard Format, version 2.0	_____	ANSI X12 835, version 3051,4B.00	_____
National Standard Format, version 2.01	_____	ANSI X12 835, version 4010	_____

In compliance with the Health Insurance Portability and Accountability Act (HIPAA), effective October 16, 2003 the only remittance format and version that NHIC will provide is ANSI X12 835, version 4010A1. If your practice management accommodates a remittance module, we recommend that you work with your vendor to install the 4010A1 version.

Provider Numbers:
    Please list all provider numbers to receive remittance. If billing with a group provider number, list only the group number. Please attach a separate sheet if necessary. The provider must sign the form to be activated.

Provider ID (9) characters	**Printed Provider Name**	**Provider Signature**
_____	_____	_____
_____	_____	_____

A billing service or clearinghouse may accept remittance files on behalf of a provider(s), but the billing service or clearinghouse is prohibited from viewing, storing, modifying, or reporting the data for its own use. The billing service or clearinghouse's signature on this form signifies their agreement with this requirement.

Billing Service/Clearinghouse Representative (if applicable)

Please fax or mail this form to the NHIC office that processes your Medicare Part B claims:

Fig. 5-11   Electronic remittance advice enrollment form.

downcoding. Many audits target physicians' offices that practice downcoding because this type of practice "raises a red flag" to auditors. Downcoding on a claim is discouraged when the reason for doing so is simply that documentation in the health record does not meet the carriers' guidelines. If a particular code accurately describes the service or procedure performed, a provider should not lower the code simply because he or she fears a documentation deficiency.

STOP AND THINK

You are having lunch with your friend Nellie Shumway, who works for a family practice clinic across the courtyard from your building. Over lunch one day, Nellie confides, "In our office, we code all new Medicare patient visits at Level 1 (99201). It's so much easier, and we don't have to worry about Medicare auditing our records." What, if anything, might you tell your friend?

If a carrier believes that a provider has a universal billing problem, the carrier may place that provider on prepayment review, which requires the provider to submit documentation for every claim before Medicare allows reimbursement. Prepayment review is a tremendous burden on the medical facility because it no longer can submit electronic claims. If the prepayment review involves documentation of hospital visits, the physician must obtain the records from the facility for each visit before submitting the claim; this delays reimbursement and creates administrative problems.

Postpayment audits are triggered most commonly by statistical irregularities. A postpayment audit can result if a provider uses a certain code much more frequently or less frequently than other providers of the same specialty in the same area. Patient complaints also can trigger audits and reviews.

Appeals

Medicare regulations allow providers and beneficiaries who are dissatisfied with Medicare's

CONQUERING MEDICARE'S CHALLENGES   183

AUTHORIZATION AGREEMENT FOR ELECTRONIC FUNDS TRANSFER (EFT)

Reason for Submission: ❑ New EFT Authorization
                                  ❑ Revision to Current Authorization *(i.e. account or bank changes)*
                                  ❑ EFT Termination Request

Chain Home Office: ❑ Check here if EFT payment is being made to the Home Office of Chain Organization
                                  (Attach letter Authorizing EFT payment to Chain Home Office)

Physician/Provider/Supplier Information

Physician's Name _____

Provider/Supplier Legal Business Name _____

_____

Chain Organization Name _____

Home Office Legal Business Name *(if different from Chain Organization Name)* _____

Tax ID Number: *(Designate SSN* ❑ *or EIN* ❑*)* ___ ___ ___ ___ ___ ___ ___ ___ ___

Doing Business As Name_____

Medicare Identification Number (*OSCAR, UPIN, or NSC only*) _____

Depository Information (Financial Institution)

Depository Name _____

Account Holder's Name _____

Street Address _____

City _____ State _____ Zip Code _____

Depository Telephone Number_____

Depository Contact Person _____

Depository Routing Transit Number *(nine digit)* ___ ___ ___ ___ ___ ___ ___ ___ ___

Depositor Account Number _____

Type of Account *(check one)* ❑ Checking Account   ❑ Savings Account

Please include a voided check, preprinted deposit slip, or confirmation of account information on bank letterhead with this agreement for verification of your account number.

Authorization

I hereby authorize the Medicare contractor, _____, hereinafter called the COMPANY, to initiate credit entries, and in accordance with 31 CFR part 210.6(f) initiate adjustments for any credit entries made in error to the account indicated above. I hereby authorize the financial institution/bank named above, hereinafter called the DEPOSITORY, to credit and/or debit the same to such account.

If payment is being made to an account controlled by a Chain Home Office, the Provider of Services hereby acknowledges that payment to the Chain Office under these circumstances is still considered payment to the Provider, and the Provider authorizes the forwarding of Medicare payments to the Chain Home Office.

If the account is drawn in the Physician's or Individual Practitioner's Name, or the Legal Business Name of the Provider/Supplier, the said Physician/Provider/Supplier certifies that he/she has sole control of the account referenced above, and certifies that all arrangements between the DEPOSITORY and the said Physician/Provider/Supplier are in accordance with all applicable Medicare regulations and instructions.

FORM CMS-588 (09/03)

Fig. 5-12 Authorization agreement for electronic funds transfer. *(Source: U.S. Department of Health and Human Services, Centers for Medicare and Medicaid Services.)*

This authorization agreement is effective as of the signature date below and is to remain in full force and effect until the COMPANY has received written notification from me of its termination in such time and such manner as to afford the COMPANY and the DEPOSITORY a reasonable opportunity to act on it. The COMPANY will continue to send the direct deposit to the DEPOSITORY indicated above until notified by me that I wish to change the DEPOSITORY receiving the direct deposit. If my DEPOSITORY information changes, I agree to submit to the COMPANY an updated EFT Authorization Agreement.

Signature Line

Authorized/Delegated Official Name *(Print)* _____

Authorized/Delegated Official Title _____

Authorized/Delegated Official Signature_____Date_____

PRIVACY ACT ADVISORY STATEMENT

Sections 1842, 1862(b) and 1874 of title XVIII of the Social Security Act authorize the collection of this information. The purpose of collecting this information is to authorize electronic funds transfers.

The information collected will be entered into system No. 09-70-0501, titled "Carrier Medicare Claims Records," and No. 09-70-0503, titled "Intermediary Medicare Claims Records" published in the Federal Register Privacy Act Issuances, 1991 Comp. Vol. 1, pages 419 and 424, or as updated and republished. Disclosures of information from this system can be found in this notice.

Furnishing information is voluntary, but without it we will not be able to process your electronic funds transfer.

You should be aware that P.L. 100-503, the Computer Matching and Privacy Protection Act of 1988, permits the government, under certain circumstances, to verify the information you provide by way of computer matches.

According to the Paperwork Reduction Act of 1995, no persons are required to respond to a collection of information unless it displays a valid OMB control number.The valid OMB control number for this information collection is 0938-0626. The time required to complete this information collection is estimated to average 2 hours per response, including the time to review instructions, search existing data resources, gather the data needed, and complete and review the information collection. If you have any comments concerning the accuracy of the time estimate(s) or suggestions for improving this form, please write to: CMS, Attn: PRA Reports Clearance Officer,7500 Security Boulevard, Baltimore, MD 21244-1850.

FORM CMS-588 (09/03)

Fig. 5-12, cont'd

determination to request that the determination be reconsidered. Through the appeals process, Medicare seeks to ensure that the correct payment is made, or a clear and adequate explanation is given supporting nonpayment.

A physician or supplier providing items and services payable under Medicare Part B may appeal an initial determination if

- the provider accepted assignment;
- the provider did not accept assignment on a claim that was denied on the basis as being not reasonable and necessary;
- the beneficiary did not know or could not have been expected to know that the service would not be covered, requiring the provider/supplier to refund the beneficiary any payment received for the services; or
- the provider did not accept assignment but is acting as the authorized representative of the beneficiary and indicates this in the appeal (attaching a copy of the beneficiary's MSN indicates the provider/supplier is authorized to act on the beneficiary's behalf).

Claims submitted with incomplete or invalid information are not given appeal rights and are returned as unprocessable. The provider has two options for correcting the claim, as follows:

- Submit an entirely new claim (electronic or paper) with complete, valid information
- Submit corrections in writing

Table 5-12 lists the types of appeal actions available to Medicare beneficiaries and providers.

Telephone Review Requests

Providers or suppliers may request a review by telephone, if the appeal request is not complex. If an appeal from a provider or supplier is complex, or if significant documentation is needed to adjudicate the appeal request, a written review must be filed within the timely filing period. Review request clarifications or problems that can be handled over the telephone include the following:

- The diagnosis was not linked properly on the original claim.
- The number of services or units is incorrect or missing.
- The anesthesia time is missing.
- The date of service is incorrect (except for changes to the year).
- The CPT code is incorrect, and changing it would not create an overpayment.

- The services are incorrectly denied as duplicate charges.
- A modifier is being added or corrected (except for returned unprocessable claim rejections).
- The place of service is incorrect.

Written Part B Determination

For Part B appeals, Medicare regulations state that any party who is dissatisfied with the initial determination may request that the carrier review such determination. Effective January 1, 2003, a request for review must be filed within 4 months after the date of the notice of the initial determination. Medicare cannot accept an appeal for which no initial determination has been made. The request for review not only must identify the initial determination with which the party is dissatisfied but also must meet the requirements for the contents of an appeal request as follows:

- A request for a review may be filed on HCFA-1964, Request for Review of Part B Medicare Claim.
- A request for a review may be a signed written statement from the provider or supplier expressing disagreement with the initial determination or indicating that the review or a re-examination should be made.
- A request for a review may be filed on the provider's or supplier's letterhead or on a Physician/Supplier Inquiry Form (this form may be requested by calling your carrier).

The review request must include the following information:

- Beneficiary name
- Medicare HICN
- Name and address of provider/supplier of item/service
- Date of initial determination
- Date of service for which the initial determination was issued (dates must be reported in a manner that comports with the Medicare claims filing instructions; ranges of dates are acceptable only if a range of dates is properly reportable on the Medicare claim form)
- The item, if any, and service that is at issue in the appeal

The provider RA should accompany the review request along with any pertinent data that provide additional information (information not submitted with the initial claim). It is unnecessary to send another CMS-1500 form. Any corrected information should be included with the written request.

TABLE 5-12	Types of Appeal Actions	
Type of Appeal	**Criteria Necessary**	**Time Limits**
Telephone review	May be requested by providers, beneficiaries, or their representative. Allowed only for assigned claims, unless beneficiary is present at the time of the request and gives Medicare the authorization to proceed with review. Providers may be limited in the number of reviews made per call (see "Telephone Review Requests" section)	Before January 1, 2007: Must be requested within 6 mo of date of initial determination January 1, 2007, and after: Must be requested within 4 mo of initial determination
Written review	Requests must be made in writing and must be signed	Before January 1, 2007: Must be requested within 6 mo of date of initial determination January 1, 2007, and after: Must be requested within 4 mo of initial determination
Fair hearing	Requested if provider is dissatisfied with the review determination. Amount in controversy must be at least $110.00. May request the hearing be held in person, by telephone, or on-the-record. If a hearing on-the-record is requested, a decision is made on the basis of information currently on file. If an in-person or telephone hearing is requested, it is scheduled	Must be filed within 6 mo after the date of the review determination
Administrative law judge	Filed if provider is dissatisfied with determination made by the hearing officer. Amount in controversy must be at least $500.00. May request a hearing before an Administrative Law Judge of the Social Security Administration	Must be made in writing and filed within 60 days of the date of the carrier's fair hearing decision of record
Judicial review	Requested if provider is still dissatisfied with the determination of the Administrative Law Judge. Amount in controversy must be at least $1090.00	No time limits

Providers and suppliers are responsible for submitting documentation, if any, that supports the reason for the appeal. This documentation may be supplied with the appeal request or at the request of the carrier. Failure to submit documentation in a timely manner may result in processing delays. A sample request for review form is shown in Fig. 5-13.

WHAT DID YOU LEARN?

1. Name the two categories into which Medicare audits fall.
2. List two things that might prompt a Medicare audit.
3. Under what circumstances might a provider initiate an appeal?
4. Name four types of claim errors that can be handled via a telephone review.

QUALITY REVIEW STUDIES

Regulations define a **quality review study** as "an assessment, conducted by or for a **peer review organization (PRO)** more recently referred to as a *quality improvement organization*, of a patient care problem for the purpose of improving patient care through peer analysis, intervention, resolution of the problem, and follow-up."* Quality review studies typically follow a set of related structured activities designed to achieve measurable improvement in processes and outcomes of care. Improvements are achieved through interventions that target health care providers, practitioners, plans, or beneficiaries.

* http://www.cms.hhs.gov/manuals/19_pro/pr16.asp#_1_2.

REQUEST FOR REVIEW OF PART B MEDICARE CLAIM
Medical Insurance Benefits – Social Security Act

NOTICE – Anyone who misrepresents or falsifies essential information requested by this form may upon conviction be subject to fine and imprisonment under Federal Law.

1. Carrier's Name and Address	2. Name of Patient
	3. Health Insurance Claim Number

4. I do not agree with the determination you made on my claim as described on my Explanation of Medicare Benefits dated:

5. MY REASONS ARE: (Attach a copy of the Explanation of Medicare Benefits, or describe the service, date of service, and physician's name. NOTE: If the date on the Explanation of Medicare Benefits mentioned in Item 4 is more than six months ago, include your reason for not making this request earlier.)

6. Describe illness or injury:

7. ☐ I have additional evidence to submit. (Attach such evidence to this form.)
   ☐ I do not have additional evidence.

COMPLETE ALL OF THE INFORMATION REQUESTED. SIGN AND RETURN THE FIRST COPY AND ANY ATTACHMENTS TO THE CARRIER NAMED ABOVE. IF YOU NEED HELP, TAKE THIS AND YOUR NOTICE FROM THE CARRIER TO A SOCIAL SECURITY OFFICE, OR TO THE CARRIER. KEEP THE DUPLICATE COPY OF THIS FORM FOR YOUR RECORDS.

8. SIGNATURE OF *EITHER* THE CLAIMANT *OR* HIS REPRESENTATIVE

Claimant	Representative	
Address	Address	
City, State and ZIP Code	City, State and ZIP Code	
Telephone Number	Date	Telephone Number	Date

Form CMS-1964 (9/91)

Carrier's Copy

Fig. 5-13   Request for review of Medicare Part B claim. *(Source: U.S. Department of Health and Human Services, Centers for Medicare and Medicaid Services.)*

Quality Improvement Organizations

Medicare **quality improvement organizations** (QIO) work with consumers, physicians, hospitals, and other caregivers to refine care delivery systems to ensure patients receive the right care at the right time, particularly among underserved populations. The program also safeguards the integrity of the Medicare trust fund by ensuring payment is made only for medically necessary services and investigates beneficiary complaints about quality of care. Under the direction of CMS, the program consists of a national network of 53 quality improvement organizations responsible for each state, territory, and the District of Columbia.

HIPAA TIP

Covered entities may disclose protected health information about non-Medicare patients without their permission when the information involves Quality Improvement Organizations quality-related activities under its contract. (Under HIPAA, a "covered entity" is a health plan, health care clearinghouse, or health care provider who transmits information in electronic form.)

Medicare Beneficiary Protection Program

Medicare quality improvement organizations, such as the **Medicare Beneficiary Protection Program**, help protect the safety and health of Medicare beneficiaries through numerous activities, such as

- responding to beneficiary complaints,
- Hospital Issued Notice of Noncoverage (HINN) and Notice of Discharge and Medicare Appeal Rights (NODMAR) reviews, and
- physician review of medical records.

Beneficiary Complaints

If a Medicare beneficiary or representative has a concern about the quality of care, especially if the beneficiary believes that the care was inadequate or inappropriate, the beneficiary may contact one of the Medicare beneficiary protection programs and initiate a complaint. More information about Medicare beneficiary rights is available on the Medicare website.

Hospital Issued Notice of Noncoverage and Notice of Discharge and Medicare Appeal Rights Reviews

When a hospital issues a HINN, or a managed care organization issues a NODMAR, a beneficiary or representative may request an immediate review. The purpose of the review is to ensure that the HINN or NODMAR is correct and that beneficiaries are not discharged prematurely from care.

Peer Review Organizations

PRO review is governed by Titles XI and XVIII of the Social Security Act and by regulations contained in various sections of the Social Security Act. Each state has its own PRO, and although each is unique, there are certain guidelines they all must follow in relation to the review of items or services provided to Medicare beneficiaries to determine the following:

- Whether services provided or proposed to be provided are reasonable and medically necessary for the diagnosis and treatment of illness or injury, or to improve functioning of a malformed body member, or (with respect to pneumococcal vaccine and mammograms) for prevention of an illness, or (in the case of hospice care) for the relief of symptoms or effects of and management of terminal illness.
- Whether the services furnished or proposed to be furnished on an inpatient basis could be performed effectively on an outpatient basis or in an inpatient health care facility of a different type.
- The medical necessity, reasonableness, and appropriateness of inpatient hospital care for which additional payment is sought under the outlier provisions of the **prospective payment system (PPS)**. PPS is a method of reimbursement in which Medicare payment is made based on a predetermined, fixed amount. The payment amount for a particular service is derived on the basis of the classification system of that service (e.g., DRGs for inpatient hospital services).
- Whether a hospital has misrepresented admission or discharge information or has taken an action that results in the unnecessary admission of an individual entitled to benefits under Part A, unnecessary multiple admissions of an individual, or other inappropriate medical or other practices with respect to beneficiaries, or billing for services furnished to beneficiaries.
- The validity of diagnostic and procedural information supplied by the provider to the intermediary for payment purposes.
- The completeness and adequacy of hospital care provided.
- Whether the quality of services meets professionally recognized standards of health care.

Physician Review of Medical Records

Physician reviewers conduct medical record review to determine if the care received was medically necessary and appropriate. Reviews may include utilization, coding, or quality of care issues. The reviewer is generally from the same specialty as the physician who provided the care. This peer review is an important component of the quality-of-care oversight provided by Medicare quality improvement organizations and external quality review organizations.

Health Care Quality Improvement Program

The **Health Care Quality Improvement Program** was created to improve health outcomes of all Medicare beneficiaries regardless of personal characteristics (e.g., socioeconomic status, health status, ethnic group), physical location (urban or rural), or setting (e.g., physicians' offices, Medicare Advantage organizations, hospitals, nursing homes). The PRO's Statement of Work sets forth specific quality indicators for national health improvement priorities, which reflect the current state of PRO program experience, measurement systems, and data sources. These quality indicators neither address the entire spectrum of health care nor reflect fully the unique circumstances of each state. CMS requires state PROs to conduct the following:

- For Medicare beneficiaries in a specific state, implement quality improvement projects on a standardized set of quality indicators in each of the following six clinical topics:
  - Acute myocardial infarction
  - Pneumonia
  - Diabetes
  - Breast cancer
  - Stroke, transient ischemic attack, or atrial fibrillation
  - Congestive heart failure
- Initiate local projects within the specific state in the following three areas:
  - Quality improvement projects in alternative settings
  - Projects designed to reduce the disparity of care received by members of disadvantaged groups and all other beneficiaries in the PRO's state
  - Projects in response to local interests and needs
- For Medicare Advantage organizations in a specific state, offer technical assistance services, and encourage the organizations to collaborate with health care facilities in any or all of their health improvement projects. This specifically includes the diabetes and influenza immunization projects that the Medicare Advantage organizations are required to

conduct under their Quality Improvement System for Managed Care regulations.

Payment Error Prevention Program

The Office of Inspector General Audit Opinion Financial Statement found that a considerable amount of improper payments were made for inpatient services under the PPS. To reduce this payment error rate, the PRO must initiate a program of payment error prevention projects. CMS defines the payment error rate as the number of dollars found to be paid in error out of the total of all dollars paid for inpatient PPS services. CMS implements a surveillance system to provide state-specific estimates of the payment error rate. These estimates are used as performance indicators on which to evaluate performance.

Clinical Laboratory Improvement Act

Congress established the **Clinical Laboratory Improvement Act (CLIA)** program in 1988 to regulate quality standards for all laboratory testing done on humans to ensure the safety, accuracy, reliability, and timeliness of patient test results regardless of where the test was performed. CMS assumes primary responsibility for financial management operations of the CLIA program. Although all clinical laboratories must be certified properly to receive Medicare or Medicaid payments, CLIA has no direct Medicare or Medicaid program responsibilities.

To enroll in the CLIA program, laboratories (including laboratories located in physician offices) first must register by completing an application, paying a fee, being surveyed if applicable, and becoming certified. CLIA fees are structured depending on the type of certificate requested by the laboratory based on the complexity of the tests it performs. After all these preliminary measures are taken, the laboratory is issued an 11-digit CLIA certificate number. This information is significant to the health insurance professional because the 11-digit CLIA certificate number must appear in Block 23 of the CMS-1500 form for Medicare claims when laboratory services have been performed in a physician office laboratory.

WHAT DID YOU LEARN?

1. Define a "quality review study."
2. How does the Medicare Beneficiary Protection Program aid beneficiaries?
3. What is the purpose of PROs?
4. Where on the CMS-1500 form should the CLIA number be entered?

SUMMARY CHECK POINTS

☑ Medicare is a comprehensive federal insurance program established by Congress in 1966 to provide limited health care to individuals age 65, certain categories of disabled individuals younger than age 65, and individuals of any age who have ESRD. Medicare is administered by CMS.

☑ *Medicare Part A* (hospital insurance) helps pay for medically necessary services for the following types of health care:
- Inpatient hospital care
- Inpatient care in SNF
- Home health care
- Hospice care

☑ *Medicare Part B* is medical insurance financed by a combination of federal government funds and beneficiary premiums, which helps pay for
- medically necessary physicians' services,
- outpatient hospital services,
- DME, and
- some other services/supplies not covered by Part A.

☑ *Medicare Part C* (Medicare Advantage, formerly Medicare+Choice) is a managed health care structure that offers regular Part A and Part B Medicare coverage and other services. Primary Medicare Part C plans include
- Medicare managed care plans;
- Medicare private, unrestricted fee-for-service plans; and
- MSA plans.

☑ Medicare Part C not only includes Part A and Part B coverage but also pays for services not covered under the original Medicare plan, such as
- preventive care,
- prescription drugs,
- eyeglasses,
- dental care, and
- hearing aids.

☑ As of January 2006, *Medicare Part D* (Prescription Drug Plan) pays a portion of prescription drug expenses and cost sharing for qualifying individuals.

☑ *Medi-Medi* refers to individuals who qualify for benefits under the Medicare and Medicaid programs, sometimes referred to as *dual eligibles*. Most individuals who qualify for Medi-Medi are low-income elderly and individuals younger than 65 with disabilities.

☑ *Medigap* is a Medicare supplement insurance policy sold by private insurance companies to fill "gaps" in the original (fee-for-service) Medicare plan coverage. There are 12 standardized plans labeled Plan A through Plan L. Medigap policies work only with the original Medicare plan.

☑ *MSP* is the term used when Medicare is not responsible for payment of health care charges first when the beneficiary is covered under another insurance policy. Medicare may be the secondary payer in any of the following situations:
- Workers' compensation
- Working aged (individuals older than 65 years who are covered by a group health plan through their own or their spouse's current employment)
- Disabled individuals age 64 and younger who are covered by a large group health plan (more than 100 employees) through their own or a family member's current employment
- Medicare beneficiaries with ESRD who are covered under a group health plan
- Individuals covered under the Federal Black Lung Program
- Individuals receiving Veterans Administration benefits
- Individuals who are covered under a Federal Research Grant Program

☑ Advantages of Medicare HMOs include the following:
- HMOs often do not health screen; enrollment may not be denied because of health status.
- HMOs may cover services that traditional Medicare does not cover, such as routine physical examinations, eyeglasses, hearing aids, prescriptions, and dental coverage.
- Enrollees do not need Medigap insurance.
- There is limited or no paperwork to deal with, in contrast to traditional Medicare coverage.
- Enrollees do not have to pay the Medicare deductibles and co-insurance.

☑ Disadvantages of Medicare HMOs include the following:
- Choice of health care providers and medical facilities is limited.

- Members/enrollees are covered only for health care services received through the HMO except in emergency and urgent care situations.
- Prior approval usually is needed from a primary care physician for a specialist's services, surgical procedures, medical equipment, and other health care services.
- Enrollees who travel out of the HMO's service area do not receive coverage except in emergency and urgent care situations.
- If an enrollee decides to switch from the HMO to the traditional Medicare plan, coverage does not begin until the first day of the month after the disenrollment request.

☑ For a service or procedure to be determined *medically necessary* under Medicare guidelines, the service or procedure must meet the following criteria:
- Consistent with the symptoms or diagnosis of the illness or injury being treated
- Necessary and consistent with generally accepted professional medical standards
- Not furnished primarily for the convenience of the patient or physician
- Furnished at the most appropriate level that can be provided safely to the patient

☑ The ABN is a form that Medicare requires all health care providers to use when Medicare does not pay for a service to ensure that beneficiaries have a choice about their health care in the event that Medicare does not pay. When patients are asked to sign an ABN, they have two options:
- To receive the test or procedure, agree to be responsible for payment, and sign the ABN
- Not to receive the test or procedure, refuse to be responsible for payment, and sign the ABN

☑ The health insurance professional must use the Medicare fee schedule to determine the amount Medicare allows PARs and nonPARs accepting assignment to charge a patient for a particular service or procedure. Medicare PARs use the amount shown under the heading "PAR." A Medicare nonPAR can charge the amount in the next column under the heading "NON-PAR." The limiting charge for providers *not accepting* assignment is the amount under the heading "LIMITING," which is 15% more than the nonPAR amount.

☑ The Medicare Crossover Program is a service that Medicare Part B offers to private insurers and retirement plans, such as Medigap insurers, supplemental retirement plans, or other health care payers wherein the insurer sends an eligibility file to Medicare and Medicare sends corresponding claim information back to the health care payer. The eligibility file contains the beneficiary's name, Medicare HICN, and policy effective dates. Medicare matches the trading partner's HICN against its own Medicare files. Any resulting claims are sent automatically to the payer for additional payment considerations.

☑ A *small provider* is defined as follows:
- A provider of services (as that term is defined in section 1861(u) of the Social Security Act) with less than 25 FTE employees
- A physician, practitioner, facility, or supplier that is not otherwise a provider under section 1861(u) with less than 10 FTE employees

☑ MSN is a document sent to the Medicare beneficiary after a provider files a claim for Part A and Part B services in the original Medicare plan. It explains what the provider billed for, the Medicare-approved amount, how much Medicare paid, and what the beneficiary must pay (sometimes called an Explanation of Medicare Benefits).

☑ A Medicare RA is the document Medicare sends to the provider of services that explains how claims were adjudicated. The RA contains detailed processing information, including claims adjustment reason codes that tell why an adjustment was made to the claim payment and remittance remark codes, which represent nonfinancial information. The health insurance professional must be able to decipher these codes to understand why the payment is less than that shown on the claim.

☑ Any Medicare provider (PAR and nonPAR) who submits electronic claims can receive an ERA. Additionally, providers may allow a billing agent (billing service, clearinghouse) to receive ERAs on their behalf. The provider receives a paper Medicare check and SPRA just as before. The check number appears on paper and electronic versions of the RA.

☑ Medicare payments can be automatically deposited to a provider's designated bank account using EFT. With EFT, each transaction is assigned a unique number, which functions the same way as a Medicare check number. EFT is instantaneous, which allows funds to become immediately available for practice or other expenses.

 Quality review studies are performed to
- improve the processes and outcomes of patient care,
- safeguard the integrity of the Medicare trust fund by ensuring that payments are made only for medically necessary services, and
- investigate beneficiary complaints.

☑ CLIA was established to set quality standards for all laboratory testing to ensure the safety, accuracy, reliability, and timeliness of patient test results regardless of where the test was performed.

Closing Scenario

Rita felt relieved yet satisfied after completing the chapter on Medicare. As she had anticipated at the beginning, there was a lot to learn. Each evening after class, Grandma Nan had waited up for Rita, and they talked about what the lesson had been about that day. Grandma Nan's interest inspired Rita to listen closely, take detailed notes, and ask questions when she did not understand a particular concept. Soon, Rita found herself caught up in Medicare's challenges.

Rita became a big help to Grandma Nan and her elderly friends. When one of them brought over a Medi-care Summary Notice, Rita went through it with them, explaining each detail line by line. She also was able to explain to them the concept of "medically necessary" and the fact that Medicare pays only 80% of "covered" charges—not *all* services and supplies. The light of understanding in their eyes was the only reward Rita needed, and she decided then and there that she wanted to work in a medical facility specializing in the treatment of elderly patients. Rita believed that she could establish a similar rapport with elderly patients as she had with Grandma Nan and her friends.

WEBSITES TO EXPLORE

- For extensive information on Medicare, log on to
  http://www.medicare.gov

- National Medicare Coverage Policies are found on the following website:
  http://cms.hhs.gov

- For more information about CMS, log on to
  http://www.cms.hhs.gov/home/aboutcms.asp

- To peruse an issue of *The CMS Quarterly Provider Update,* log on to
  http://www.cms.hhs.gov/
  QuarterlyProviderUpdates/01_Overview.asp

- LMRPs can be found on the following link:
  http://www.apa.org/pi/aging/lmrp/toolkit/
  part1.html

- The Medicare Coverage Issues Manual is searchable on the following website:
  http://cms.hhs.gov

- For information on how to submit MSP claims electronically, log on to the website for the American National Standards Institute (ANSI) ASC X12N Implementation Guide:
  http://www.ansi.org

- Or for the National Standard Format (NSF) Specifications, log on to
  http://www.hipaanet.com/hisb_nsf.htm

- For instructions on how to read the beneficiary MSN, log on to the following website:
  http://www.medicare.gov/Basics/Summary
  Notice_HowToRead.asp

- Information on filing complaints for Medicare beneficiaries is available at
  www.medicare.gov/Publications/Pubs/
  pdf/10050.pdf

- For more information on CLIA, log on to the CMS website and click on "CLIA" in the left-hand column:
  http://www.cms.hhs.gov

Assessment

Multiple Choice

Directions: *In the questions/statements presented, choose the response that **best** answers/completes the stem, and circle the letter that precedes it.*

1. Medicare was established by Congress in 1966 to provide financial assistance with medical expenses to _____.
   A. people older than 65
   B. people with end-stage renal disease
   C. people younger than 65 with disabilities
   D. all of the above

2. Medicare requires its beneficiaries to pay premiums, deductibles, and co-insurance, which is referred to as _____.
   A. Medigap
   B. taxation
   C. cost sharing
   D. allowable charges

3. Medicare Part A, the hospital insurance part of Medicare, is funded through _____.
   A. taxes withheld from employees' wages
   B. taxes paid by employers
   C. state funds
   D. A and B are correct

4. Coverage requirements under Medicare state that for a service to be covered, it must be considered _____.
   A. proper and timely
   B. reasonable and customary
   C. medically necessary
   D. Medicare has no coverage requirements

5. Part A coverage is available free of charge to eligible Medicare beneficiaries who _____.
   A. have no other insurance
   B. are "dual eligibles"
   C. are eligible to receive Social Security benefits
   D. Medicare Part A is not free of charge to anyone

6. A private organization that contracts with Medicare to pay Part A and some Part B bills and determines payment to Part A facilities is called a _____.
   A. fiscal intermediary (FI)
   B. Part A negotiator
   C. beneficiary
   D. participating provider (PAR)

7. Medicare Part B helps pay for _____.
   A. medically necessary physician's services
   B. acute care hospitalization
   C. custodial and long-term care
   D. all of the above

8. Medicare pays _____% of allowable charges after the annual deductible is met.
   A. 20
   B. 50
   C. 80
   D. 100

9. The _____ is the duration of time during which a Medicare beneficiary is eligible for Part A benefits for services incurred in a hospital or skilled nursing facility (SNF) or both.
   A. donut hole
   B. Medicare gap
   C. benefit period
   D. open enrollment period

10. Managed health care plans that offer regular Part A and Part B Medicare coverage and additional coverage for certain other services are called _____.
    A. Medicare Part A
    B. Medicare Part B
    C. Medicare Part C
    D. Medicare Part D

11. The prescription drug coverage plan, which began in January 2006, is called _____.
    A. Medicare Part A
    B. Medicare Part B
    C. Medicare Part C
    D. Medicare Part D

12. The period during which a Medicare beneficiary is responsible for all prescription drug expenses until a total of $3850 (2007 figure) is spent out-of-pocket is referred to as the _____.
    A. Medigap
    B. donut hole
    C. crosswalk
    D. nonbenefit period

13. An individual qualifying for Medicare and Medicaid benefits is referred to as a _____.
    A. dual eligible
    B. Medimax
    C. medical qualifier
    D. categorically eligible

14. The program that provides community-based acute and long-term care services to Medicare beneficiaries is called _____.
    A. FICA
    B. PACE
    C. CLIA
    D. LMRP

15. A health insurance plan sold by private insurance companies to help pay for health care expenses not covered by Medicare is called a _____.
    A. commercial policy
    B. trading partner plan
    C. prospective payment plan
    D. supplemental policy

16. The term used when another insurance policy is primary to Medicare is _____.
   A. Medigap
   B. Medicare Supplement Insurance
   C. Medicare secondary payer (MSP)
   D. other health insurance

17. Some Medicare health maintenance organization (HMO) enrollees are allowed to see specialists outside the "network" without going through a primary care physician. This is called _____.
   A. self-referring
   B. open enrollment
   C. noncovered services
   D. not medically necessary

18. A group of medical providers that skips the insurance company middleman and contracts directly with patients is referred to as a _____.
   A. coordination of benefits (COB)
   B. nonparticipating provider (nonPAR)
   C. trading partner agreement
   D. provider sponsored organization

19. Local medical review policies (LMRPs) were replaced in 2003 by _____.
   A. CLIAs
   B. LCDs
   C. COBs
   D. QIOs

20. A form that Medicare requires all health care providers to use when Medicare does not pay for a service is the _____.
   A. SPRA
   B. COB
   C. ABN
   D. EOB

True/False

Directions: *Place a "T" in the blank preceding the sentence if it is true; place an "F" if it is false.*

_____ 1. Medicare Parts A and B are provided free of charge for qualifying individuals.

_____ 2. Part A covers custodial and long-term care.

_____ 3. Neither Medicare Part A nor Part B covers any preventive care services.

_____ 4. For durable medical equipment to qualify for Medicare payment, it must be ordered by a physician for use in the home, and items must be reusable.

_____ 5. Most Medicare Part B beneficiaries pay for Part B coverage in the form of a premium deducted from their monthly Social Security check.

_____ 6. Medicare beneficiaries are allowed only one "benefit period" per year.

_____ 7. An individual must be eligible for Part A or B to enroll in a Medicare Advantage Plan.

_____ 8. If a beneficiary has a Medicare Advantage Plan, he or she still needs a supplemental policy.

_____ 9. An individual who has Medicare Parts A and B must have a supplement policy.

_____ 10. The private organization that determines payment of Part B covered items and services is called a peer review organization.

_____ 11. If individuals do not sign up for Medicare Part B when first becoming eligible and later decide to enroll, the monthly premiums may be higher because of penalties.

_____ 12. When an individual turns 65 and enrolls in Medicare, federal law forbids insurance companies from denying eligibility for Medigap policies for 6 months.

_____ 13. Workers' compensation would likely be a primary payer to Medicare.

_____ 14. Medicare HMOs typically screen potential enrollees for preexisting conditions.

_____ 15. Under certain circumstances, a signed release of information form for Medicare beneficiaries can be valid for more than 1 year.

_____ 16. Medicare's definition of medical necessity must meet specific criteria.

_____ 17. Medicare health insurance claim numbers are typically in the format of nine numerical characters followed by one alpha character.

_____ 18. The Medicare fee schedule is now based on a resource-based relative value system.

_____ 19. Medicare nonPARs do not have to submit claims for their Medicare patients.

_____ 20. The process of matching one set of data elements or category of codes to their equivalents within a new set of elements or codes is called a crossover.

Short Answer/Fill-in-the-Blank

1. The second cost sharing requirement in Medicare Part B is an annual deductible of

   $_____, after which Medicare pays _____% of _____.

2. The duration of time Medicare uses for hospital and SNF services is called a(an) _____.

3. This duration of time begins the day an individual is _____ to a hospital or SNF and ends

   when the beneficiary has not received care in a hospital or SNF for _____ days in a row.

4. Medicare Part C, previously called _____, was renamed _____

   _____ by the Medicare Prescription Drug, Improvement, and Modernization Act of 2003.

5. The Balanced Budget Act of 1997, which went into effect in January 1999, expanded the role of

   private plans to include _____ plans.

6. List the various managed care choices included under Medicare Part C.

   _____

   _____

   _____

7. Medicare managed care plans (Medicare Part C) coverage not only includes Part A and Part B coverage but also pays for services not covered under the original Medicare plan, such as

_____

_____

_____

8. What main change did Medicare Part D introduce in January 2006?

_____

9. Explain Medicare's basic payment structure for Medicare Part D.

_____

10. How does Medicare's Part D payment structure differ for dual eligibles compared with that for Medicare beneficiaries who do not qualify for dual eligibility?

_____

Matching

Directions: *Place the letter that precedes the word or words that correctly answer the question/statement.* (**Note:** *Not all answers will be used.*)

_____ 1. The program that provides community-based acute and long-term care services.

_____ 2. A health insurance plan sold by private insurance companies to help pay for expenses not covered by Medicare.

_____ 3. The time period Medicare allows for enrolling in a Medicare supplement plan without penalty.

_____ 4. The term used when Medicare is not the primary payer, and the beneficiary is covered under another insurance policy.

_____ 5. The individual responsible for initial MSP development activities formerly performed by Medicare FIs and carriers.

A. COB contractor

B. MSP

C. Program of All-Inclusive Care for the Elderly

D. Medigap

E. Open enrollment

F. Medi/Medi

G. Preferred provider organization

Critical Thinking Activities

A. You are employed as a health insurance professional at Broadmoor Medical Clinic, where there is a standing policy that patients cannot be seen until they produce "proof of insurance." When you ask Averil Potter, a 76-year-old new patient, for his Medicare ID card, he informs you that he does not carry it with him because he is afraid of "identity theft." He informs you that he has memorized his Medicare number, which is his Social Security number with an ending alpha character. In light of the growing incidence of identity theft and the fact that many insurance companies use Social Security numbers as policy identifiers, would you recommend that the clinic's policy be changed? If so, how; if not, why not?

B. Members of the health care team of the Broadmoor Medical Center's emergency department are not allowed to ask for proof of insurance before treating a patient who has arrived for emergency treatment. What is the rationale for this difference in policy as opposed to that of the Clinic?

C. Because a Medicare nonPAR can charge 15% over and above the Medicare allowable charge and bill the patient for this excess amount, why do many providers become Medicare PARs?

D. Frieda Dawson is a 66-year-old Medicare established patient. She was seen on March 16, 20XX, and had a mammogram the next day. Frieda returns on November 30 of that same year for treatment of a severe urinary tract infection, at which time she requests another mammogram. She is worried because her 73-year-old sister was recently diagnosed with breast cancer. You schedule the second mammogram as Frieda requests; however, Medicare disallows it as not being "medically necessary." You failed to get an advance beneficiary notice because you thought Medicare paid for mammograms. How should you handle this situation?

Case Studies

A. **Medicare Part B benefits:** When Phyllis Trent, age 72, was in the hospital, she received services from several providers in addition to the hospital. Some providers were PAR; some were nonPAR.

1. The first provider to visit Phyllis was Dr. Frank McDonald, her internist and her regular physician. Dr. McDonald examined Phyllis and referred her to a surgeon, Dr. Maxwell Leonard. (**Note:** Phyllis has not met her deductible for the year.) Dr. McDonald's charges to Medicare were processed as follows:

   Charged for professional services: $500
   Medicare-approved charges: $400

   Phyllis owes deductible of _____

   Medicare paid _____% × $_____ = _____

   Phyllis owes co-insurance of _____% × $_____ = $_____

2. Dr. Leonard, the surgeon, is a Medicare PAR provider. He bills Medicare as follows:

   Charges for professional services: $1800
   Medicare-approved charges: $1200

   Medicare paid _____% × $_____ = _____

   Phyllis owes deductible of _____

   Phyllis owes co-insurance of _____% × $_____ = $_____

3. Phyllis received a statement from the anesthesiologist, who is nonPAR with Medicare and does not accept assignment. The anesthesiologist billed Medicare as follows:

Charges for professional services: $920
Medicare-approved charges: $800

Medicare paid _____% × $_____ = _____

Phyllis owes deductible of _____

Phyllis owes co-insurance of _____% × $_____ = $_____

Plus **excess** charges of _____% × $_____ = $_____

4. Phyllis was transported to the hospital by ambulance. Medicare determined it was medically necessary because it was an emergency. The ambulance claim was processed as follows:

Charges for ambulance transport: $720
Medicare-approved charge: $300

Medicare paid _____% × $_____ = _____

Phyllis owes deductible of _____

Phyllis owes co-insurance of _____% × $_____ = $_____

Plus **excess** charges of _____% × $_____ = $_____

5. Before her surgery, Phyllis had several procedures performed on an outpatient basis at the hospital. The hospital billing was processed as follows:

Hospital charges	$3000
Medicare paid	$1215
Beneficiary co-pay	$571

What is the total amount Phyllis owes?

6. Phyllis had a series of clinical diagnostic laboratory tests while in the hospital. This claim was processed as follows:

Blood series charge: $280
Medicare-approved charge: $220

Phyllis owes co-insurance of _____% × $_____ = $_____

Plus **excess** charges of _____% × $_____ = $_____

7. How would Phyllis's responsibility for the laboratory tests change if she had not yet satisfied her Part B deductible?

8. Medicare denied one laboratory test as "not medically necessary." What was Phyllis' responsibility for this charge?

B. **Interpreting a Medicare Summary Notice (MSN):** Study the MSN in Fig. 5-14, then answer the following questions:

1. What does the "A" indicate following this patient's Medicare ID number?
2. If the alpha character had been a "D," what would that indicate?

3. This claim was for a _____ day _____.
4. Has the patient met the deductible for this benefit period?
5. What is the total amount the patient may have to pay out-of-pocket?

Page 1 of 1

Medicare Summary Notice

Jane Beneficiary
123 Any Street
Anytown, Iowa 50000

HELP STOP FRAUD: Beware of door-to-door solicitors offering free or discounted Medicare items or services.

Customer Service Information

Your Medicare Number: 123-45-6789A

If you have questions, write or call:
Medicare
555 Medicare Blvd.
Suite 200
Medicare Building
Medicare, US XXXXX-XXXX

Local: (XXX)XXX-XXXX
Toll-free: 1-800-XXX-XXXX
TTY for Hearing Impaired: 1-800-XXX-XXXX

This is a summary of claims processed from 09/15/2000 through 10/15/2000.

PART A HOSPITAL INSURANCE – INPATIENT CLAIMS

Dates of Service	Benefit Days Used	Amount Charged	Non-Covered Charges	Deductible and Coinsurance	You May Be Billed	See Notes Section
Claim number 0000-0000-0000 Broadmoor Medical Clinic Milton, XY 12345 R. L. Jones, MD						a
09/06/00-09/08/00	2 days	$2,399.55	$34.00	$776.00	$810.00	b,c,d

Notes Section:

a. This information is being sent to your private insurer(s). Send any questions regarding benefits to them.

b. $776.00 was applied to your inpatient deductible.

c. Days used are being subtracted from your total inpatient benefits for this benefit period.

d. $34.00 for noncovered charges for which you are liable.

Deductible Information:

You have now met the Part A deductible for this benefit period.

General Information:

If you were offered free items or services but Medicare was billed, please call your local Customer Service at (XXX)XXX-XXXX or toll-free 1-800-XXX-XXXX.

Appeals Information – Part A

If you disagree with any claims decision on this notice, you can request an appeal by **December 15, 2000.** Follow the instructions below:

1) Circle the item(s) you disagree with and explain why you disagree.

2) Send this notice, or a copy, to the address in the "Customer Service Information" box on Page 1.

3) Sign here _____   Phone number (___) _____

THIS IS NOT A BILL – Keep this notice for your records.

Fig. 5-14   Medicare Summary Notice.

C. Elizabeth Franklin has a Medicare supplement policy with Blue Cross and Blue Shield of Iowa. Study the explanation of benefits (EOB) in Fig. 5-15 and answer the following questions:

1. What was the date of service? _____

2. Milton Gastroenterology charged _____.

3. Medicare-approved charge is _____.

4. How much did Medicare pay? _____

5. How much did Blue Cross and Blue Shield pay? _____

6. How much does Ms. Franklin owe on this claim? _____

D. Study the EOB from the Medicare Supplemental Policy in Fig. 5-16.

1. Dr. Jones charged Harold Shalladay $32 for an office visit on 01/03/20XX, and Medicare approved $17.17. Did Medicare pay anything on this claim? If so, why? If not, why not?

2. Medicare sent Mr. Shalladay's claim to his Medicare supplemental carrier, Mutual of Omaha Companies. How much, if anything, did Mutual of Omaha pay toward this claim?

3. What amount can you bill Mr. Shalladay after Medicare and Mutual of Omaha have paid their share of the claim?

4. Can you determine from the EOB if Dr. Jones is Medicare PAR or nonPAR?

5. If Mr. Shalladay were eligible for the QMB program, how much would he have to pay out-of-pocket for this claim?

Internet Exploration

A. Log on to **http://www.medicare.gov** and choose "Learn More About Plans in Your Area." Enter your state and county and click "Continue." Study the relevant information about Medigap plans in your state. Compare this information to plans in neighboring states.

B. Local coverage determinations have replaced LMRPs. Log on to **http://www.cms.hhs.gov/ coverage/lmrp_contractors_index.asp.** Find the contractor who administers Medicare in your state. Research the site to learn what resources are available to learn more about this topic.

BlueCross BlueShield of Iowa

Page   1

Identification Number:

Explanation of Health Benefits
Medicare Supplement

Claim Number: 43900190CLJX

Provider Number: 4486942

Provider Name: MILTON GASTROENTEROLOGY CLINIC

This is not a bill. It is a statement showing how we applied your Blue Cross and Blue Shield of Iowa coverage to claims submitted to us. If you have a question, please detach the top of this form and send it to us with a letter or call: Customer Service is available to answer calls Mon.–Fri. 8:00 a.m.–4:00 p.m.

Date of Service		SER-VICE CODE	Charge		Medicare Approved		Medicare Benefit Amount		BC/BS Benefit Amount		Notes	Claim Summary
From	Through											
11-01	11-01-20XX	3G	50	00	26	99	21	59	5	40		Total Charges Submitted
												50.00
												Medicare Approved
												26.90
												Medicare Benefit Amount
												21.50
												Noncovered Services
												.00
												Amount You Owe*
												.00
												Blue Cross Blue Shield Benefit Amount For This Claim
This is not a bill and you should not send us money. However, if you have not paid for the service shown here, you may owe the provider. You may want to keep this statement for your records.												5.40

Notes

*This is the amount you owe the provider indicated above. If you have already paid this provider, please disregard this amount.

Identification Number	**Group Number**	**Claim Number**	**Account Number**
Claim Received 12-22-20XX	**Claim Processed** 01-13-20XX	**Provider Name** MILTON GASTROENTEROLOGY CLINIC	**Patient Name**

Fig. 5-15 Blue Cross and Blue Shield explanation of benefits.

```
                                                         Page 1 of 1

              Medicare Summary Notice
```

Customer Service Information

Your Medicare Number: 123-45-6789A

Harold Shalladay
1552 Airline Drive
Milton, XY 12345

If you have questions, write or call:
  Medicare
  555 Medicare Blvd.
  Suite 200
  Medicare Building
  Medicare, US XXXXX-XXXX

Local: (XXX)XXX-XXXX
Toll-free: 1-800-XXX-XXXX
TTY for Hearing Impaired: 1-800-XXX-XXXX

HELP STOP FRAUD: Beware of door-to-door
solicitors offering free or discounted Medicare
items or services.

This is a summary of claims processed from 02/15/2000 through 03/15/2000.

PART B MEDICAL INSURANCE – ASSIGNED CLAIMS

Dates of Service	Services Provided	Amount Charged	Medicare Approved	Medicare Paid Provider	You May Be Billed	See Notes Section
Claim number 0000-0000-0000 Broadmoor Medical Clinic Milton, XY 12345 R. L. Jones, MD						a
01/31/00	1 Office/Outpatient visit, Est. (99212)	$32.00	$17.17	$0.00	$17.17	b

Notes Section:
a. This information is being sent to your private insurer(s). Send any questions regarding benefits to them.
b. $17.17 of this approved amount has been applied toward your deductible

Deductible Information:

You have now met $38.73 of your Part B deductible.

General Information:

If you were offered free items or services but Medicare was billed, please call your local Customer Service at (XXX)XXX-XXXX or toll-free 1-800-XXX-XXXX.

Appeals Information – Part B

If you disagree with any claims decision on this notice, you can request an appeal by **September 15, 2000.** Follow the instructions below:

1) Circle the item(s) you disagree with and explain why you disagree.

2) Send this notice, or a copy, to the address in the "Customer Service Information" box on Page 1.

3) Sign here _____ Phone number (___)_____

THIS IS NOT A BILL – Keep this notice for your records.

Fig. 5-16   Medicare Summary Notice (Shalladay).

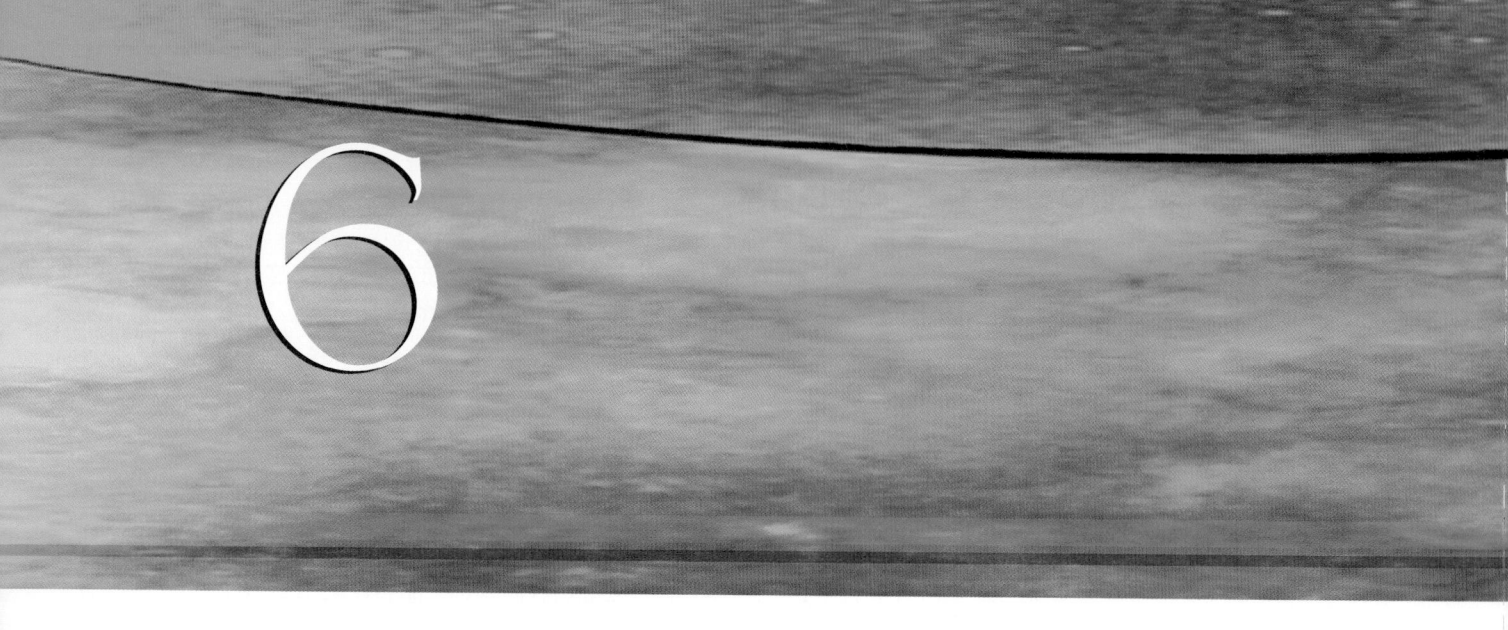

OBJECTIVES

After completion of this chapter, the student should be able to:

1. Discuss the history and development of diagnostic coding.
2. Outline the format of the ICD-9-CM manual.
3. Describe the organization and use of Volume 2, the Alphabetic Index.
4. Explain what "main terms" are and how to locate them.
5. Differentiate between an essential and nonessential modifier.
6. Discuss the importance of understanding coding conventions.
7. Explain the organization of codes in Volume 1, the Tabular List.
8. List the essential steps to diagnostic coding.
9. Give an overview of ICD-10.

DIAGNOSTIC CODING

KEY TERMS

adjectives
category
code set
coding
combination code
conditions
diagnosis
diseases
E codes
eponyms

essential modifiers
etiology
hypertension
in situ
International Classification of Diseases,
   Ninth Revision, Clinical Modification
   (ICD-9-CM)
International Classification of Diseases,
Tenth Revision (ICD-10)
main term

manifestation
morbidity
mortality
neoplasm
nonessential modifiers
notes
noun
subcategory
subclassification
V codes

Opening Scenario

Since Park Chalmers was a little boy, he had wanted to be a doctor; however, when he fainted after witnessing a bicycle accident that severely injured his best friend's arm, Park realized that the clinical side of medicine was not for him. Still, the field of medicine intrigued him. After high school, Park moved from one dead-end job to another. He soon faced the fact that without specialized career training, the prospect of living comfortably in an apartment of his own appeared grim.

In his search for more meaningful employment, Park noticed an advertisement in the classified section of the newspaper for a coder at a local medical clinic. The position required coursework or on-the-job experience in ICD-9-CM and CPT coding. The pay range noted in the ad was enticing to Park; however, he had no idea what ICD-9-CM or CPT coding was. The terms themselves were "codes" to Park.

Curious about the meaning of ICD-9-CM and CPT coding, Park made inquiries when he attended a job fair at the community college. He was directed to the health careers booth where current health insurance students, along with the aid of an instructor, answered all his questions and gave a brief demonstration on diagnostic coding.

"I think I can learn this coding stuff," Park decided, and headed for the Student Services Department to enroll in the upcoming health insurance program.

HISTORY AND DEVELOPMENT OF DIAGNOSTIC CODING

Dorland's Illustrated Medical Dictionary defines **diagnosis** as "the determination of the nature of a cause of disease," or "the art of distinguishing one disease from another." **Coding**, as it applies to this topic, is the process of assigning a series of numbers or alphanumerical characters to a diagnosis for the purpose of identification or classification or both.

Diagnostic coding dates back to 17th century England, where statistical data were collected through a system called the *London Bills of Mortality*. By 1937, this method of tracking information had evolved into the International List of Causes of Death. The World Health Organization (WHO) published a statistical listing in 1948 that tracked **morbidity** (the presence of illness or disease) and **mortality** (the deaths that occur from a disease). This statistical WHO listing was called the International Classification of Diseases (ICD) and ultimately became the book used worldwide today for coding diagnoses—the *International Classification of Diseases, Ninth Revision* (ICD-9).

Use of ICD-9 began in the United States when the U.S. National Center for Health Statistics modified the system in 1977 with clinical information. This modification provided a way to classify morbidity data for the indexing of medical records,

medical case reviews, ambulatory and other medical care programs, and basic health statistics. The result was the ***International Classification of Diseases, Ninth (BF) Revision, Clinical Modification*** (ICD-9-CM). This modified version precisely describes the clinical picture of each patient and provides exact information above and beyond that needed for statistics and analysis of health care trends.

In 1988, Congress passed the Medicare Catastrophic Coverage Act. This act mandated the use of ICD-9 coding for all Part B Medicare Claims. A portion of this act was later revoked, but the part requiring use of ICD-9 codes for Medicare claims was upheld and became effective in April 1989. Basic guidelines regarding the use of ICD-9 codes were published by the Centers for Medicare and Medicaid Services (CMS), previously known as the Health Care Financing Administration. Soon after Medicare began using ICD-9 codes, other insurance companies followed. Today, most third-party payers require the use of these diagnosis codes on all claims.

The ICD-9-CM currently comprises three volumes:

- Volume 1, Tabular List
- Volume 2, Alphabetic List
- Volume 3, Used for Hospital Inpatient Procedure Coding

Generally, most publishers combine Volumes 1 and 2 in the same manual. Although most insurance companies do not require the use of Volume 3 for physician billing, Volume 3 is still used for hospital inpatient coding. (Medicare Part B does not accept codes from Volume 3; if they are used, the claim is denied.) The health insurance professional should obtain and use the most recent version of the ICD-9 for effective and accurate coding. Any questions regarding which volume to use should be addressed to the appropriate carrier, fiscal intermediary, or billing consultant.

WHAT DID YOU LEARN?

1. When did diagnostic coding get its start in the United States?
2. How did the Medicare Catastrophic Coverage Act affect diagnostic coding?
3. Name the three volumes that make up the ICD-9-CM.
4. What ICD-9-CM volumes are generally used for physician billing?

ICD-9-CM MANUAL

Before any attempt is made to code a diagnosis, the health insurance professional must become familiar with the contents and structure of the ICD-9 manual. The format of the ICD-9 differs from one publisher to the next as far as how the material is arranged; however, the basic information is the same. The prefacing instructions given here are generic because the ICD-9-CM manual is available from several different publishers in a variety of formats. The information, coding instructions, and codes were current at the time of this writing. For up-to-date information, the health insurance professional should consult the most recent ICD-9-CM coding manual.

The first several pages of the ICD-9 manual contain an introduction and guide to using the ICD-9. Informational items typically include (but are not limited to) the following:

- Introduction
    A discussion of the history and future of the ICD-9-CM system
    The background of the ICD-9-CM
    Characteristics of ICD-9-CM
    The disease classification
- Instructional steps for using Physicians Volumes 1 and 2 correctly
    Ten steps to correct coding
    Organization

- A listing of ICD-9-CM Official Conventions, footnotes, symbols, and instructional notes
- A summary of code changes
- Valid three-digit ICD-9 codes
- General coding guidelines

No matter which ICD-9-CM manual is used, it is important that the health insurance professional study thoroughly the prefacing information contained in the introductory pages because it serves as a basic foundation for diagnostic coding and aids in assigning diagnosis codes correctly. The following sections complete a typical format of an ICD-9-CM manual:

- Volume 2, Index to Diseases
- Volume 1, Tabular List
- Appendix A, Morphology of Neoplasms
- Appendix B, Glossary of Mental Disorders
- Appendix C, Classification of Drugs by American Hospital Formulary Service List
- Appendix D, Industrial Accidents According to Agency
- Appendix E, Three-Digit Categories (Infectious and Parasitic Diseases)

Volume 2, the Alphabetic List (Index)

Volume 2, the Alphabetic List, typically is located in the front half of the ICD-9-CM and is presented before Volume 1, the Tabular List. Volume 2 contains an alphabetical listing that provides detailed instructions that can help the coder determine if a diagnosis requires the use of additional or alternative codes. A diagnosis should *never* be coded strictly from the Alphabetic List.

A diagnosis code consists of three to five characters, depending on whether a three-digit, four-digit, or five-digit code best represents the patient's diagnosis. ICD-9-CM codes range from 001 to V85.4 (2006) and identify symptoms, conditions, problems, complaints, or other reasons for the procedure, service, or supply provided. It is crucial that a diagnosis is coded to the "highest level of specificity." By consulting the Alphabetic List first, the health insurance professional can determine more accurately whether a three-digit code sufficiently describes the diagnosis or whether additional numbers are required for specificity. Diagnoses that are coded inadequately or inappropriately can result in a claim being underpaid, overpaid, delayed, or denied.

Three Sections of Volume 2

Section 1, the Index to Diseases
Volume 2 contains three separate sections or indexes. The largest one, the Index to Diseases, is

organized alphabetically by **main terms**, which are always printed in boldface type for ease of reference. Main terms include the following:

- **Diseases**, such as influenza or bronchitis
- **Conditions**, such as fatigue, fracture, or injury
- **Nouns**, such as disease, disturbance, syndrome, or eponyms
- **Adjectives**, such as double, large, or kinked

Anatomical sites are not listed as main terms. If a patient has a diagnosis of deviated nasal septum, it would be found in Volume 2 under the main term "deviation," rather than "nasal." Ankle sprain would be located under "sprain," rather than "ankle." Fig. 6-1 shows a sample page from Volume 2.

STOP AND THINK

Marlee Davis is employed as a health insurance professional for cardiologist Ferris Barnes. Marlee is in charge of all the billing, coding, and insurance. While preparing to submit an insurance claim for patient Eloise Hardy, Marlee notes that the patient's health care record documents a diagnosis of "congestive heart failure." Identify the "main term" in this diagnosis.

Many conditions can be found in more than one place in the Alphabetic Index, which can be confusing sometimes. Obstetrical conditions can be found under the name of the condition and under the entries for "delivery," "pregnancy," and "puerperal" (after delivery). Fig. 6-2 provides examples of how each of these three terms are shown in Volume 2. Complications of medical and surgical care are indexed under the *name of condition* and under *complications*.

EPONYMS. **Eponyms** are diseases, procedures, or syndromes named for individuals who discovered or first used them. They typically are located alphabetically by the individual's name and by the common name. Vincent's disease (trench mouth) can be found under "Vincent's," "disease," and "trench" (Fig. 6-3).

ESSENTIAL MODIFIERS. **Essential modifiers** are indented under the main term, as shown in the example in Fig. 6-4. They modify the main, term describing different sites, **etiology** (the cause or origin of a disease or condition), and clinical types. Essential modifiers must be a part of the documented diagnosis.

NONESSENTIAL MODIFIERS. **Nonessential modifiers** are terms in parentheses following the main terms. They typically give alternative terminology for the main term and are provided to assist the coder in locating the applicable main term. Fig. 6-5 shows an example of how nonessential modifiers are depicted in Volume 2. Nonessential modifiers are usually not a part of the diagnostic statement.

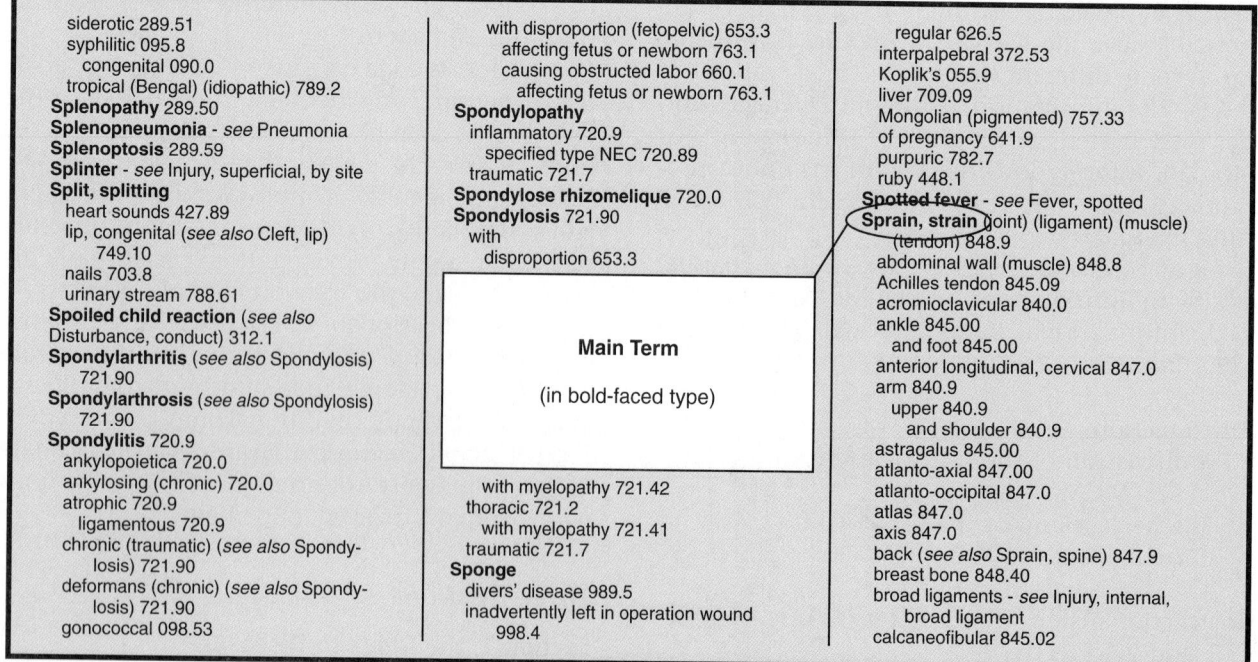

Fig. 6-1 Sample page of section of the ICD-9 Volume 2. (*Data from* International Classification of Diseases, *Ninth Revision. U.S. Department of Health and Human Services, Public Health Service, Centers for Medicare and Medicaid Services.*)

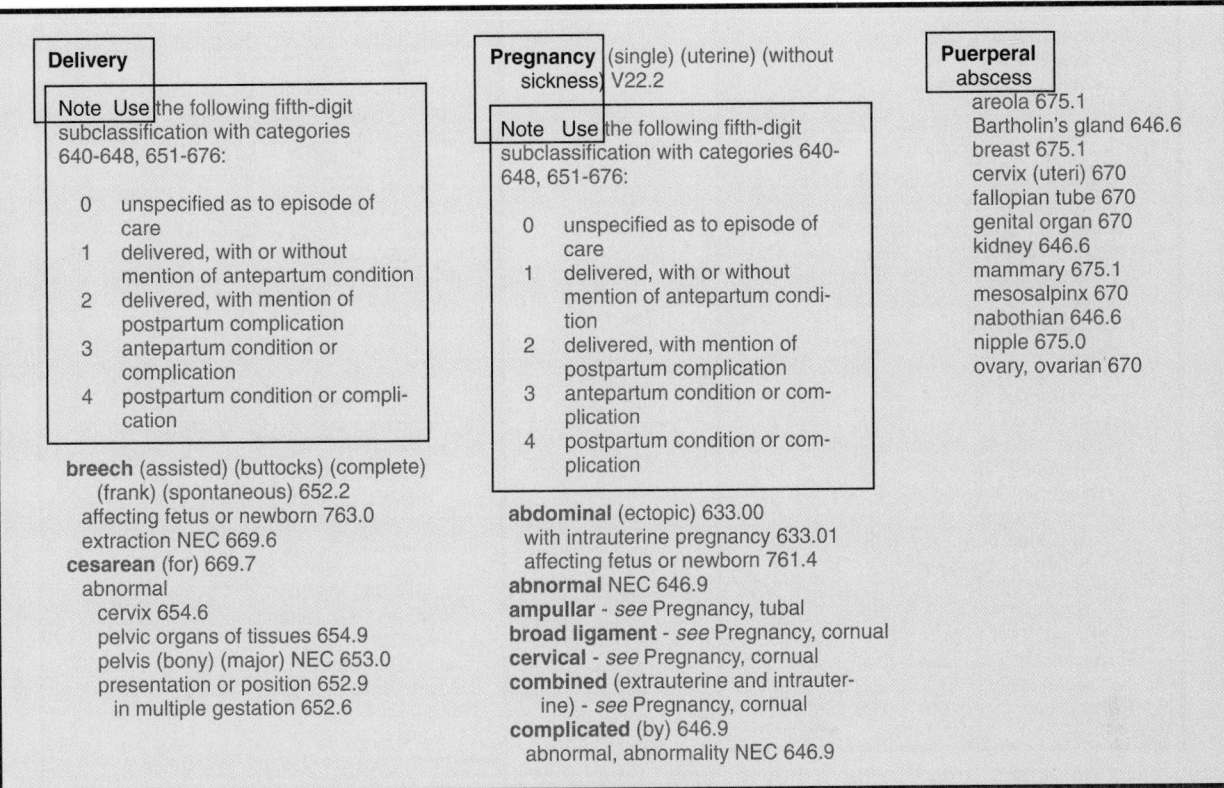

Delivery

Note Use the following fifth-digit subclassification with categories 640-648, 651-676:

   0   unspecified as to episode of care
   1   delivered, with or without mention of antepartum condition
   2   delivered, with mention of postpartum complication
   3   antepartum condition or complication
   4   postpartum condition or complication

breech (assisted) (buttocks) (complete) (frank) (spontaneous) 652.2
   affecting fetus or newborn 763.0
   extraction NEC 669.6
cesarean (for) 669.7
   abnormal
      cervix 654.6
      pelvic organs of tissues 654.9
      pelvis (bony) (major) NEC 653.0
      presentation or position 652.9
         in multiple gestation 652.6

Pregnancy (single) (uterine) (without sickness) V22.2

Note Use the following fifth-digit subclassification with categories 640-648, 651-676:

   0   unspecified as to episode of care
   1   delivered, with or without mention of antepartum condition
   2   delivered, with mention of postpartum complication
   3   antepartum condition or complication
   4   postpartum condition or complication

abdominal (ectopic) 633.00
   with intrauterine pregnancy 633.01
   affecting fetus or newborn 761.4
abnormal NEC 646.9
ampullar - *see* Pregnancy, tubal
broad ligament - *see* Pregnancy, cornual
cervical - *see* Pregnancy, cornual
combined (extrauterine and intrauterine) - *see* Pregnancy, cornual
complicated (by) 646.9
   abnormal, abnormality NEC 646.9

Puerperal
abscess
   areola 675.1
   Bartholin's gland 646.6
   breast 675.1
   cervix (uteri) 670
   fallopian tube 670
   genital organ 670
   kidney 646.6
   mammary 675.1
   mesosalpinx 670
   nabothian 646.6
   nipple 675.0
   ovary, ovarian 670

Fig. 6-2 Example showing how each of the above three terms is shown in Volume 2. (*Data from* International Classification of Diseases, *Ninth Revision. U.S. Department of Health and Human Services, Public Health Service, Centers for Medicare and Medicaid Services.*)

VIN II (vulvar intraepithelial neoplasia I) 624.8
VIN III (vulvar intraepithelial neoplasia I) 233.3
Vincent's
   angina 101
   bronchitis 101
   disease 101
   gingivitis 101
   infection (any site) 101
   laryngitis 101
   stomatitis 101
   tonsillitis 101
Vinson-Plummer syndrome (sideropenic dysphagia) 280.8
Viosterol deficiency (*see also* Deficiency, calciferol) 268.9
Virchow's disease 733.99
Viremia 790.8

Fig. 6-3 Example of an eponym listing. (*Data from* International Classification of Diseases, *Ninth Revision. U.S. Department of Health and Human Services, Public Health Service, Centers for Medicare and Medicaid Services.*)

   traumatic - *see* Injury, nerve, spinal
   nontraumatic - *see* Myelitis
stomach 536.9
   psychogenic 306.4
sympathetic nerve NEC (*see also* Neuropathy, peripheral, autonomic) 337.9
ulnar nerve 354.2
vagina 623.9
Isambert's disease 012.3
Ischemia, ischemic 459.9
→ basilar artery (with transient neurologic deficit) 435.0
   bone NEC 733.40
   bowel (transient) 557.9
      acute 557.0
      chronic 557.1
      due to mesenteric artery insufficiency 557.1
   brain - *see also* Ischemia, cerebral
      recurrent focal 435.9
   cardiac (*see also* Ischemia, heart) 414.9

Fig. 6-4 Example of an essential modifier. (*Data from* International Classification of Diseases, *Ninth Revision. U.S. Department of Health and Human Services, Public Health Service, Centers for Medicare and Medicaid Services.*)

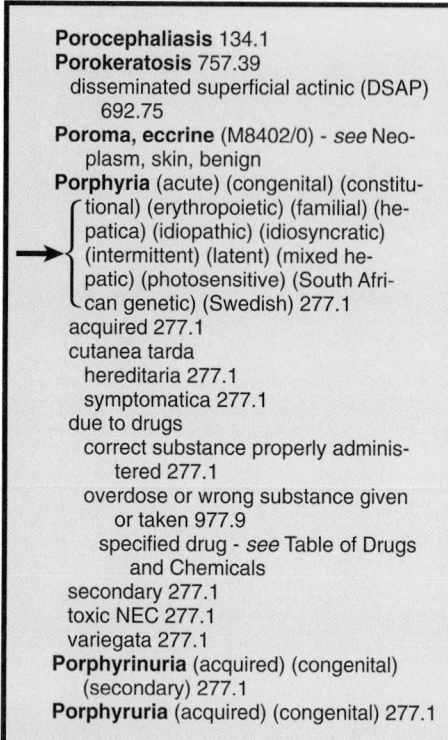

Fig. 6-5 Section of page from Volume 2 showing nonessential modifiers using porphyria. *(Data from International Classification of Diseases, Ninth Revision. U.S. Department of Health and Human Services, Public Health Service, Centers for Medicare and Medicaid Services.)*

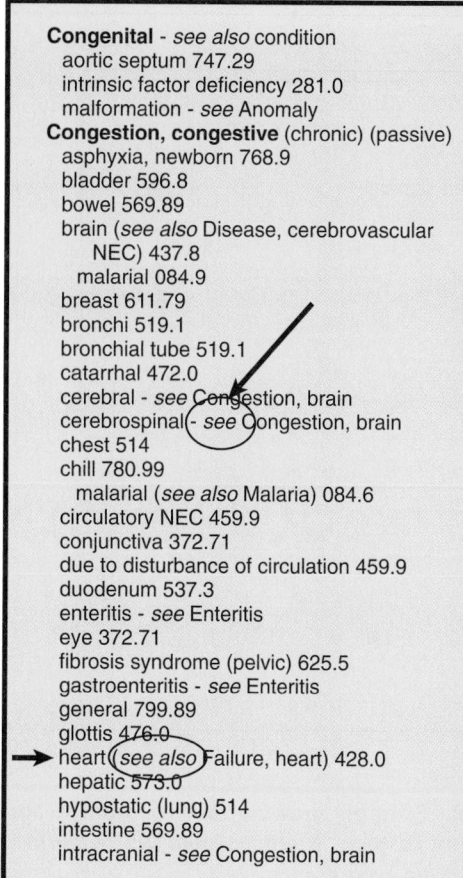

Fig. 6-6 Section from Volume 2 using congestive heart failure. *(Data from International Classification of Diseases, Ninth Revision. U.S. Department of Health and Human Services, Public Health Service, Centers for Medicare and Medicaid Services.)*

NOTES.   Cross-reference **notes**, such as *see*, *see* also, and *see condition*, typically refer the coder to continue the search under another main term. Referring to the patient described in the Stop and Think box with a diagnosis of *congestive heart failure*, the main term "congestive" and the essential modifier "heart" are located in the Alphabetic Index, and there is a parenthetical notation *(see also* Failure, heart 428.0). This notation guides the coder to an alternate page in the Index, where the main term "failure, failed" is located. After the essential modifiers ("heart" and "congestive") code 428.0 is located, the coder must cross-reference this code to the Tabular List to determine if 428.0 describes this diagnosis to its "greatest specificity" or if a fifth digit is needed. Fig. 6-6 shows an example of how *see also* is used in Volume 2.

HYPERTENSION AND NEOPLASM TABLES. Also listed within the Alphabetic Index to Diseases are two tables: (1) Hypertension Table and (2) Neoplasm Table. If a patient is diagnosed with a type of **hypertension** (high blood pressure), the health insurance professional must locate the specific type in the hypertension table and determine whether it is "malignant," "benign," or "unspecified" as indicated in the columnar codes (Fig. 6-7). If the patient's diagnosis is essential benign hypertension, the ICD-9 code would be 401.1. As with other code searches, hypertension and **neoplasm** (new growth) coding does not stop with the indexed tables in Volume 2.

Section 2, Table of Drugs and Chemicals

Section 2 of Volume 2 consists of the Table of Drugs and Chemicals, which contains the Alphabetic Index to Poisoning and External Causes of Adverse Effects of Drugs and Other Chemical Substances. Codes in this table are used when documentation

IMAGINE THIS!

Tricia Lorber, a health insurance professional, was preparing a claim for patient Arthur Renteria, whose health record documented "hemorrhoids, internal and external." Tricia used a diagnosis code of 455.3, but if she had coded to the "greatest specificity," two codes should have been reported: 455.0 and 455.3. This error cost the practice $100.

	Malignant	Benign	Unspecified
Hypertension, hypertensive (arterial) (arteriolar) (crisis) (degeneration) (disease) (essential) (fluctuating) (idiopathic) (intermittent) (labile) (low renin) (orthostatic) (paroxysmal) (primary) (systemic) (uncontrolled) (vascular)	401.0	401.1	401.9
with			
chronic kidney disease	403.01	403.11	403.91 ◄
heart involvement (conditions classifiable to 429.0-429.3, 429.8, 429.9 due to hypertension) (*see also* Hypertension, heart)	402.00	402.10	402.90
with kidney involvement-*see* Hypertension, cardiorenal			
renal involvement (only conditions classifiable to 585, 586, 587) (excludes conditions classifiable to 584) (*see also* Hypertension, kidney)	403.00	403.10	403.90
with heart involvement-*see* Hypertension, cardiorenal			
failure (and sclerosis) (*see also* Hypertension, kidney)	403.01	403.11	403.91
sclerosis without failure (*see also* Hypertension, kidney)	403.00	403.10	403.90
accelerated (*see also* Hypertension, by type, malignant)	401.0	-	-
antepartum-*see* Hypertension, complicating pregnancy, childbirth, or the puerperium			
cardiorenal (disease)	404.00	404.10	404.90
with			
chronic kidney disease	403.01	403.11	403.91 ◄
and heart failure	404.03	404.13	404.93 ◄
heart failure	404.01	404.11	404.91
and chronic kidney disease	404.03	404.13	404.93 ◄
and renal failure	404.03	404.13	404.93
renal failure	404.02	404.12	404.92
and heart failure	404.03	404.13	404.93
cardiovascular disease (arteriosclerotic) (sclerotic)	402.00	402.10	402.90
with			
heart failure	402.01	402.11	402.91
renal involvement (conditions classifiable to 403) (*see also* Hypertension, cardiorenal)	404.00	404.10	404.90
cardiovascular renal (disease) (sclerosis) (*see also* Hypertension, cardiorenal)	404.00	404.10	404.90
cerebrovascular disease NEC	437.2	437.2	437.2
complicating pregnancy, childbirth, or the puerperium	642.2	642.0	642.9
with			
albuminuria (and edema) (mild)	-	-	642.4
severe	-	-	642.5
edema (mild)	-	-	642.4
severe	-	-	642.5
heart disease	642.2	642.2	642.2
and renal disease	642.2	642.2	642.2
renal disease	642.2	642.2	642.2
and heart disease	642.2	642.2	642.2
chronic	642.2	642.0	642.0
with pre-eclampsia or eclampsia	642.7	642.7	642.7
fetus or newborn	760.0	760.0	760.0
essential	-	642.0	642.0
with pre-eclampsia or eclampsia	-	642.7	642.7
fetus or newborn	760.0	760.0	760.0
fetus or newborn	760.0	760.0	760.0
gestational	-	-	642.3
pre-existing	642.2	642.0	642.0

Fig. 6-7   Section from hypertension table. (*Data from* International Classification of Diseases, *Ninth Revision. U.S. Department of Health and Human Services, Public Health Service, Centers for Medicare and Medicaid Services.*)

in the health record indicates a poisoning, overdose, wrong substance given or taken, or intoxication. The table also lists external causes of adverse effects resulting from ingestion or exposure to drugs or other chemical substances. A section of a page from the Table of Drugs and Chemicals is shown in Fig. 6-8.

Section 3, Index to External Causes of Injury and Poisoning (E Codes)

Section 3 is the Alphabetic Index to External Causes of Injury and Poisoning, which contains **E codes** (Fig. 6-9). Codes in this section are used to classify environmental events, circumstances, and other conditions that are the cause of injury and other adverse effects. E codes are organized by main

terms that describe the accident, circumstance, event, or specific agent causing the injury or adverse effect.

STOP AND THINK

Twenty-year-old Bob Timmerman was driving his 1978 Trans-Am on a two-lane country road at dusk when he accidentally struck a slow-moving Amish carriage, injuring a 4-year-old child. The child sustained a fractured ulna and multiple lacerations and contusions. In what section of ICD-9 would the health insurance professional look to begin the search for the appropriate diagnostic code?

TABLE OF DRUGS AND CHEMICALS / Antibiotics

		External Cause (E-Code)				
Substance	Poisoning	Accident	Therapeutic Use	Suicide Attempt	Assault	Undetermined
Antibiotics *(Continued)*						
specified NEC	960.8	E856	E930.8	E950.4	E962.0	E980.4
tetracycline (group)	960.4	E856	E930.4	E950.4	E962.0	E980.4
Anticancer agents NEC	963.1	E858.1	E933.1	E950.4	E962.0	E980.4
antibiotics	960.7	E856	E930.7	E950.4	E962.0	E980.4
Anticholinergics	971.1	E855.4	E941.1	E950.4	E962.0	E980.4
Anticholinesterase (organophosphorus) (reversible)	971.0	E855.3	E941.0	E950.4	E962.0	E980.4
Anticoagulants	964.2	E858.2	E934.2	E950.4	E962.0	E980.4
antagonists	964.5	E858.2	E934.5	E950.4	E962.0	E980.4
Anti-common cold agents NEC	975.6	E858.6	E945.6	E950.4	E962.0	E980.4
Anticonvulsants NEC	966.3	E855.0	E936.3	E950.4	E962.0	E980.4
Antidepressants	969.0	E854.0	E939.0	E950.3	E962.0	E980.3
Antidiabetic agents	962.3	E858.0	E932.3	E950.4	E962.0	E980.4
Antidiarrheal agents	973.5	E858.4	E943.5	E950.4	E962.0	E980.4
Antidiuretic hormone	962.5	E858.0	E932.5	E950.4	E962.0	E980.4
Antidotes NEC	977.2	E858.8	E947.2	E950.4	E962.0	E980.4
Antiemetic agents	963.0	E858.1	E933.0	E950.4	E962.0	E980.4
Antiepilepsy agent NEC	966.3	E855.0	E936.3	E950.4	E962.0	E980.4
Antifertility pills	962.2	E858.0	E932.2	E950.4	E962.0	E980.4
Antiflatulents	973.8	E858.4	E943.8	E950.4	E962.0	E980.4
Antifreeze	989.89	E866.8	-	E950.9	E962.1	E980.9
alcohol	980.1	E860.2	-	E950.9	E962.1	E980.9
ethylene glycol	982.8	E862.4	-	E950.9	E962.1	E980.9
Antifungals (nonmedicinal) (sprays)	989.4	E863.6	-	E950.6	E962.1	E980.7
medicinal NEC	961.9	E857	E931.9	E950.4	E962.0	E980.4
antibiotic	960.1	E856	E930.1	E950.4	E962.0	E980.4
topical	976.0	E858.7	E946.0	E950.4	E962.0	E980.4

Fig. 6-8 Section from Table of Drugs and Chemicals. *(Data from* International Classification of Diseases, *Ninth Revision. U.S. Department of Health and Human Services, Public Health Service, Centers for Medicare and Medicaid Services.)*

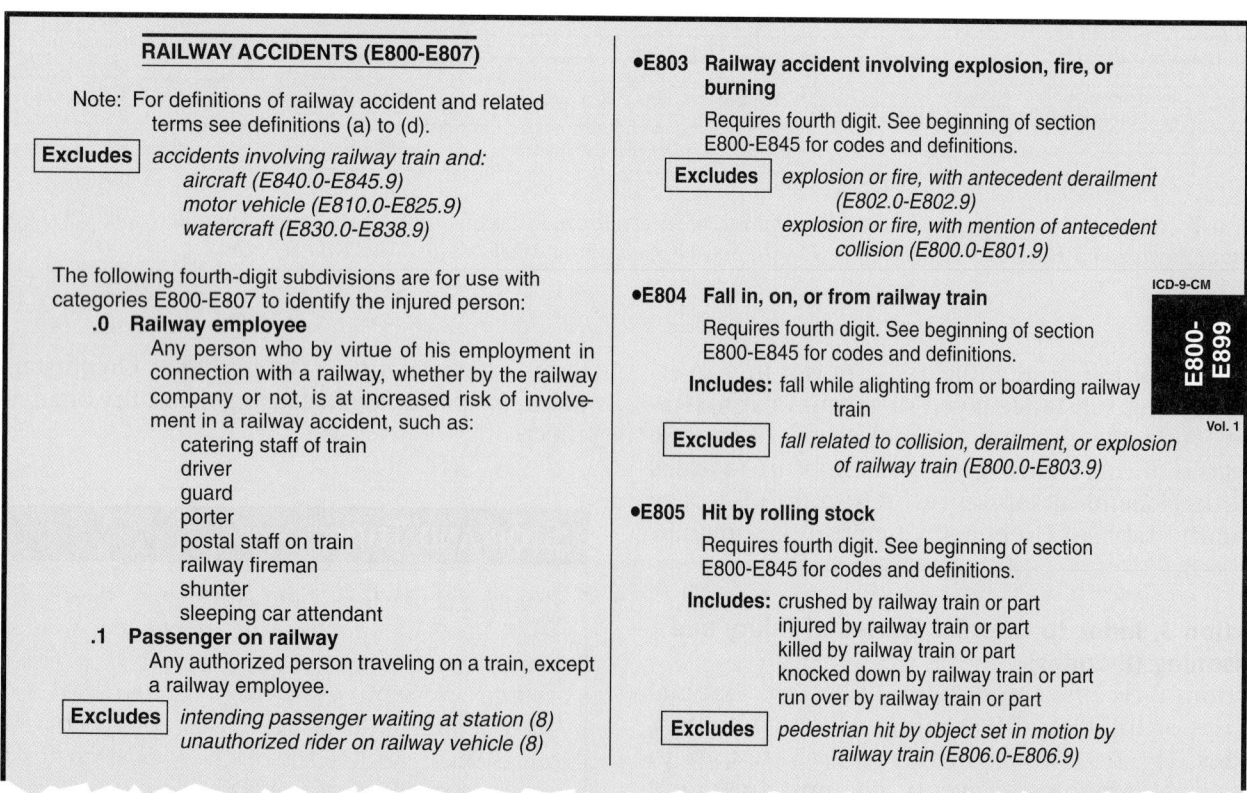

Fig. 6-9 Section from Index to External Causes. *(Data from* International Classification of Diseases, *Ninth Revision. U.S. Department of Health and Human Services, Public Health Service, Centers for Medicare and Medicaid Services.)*

DIAGNOSIS: Chk or 1 = Primary		2 = Secondary					Chlamydia / GC Screen	86631	
							Digoxin	80162	
							Dilantin	80185	
Abdominal Pain	789.00	COPD	496	Hypothyroidism	244.9		MSAFP	82105	
Allergies	995.3	CVA, Old	438.9	Long term med use	V58.69		Pap Smear	88150	
Anemia	285.9	Depression	311	Nasopharyngitis	460		RA	86430	
Anticoagulation Therapy	V58.61	Dermatitis	692.9	Otitis Media	382.00		T-4, Free-RIA	84439	
Anxiety	300.00	Diabetes (Non-Insulin)	250.00	Pharyngitis	462		Sensitivity	87186	
Arthritis	716.90	Diabetes (Insulin-Depend.)	250.01	Physical Exam	V70.0		Theophylline	80198	
Arthritis, degen.	715.90	Dizziness	780.4	Physical, Athletic	V70.3		Urine Culture	87086	
Arthritis, Rheumatoid	714.0	Elevated BP	796.2	Physical, Preemployment	V70.5		☐ Cash ☐ Credit Card	INITIALS	
Asthma	493.90	Fatigue	780.79	Pneumonia	486		Check # 3204	GSM	
Atrial Fibrillation	427.31	Gastroenteritis, viral	008.8	Pregnancy	V22.2				
Backache, unspec.	724.5	Gastroesophageal Reflux	530.81	Routine Child Exam	V20.0		PREVIOUS BALANCE	.00	
Bronchitis	490	GYN Exam w/Pap	V72.3	Sinusitis, Acute	461.9		CREDIT BALANCE	.00	
CAD	414.00	Headaches	784.0	Sinusitis, Chronic	473.9		TODAY'S CHARGES		
Chest Pain	786.50	Hypercholesterolemia	272.0	Tonsillitis	463			47.00	
CHF	428.0	Hyperlipidemia	272.4	URI	465.9				
Conjunctivitis	372.30	Hypertension, Benign	401.1	UTI	599.0				

OTHER DIAGNOSIS (NOT LISTED)   CODE

		PAYMENT ON TODAY'S CHARGES	47.00
		PAYMENT ON PREVIOUS BALANCE	

OFFICE RETURN
10   15   20   30   40   OTH_____
_____ _____ _____ FU_____
DAYS   WEEKS   MONTHS
WITH: PE

LAB RETURN
_____ _____ _____
DAYS   WEEKS   MONTHS
TESTS:

NEW BALANCE

Fig. 6-10 Portion of an encounter form showing list of diagnoses.

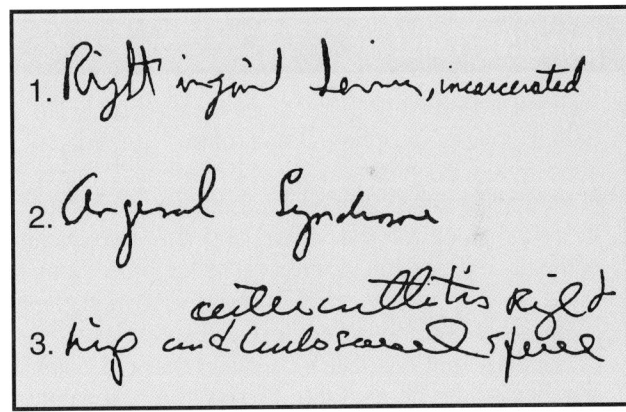

1. Right inguinal hernia, incarcerated
2. Argonal Syndrome
3. hip and tuberculosis of spine   cellunitis right

Fig. 6-11 Examples of handwritten diagnoses.

PROCESS OF CLASSIFYING DISEASES

Coding involves transforming verbal descriptions of a diagnosis into numbers or a combination of alphanumerical characters. In the insurance and billing department of a medical facility, coding might be done by a professional certified coder; however, in smaller offices, this task may fall under the responsibilities of the health insurance professional. Assuming the latter, the first thing that the health insurance professional must do in the coding process is to locate the diagnosis in the health record. This can be straightforward sometimes because many encounter forms list the more frequently used diagnoses within a certain medical specialty along with their corresponding ICD-9 codes (Fig. 6-10). Other times, the health insurance professional may have to refer back to the clinical notes to locate the diagnosis. If the notes are written, deciphering the health care professional's handwriting sometimes can be challenging (Fig. 6-11). With practice and experience, locating the diagnosis within the clinical notes and translating a physician's handwriting become easier.

After the diagnosis has been determined, the health insurance professional should identify the main term within the diagnosis. If the diagnosis is "breast mass," the main term would be *mass*. (The anatomic site *breast* is not used in the Alphabetic Index to Diseases.) Fig. 6-12 illustrates how the main term "mass" appears in Volume 2.

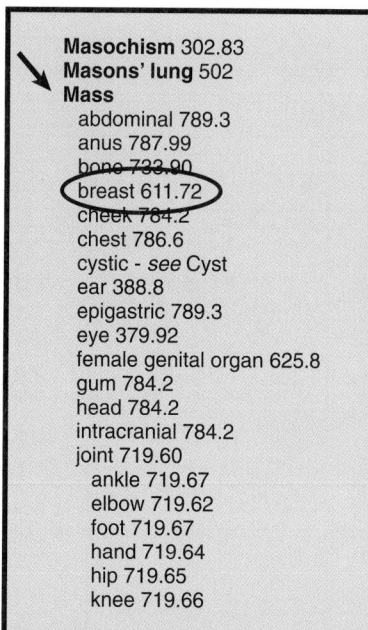

Fig. 6-12   Section of Volume 2 showing Mass, breast. *(Data from* International Classification of Diseases, *Ninth Revision. U.S. Department of Health and Human Services, Public Health Service, Centers for Medicare and Medicaid Services.)*

IMAGINE THIS!

Marlee Davis, the health insurance professional in Dr. Barnes' office, deciphered one of the physician's handwritten diagnoses as "atrophic arthritis," rather than "aortic arteritis." The error was not caught before the submission of the claim, and the insurance company rejected the claim because the procedures listed on the claim form did not coincide with the diagnosis. When the patient received an explanation of benefits from his insurance carrier that the claim was denied, he phoned the office with a complaint. Marlee had to apologize to the patient and resubmit the CMS-1500 claim form.

HIPAA TIP

HIPAA requires that ICD-9-CM diagnosis codes be included on all Medicare claims billed to Part B carriers, with the exception of ambulance claims. Providers and suppliers rely on physicians to provide a diagnosis code or narrative diagnostic statement on orders/referrals.

Note the numbers 611.72 following "breast" shown in the portion of Volume 2 in Fig. 6-13. This is the five-digit diagnosis code for breast mass. The number one cardinal rule in coding is *never* to code

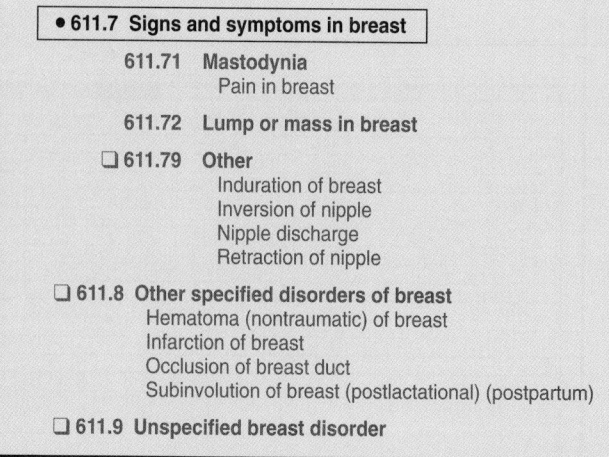

Fig. 6-13   Portion of tabular listing in Volume 2 showing the above code. *(Data from* International Classification of Diseases, *Ninth Revision. U.S. Department of Health and Human Services, Public Health Service, Centers for Medicare and Medicaid Services.)*

1. Infectious and Parasitic Diseases (001-139)
2. Neoplasms (140-239)
3. Endocrine, Nutritional & Metabolic Diseases & Immunity Disorders (240-279)
4. Diseases of the Blood & Blood-Forming Organs (280-289)
5. Mental Disorders (290-319)
6. Nervous System and Sense Organs (320-389)
7. Diseases of the Circulatory System (390-459)
8. Diseases of the Respiratory System (460-519)
9. Diseases of the Digestive System (520-579)
10. Diseases of the Genitourinary System (580-629)
11. Complications of Pregnancy, Childbirth, and the Puerperium (630-677)
12. Diseases of the Skin & Subcutaneous Tissue (680-709)
13. Diseases of the Musculoskeletal System & Connective Tissue (710-739)
14. Congenital Anomalies (740-759)
15. Certain Conditions Originating in the Perinatal Period (760-779)
16. Symptoms, Signs, and Ill-Defined Conditions (780-799)
17. Injury and Poisoning (800-999)

Fig. 6-14   List of 17 sections in Volume 1.

from the Alphabetic Index (Volume 2) alone. Before assigning this code, it is important to read any special notes or instructions, after which the health insurance professional turns to Volume 1, the Tabular Index, and locates the code 611.72.

Volume 1, the Tabular List

Volume 1, the Tabular List, comprises 17 sections (Fig. 6-14). These 17 sections represent anatomical systems or types of conditions. The titles describe the content of the section followed by the range of codes in a specific category.

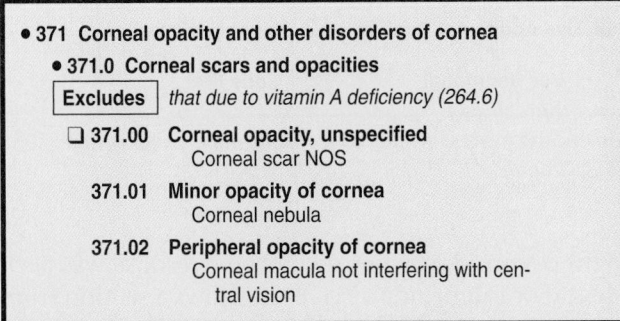

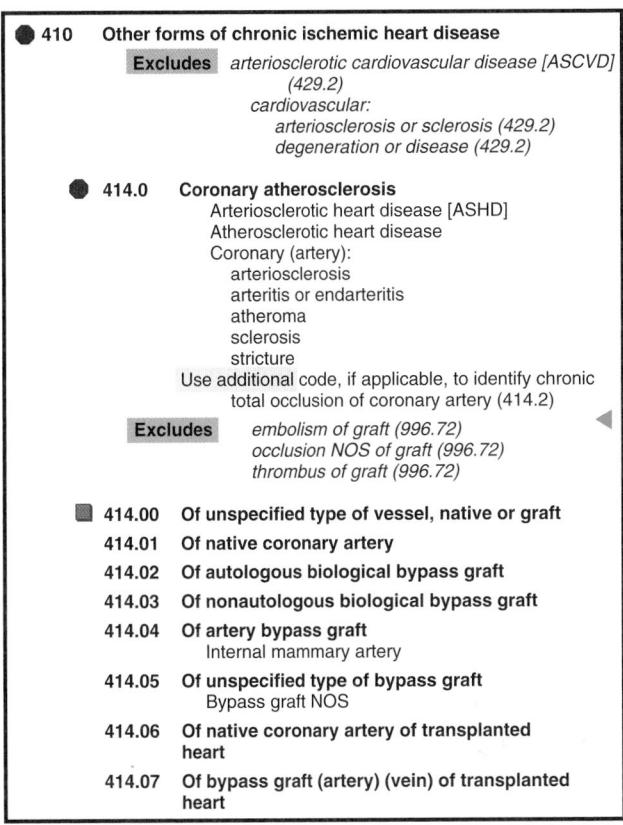

Fig. 6-15 Section of a page from Volume 1 showing one-digit, two-digit, and three-digit codes. (*Data from International Classification of Diseases, Ninth Revision. U.S. Department of Health and Human Services, Public Health Service, Centers for Medicare and Medicaid Services.*)

Fig. 6-16 Category 414. (*Color codes from Buck C: Saunders 2008 ICD-9-CM, Volumes 1, 2, and 3, Professional Edition. St Louis, 2008, Saunders.*)

Organization of Volume 1 Codes

There are three types of codes in Volume 1:

- Three-digit **category** codes (e.g., 220, "benign neoplasm of ovary")
- Four-digit **subcategory** codes (e.g., 370.0, "corneal ulcer")
- Five-digit **subclassification** codes (e.g., 370.00, "corneal ulcer, unspecified")

Study the section of a page from Volume 1 that illustrates these three types of codes (Fig. 6-15).

To clarify further the four-digit and five-digit necessity, say that a patient's diagnosis in the health record is coronary atherosclerosis. Note in the example shown in Fig. 6-16 that the color coding (bullet) of category 414 (other forms of chronic ischemic heart disease) indicates a fourth digit is needed, and the subcategory 414.0 (coronary atherosclerosis) needs a fifth digit to describe the patient's diagnosis to the greatest specificity. It must be determined which of the subclassifications (414.00 through 414.06) best describes the patient's heart condition. If the four-digit code (414.0) is indicated in Block 21 of the CMS-1500 form, it no doubt would be rejected and returned unpaid because a fifth digit is needed.

Color Coding

Most ICD-9 manuals use color coding in Volume 1 to alert the coder to special edits and other important issues. In the American Medical Association (AMA) publication, a fourth color-coded notation preceding a three-digit code category indicates that a fourth digit is required. Other publications use a circle with either a 4 or a 5 inside to indicate additional digits are needed.

Another type of color coding is the age symbols (used in the AMA publication). Age-related color-coded alpha characters are white on a yellow background as follows:

- N—newborn age, 0
- P—pediatric age, 0-17
- M—maternity age, 12-55
- A—adult age, 15-124
- MSP—Medicare Secondary Payer

Unspecified Code, Other Specified Code, and Manifestation Code also have special color coding in the AMA ICD-9 manual. Fig. 6-17 illustrates how the AMA ICD-9-CM manual uses color coding in Volume 1 to help guide the individual in selecting the right code and coding to the greatest specificity.

Remember: The health insurance professional must *not* use a three-digit code if a four-digit code is available and must *not* use a four-digit code if a five-digit code is available.

Supplementary Sections of Volume 1

V Codes

The **V codes**, Supplementary Classification of Factors Influencing Health Status and Contact with Health Services (V01-V83), follow the aforementioned 17 sections. Codes in this section are used when circumstances other than a disease or injury

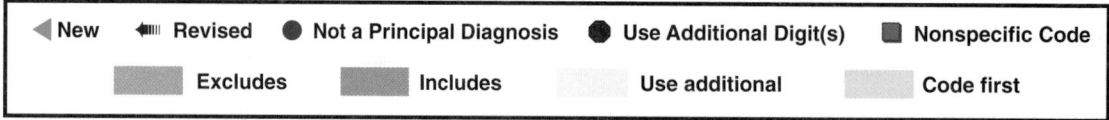

Fig. 6-17 Section at bottom of Volume 1 pages showing color coding notes. *(Color codes from Buck C: Saunders 2008 ICD-9-CM, Volumes 1, 2, and 3, Professional Edition. St Louis, 2008, Saunders.)*

are recorded as a diagnosis or problem. This can appear in the health record in one of three ways:

1. When an individual who is not sick visits the medical facility for a specific purpose, such as donating a tissue sample or to receive a vaccination.
2. When an individual with a known disease or injury comes in for specific treatment for that problem, such as dialysis for kidney disease, chemotherapy for cancer, or a cast change.
3. When a problem is present that influences the individual's health status but is not, in itself, a current illness or injury. An example is an individual with a history of a certain disease or an individual who has an artificial heart valve, which may affect his or her present condition.

When the following terms are seen as the diagnosis in a health record, it is usually a clue that a V code is needed:

- Aftercare
- Examination
- Problem with
- Attention to
- Observation
- Screening for
- Admission
- Tests
- Vaccinations

Some V codes can be used alone, and some require a medical diagnosis from the main ICD-9 sections. Examples of common V code diagnoses include the following:

- Family history of malignant neoplasm
- Health supervision of infant or child
- Normal pregnancy
- Supervision of high-risk pregnancy

E Codes

The Supplementary Classification of External Causes of Injury and Poisoning, referred to as *E codes* (codes E800 through E999), follows the section on V codes. Codes in this section classify external causes of environmental events, circumstances, or conditions that caused the injury, condition, poisoning, or adverse effect being described, such as how an acci-

dent occurred or whether a drug overdose was accidental or intentional. Fig. 6-18 shows a section from a page in this section to illustrate how codes in this portion of the ICD-9-CM manual are structured.

E codes are never used alone or as the primary diagnosis on a claim. They typically are combined with a code from one of the main chapters of the ICD-9 that indicates the nature of the condition. Health care providers usually are not required to assign E codes, unless there is an adverse reaction to a medication that has been taken according to directions. A typical example of this might be as follows:

780.4 Dizziness due to
E939.4 Valium, correct dose

Also, some third-party payers prefer that E codes not be used at all on claims. The health insurance professional should contact the carrier or fiscal intermediary to determine if E codes are allowed.

The steps for selecting the correct E code for adverse effects are as follows:

1. Locate the drug in the index on the Table of Drugs and Chemicals.
2. Search for the code in the column titled "Therapeutic Use."
3. Verify the code.
4. Do not use an E code as the first diagnosis.
5. Note the corresponding code under "Poisoning," and use this as the primary code.

HIPAA TIP

Always protect the confidentiality of all ICD-9 codes because these codes are part of the patient's record. HIPAA addresses coding issues and sets standards for their use, along with other issues regarding confidentiality in dealing with patient health records.

Locating a Code in the Tabular List (Volume 1)

Codes in Volume 1 are arranged numerically, so they are relatively easy to find. Use the numerical range descriptors at the top corners of each page to narrow down your search (Fig. 6-19). First, locate the three-digit code that defines the category. Using the breast

TABLE OF DRUGS AND CHEMICALS / Antibiotics

Substance	Poisoning	External Cause (E-Code)				
		Accident	Therapeutic Use	Suicide Attempt	Assault	Undetermined
Unna's boot	976.3	E858.7	E946.3	E950.4	E962.0	E980.4
Uracil mustard	963.1	E858.1	E933.1	E950.4	E962.0	E980.4
Uramustine	963.1	E858.1	E933.1	E950.4	E962.0	E980.4
Urari	975.2	E858.6	E945.2	E950.4	E962.0	E980.4
Urea	974.4	E858.5	E944.4	E950.4	E962.0	E980.4
topical	976.8	E858.7	E946.8	E950.4	E962.0	E980.4
Urethan(e) (antineoplastic)	963.1	E858.1	E933.1	E950.4	E962.0	E980.4
Urginea (maritima) (scilla) - *see* Squill	—	—	—	—	—	—
pertussis component	978.6	E858.8	E948.6	E950.4	E962.0	E980.4
rickettsial component	979.7	E858.8	E949.7	E950.4	E962.0	E980.4
yellow fever	979.3	E858.8	E949.3	E950.4	E962.0	E980.4
Vaccinia immune globulin (human)	964.6	E858.2	E934.6	E950.4	E962.0	E980.4
Vaginal contraceptives	976.8	E858.7	E946.8	E950.4	E962.0	E980.4
Valethamate	971.1	E855.4	E941.1	E950.4	E962.0	E980.4
Valisone	976.0	E858.7	E946.0	E950.4	E962.0	E980.4
Valium	969.4	E853.2	E939.4	E950.3	E962.0	E980.3
Valmid	967.8	E852.8	E937.8	E950.2	E962.0	E980.2
Vanadium	985.8	E866.4	—	E950.9	E962.1	E980.9
Vancomycin	960.8	E856	E930.8	E950.4	E962.0	E980.4

Fig. 6-18 Section from E code pages. (*Data from* International Classification of Diseases, *Ninth Revision. U.S. Department of Health and Human Services, Public Health Service, Centers for Medicare and Medicaid Services.*)

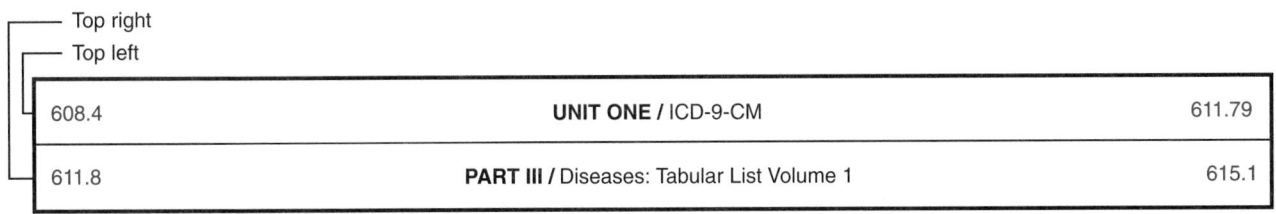

Top right		
Top left		
608.4	**UNIT ONE** / ICD-9-CM	611.79
611.8	**PART III** / Diseases: Tabular List Volume 1	615.1

Fig. 6-19 Top portion of page showing range descriptors. (*Color codes from Buck C:* Saunders 2008 ICD-9-CM, *Volumes 1, 2, and 3, Professional Edition. St Louis, 2008, Saunders.*)

mass example, this would be 611, "other disorders of breast." The color coding indicates that a fourth digit is required for each subcategory. Read down through the subcategory entries until 611.7 is found, "signs and symptoms in breast." Note that a fifth digit is required. Locate the subclassification entry 611.72, "lump or mass in breast." If no other notes, symbols, or special editing codes are shown, it can be reasonable to assume that this diagnosis has been coded to its greatest specificity (Fig. 6-20).

WHAT DID YOU LEARN?

1. Briefly explain what coding involves.
2. List and identify the 17 main sections in Volume 1.
3. List and give an example of the three types of codes in the 17 sections of Volume 1.
4. What is the purpose of color coding?
5. Give four examples of common V code diagnoses.
6. When are E codes used?

CONVENTIONS USED IN ICD-9-CM

The conventions used in Volumes 1 and 2 of the ICD-9 manual include abbreviations, punctuation, symbols, footnotes, and other instructional notes. Many of these conventions are used in all three volumes; however, some are used only in Volumes 1 and 2. Although each publication typically has its own special list of conventions, the ones discussed subsequently are the ones used in the AMA publication and are basically the same as the ones used in the government's official version. Codes on health insurance forms must conform to the standards that are published in the *Federal Register*. The *Federal Register* is a daily publication that provides a uniform system for publishing federal regulations, legal notices, presidential proclamations, and executive orders. See Websites to Explore at the end of this chapter for the *Federal Register* website. To code accurately, the health insurance professional must understand what each of these elements means (Fig. 6-21).

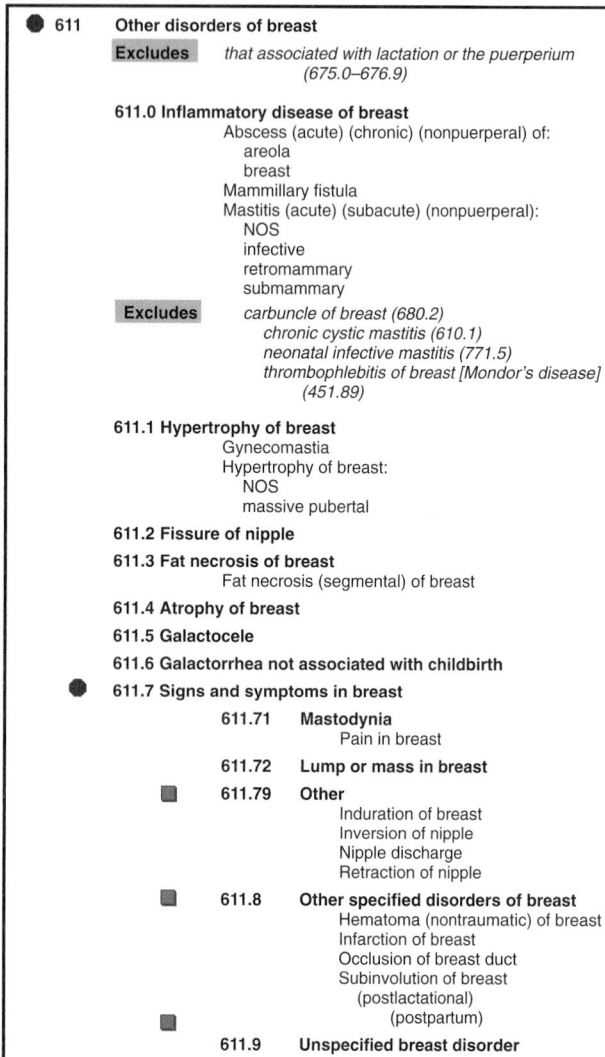

● 611   Other disorders of breast
   Excludes   *that associated with lactation or the puerperium*
                  (675.0–676.9)

   611.0 Inflammatory disease of breast
            Abscess (acute) (chronic) (nonpuerperal) of:
                areola
                breast
            Mammillary fistula
            Mastitis (acute) (subacute) (nonpuerperal):
                NOS
                infective
                retromammary
                submammary
   Excludes   *carbuncle of breast (680.2)*
                  chronic cystic mastitis (610.1)
                  neonatal infective mastitis (771.5)
                  thrombophlebitis of breast [Mondor's disease]
                  (451.89)

   611.1 Hypertrophy of breast
            Gynecomastia
            Hypertrophy of breast:
                NOS
                massive pubertal

   611.2 Fissure of nipple
   611.3 Fat necrosis of breast
            Fat necrosis (segmental) of breast
   611.4 Atrophy of breast
   611.5 Galactocele
   611.6 Galactorrhea not associated with childbirth
● 611.7 Signs and symptoms in breast
            611.71   Mastodynia
                          Pain in breast
            611.72   Lump or mass in breast
         ■ 611.79   Other
                          Induration of breast
                          Inversion of nipple
                          Nipple discharge
                          Retraction of nipple
         ■ 611.8   Other specified disorders of breast
                          Hematoma (nontraumatic) of breast
                          Infarction of breast
                          Occlusion of breast duct
                          Subinvolution of breast
                              (postlactational)
                              (postpartum)
         ■ 611.9   Unspecified breast disorder

Fig. 6-20 Section of ICD-9 showing symbols, color coding, and instructional notes in the ICD-9-CM. *(Color codes from Buck C:* Saunders 2008 ICD-9-CM, *Volumes 1, 2, and 3, Professional Edition. St Louis, 2008, Saunders.)*

STOP AND THINK

Marlee, the health insurance professional in Dr. Ferris Barnes' office, was searching for a particular code in the ICD-9, when she noticed a blackened triangle (▲) in front of the diagnosis code that she sought. What does this symbol indicate to Marlee?

Typefaces

The AMA (and other publications) ICD-9-CM manual varies the format of the type to indicate other conventions, as follows:

- **Boldface:** Boldface type is used for main terms in the Alphabetic Index (Volume 2) and all codes and titles in the tabular list.

- ***Italics:*** Italicized type is used for all exclusion notes and to identify codes that should not be used for describing the primary diagnosis.

Examples of these two typeface formats are shown in Fig. 6-22.

Instructional Notes

In addition to abbreviations, punctuation, and symbols, the ICD-9 uses instructional notes to help the health insurance professional choose the correct code (Fig. 6-23).

WHAT DID YOU LEARN?

1. What is the function and purpose of boldface type?
2. What does NOS mean?
3. What does it mean when a colon (:) is used?
4. What does the bullet symbol (•) preceding a code indicate?
5. What does italicized type indicate?

ESSENTIAL STEPS TO DIAGNOSTIC CODING

Now that the basic background for ICD-9 coding has been presented, let's look at the essential steps of diagnostic coding.

1. Locate the diagnosis in the patient's health record (or on the encounter form).
2. Determine the "main term" of the stated diagnosis.
3. Find the main term in the Alphabetic Index (Volume 2) of the most recent version of the ICD-9-CM manual.
4. Read and apply any notes or instructions contained in the Alphabetic Index. *Reminder: Never code directly from the Alphabetic Index.*
5. Cross-reference the code found in the Alphabetic Index (Volume 2) to the Tabular List (Volume 1).
6. Read and be guided by the conventions and symbols, paying close attention to any footnotes or cross-references.
7. Read through the entire category, and code to the *highest level of specificity,* taking special care to assign a fourth or fifth digit to the code if the color coding indicates it is necessary.

Box 6-1 contains a list of ICD-9 coding compliance tips. In addition, the AMA has published "The

NEC	**Not elsewhere classifiable.** NEC tells the coder that a specified form of the listed condition is classified differently. The category number for the term including NEC is to be used only when the coder lacks the information necessary to code to a more specific category. 244.8 **Other specified acquired hypothyroidism** Secondary hypothyroidism NEC
NOS	**Not otherwise specified.** This abbreviation is the equivalent of "unspecified" and is used only when there is not enough information available to code to a more specific, 4-digit subcategory. ● 410 **Acute myocardial infarction** ● 410.1 **Of other anterior wall** Infarction (wall) ⎱ NOS with contiguous portion anterior ⎰ of intraventricular septum
[ ]	**Square brackets are used to enclose synonyms, alternative terminology, or explanatory phrases.** They may appear within code descriptions or within instructional notes. ● 483 **Pneumonia due to other specified organism** 483.0 **Mycoplasma pneumoniae** Eaton's agent Pleuropneumonia-like organism [PPLO]
( )	**Parentheses enclose supplementary words, called** *nonessential modifiers,* that serve as guides in finding the correct code. These words may or may not be present in the narrative description of a disease and do not affect the code assignment. ● 626 **Disorders of menstruation and other abnormal bleeding from female genital tract** 626.0 **Absence of menstruation** Amenorrhea (primary) (secondary)

Fig. 6-21   List of conventions and symbols.

Continued

BOX 6-1   ICD-9 Coding Compliance Tips

1. Maintain access to and be versed in federal, state, and private payer requirements.
2. Review medical documentation to ensure that the health record supports the codes selected to avoid claim denials.
3. Use only the most recent ICD-9 coding manual.
4. Conduct self-audits of coded claims.
5. When updates occur, perform audits to identify invalid or old codes, avoiding potential claim rejection problems.
6. Avoid abbreviated coding "cheat sheets," which can cause improper coding.
7. Do not code on the basis of on assumptions. Never assume that because a patient is receiving a specific treatment or is on a certain medication that the diagnosis must always be the same.
8. Never alter documentation. Making changes because something sounds "better" could lead to serious problems in the future. Always check with the health care professional when questions arise regarding documentation, and always document the discussion for any changes made to the claim.
9. Know all qualified and licensed personnel. Establish procedures to ensure that all staff members have the requisite qualifications and renew their licenses on time.
10. Review all claims rejected because of improper coding. This step should be done by an experienced coder and should be part of a medical facility's internal coding practices.
11. Recognize and use the official HIPAA Guidelines in coding.

:	A colon is used in the tabular list after an incomplete term that needs one or more modifiers to make it a complete statement. (An exception to this rule pertains to the abbreviated NOS.)
	
	⬤ **415 Acute Pulmonary Heart Disease**
	
	   ⬤ **415.1 Pulmonary embolism and infarction**
	     Pulmonary (artery) (vein):
	      apoplexy
	      embolism
	      infarction (hemorrhagic)
	      thrombosis

{ }	Braces are used to connect a series of terms to a common step. Each term to the left of the brace is incomplete and must be completed by a term to the right of the brace.
	
	⬤ **Arthropathy associated with infections**
	
	  Includes arthritis associated with
	             arthropathy conditions
	             polyarthritis classifiable
	             polyarthropathy below

§	When the section mark (§) precedes a code, it indicates there is a footnote on the page. The section mark is used only in the Tabular List (Volume 1). § ⬤ **E812** **Other motor vehicle traffic accident involving collision with motor vehicle** The footnote indicates that this code requires a 4th digit. See beginning of section E810-E819 for codes and definitions.
●	This symbol is referred to as a "bullet." The bullet indicates that the code is new to this revision of the ICD-9. The 2003 ICD-9 added several new E-codes associated with terrorism.
▲	A triangle in the Tabular List (Vol. 1) indicates that the code title is revised. In the Alphabetic Index (Vol. 2), the triangle indicates that a code has been changed.
►◄	These "sideways triangles" appear at the beginning and end of a section of new or revised text. The right-facing triangle appears at the beginning of the text; the left-facing one appears at the end.
<u>word</u>	Underlined words set off text that has been revised or added for 2008. This feature is relevant only in the 2008 ICD-9-CM code changes table.
~~word~~	A word(s) with a strikethrough highlights a word(s) that has been deleted from a particular code description for 2008. This feature is relevant only in the 2008 ICD-9-CM code changes table.

Fig. 6-21, cont'd

Ten Commandments of Diagnosis Coding," which are shown in Box 6-2.

WHAT DID YOU LEARN?

1. List the seven essential steps of diagnostic coding.
2. What should the health insurance professional do if he or she thinks a diagnosis documented in a health record can be worded better?

SPECIAL CODING SITUATIONS

Coding Signs and Symptoms

If a patient's condition has not been specifically diagnosed, the health insurance professional must code the signs or symptoms. Section 16 of the ICD-9 (codes 780 through 799) contains a list of codes classifying symptoms, signs, abnormal results of laboratory tests or other investigative procedures, and ill-defined conditions for which no diagnosis classifiable elsewhere is recorded. Common examples of signs and symptoms include the following:

Bold face type

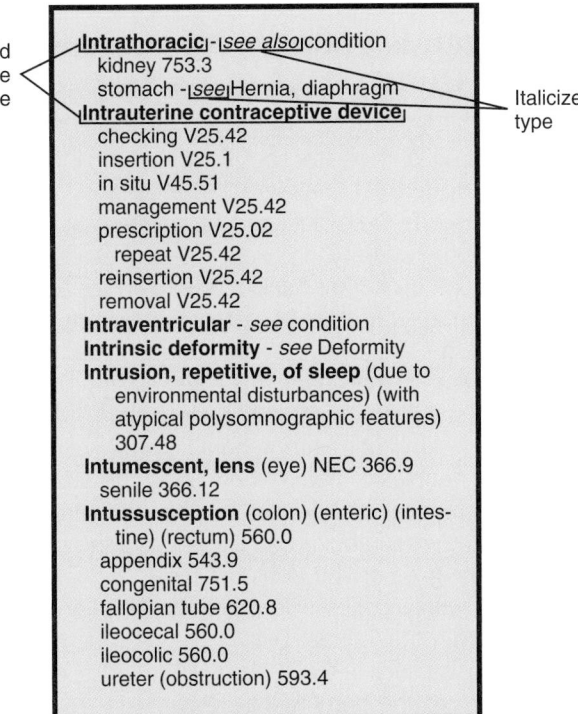

Italicized type

Intrathoracic - *see also* condition
  kidney 753.3
  stomach - *see* Hernia, diaphragm
Intrauterine contraceptive device
  checking V25.42
  insertion V25.1
  in situ V45.51
  management V25.42
  prescription V25.02
    repeat V25.42
  reinsertion V25.42
  removal V25.42
Intraventricular - *see* condition
Intrinsic deformity - *see* Deformity
Intrusion, repetitive, of sleep (due to
  environmental disturbances) (with
  atypical polysomnographic features)
  307.48
Intumescent, lens (eye) NEC 366.9
  senile 366.12
Intussusception (colon) (enteric) (intestine) (rectum) 560.0
  appendix 543.9
  congenital 751.5
  fallopian tube 620.8
  ileocecal 560.0
  ileocolic 560.0
  ureter (obstruction) 593.4

Fig. 6-22   Example of boldface and italicized type. *(Data from* International Classification of Diseases, *Ninth Revision. U.S. Department of Health and Human Services, Public Health Service, Centers for Medicare and Medicaid Services.)*

- Dizziness
- Fever
- Insomnia
- Nausea
- Shortness of breath
- Headache

If a patient visits the medical facility with the chief complaint of nausea, but the health care provider has not yet determined what is causing the nausea, the code for nausea must be used. Looking in the Alphabetic Index (Volume 1) under "nausea," we find 787.02 for nausea without vomiting and 787.01 for nausea with vomiting. Cross-referencing to the Tabular Index, we first locate the three-digit category: "787, symptoms involving digestive system." Reading down through the subcategory and subclassification sections, note that five digits are needed. For accurate coding, it must be determined if the patient has nausea with vomiting, nausea alone, or vomiting alone. This should be documented in the clinical notes. If the clinical notes are nonspecific as to whether there is vomiting, it should be assumed there is not vomiting unless it is documented.

Includes	The instructional note **Includes** further defines or clarifies the content of the category, subcategory, or subclassification.
Excludes	Terms following the instructional note **Excludes** are not classified to the category, subcategory, or specific subclassification code under which it is found. The note may also provide the location of the excluded diagnosis.
Use additional code	When this note appears, an additional code(s) must be used to provide a more complete description of the diagnosis.
Code first underlying disease	This italicized note indicates that the description given should not be used for coding the primary diagnosis. The italicized notation is followed by the code(s) for the most common underlying disease. These codes, referred to as manifestation codes, should not be used alone or indicated as the primary diagnosis (i.e., sequenced first). They must always be preceded by another code. Record the code for the primary disease first, and then record the italicized manifestation code.
▉ Nonspecified Code	Use these codes only when neither the diagnostic statement nor the documentation provides enough information to assign a more specific code. (Note: Check with the carrier or FI to see if unspecified codes are acceptable on the claim form.)
Code, if applicable, any causal condition first	A code with this notation may be principal if no causal condition is applicable or known.
"And" and "with"	"and" means and/or; "with" indicates another condition is included in the code.

Fig. 6-23   Examples of how boldface and italicized type and other special notations are identified. *(Color codes from Buck C:* Saunders 2008 ICD-9-CM, *Volumes 1, 2, and 3, Professional Edition. St Louis, 2008, Saunders.)*

BOX 6-2 **AMA's "The Ten Commandments of Diagnosis Coding": An Irreverent Summary of Rules with Practical Coding Hints**

I. The largest number of digits wins.
   Do not report three if there are four; do not report four if there are five.

II. Numerical codes win over alphanumerical.
   If the code is listed twice, once with a letter and once with all numbers, use the one with all numbers, if possible.

III. Watch out for punctuation.
   Do not even think it. Do not think "427 point 0" or "250 point 00." These codes are 4270 and 25000. Many claim form scanners and electronic claim programs cannot process the punctuation mark.

IV. Use only the codes related to the services performed.
   A patient with acute bronchitis and heart disease is seen for the bronchitis. The chart indicates it is time for an electrocardiogram. If you code the electrocardiogram for bronchitis, it may not pay. With Medicare, it could result in a "not medically necessary" rejection.

V. Diagnosis coding does not increase the payment; it only allows it.

VI. Do not code in greater specificity than the information provided.
   Do not code "rule out" and "suspected" as if the condition existed. The patient is seen because she thinks she broke her hand. Code "pain" or "contusion" if the x-ray does not confirm the fracture.

VII. Neoplasms are always benign unless stated to be malignant. If malignant, they are always primary unless stated to be secondary or in situ.
   Some lesion codes are general; others are found in the neoplasm table. When using the table, be certain to select the correct column, and verify that code with the Tabular List. Do not give the patient something he or she does not have.

VIII. Always verify codes selected from the Alphabetic Index with the Tabular List.

IX. Diagnosis codes in the Tabular List, in italics, cannot be used as the primary diagnosis.
   These codes are listed as "excludes" or "code also the underlying disease." Be certain the correct code is selected and verified.

X. Sometimes the best diagnosis code is going to be the one that is least incorrect.

Etiology and Manifestation Coding

When the notation "code first underlying disease" is seen, this indicates that the etiology (cause or origin of the disease) is coded before the **manifestation** (sign or symptom of the disease). If the patient's diagnosis is diabetic ulcer of the heel, the disease process (diabetes) is coded first before the heel ulcer.

Symptoms, Signs, and Ill-Defined Conditions

In Section 16 in the ICD-9-CM manual is a listing of codes (780 through 799.9) for "signs, abnormal results of laboratory or other investigative procedures, and ill-defined conditions regarding which no diagnosis classifiable elsewhere is recorded." These codes are used when no definitive diagnosis can be arrived at conclusion of the initial encounter. It may take two or more visits before a specific diagnosis is confirmed. Documentation in the assessment segment of the patient record may use such terms as "probable," "questionable," "rule out," or "suspected"; however, the coder should not use any one of these terms as if it were the final

diagnosis. Coding guidelines for inconclusive diagnoses (e.g., probable, suspected, rule out) were developed for inpatient reporting and do not apply to outpatients.

STOP AND THINK

Lonny Chadwick noticed a suspicious-looking mole on his lower right leg and went to his dermatologist. Lonny's father died as a result of malignant melanoma, and Lonny was concerned that his mole also was malignant. The dermatologist examined the mole and removed a section of tissue for a biopsy. When the biopsy results were returned, the laboratory report stated that the tissue sample was "abnormal, but inconclusive." Documentation in Mr. Chadwick's health record noted the fact that his father had died of malignant melanoma. The diagnosis stated "suspicious lesion, lower right leg, rule out melanoma." Subsequently, the health insurance professional submitted the claim with the diagnosis of "melanoma." What problems might arise from this incorrect coding process?

Combination Codes

A **combination code** is used when more than one otherwise individually classified disease is combined with another disease and one code is assigned for both, or when a single code is used to describe conditions that frequently occur together. An example of this is the code 034.0, "streptococcal sore throat," because a sore throat is often caused by the streptococci bacteria. If a patient has hypertensive heart and renal disease, these conditions are combined under one code (category 404), rather than assigning codes from the 402 and 403 categories.

Coding Neoplasms

A neoplasm results when abnormal cells grow uncontrollably, usually resulting in a tumor. Neoplasms may be classified as follows:

- Benign
- Malignant
- **In situ** (confined to the site of origin without invasion)
- Uncertain behavior
- Unspecified behavior

The anatomic site of the neoplasm may be the organ or area of the body where the tumor originated (primary) or the organ or area of the body where the tumor has spread (secondary). To code neoplasms, first find the main term in the Alphabetic Index (Vol. 2). Using "fibroadenoma of the breast" as an example, assign the correct code using the following steps:

1. Locate the main term ("fibroadenoma") in the Alphabetic Index (Vol. 2) under "by site, benign." Note it refers the coder to the Neoplasm Table.
2. Because we know the site, we cross-reference to the Neoplasm Table.
3. Noting that the anatomical sites are listed alphabetically, locate "breast."
4. Identify the code under the column titled "benign."
5. If no additional information is available, the correct code is 217.

If a detailed diagnosis is given, such as "malignant adenoma of the colon, primary," the resulting code is more specific:

1. Locate the main term ("adenoma") in the Alphabetic Index. (See also "neoplasm, by site, benign.")
2. Cross-reference to the Neoplasm Table.
3. Cross-reference "colon" to "intestine, intestinal, large, colon."
4. Assign the correct code under the "malignant, primary" column heading (153.9).

V codes are sometimes used if there is a family or personal history of malignant neoplasms.

Coding Hypertension

One of the most common conditions coded is that of hypertension (high blood pressure). If a patient has a documented diagnosis of "hypertension, essential, benign," the steps to follow for coding this condition are as follows:

1. Locate the main term "hypertension" in the Alphabetic Index.
2. Note the three column headings in the Table: "malignant," "benign," and "unspecified."
3. The various terms in parentheses (nonessential modifiers) listed behind the main terms in boldface type (hypertension, hypertensive) include the word "essential."
4. Because "essential" is a nonessential modifier included under the main term category, cross-reference it to the "benign" column.
5. Assign the code 401.1.

WHAT DID YOU LEARN?

1. List four common examples of signs and symptoms.
2. Which should be coded first, the etiology or the manifestation?
3. What is a combination code?
4. Compare a "primary" neoplasm site with a "secondary" site.

≋ HIPAA AND CODING

Code sets for medical data are required for data elements in the administrative and financial health care transaction standards adopted under the Health Insurance Portability and Accountability Act (HIPAA) for diagnoses, procedures, and drugs. Under HIPAA, a **code set** is any set of codes used for encoding data elements, such as tables of terms, medical concepts, medical diagnosis codes, or medical procedure codes. Medical data code sets used in the health care industry include coding systems for

- diseases, impairments, other health-related problems, and their manifestations;
- causes of injury, disease, impairment, or other health-related problems;
- actions taken to prevent, diagnose, treat, or manage diseases, injuries, and impairments; and
- any substances, equipment, supplies, or other items used to perform these actions.

HIPAA TIP

Although the HIPAA requirements apply only to electronic claims, to maintain consistency in claims processing, CMS has mandated that ICD-9-CM requirements be applied to paper claims and electronic claims.

Code Sets Adopted as HIPAA Standards

The following code sets have been adopted as the standard medical data code sets:

- ICD-9-CM, Volumes 1 and 2 (including *The Official ICD-9-CM Guidelines for Coding and Reporting*), as updated and distributed by the Department of Health and Human Services (HHS), for the following conditions:
    Diseases
    Injuries
    Impairments
    Other health-related problems and their manifestations
    Causes of injury, disease, impairment, or other health-related problems
- ICD-9-CM, Volume 3 Procedures (including *The Official ICD-9-CM Guidelines for Coding and Reporting*), as updated and distributed by HHS, for the following procedures or other actions taken for diseases, injuries, and impairments in hospital inpatients reported by hospitals:
    Prevention
    Diagnosis
    Treatment
    Management
- National Drug Codes, as updated and distributed by HHS, in collaboration with drug manufacturers, for certain drugs and biologics
- Codes on Dental Procedures and Nomenclature, as updated and distributed by the American Dental Association, for dental services
- The combination of CMS *Common Procedure Coding System* (HCPCS), as updated and distributed by HHS, and *Current Procedural Terminology*, Fourth Edition (CPT-4), as updated and distributed by the AMA, for physician services and other health-related services. These services include, but are not limited to, the following:
    Physician services
    Physical and occupational therapy services
    Radiologic procedures
    Clinical laboratory tests
    Other medical diagnostic procedures
    Hearing and vision services
    Transportation services including ambulance
- The HCPCS, as updated and distributed by CMS and HHS, for all other substances, equipment, supplies, or other items used in health care services. These items include, but are not limited to, the following:
    Medical supplies
    Orthotic and prosthetic devices
    Durable medical equipment

HCPCS Level 3 Codes

HCPCS Level 3 codes are known as local codes. Under the intent of HIPAA, the Level 3 codes were to be eliminated; however, some payers still require Level 3 codes for payment and reimbursement. As always, if questions arise, contact your local carrier or fiscal intermediary for guidelines for using Level 3 codes.

HIPAA TIP

HIPAA compliant claims cannot contain ICD-9 Volume 3 procedure codes on claims submitted by physicians' offices.

WHAT DID YOU LEARN?

1. Explain what a "code set" is under HIPAA.
2. List the standard code sets adopted by HIPAA.

ICD-10

The WHO typically releases an updated version of the ICD manual approximately every 10 years. The *International Classification of Diseases, Tenth Revision* (ICD-10), was issued in three volumes from 1992 to 1994 and is now being used in some parts of the world. The intent of this revision was to address some of the problems that had been identified in the current ICD-9 and to improve classification of mortality and morbidity data.

ICD-10 provides increased clinical detail and addresses information regarding previously classified diseases and new diseases discovered since the ninth revision. Conditions are grouped according to those most appropriate for general epidemiological purposes and the evaluation of health care. Although the format and conventions of the classification remain, for the most part, unchanged, ICD-10 differs from ICD-9-CM in the following ways:

- ICD-10 is printed in a three-volume set compared with the physician's ICD-9 two-volume set.
- ICD-10 has alphanumerical categories rather than numerical categories.
- Some chapters have been rearranged, some titles have changed, and conditions have been regrouped.
- ICD-10 has almost twice as many categories as ICD-9.
- Some minor changes have been made in the coding rules for mortality.

Three Volumes of ICD-10

Volume 1, the Tabular List

The first volume (which is more than 1000 pages) contains the classification at the three-character and four-character levels, the classification of the morphology of neoplasms, special tabulation lists for mortality and morbidity, definitions, and the nomenclature regulations. The volume also reproduces the report of the International Conference for the Tenth Revision, which indicates the many complex considerations behind the revisions.

Volume 2, Instruction Manual

The second volume consolidates notes on certification and classification formerly included in Volume 1, supplemented by a great deal of new background information, instructions, and guidelines for users of the tabular list. Historical information about the development of the classification, which dates back to 1893, also is included.

Volume 3, Alphabetic Index

The final volume presents the detailed alphabetical index. Expanded introductory material is complemented by practical advice on how to make the best use of the index. To facilitate efficient coding, the index includes numerous diagnostic terms commonly used as synonyms for the terms officially accepted for use in the classification.

Hard copy and electronic versions of the three-volume set of ICD-10 are available through the WHO Publications Center USA. There also is an ICD-10 homepage at the WHO website.

ICD-10-PCS

The *International Classification of Diseases Tenth Revision Procedure Classification System* (ICD-10-PCS) has been developed as a replacement for Volume 3 of the ICD-9. The CMS has developed a training manual that can be downloaded and reviewed using the Adobe Acrobat System.

Implementation of ICD-10

Revisions have been made to the initial version of ICD-10-CM based on the comments received from reviewers. An updated edition of ICD-10-CM became available in late 2003 for public viewing. As of this writing, however, the codes in ICD-10-CM are not currently valid for any purpose or uses. Testing of ICD-10-CM will occur using this prerelease version. It is anticipated that updates to this draft will occur before implementation of ICD-10-CM.

No deadline has been established as yet for the mandatory use of the ICD-10 in the United States.

Implementation will be based on the process for adoption of standards under HIPAA. There will be a 2-year implementation window when the final notice to implement has been published in the *Federal Register*. In the meantime, the health insurance professional can download and view a version of this manual for the purpose of keeping up with coming changes in diagnostic coding.

WHAT DID YOU LEARN?

1. What is the intent of the ICD-10 revision?
2. List three ways ICD-10 differs from ICD-9.
3. Name the three volumes of ICD-10.
4. What does the ICD-10-PCS replace?
5. What date has been established for the mandatory use of ICD-10 codes in the United States?

SUMMARY CHECK POINTS

☑ Diagnostic coding got its start in 17th-century England. In 1948, the WHO developed and published a listing of morbidity and mortality statistics that eventually evolved into what is now known as the ICD. This publication is now in its ninth revision (ICD-9). The U.S. National Center for Health Statistics modified the ICD further, providing a way to use these data for indexing medical information, which precisely describes every patient's clinical picture (diagnosis). This revised version, by adding these *clinical modifications*, resulted in the ICD-9-CM. The CMS adopted the ICD-9-CM in 1988 and mandated that this coding system be used on all Medicare Part B claims. Today, most third-party payers also require ICD-9-CM diagnostic codes on health insurance claims.

☑ The ICD-9-CM manual comprises three volumes: Volume 1, the Tabular List; Volume 2, the Alphabetic List; and Volume 3, Inpatient Procedural Coding. (Typically, Volumes 1 and 2 are combined into one book.) Although various publications are available, most follow a similar format. The first several pages of the manual consist of an introduction, providing a guide for using the ICD-9. The following sections complete the format:
- Volume 2, the Index to Diseases
- Volume 1, the Tabular List
- Appendix A, Morphology of Neoplasms
- Appendix B, Glossary of Mental Disorders
- Appendix C, Classification of Drugs by American Hospital Formulary Service List
- Appendix D, Industrial Accidents According to Agency
- Appendix E, Three-Digit Categories (Infectious and Parasitic Diseases)

☑ Volume 2, the Alphabetic Index (typically presented before Volume 1, the Tabular List) contains three separate sections (indexes). The first section, the Index to Diseases, contains diagnostic terms for illnesses, injuries, and reasons for encounters with health care professionals. Within this section are two tables: the Hypertension Table and the Neoplasm Table. Section 2 contains the Table of Drugs and Chemicals, and Section 3 is the Alphabetic Index to External Causes of Injury and Poisoning.

☑ Main terms consist of diseases, conditions, nouns, adjectives, and eponyms. (Anatomical sites are not considered main terms in diagnostic coding.) Main terms are printed alphabetically in boldface type in Volume 2. The health insurance professional first must determine the main term within a clinical diagnosis and locate that term in the Index to Diseases. Some conditions can be found in more than one place. Obstetrical main terms can be found under the name of the condition and under individual entries, such as "delivery," "pregnancy," and "puerperal."

☑ Modifiers are words added to main terms that supply more specific information about the patient's clinical picture. *Essential* modifiers are the indented terms listed under a main term. They describe different anatomical sites, etiology, and clinical types. To be considered essential, a modifier must be a part of the documented diagnosis. *Nonessential* modifiers are terms in parentheses immediately following a main term. They give alternative terminology and are provided simply to assist the health insurance professional in locating the correct main term. Nonessential modifiers usually are not part of the documented diagnostic statement.

☑ ICD-9-CM uses a variety of coding conventions, which include abbreviations, punctuation, symbols, typefaces, footnotes, and other instructional notes. It is important that the health insurance professional understand what each one means because each has a significant impact on the process of accurate coding. The ultimate goal of coding is to "code to the greatest level of specificity." Coding conventions provide a means for accomplishing this goal by guiding the coder through this intricate process.

Volume 1, the Tabular List, comprises 17 sections plus a section listing V codes (Supplementary Classification of Factors Influencing Health Status and Contact with Health Services) followed by the section containing E codes (Supplementary Classification of External Causes of Injury and Poisoning). Five appendixes, A through E, complete Volume 1. There are three types of codes used in the main part of Volume 1: three-digit codes, four-digit codes, and five-digit codes. Codes are organized first by category (three-digit codes), then by subcategory (four-digit codes), and finally by subclassification (five-digit codes). The health insurance professional must follow all notes and conventions and code to the greatest level of specificity to ensure accurate coding. A three-digit code must not be used if a four-digit or five-digit code describes the patient's diagnosis more precisely.

 The essential steps in accurate diagnostic coding are as follows:

- Step 1—Locate the diagnosis in the patient's health record (or on the encounter form).
- Step 2—Determine the "main term" of the stated diagnosis.
- Step 3—Find the main term in the Alphabetic Index (Volume 2) of the most recent version of ICD-9-CM.
- Step 4—Read and apply any notes or instructions contained in the Alphabetic Index. *Remember: Never code directly from the Alphabetic Index.*

- Step 5—Cross-reference the code found in the Alphabetic Index (Volume 2) to the Tabular List (Volume 1).
- Step 6—Read and be guided by the conventions and symbols, paying close attention to any footnotes or cross-references.
- Step 7—Read through the entire category, and code to the highest level of specificity, taking special care to assign a fourth or fifth digit to the code if the color coding indicates it is needed.

 ICD-10 was issued in three volumes from 1992 to 1994 and is now being used in some parts of the world. The intent of this revision was to correct some of the problems contained in the ICD-9 and to improve classification of mortality and morbidity data. It is published in three volumes: Volume 1, the Tabular List; Volume 2, the Instruction Manual; and Volume 3, the Alphabetic Index. Although the format and conventions remain basically the same, the major differences (in addition to those already mentioned) include the following:

- ICD-10 has alphanumerical categories rather than numerical categories.
- Some chapters have been rearranged, some titles have changed, and conditions have been regrouped.
- ICD-10 has almost twice as many categories as ICD-9.

Closing Scenario

Park Chalmers found this introductory chapter on ICD-9-CM coding extremely interesting; he was convinced coding would meet his need for a challenging and meaningful career. Park thought he needed a "structured" approach to learning, and the clear-cut steps to coding enhanced his ability to comprehend the process. After completing the chapter on ICD-9-CM coding, Park decided that his search for a meaningful career might be over.

With a career in coding, he could realize both of his goals—a challenging career and an opportunity to work in the field of medicine. Although becoming a health insurance professional was not the same as becoming a physician, the anticipation of becoming an expert in insurance and coding spurred Park on, and he already was looking forward to the next chapter.

WEBSITES TO EXPLORE

- Central Office for ICD-9-CM website:
  http://www.icd-9-cm.org

- Information abut the *Federal Register* and how the documentation found in the *Federal Register* affects the coding process can be found on their website at
  http://www.archives.gov/federal-register

- For more information on ICD-10, log on to http://www.who.int/en and use "ICD-10" as your search word

- For more information about the HIPAA standardized code sets, search the following websites:
  http://cms.hhs.govhttp://www.fda.gov/cder/ndc/index.htm

- The American Association of Medical Assistants (AAMA) website provides information about coding in the medical office and details about various educational workshops pertaining to this subject:
  http://www.aama-natl.org

- For information on becoming a certified professional coder, log on to the American Academy of Professional Coders' website at
  http://www.aapc.com
  or the American Health Information Management Association's website at
  http://www.ahima.org

- ICD-9 Internet access for diagnostic coding:
  http://www.eicd.com/EICDMain.htm

Chapter Review

Assessment

Multiple Choice

Directions: In the questions/statements presented, choose the response that **best** answers/completes the stem, and circle the letter that precedes it.

1. The determination of the nature of a cause of disease, or the art of distinguishing one disease from another, is commonly referred to as _____.
   A. assignation
   B. coding
   C. diagnosis
   D. insurance

2. Use of ICD-9 began in the United States when the U.S. National Center for Health Statistics (NCHS) modified the system in _____.
   A. 1937
   B. 1966
   C. 1977
   D. 1988

3. The transformation of verbal descriptions of a diagnosis into numbers or a combination of alphanumeric characters is called _____.
   A. coding
   B. classifying
   C. documenting
   D. modifying

4. The first several pages of the ICD-9 manual constitute _____.
   A. a list of anatomic sites
   B. an introduction
   C. conventions and symbols
   D. a guide to clinical procedures

5. An alphabetical listing of diagnoses is contained in _____.
   A. Volume 1
   B. Volume 2
   C. Appendix A
   D. Appendix B

6. *Italics* are used in Volumes 1 and 2 to _____.
   A. identify new codes
   B. highlight all exclusionary notes
   C. identify rubrics that should not be listed as primary codes
   D. B and C

7. The largest section in Volume 2, the Index to Diseases, is organized _____.
   A. by anatomic sites
   B. alphabetically by main terms
   C. numerically
   D. by body systems

8. Diseases, procedures, or syndromes named for individuals who discovered or first used them are called _____.
   A. eponyms
   B. main terms
   C. modifiers
   D. diagnoses

9. Essential modifiers describe _____.
   A. various anatomic sites
   B. the cause or origin of a disease or condition
   C. clinical types
   D. all of the above

10. Terms in parentheses following main terms are called _____.
    A. subterms
    B. essential modifiers
    C. nonessential modifiers
    D. eponyms

11. The codes used to classify environmental events, circumstances, and other conditions that are the cause of injury and other adverse effects are referred to as _____.
    A. main terms
    B. V codes
    C. E codes
    D. modifiers

12. Codes in the Tabular List (Volume 1) are arranged _____.
    A. alphabetically
    B. numerically
    C. alphanumerically
    D. by anatomic site

13. Codes on health insurance forms must conform to the standards that are published in/on _____.
    A. *JAMA*
    B. the Centers for Medicare and Medicaid Services (CMS) website
    C. the *Federal Register*
    D. the Health Insurance Portability and Accountability Act (HIPAA) manual

14. If a patient's condition has not been specifically diagnosed, the health insurance professional must code the _____.
    A. "suspected" disease(s)
    B. disease(s) to be "ruled out"
    C. probable disease(s)
    D. signs or symptoms

15. When a single code is used to describe conditions that frequently occur together, a(an) _____ code is used.
    A. V
    B. E
    C. combination
    D. Volume III

16. Under HIPAA, any set of codes used for encoding data elements, such as tables of terms, medical concepts, medical diagnosis codes, or medical procedure codes, is called a _____.
    A. code set
    B. coding rubric
    C. HIPAA cluster
    D. concept set

17. The main term for *acute depressive reaction* is _____.
    A. acute
    B. depressive
    C. reaction
    D. either A or C

18. The following instruction "*330—Cerebral degenerations usually manifest in childhood. Use additional code to identify associated mental retardation*" indicates to the health insurance professional _____.
    A. a fourth and fifth digit must be assigned to the code
    B. an additional code should be used for better clarification
    C. A and B are correct.
    D. There is not enough information to answer correctly.

19. V codes show problems or situations that influence a patient's health status but are not a current illness or injury, such as _____.
    A. family history of cancer
    B. routine physical examination
    C. colonoscopy screening
    D. all of the above

20. E codes provide a classification of external causes, such as _____.
    A. how an accident occurred
    B. whether a drug overdose was accidental or purposeful
    C. A and B
    D. neither A nor B

True/False

Directions: *Place a "T" in the blank preceding each of the following statements if it is true; place an "F" if it is false.*

_____ 1. A diagnosis should never be coded from the Alphabetic List alone.

_____ 2. You can show only one diagnosis code in Block 21.

_____ 3. Anatomic sites are often listed as main terms in ICD-9-CM.

_____ 4. Essential modifiers must be a part of the diagnosis documented in the health record.

_____ 5. Nonessential modifiers usually are not a part of the diagnostic statement.

_____ 6. *See* or *see also* tells the coder to continue the search under another main term.

_____ 7. V codes are used when circumstances other than a disease or injury are recorded as diagnosis or problem.

_____ 8. V codes can never be used alone on the CMS-1500 claim form.

_____ 9. *Italicized type* is used for main terms in the Alphabetic Index (Volume 2) and all codes and titles in the tabular list.

_____ 10. **Boldface type** is used for all exclusion notes and to identify codes that should not be used for describing the primary diagnosis.

_____ 11. When the notation "code first underlying disease" is seen, the etiology is coded before the manifestation.

_____ 12. HCPCS Level 3 codes, known as local codes, have mostly been eliminated from use.

_____ 13. A colon is used in the tabular list after an incomplete term that needs one or more modifiers to make it a complete statement.

_____ 14. If the health care provider inadvertently omits a diagnosis in the patient's health record, an experienced health insurance professional may abstract the correct diagnosis for coding purposes without consulting the physician.

_____ 15. The abbreviation NOS is the equivalent of "unspecified."

Short Answer/Fill-in-the-Blank

1. Define diagnosis in your own words.

   _____

2. A diagnosis code can be _____ to _____ digits.

3. ICD-9-CM stands for _____.

4. The "primary diagnosis" is used by _____; the "principal diagnosis" is used by

   _____.

5. Name the three volumes of ICD-9-CM and what each contains.

   _____

   _____

   _____

6. Why is it important for the health insurance professional to use the most recent volume of ICD-9-CM?

   _____

7. In the blank following the name of the volume or appendix, list what is contained in that portion of the ICD-9-CM manual.

   Volume 2: _____

   Volume 1: _____

   Appendix A: _____

   Appendix B: _____

   Appendix C: _____

   Appendix D: _____

   Appendix E: _____

8. The first step in diagnostic coding is to identify the _____.

9. List the four ways main terms appear in the Index to Diseases, and give an example of each.

_____

_____

_____

_____

10. Name the tables that appear in the Alphabetic Index to Diseases.

_____

_____

11. Explain the content and purpose of the Table of Drugs and Chemicals.

_____

_____

12. List the seven essential steps to diagnostic coding.

_____

_____

_____

_____

_____

_____

13. List steps for selecting the correct E code.

_____

_____

_____

14. ICD-10 is now being used in some parts of the world. Describe this revised method of coding, and explain some of the differences compared with ICD-9.

_____

_____

_____

Critical Thinking Activities

A. Underline the main term in each of the following:

    1. breast mass
    2. deviated nasal septum
    3. heel spurs
    4. excessive eye strain
    5. tension headache
    6. bronchial croup
    7. senile cataract
    8. paranoid delusions
    9. acute hemorrhagic otitis media with effusion
  10. coronary insufficiency

B. Explain what an eponym is and give two examples.

C. Underline the main terms in the following diseases/conditions, and assign the correct ICD-9-CM code.

    1. angina pectoris: _____

    2. hemorrhoids: _____

    3. irregular menstruation: _____

    4. Parkinson disease: _____

    5. Skene gland abscess: _____

D. Explain each of the following conventions/symbols:

NOS: _____

NEC: _____

[ ]: _____

§: _____

✔5ᵗʰ: _____

E. A diagnostic statement from the physician may contain many medical terms, but there is only one main term that describes the patient's illness or injury. All accompanying words that describe the main term further are called *modifiers*. These are found in the Alphabetic Index following the main terms.

    1. Name the two types of modifiers.
    2. Explain how these two types of modifiers are differentiated, how they are used, and their effect on assigning a correct diagnostic code.

F. Cross-references assist the coder in locating the appropriate code. They are found only in the Alphabetic Index. There are three types of cross-references; name them and explain what each means.

G. There are four kinds of punctuation marks used in the Tabular List, and each punctuation mark has a different meaning. List these four punctuation marks and explain what each means to the coder.

H. Four symbols appear in Volume 1 (the Tabular List) of ICD-9-CM. List these four symbols, and give a detailed explanation of what each one tells the coder.

I. The following instructional notes appear only in the Tabular List of Diseases. Explain what each means in your own words.

Includes
Excludes
Use additional code
Code first underlying disease
Code, if applicable, any causal condition first
Omit code

J. Other conventions include two different styles of type. Explain where and for what purpose each of these style types are used.

Boldface: _____

Italicized: _____

Case Studies

A. Aileen Fortune visited Broadmoor Medical Clinic on 12/29/20_____. On examining her health record, you find the following diagnoses:

Hypertension, essential, benign: _____

Urinary incontinence: _____

Multiple vesicovaginal fistula of bladder: _____

Underline the main terms and assign the correct ICD-9-CM codes to each.

B. Patient Marcus Aberle's chief complaint and diagnoses are documented as follows:

CC: shortness of breath, chest discomfort, nausea, and profuse sweating
DX: (1) probable myocardial infarction; (2) rule out gastroesophageal reflux disease
What would the correct ICD-9-CM code(s) be for this patient?

C. A 51-year-old man is seen at Broadmoor Medical Clinic for an annual health maintenance examination. In addition to the examination, three diagnoses are listed in his health record as follows:

1. Health maintenance examination, 51-year-old man
2. Tobacco dependence
3. Gastroesophageal reflux disease
4. Arthritis of spine (degenerative)

Underline the main terms for this patient's diagnoses/conditions, and assign the proper codes to each.

D. Archie Simpson, a 14-year-old boy, presents to the clinic with an insect bite to the right hand, etiology unknown. What would this diagnostic code be?

E. Katie Olivier, a 6-year-old girl, comes to the clinic with complaints of fever of 101.5° F, chills, sweats, mild earache, stuffy nose, sinus pain and pressure, an episodic cough (that is worse in the evening), wheezing, and dyspnea that started approximately 5 days ago. The diagnosis documented in Katie's health record is *acute upper respiratory infection with mild sinusitis, possibly allergy related.* How many diagnostic codes would you list on the claim form? What would this/these code(s) be?

F.

   1. David Scott presented to the clinic as a new patient on 08/05/2004. The documentation in his health record states a diagnosis of *ulcer of the midfoot* on this first visit. What is the code for the diagnosis?

   2. Over the next 2 years, Mr. Scott continues to come to the clinic on follow-up visits for treatment of his foot ulcer, which tends to heal and then recur. Would the ICD-9 code be the same for this patient's follow-up visit on 04/09/2006?

   3. If not, what is the correct code for this follow-up visit?

G. Assign the correct diagnosis for a 6-year-old boy who presents to the clinic with a cat bite and associated cellulitis of the right lower leg.

H. Marcie Emmerson, a 22-year-old woman, presents to the clinic with a chief complaint of sore throat, mild discomfort with swallowing, hoarseness in her voice, nasal congestion with a greenish nasal discharge, and slight postnasal drainage. She denies sinus pain and pressure. She has had a minimal cough with no wheezing, shortness of breath, or dyspnea. The patient is afebrile. Impression: Acute pharyngitis.

   1. How many diagnosis codes are needed for this patient's claim form?
   2. State the diagnosis(es).
   3. Assign the correct code(s).

Internet Exploration

A. The following website contains helpful information and ICD-9-CM coding resources: **http://www. cms.hhs.gov/ICD9ProviderDiagnosticCodes**. Explore this expansive website for additional information on diagnostic coding.

B. On the above-mentioned website, locate and click on the following topics:

   - New, Deleted, and Revised ICD-9-CM Codes-Summary Tables
   - ICD-9-CM Official Coding Guidelines
   - ICD-9-CM Conversion Table (this table shows the date the new code became effective and its previously assigned code equivalent)
   - ICD-10-PCS Draft Coding System and Manual

C. The NCHS is dedicated to monitoring health in the United States. Their website, **http://www.cdc. gov/nchs/icd9.htm**, provides information on "What's New" in health care. Explore the topic "Classification of Death and Injury Resulting from Terrorism," which discusses how the events of 9/11 affected coding.

Additional Coding Exercises

Using the guidelines given in the text and the most current ICD-9-CM manual, code the following diagnoses/ conditions to their greatest level of specificity. (Some may need more than one code.)

Exercise 1

Abdominal discomfort: _____

Abdominal pain, right upper quadrant: _____

Acute conjunctivitis: _____

Acute cephalgia: _____

Acute hemorrhagic otitis media with effusion: _____

Acute otitis media: _____

Acute rheumatoid juvenile arthritis: _____

Acute, obstructed gastric ulcer with hemorrhage and perforation: _____

Alcoholic gastritis: _____

Cardiovascular disease, angina pectoris: _____

Pelvic inflammatory disease: _____

Contact dermatitis: _____

Breast mass: _____

Bronchial croup: _____

Chest pain: _____

Closed fracture of fifth cervical vertebra: _____

Color blindness (congenital): _____

Exercise 2

Compound fracture of right humerus: _____

COPD: _____

Coronary insufficiency: _____

Cystic fibrosis: _____

Deviated septum: _____

Diabetes mellitus: _____

Dietary counseling with dietitian for diabetes: _____

Diverticulitis of duodenum: _____

Exertional dyspnea: _____

Extra thyroid gland: _____

Follow-up examination after surgery: _____

Food poisoning NOS with vomiting: _____

Acute idiopathic pericarditis: _____

Chronic lymphadenitis: _____

Gangrene due to insulin-dependent diabetes: _____

Heartburn: _____

Ileitis, noninfectious: _____

Infected rectal polyps (2): _____

Infection, base of left great toe: _____

Inflammatory cystic lesion of scalp ($\frac{1}{5}$ cm): _____

Klebsiella pneumonia: _____

Exercise 3

Lumbago due to displacement of intervertebral disc: _____

Lung abscess: _____

Myocardial infarction with hypertension, subsequent episode of care: _____

Nasal laceration: _____

Necrosis of liver: _____

Onychauxis and onychocryptosis: _____

Osteoarthrosis, localized, primary of ankle: _____

Paranoid delusions: _____

Parkinson disease: _____

Potassium deficiency: _____

Premature ventricular contractions: _____

Pulmonary emphysema: _____

Exposure to rabies: _____

Reflux esophagitis: _____

Right hip fracture, closed: _____

Right otitis media, necrotizing with rupture of eardrum: _____

Ringing in the ears: _____

Routine chest x-ray: _____

Sebaceous cyst: _____

Senile cataract: _____

Exercise 4

Severe onychocryptosis, both margins of left hallux: _____

Shortness of breath: _____

Tension headache: _____

Toxic nodular goiter with crisis: _____

Urinary tract infection due to *Trichomonas*: _____

Varicose veins, lower extremities: _____

Well-baby examination: _____

Yellow jaundice: _____

Actinic keratosis: _____

Common migraine with blurred vision: _____

Urinary tract infection with vaginitis (NOS): _____

Food poisoning (NOS) without vomiting: _____

Colles fracture: _____

Irritable colon: _____

6-week postpartum checkup: _____

Accidental drowning after fall from motorboat: _____

Measles (no complications documented): _____

Irritable bladder: _____

Kaposi sarcoma: _____

Adverse reaction to pertussis vaccine: _____

Hypokalemia: _____

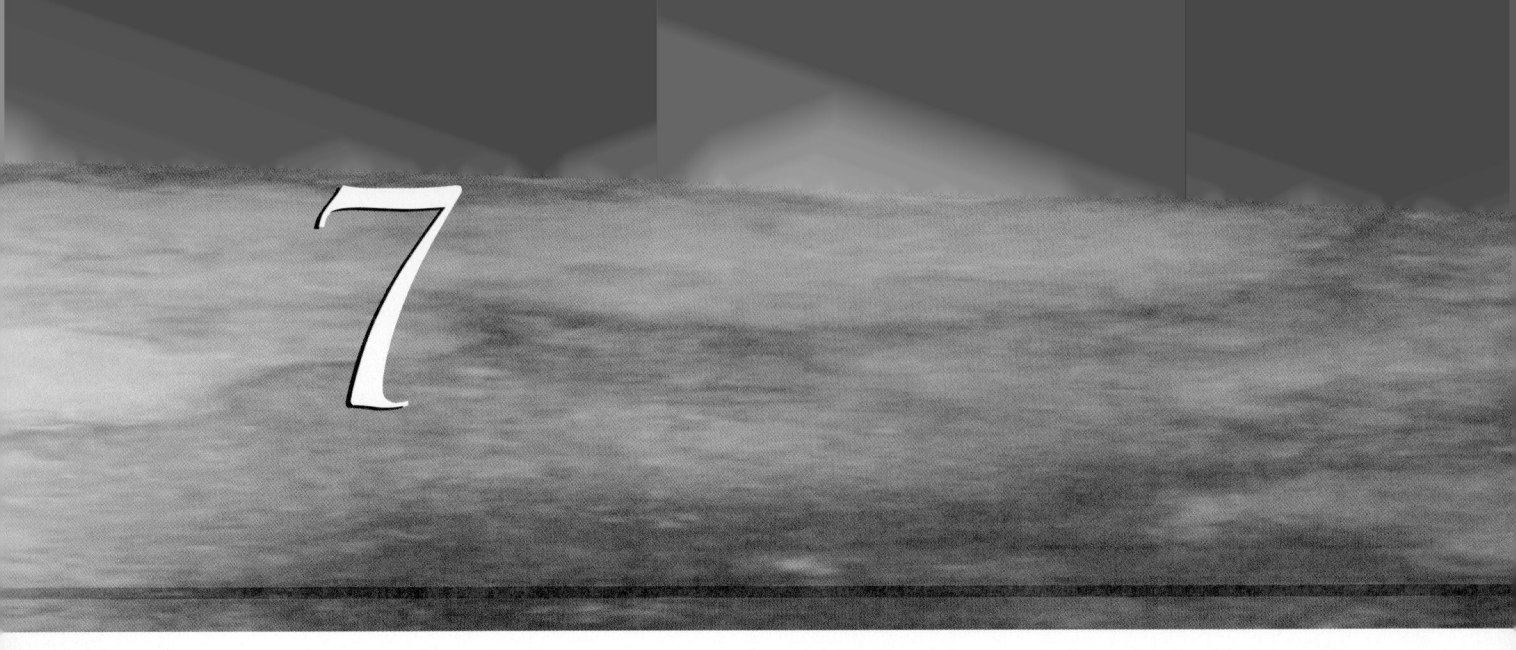

OBJECTIVES

After completion of this chapter, the student should be able to:

1. Discuss the purpose and development of the CPT-4 Manual.
2. Explain the format of CPT.
3. Interpret the symbols used in CPT.
4. Explain the significance of the semicolon in CPT.
5. List the basic steps in CPT coding.
6. Differentiate between a "new" and "established" patient in E/M coding.
7. List and explain the three key components that establish the level in E/M coding.
8. Name the four contributing factors that can affect the level of E/M coding.
9. Explain how time can be measured in E/M coding.
10. Compare and contrast the main differences in the 1995 versus 1997 E/M documentation guidelines.
11. Explain the HCPCS coding system.
12. Discuss HIPAA's requirements in relation to standardizing procedural coding.

PROCEDURAL, EVALUATION AND MANAGEMENT, AND HCPCS CODING

KEY TERMS

category
Category III codes
Centers for Medicare and Medicaid
  Services (CMS)
chief complaint (CC)
concurrent care
consultation
counseling
critical care
crosswalk
emergency care
established patient
Evaluation and Management (E/M) codes
face-to-face time
HCFA's Common Procedure Coding
  System (HCPCS)

HCPCS codes
Health Care Financing Administration
  (HCFA)
history of present illness (HPI)
indented code
inpatient
key components
Level I (codes)
Level II (codes)
Level III (codes)
modifier
modifying term
neonates
new patient
observation
outpatient

past, family, and social history (PFSH)
*Physicians' Current Procedural
  Terminology*, Fourth Edition (CPT-4)
*Physicians' Current Procedural
  Terminology*, Fifth Edition (CPT-5)
review of systems (ROS)
section
see
special report
stand-alone code
subheading
subjective information
subsection
unit/floor time

Opening Scenario

Park Chalmers found that ICD-9 coding met his needs for a chance at a challenging career and his desire to work in the medical field. He hoped that he also would find CPT coding to his liking. Melanie Sanders, another student in Park's medical insurance class, had struggled with diagnostic coding, and she confessed to Park that the chapter on CPT intimidated her. "If I don't get this coding stuff," Melanie confided to Park, "I'm going to have to drop the course." Melanie is not interested in becoming a professional coder—her career goal is to work in the clinical side of medical assisting. "I don't know why I have to know this stuff anyway," she tells Park, "I won't have to deal with coding once I've finished the program."

"Being familiar with all facets of administrative work in the medical office, including billing, insurance, and coding, makes you more employable," Park reminded her. "For instance, if you and one other applicant are competing for a job, and you know how to code, but the other individual doesn't, you'd have the edge. If you stick with it, I'll help you," Park promised.

Park gave Melanie an important tip: "The secret to coding is in its structure. There is a very systematic method for finding the appropriate code," he explained. "The most important thing is to follow the steps outlined in the chapter, and never code from the Alphabetic Index alone." Melanie, encouraged by Park's positive outlook toward coding and his pledge to help her, decides to give coding a second chance. With Park's help, she determined that perhaps she could understand CPT coding well enough to pass the course.

OVERVIEW OF CPT CODING

The *Physicians' Current Procedural Terminology*, **Fourth Edition (CPT-4)**, is a manual containing a list of descriptive terms and identifying codes used in reporting medical services and procedures performed and supplies used by physicians and other professional health care providers in the care and treatment of patients. CPT was first developed and published by the American Medical Association (AMA) in 1966. The CPT system is governed by the CPT editorial panel, a group of 16 individuals (virtually all physicians) who are empowered to make final decisions with regard to the content of CPT. The CPT coding system was adopted by the **Health Care Financing Administration (HCFA)**, now called the **Centers for Medicare and Medicaid Services (CMS)**, as Level I codes to help establish a more uniform payment schedule for Medicare carriers to use when reimbursing providers, and became the preferred method of coding when the federal government developed the Health Care Financing Administration (HCFA) Common Procedure Coding System (HCPCS), Level II codes, for the Medicare Program. CPT is published by the AMA and updated annually.

Since the early 1970s, HCFA has asked the AMA to work with physicians of every specialty to determine appropriate definitions for CPT codes and to try to determine accurate reimbursement amounts for each code. Two committees within the AMA act on these issues: the CPT Committee, which updates the definitions of the codes, and the Relative Value Update Committee, which recommends reimbursement values to the CMS based on data collected by medical societies on the current rate of services described in the codes.

Because medicine is constantly changing, the AMA publishes an updated version of the CPT manual every year. The health insurance professional must use the most recent edition of CPT when coding professional procedures and services for claims submissions.

Today, not only Medicare and Medicaid but also most managed care and other insurance companies base their reimbursements on the values established by the CMS. As with ICD-9-CM diagnostic coding, it is important that the health insurance professional have a thorough understanding of CPT coding to facilitate accurate claims completion for maximal reimbursement. The main reason for this is because CPT codes are used instead of a narrative description in Block 24d of the CMS-1500 form to describe what services or procedures were rendered or what supplies were used during the patient encounter.

Purpose of CPT

The purpose of CPT coding is to provide a uniform language that accurately describes medical, surgical, and diagnostic services, serving as an effective means for reliable nationwide communication among physicians, insurance carriers, and patients. CPT codes also are used by most third-party payers and government agencies as a record of an individual health care provider's activities.

HIPAA TIP

Providers submitting claims for professional services on the CMS-1500 form should use the current ICD-9-CM diagnosis codes, current CPT procedural codes, and current Point-of-Service codes.

Development of CPT

As mentioned previously, the AMA developed and published the first CPT in 1966. This first edition

- helped encourage the use of standard terms and descriptors to document procedures in the health record,
- helped communicate accurate information on procedures and services to agencies concerned with insurance claims,
- provided the basis for a computer-oriented system to evaluate operative procedures, and
- contributed basic information for actuarial and statistical purposes.

The first edition of CPT contained primarily surgical procedures, with limited sections on medicine, radiology, and laboratory procedures.

The second edition was published in 1970 and presented an expanded system of terms and codes to designate diagnostic and therapeutic procedures in surgery, medicine, and other specialties. At that time, the five-digit coding system was introduced, replacing the former four-digit classification. Another significant change was a listing of procedures relating to internal medicine. The third and fourth editions of CPT were introduced in the mid to late 1970s. The fourth edition, published in 1977, presented significant updates in medical technology, and a system of periodic updating was introduced to keep pace with the rapidly changing medical environment.

In 1983, CPT was adopted as part of **HCFA's Common Procedure Coding System (HCPCS)**. With this adoption, HCFA mandated the use of HCPCS (pronounced "hick picks") to report services for Part B of the Medicare Program. In October 1986, HCFA also required state Medicaid agencies to use HCPCS in the Medicaid Management Information System. In July 1987, as part of the Omnibus Budget Reconciliation Act, HCFA mandated the use of CPT for reporting outpatient hospital surgical procedures. Today, in addition to use in federal

programs (Medicare and Medicaid), CPT is used extensively throughout the United States as the preferred system of coding and describing health care services.

WHAT DID YOU LEARN?

1. What is CPT?
2. What is the purpose of CPT?
3. Why were CPT codes developed?
4. Who publishes CPT-4?
5. How often is CPT updated?

THREE LEVELS OF PROCEDURAL CODING

HCPCS codes are descriptive terms with letters or numbers or both used to report medical services and procedures for reimbursement. As discussed earlier, they provide a uniform language to describe medical, surgical, and diagnostic services. HCPCS codes are used to report procedures and services to government and private health insurance programs, and reimbursement is based on the codes reported. A code, rather than a narrative description, can summarize the services or supplies provided when billing a third-party payer. HCPCS codes are grouped into three levels, as follows:

Level I. Level I contains the AMA Physicians' CPT codes. These are five-digit codes, accompanied by descriptive terms, used for reporting services performed by health care professionals. Level I codes are developed and updated annually by the AMA.

Level II. Level II consists of the HCPCS National Codes used to report medical services, supplies, drugs, and durable medical equipment not contained in the Level I codes. These codes begin with a single letter, followed by four digits. Level II codes supersede Level I codes for similar encounters, evaluation and management (E/M) services, or other procedures and represent the portion of procedures involving supplies and materials. National Level II Medicare Codes are not restricted to Medicare as their title may suggest. An increasing number of private insurance carriers are encouraging, and some are even requiring, the use of HCPCS National Codes. HCPCS Level II codes are in a separate manual from Level I codes (CPT). Level II codes are developed and updated annually by the CMS and their contractors.

Level III. In preparation of standardization for the full implementation of the Health Insurance Portability and Accountability Act

(HIPAA), CMS has instructed carriers to eliminate local procedures and modifier codes from their claim processing systems. Official HCPCS Level III procedure and modifier codes are defined as codes and descriptors developed by local Medicare contractors for use by physicians, practitioners, providers, and suppliers in completion of claims for payment.

HIPAA TIP

The combination of HCPCS and CPT-4 (including codes and modifiers) is the HIPAA adopted standard for reporting physician services and other health care services on standard transactions.

WHAT DID YOU LEARN?

1. What are HCPCS codes?
2. List the three levels of HCPCS codes.

CPT MANUAL FORMAT

Introduction and Main Sections

Similar to the ICD-9-CM manual, CPT-4 is composed of several sections beginning with an introduction, identified by lower case Roman numerals. The main body of the manual follows the introduction and is organized in six sections. Within each section are subsections with anatomical, procedural, condition, or descriptor subheadings. Table 7-1 lists the CPT sections and their number range sequence. The listed procedures and services and their identifying five-digit codes are presented in numerical order except for the E/M section. Because E/M codes are used by most physicians for reporting key categories of their services, this section is presented first.

Five-digit CPT codes may be defined further by modifiers to help explain an unusual circumstance associated with a service or procedure. As mentioned previously, the right coding modifiers are crucial to getting claims paid promptly and for the correct amount. Conversely, missing or incorrect modifiers are one of the most common reasons that claims are denied by payers. It is easy to get confused on how to use modifiers correctly, especially because, similar to CPT codes, they are constantly changing. The most important thing to remember when using modifiers is that the health record must contain adequate documentation to support the modifier (Fig. 7-1).

When coding procedures, it is important always to have the most recent edition of the CPT book available to look up current modifier codes. (Modifiers are listed in Appendix A at the back of the CPT manual.) Also, it is advisable for health care providers and their billing staff to read Medicare (and other) coding newsletters and attend coding workshops periodically.

Each main section of the CPT is preceded by guidelines specific to that section. These guidelines define terms that are necessary to interpret correctly and report the procedures and services contained in that section. The health insurance professional should read and study these guidelines before attempting to assign a code.

Category III Codes

Following the six sections listed in the main body of the CPT manual are the **Category III codes**

Modifier-22 is used to indicate that there was "something unusual about the procedure, it took longer than usual, or it was harder than usual." The only way you'll get consideration for additional payment is if you use the modifier and have good documentation.

Modifier-59 is used to indicate that a procedure or service was distinct or independent from other services performed on the same day (e.g., not normally reported together) but are appropriate under the circumstances, as documented.

Fig. 7-1 Examples of correct modifier use.

TABLE 7-1 CPT Section Numbers and Their Sequence

Section Title	Numbering Sequence
Evaluation and Management	99201-99499
Anesthesiology	00100-01999, 99100-99140
Surgery	10021-69990
Radiology (including Nuclear Medicine and Diagnostic Ultrasound)	70010-79999
Pathology and Laboratory	80048-89356
Medicine (except Anesthesiology)	90281-99199, 99500-99602

(Fig. 7-2). Category III codes were established by the AMA as a set of temporary CPT codes for emerging technologies, services, and procedures for which data collection is needed to substantiate widespread use or for the approval process of the Food and Drug Administration (FDA). If a Category III code has not been proposed and accepted into the main body of CPT (referred to as *Category I codes*) within 5 years, it is archived, unless a demonstrated need for it develops.

In the introduction of the CPT book, users are instructed not to select a code that merely approximates the service provided. The code should identify the service performed accurately. If a Category III code is available and accurately describes the service provided, it should be used instead of a Category I code. Category III codes are updated semiannually in January and July, and new codes are posted on the AMA website.

Appendixes A through L

As with ICD-9-CM, CPT-4 contains several appendixes, which follow the Category III codes. These appendixes and their contents are as follows:

Appendix A—Modifiers
Appendix B—Summary of Additions, Deletions, and Revisions
Appendix C—Clinical Examples
Appendix D—Summary of CPT Add-On Codes
Appendix E—Summary of CPT Codes Exempt from Modifier -51
Appendix F—Summary of CPT Codes Exempt from Modifier -63
Appendix G—Summary of CPS Codes that Include Moderate (Conscious) Sedation
Appendix H—Alphabetic Index of Performance Measure by Clinical Condition by Topic
Appendix I—Genetic Testing Code Modifiers
Appendix J—Electrodiagnostic Medicine Listing of Sensory, Motor, and Mixed Nerves
Appendix K—Products Pending FDA Approval
Appendix L—Vascular Families

CPT Index

Main Terms

In the CPT manual, the index is presented last. As with ICD-9-CM, the CPT index is organized by main terms (Fig. 7-3). Each main term can stand alone, or it can be followed by up to three modifying terms. There are four primary classes of main term entries, as follows:

Category III codes	0052T—0071T
0062T	Percutaneous intradiscal annuloplasty, any method, unilateral or bilateral including fluoroscopic guidance; single level
	➲ *CPT Assistant* Mar 05:2-3, Apr 05:14, 16; *CPT Changes: An Insider's View* 2005
+ 0063T	one or more additional levels (List separately in addition to 0062T for primary procedure)
	➲ *CPT Assistant* Mar 05:2; *CPT Changes: An Insider's View* 2005
	(For CT or MRI guidance and localization for needle placement and annuloplasty in conjunction with 0062T, 0063T, see 76360, 76393)
0064T	Spectroscopy, expired gas analysis (e.g., nitric oxide/carbon dioxide test)
	➲ *CPT Assistant* Mar 05:3; *CPT Changes: An Insider's View* 2005
0065T	Ocular photoscreening, with interpretation and report, bilateral
	➲ *CPT Assistant* Mar 05:3-4; *CPT Changes: An Insider's View* 2005
	(Do not report 0065T in conjunction with 99172 or 99173)
0066T	Computed tomographic (CT) colonography (i.e., virtual colonoscopy); screening
	➲ *CPT Assistant* Mar 05:4; *CPT Changes: An Insider's View* 2005
	➲ *Clinical Examples in Radiology* Winter 05:8, 12
0067T	diagnostic
	➲ *CPT Assistant* Mar 05:4; *CPT Changes: An Insider's View* 2005
	➲ *Clinical Examples in Radiology* Winter 05:8

Fig. 7-2 Example of Category III codes. *(From American Medical Association:* CPT 2007 Current procedural terminology, *2007, Standard Edition, Chicago, 2007, American Medical Association.)*

```
Endoscopy . . . . . . . . . . . 45337
Ultrasound
  Endoscopy . . . . . . . 45341-45342

Colonna Procedure
See Acetabulum, Reconstruction
Colonography
CT Scan . . . . . . . . . . 0066T, 0067T
Colonoscopy
Biopsy . . . . . . . . . . . 45380, 45392
Collection Specimen . . . . . . . 45380
  via Colotomy . . . . . . . . . . . 45355
Destruction
  Lesion . . . . . . . . . . . . . . . . 45383
  Tumor . . . . . . . . . . . . . . . . 45383
Dilation . . . . . . . . . . . . . . . . 45386
Hemorrhage Control . . . . . . . 45382
```

Fig. 7-3 Example of main terms. *(From American Medical Association:* CPT 2007 Current procedural terminology, *2007, Standard Edition, Chicago, 2007, American Medical Association.)*

1. **Procedure or service** (e.g., colonoscopy, anastomosis, debridement)
2. **Organ or other anatomical site** (e.g., fibula, kidney, nails)
3. **Condition** (e.g., infection, pregnancy, tetralogy of Fallot)
4. **Synonyms, eponyms, and abbreviations** (e.g., ECS, Pean's operation, Clagett procedure)

STOP AND THINK

Surgeon Milford Tramen saw Patrick Lovell, a 34-year-old Illinois farmer, in his office on February 19 for the repair of an injury to the patient's mouth. The chief complaint in the medical record documents that the patient was "kicked in the mouth while vaccinating hogs." The surgeon stitched up the 3.4-cm cut, and the nurse administered a tetanus shot. What would be the main term for the procedure performed by the surgeon?

Modifying Terms

As mentioned previously, each main term can stand alone, or it can be followed by up to three modifying terms (Fig. 7-4). Modifying terms are indented under the main term. All **modifying terms** should be examined closely because these subterms often have an effect on the selection of the appropriate procedural code.

Code Layout

A CPT code can be displayed one of three ways:

1. **A single code** (Proetz therapy, nose 30210)
2. **Multiple codes** (prolactin 80418, 80440, 84146)
3. **A range of codes** (prostatotomy 55720-55725)

Symbols Used in CPT

The CPT manual uses several symbols that help guide the health insurance professional in locating the correct code. Accurate procedural coding cannot be accomplished without understanding the meaning of each of these symbols (Table 7-2).

| Delay of Flap |
| Skin Graft. . . . . 15600-15630 |
| **Deligation** |
| Ureter. . . . . 50940 |
| **Deliveries, Abdominal** |
| *See* Cesarean Delivery |
| **Delivery** |
| *See* Cesarean Delivery, Vaginal Delivery |
| **Delorme Operation** |
| *See* Pericardiectomy |
| **Denervation** |
| Hip |
| Femoral. . . . . 27035 |
| Obturator. . . . . 27035 |
| Sciatic. . . . . 27035 |
| **Denervation, Sympathetic** |
| *See* Excision, Nerve, Sympathetic |
| **Denis-Browne Splint** . . . . . . 29590 |
| **Dens Axis** |
| *See* Odontoid process |
| **Denver Developmental Screening Test** . . . . . 96101-96103 |
| **Denver Krupic Procedure** |
| *See* Aqueous Shunt, to Extraocular Reservoir |
| **Denver Shunt** |
| Patency Test . . . . 78291 |
| **Denver-Krupin Procedure**. . 66180 |

Fig. 7-4 Example of main term with modifying terms. (*From American Medical Association:* CPT 2007 Current procedural terminology, *2007, Standard Edition, Chicago, 2007, American Medical Association.*)

TABLE 7-2	Symbols Used in the CPT Manual

Symbol	Explanation
Bullet (●)	A bullet (●) before a code means the code is new to the CPT book for that particular edition
Triangle (▲)	A triangle (▲) means the description for the code has been changed or modified since the previous revision of the CPT book
Horizontal triangles (►◄)	Horizontal triangles (►◄) placed at the beginning and end of a descriptive entry indicates that it contains new or revised wording
Plus sign (+)	Add-on codes are annotated by a plus sign (+)
⊘	This symbol is used to identify codes that are exempt from the use of modifier -51
☉	Reference to *CPT Assistant, Clinical Examples in Radiology and CPT Changes* book
⚡	The lightning bolt indicates codes for vaccines that are pending Food and Drug Administration approval
⊙	This symbol is used to identify codes that include conscious sedation

Modifiers

Modifiers are important to ensuring appropriate and timely payment. A health insurance professional who understands when and how to use modifiers reduces the problems caused by denials and expedites processing of claims.

A modifier provides the means by which the reporting health care provider can indicate that a service or procedure performed has been altered by some specific circumstance, but its definition or code has not been changed. The judicious application of modifiers tells the third-party payer that this case is unique. By using appropriate modifiers, the office may be paid for services that are ordinarily denied. In addition, modifiers can describe a situation that, without the modifier, could be considered inappropriate coding.

Modifiers are not universal; they cannot be used with all CPT codes. Some modifiers may be used only with E/M codes (e.g., modifier -24 or modifier -25), and others are used only with procedure codes (e.g., modifier -58 or modifier -79). Check the guidelines at the beginning of each section for a listing or description of the modifiers that may be used with the codes in that section. Appendix A of the CPT manual contains a comprehensive list of modifiers.

HIPAA TIP

HIPAA does not mandate the use of modifiers. According to the adopted HIPAA implementation guide, use of modifiers is not required. Their usage is "situational," meaning that the use of a modifier is required only when a modifier clarifies or improves the reporting accuracy of the associated procedure code.

Unlisted Procedure or Service

A health care provider may perform a service or procedure for which a code is unavailable in the CPT manual. When this happens, specific codes have been designated for reporting these unlisted procedures. At the end of each subsection or subheading in question, a code is provided under the heading "other procedures," which typically ends in "-99." In the surgery section, note the "other procedures" code 39499 at the end of the "mediastinum" subsection. This would be the code of choice for any unlisted procedures of the mediastinum.

Special Reports

When a rarely used, unusual, variable, or new service or procedure is performed, many third-party payers require a **special report** to accompany the claim to help determine the appropriateness and medical necessity of the service or procedure. Items that should be addressed in the report, if applicable, include the following:

- A definition or description of the service or procedure
- The time, effort, and equipment needed
- Symptoms and final diagnosis
- Pertinent physical findings and size
- Diagnostic and therapeutic services
- Concurrent problems
- Follow-up care

WHAT DID YOU LEARN?

1. List the six main sections of CPT.
2. What is the purpose of the guidelines that appear at the beginning of each main section of CPT?
3. What are Category III codes?
4. Name the five appendixes contained in CPT.
5. What are the four primary classes of main term entries?
6. What is the function of a "modifier"?

FORMAT OF CPT

There are two types of CPT codes: stand-alone and indented. The terminology of a **stand-alone code** is complete in and of itself. It contains the full description of the procedure without additional explanation. Some procedures do not contain the entire written description, however. These are known as **indented codes**. Indented codes refer to the common portion of the procedure listed in the preceding entry, and correct code selection requires careful attention to the punctuation in the description.

Importance of the Semicolon

In the CPT, the semicolon is used to separate main and subordinate clauses in the code descriptions. This symbol was adopted to save space in the manual where a series of related codes are found. CPT code "38100 splenectomy; total (separate procedure)" is a stand-alone code. The code immediately following it, 38101, is indented and reads "partial (separate procedure)." The semicolon after splenectomy in code 38100 becomes part of the indented code

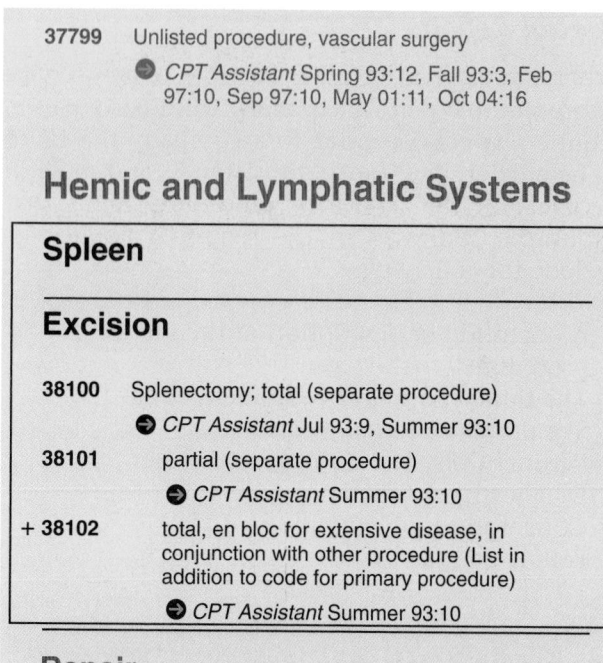

Fig. 7-5 Example of a stand-alone code followed by an indented code used in the example of Fig. 7-4. *(From American Medical Association: CPT 2007 Current procedural terminology, 2007, Standard Edition, Chicago, 2007, American Medical Association.)*

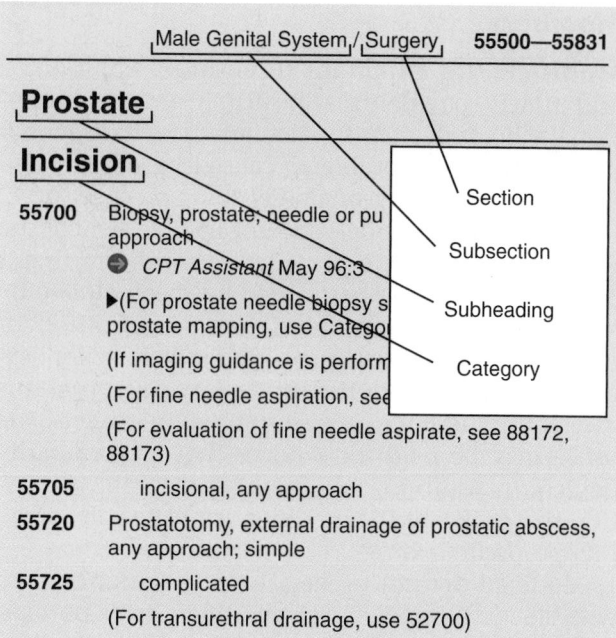

Fig. 7-6 Section of Tab List illustrating section, subsection, subheading, and category. *(From American Medical Association: CPT 2007 Current procedural terminology, 2007, Standard Edition, Chicago, 2007, American Medical Association.)*

38101. The full description of code 38101 in effect would read "splenectomy; partial (separate procedure)." Fig. 7-5 provides an example of a stand-alone code followed by an indented code used in the mentioned example.

Section, Subsection, Subheading, and Category

Codes in the tabular section of CPT are formatted using four classifications: section, subsection, subheading, and category. To illustrate this, locate the code "51020" in the Tabular List. At the top left, note the code range on that particular page (50970 through 51610), followed by the words "surgery/urinary system." "Surgery" is the **section,** and "urinary system" is the **subsection**. Moving down the page, note the word "bladder" in large, bold font. Bladder is the **subheading**. Immediately under bladder, note the word "incision," which ~~ates the **category** (Fig. 7-6).

Cross-Referencing with See

When searching for the correct main term, the word "*see*" is frequently seen. "*See*" is used as a cross-reference term in the CPT alphabetical index and directs the coder to an alternative main term (Fig. 7-7).

WHAT DID YOU LEARN?

1. Explain the significance of the semicolon in CPT coding.
2. How is a "stand-alone" code different from an "indented code"?
3. What does the cross-referencing term "*see*" indicate?

BASIC STEPS OF CPT CODING

CPT coding is a structured process, and it is important for the health insurance professional to follow a few basic steps so that the correct code is identified and assigned.

1. *Identify the procedure, service, or supply to be coded.* These are typically found on the ledger card, on the encounter form, or in the patient data in the computerized accounting software.

2. *Determine the main term.* The index is located at the back of the CPT manual. Main terms are in boldface type and are listed alphabetically with headings located in the top right and left corners, similar to a dictionary (Fig. 7-8). For the purpose of review, main terms are organized by four primary classes of main entries: a procedure or service; an organ or other anatomical site; a condition; or a synonym, eponym, or abbreviation. Subterms (if applicable) are indented under main terms.

Reminder! Do not select the final code from the alphabetical index alone.

3. Locate the main term in the alphabetical index, and note the code or codes.
4. Cross-reference the single code, multiple codes, or the code range numerically in the tabular section of the manual.
5. Read and follow any notes, special instructions, or conventions associated with the code.
6. Determine and assign the appropriate code.

Before assigning an indented code, refer to the stand-alone code above it. Read the words that *precede* the semicolon, ensuring that the combined description (the portion of the stand-alone code *up* to the semicolon *plus* the wording included in the indented description) corresponds to the documented procedure or service.

Dermatology
Actinotherapy 96900
Examination of Hair
  Microscopic 96902
Ultraviolet A Treatment 96912
Ultraviolet B Treatment
  96910-96913
Ultraviolet Light Treatment
  96900-96913
Unlisted Services and
  Procedures 96999

Dermatoplasty
Septal 30620

Dermoid
See Cyst, Dermoid

Derrick-Burnet Disease
See Q Fever

Descending Abdominal Aorta
See Aorta, Abdominal

Desipramine
Assay 80160

Desmotomy
See Ligament, Release

Desoxycorticosterone 82633

Desoxycortone
See Desoxycorticosterone

Desoxyephedrine
See Methamphetamine

Desoxynorephedrin
See Amphetamine

Fig. 7-7 Example of "*see*" used as a cross-reference. *(From American Medical Association: CPT 2007 Current procedural terminology, 2007, Standard Edition, Chicago, 2007, American Medical Association.)*

WHAT DID YOU LEARN?

1. What is the first step in CPT coding?
2. What factors should be considered before assigning an "indented code"?

≋ EVALUATION AND MANAGEMENT (E/M) CODING

The **Evaluation and Management (E/M) codes** (99201 and 99499) are found at the beginning of the CPT manual. The E/M section of the CPT is divided into broad categories, including office visits, hospital visits, and consultations. Most of the categories are divided further. There are two subcategories of office visits (new versus established patients), and two categories of hospital visits (initial versus subsequent visits).

The subcategories list codes that describe differing levels of service provided, ranging from low levels of service to higher and more intense levels of service. Initially, these codes were based on highly subjective factors that were applied inconsistently among carriers. In 1992, new uniform, national criteria were established to determine the appropriate level code to be used. Under these criteria, every visit regardless of location must include at least two of the following three components—history, examination, and medical decision making.

| Arteriovenous Fistula, Repair | Artery, Peripheral Arterial Rehabilitation |

Fig. 7-8 Example of header words at top of page in CPT manual. *(From American Medical Association: CPT 2007 Current procedural terminology, 2007, Standard Edition, Chicago, 2007, American Medical Association.)*

E/M codes represent the services provided directly to the patient during an encounter that do not involve an actual procedure. If a patient has an appointment in the office, only the office visit receives an E/M code. If any procedures are done (e.g., a urinalysis or an electrocardiogram), those procedures receive a CPT code. E/M codes are designed to classify services provided by a health care provider and are used primarily in outpatient settings. E/M codes are technically CPT codes (Level I HCPCS); however, they are referred to as *E/M* instead of *CPT* to distinguish between E/M services and procedural coding (Fig. 7-9). The level of service code selected for an office visit is given a numerical level (1 to 5). The code level assigned depends on the complexity of the history, examination, and medical decision making and usually is not affected by the time the provider spends with the patient. The range of codes for office or other outpatient services are 99201 to 99205 for new patients and 99211 to 99215 for established patients. A specific distinction between new and established patients is associated with E/M coding. The exact definitions are discussed in the next section.

Vocabulary Used in E/M Coding

To understand E/M coding more fully, the coder must become acquainted with several terms, as follows:

- **New patient**—an individual who is new to the practice, regardless of location of service, or one who has not received any medical treatment by the health care provider or any other provider in that same office *within the past 3 years.*
- **Established patient**—an individual who has been treated previously by the health care provider, regardless of location of service, within the past 3 years. If the provider saw the patient for the first time in a hospital, and that individual comes to the office for a follow-up visit after discharge, the patient is considered an established patient to the practice because health record documentation was generated from the hospital visit.
- **Outpatient**—a patient who *has not* been officially admitted to a hospital but receives diagnostic tests or treatment in that facility or a clinic connected with it.
- **Inpatient**—a patient who *has* been formally admitted to a hospital for diagnostic tests, medical care and treatment, or a surgical procedure, typically staying overnight.
- **Consultation**—when the attending health

Evaluation and Management

Office or Other Outpatient Services

The following codes are used to report evaluation and management services provided in the physician's office or in an outpatient or other ambulatory facility. A patient is considered an outpatient until inpatient admission to a health care facility occurs.

▶ To report services provided to a patient who is admitted to a hospital or nursing facility in the course of an encounter in the office or other ambulatory facility, see the notes for initial hospital inpatient care (page 11) or initial nursing facility care (page 21). ◀

For services provided by physicians in the emergency department, see 99281-99285.

For observation care, see 99217-99220.

For observation or inpatient care services (including admission and discharge services), see 99234-99236.

New Patient

99201   **Office or other outpatient visit** for the evaluation and management of a new patient, which requires these three key components:

- ■ **a problem focused history;**
- ■ **a problem focused examination;**
- ■ **straightforward medical decision making.**

Counseling and/or coordination of care with other providers or agencies are provided consistent with the nature of the problem(s) and the patient's and/or family's needs.

Usually, the presenting problem(s) are self limited or minor. Physicians typically spend 10 minutes face-to-face with the patient and/or family.

⊘ *CPT Assistant* Winter 91:11, Spring 92:13, 24, Summer 92:1, 24, Spring 93:34, Summer 93:2, Fall 93:9, Spring 95:1, Summer 95:4, Fall 95:9, Jul 98:9, Sep 98:5, Jun 99:8, Feb 00:3, 9, 11, Aug 01:2, Oct 04:11, Apr 05:3

99202   **Office or other outpatient visit** for the evaluation and management of a new patient, which requires these three key components:

- ■ **an expanded problem focused history;**
- ■ **an expanded problem focused examination;**
- ■ **straightforward medical decision making.**

Counseling and/or coordination of care with other providers or agencies are provided consistent with the nature of the problem(s) and the patient's and/or family's needs.

Fig. 7-9 Portion from E/M coding section. *(From American Medical Association:* CPT 2007 Current procedural terminology, *2007, Standard Edition, Chicago, 2007, American Medical Association.)*

care provider recommends that the patient see another physician (often a specialist) for a problem usually associated with one major body system. A family practitioner may advise a patient who presents with a suspicious mole to see a dermatologist.

Note: Do not confuse a consultation with a referral. A consultation is usually a one-time visit; the attending physician (or provider) retains control of the patient's health care, and the consultation ends when the consulting provider renders his or her opinion. With a referral, the original provider relinquishes total care of the patient to the provider to whom the patient has been referred.

- **Counseling**—a discussion with the patient or the patient's family or both. Counseling typically includes one or more of the following:
  - Discussing diagnostic test results, impressions, or recommended studies
  - Discussing prognosis
  - Explaining the risks or benefits of recommended treatment or instruction for management of care
  - Performing patient or family teaching
- **Concurrent care**—when a patient receives similar services (e.g., hospital visits) by more than one health care provider on the same day.
- **Critical care**—the constant attention (either at bedside or immediately available) by a physician in a medical crisis.
- **Emergency care**—care given in a hospital emergency department.

STOP AND THINK

Tom Galliger was in the Air Force for 4 years. During that time, he did not see Dr. Boker, his physician in his hometown of Gaithersville. Dr. Boker's office policy is to place any inactive files on microfilm after 2 years of inactivity. After Tom finished his tour of duty, he returned home to Gaithersville. Soon after returning home, he sprained his ankle hiking in the mountains and subsequently scheduled an appointment with Dr. Boker. Would Tom be considered a new or established patient?

Documentation Requirements

Because the level of the E/M codes is based on the complexity of the history, examination, or medical decision making performed during the visit, the key to reimbursement is being able to prove the level of complexity of the performed services. The only valid source of proof is the documentation in the patient's medical record.

Coding E/M services should be based on the extent of documentation in the patient's medical record (Fig. 7-10). The criteria for E/M services must be well understood by the treating provider and documented in the record. Each record needs to show elements of the history, such as the history of

---

6/10/2004

HX: This 27-year-old white male presents to the clinic today for chief complaint of an abrasion on the right knee following a fall yesterday. According to the patient, he had this soft tissue lesion before the fall; and when he fell, he basically abraded the lower half of the lesion. He is here for reevaluation and possible excision of the lesion.

PAIN ASSESSMENT: Scale 0-10, one.
ALLERGIES: DEMEROL
CURRENT MEDS: None

PE: NAD. Ambulatory. Appears well.
VS: BP: 120/74   WT: 150#
RIGHT KNEE EXAMINATION: The patient has a tibial prominence and just above that, there is what appears to be a 1.5-cm epidermal inclusion cyst with an abraded area inferiorly. There is mild erythema and serous drainage but no purulence. There is no appreciable edema. Just lateral to that lesion is a small superficial abrasion. The knee examination was totally within normal limits.

IMP: Epidermal inclusion cyst measuring 1.5 to 2 cm of the right knee, traumatized with abrasion

PLAN: The patient was empirically started on Keflex 500 mg 1 p.o. b.i.d. He was given instructions on home care and is to follow up this week for excision of the lesion. Routine follow-up as noted. RTN PRN.

Frederick Mahoney, MD

Fig. 7-10   Sample documentation.

present illness (HPI) (e.g., location, severity, frequency, duration); the review of systems (ROS); and past, family, and social history (PFSH). The physical examination should list all systems or organs examined. Medical decision making should discuss the number of options or diagnoses considered in the decision, the amount of data or complexity of data reviewed, and the risk to the patient of the decision made.

IMAGINE THIS!

Vancil Allen, a 73-year-old white man, was admitted to the hospital with chest pain and shortness of breath after a minor automobile accident. His cardiologist, Marcus Walters, was the admitting physician. While hospitalized, Vancil complained of severe pain in his right lower back. Further examination revealed a kidney stone. Subsequently, Dr. Marta Tomi, a urologist, was called in to take over the care of Vancil's kidney problems.

Three Factors to Consider

The health insurance professional must determine three factors that would direct him or her to the proper category in the E/M coding section:

1. **Place of service** (where the service was provided)
   Physician's office
   - Hospital
   - Emergency department
   - Nursing home
   - Other
2. **Type of service** (the reason the service was rendered)
   Office visit
   - Consultation
   - Admission
   - Newborn care
3. **Patient status** (type of patient)
   - New patient
   - Established patient
   - Outpatient
   - Inpatient

When these three factors are determined, the health insurance professional can move on to determining the key components, the next step in E/M coding.

For example, Cindy Carlson recently moved to Jackson City because of a job transfer. Shortly after arriving in Jackson City, Cindy sprained her ankle while jogging in the park. She scheduled an appointment with Dr. Allen Schubert, a family practitioner, for medical treatment. In this scenario

- the place of service would be the physician's office,
- the type of service would be an office visit, and
- the patient status would be "new" because Cindy has never been seen in Dr. Schubert's office before.

Now that the first three factors have been established, the next step is to determine the three key components of the encounter.

Key Components

The health insurance professional must establish what level of service the patient received. Levels of service are based on three **key components**:

- History
- Examination
- Complexity of medical decision making

All three key components must be met or exceeded for new patients; only two must be met for established patients. In addition to these three key components, there may be contributing factors that affect the E/M coding level reported, including

- counseling,
- coordination of care,
- nature of presenting problem, and
- time.

History

A patient history is **subjective information**. The essentials of the history are based on what the patient tells the health care provider in his or her own words. An experienced health insurance professional should be able to identify the various elements and levels of a history by reading the clinical notes entered into the health record.

ELEMENTS OF A PATIENT HISTORY.   A patient history is based on four elements:

1. **Chief complaint (CC)**—the reason the patient is seeing the physician, usually in the patient's own words; the CC might be "I feel awful, and I can't keep anything down."
2. **History of present illness (HPI)**—details of the severity and duration of signs and symptoms regarding the CC (e.g., fever for 2 days, severe cough, chest pains on and off since breakfast). The HPI typically consists of the following eight qualifiers:

- *Location* (where the symptom is occurring, such as neck, stomach, or ankle)
- *Quality* (burning, stabbing, throbbing)
- *Severity* (8 on a scale of 1 to 10)
- *Duration* (how long symptom has been present, or how long it lasts when it occurs)
- *Timing* (constant, after meals, during exercise)
- *Context* (the situation associated with symptom, such as began after altercation at work, after a big meal, while exercising)
- *Modifying factors* (cold rag to back of neck helps)
- *Associated signs and symptoms* (nausea, vomiting, jagged lights in field of vision)

Using the Cindy Carlson scenario described earlier, the HPI might be as follows: "Patient describes pain and swelling in the right ankle area. Applying weight on the ankle increases the pain. Ibuprofen and ice packs relieve the pain and swelling temporarily."

Note: The HPI is typically written in present tense.

3. **Review of systems (ROS)**—involves a series of questions the provider asks the patient to identify what body parts or body systems are involved, for example:
   - Constitution: denies recent weight gain/loss
   - Eyes: jagged lights in peripheral vision
   - Ear, nose, throat: denies sore throat or ear pain
   - Cardiovascular: denies chest pain, orthopnea
   - Respiratory: denies hemoptysis
   - Gastrointestinal: negative
   - Genitourinary: denies nocturia or frequent urinary tract infections
   - Musculoskeletal: denies joint pain
   - Skin: denies rashes, skin lesions
   - Neurological: denies seizures or tremors
   - Psychological: denies suicidal ideation
   - Endocrine: denies polydipsia, polyphagia
   - Hematological/lymph: denies easy bruising
   - Allergy/immunological: allergic to citrus fruit/strawberries

Typical documented ROS notation would be as follows:

Pulmonary: cough × 4 weeks; otherwise negative
Cardiac: negative except for complaints of fatigue
All other systems negative

The ROS for Cindy Carlson's condition would be limited to one body part (right ankle) or one organ system (musculoskeletal).

4. **Past, family, and social history (PFSH)**—includes the patient's past illnesses, operations, injuries, treatments, and any diseases or conditions other members of the patient's family have that could be hereditary. A social history includes a review of the patient's past and current activities, such as marital status, employment, drug and alcohol use, and any other pertinent social factors that might affect the current problem.

These history-taking elements, with the exception of PFSH, are involved to some degree in all patient encounters. The extent or level of history is determined by these elements.

HISTORY LEVELS.   The first element to consider is the level of patient history:

- *Problem-focused history*—provider concentrates on the CC and takes a *brief* history (HPI) centering around the severity, duration, or symptoms with regard to the CC. Typically, there would be no PFSH or ROS conducted.
  - *Example:* A 6-month-old infant presents with diaper rash.
- *Expanded problem-focused history*—provider considers the CC, obtains a brief history of the problem, and performs a problem-pertinent ROS centered on the organ system involved.
  - *Example:* A 13-year-old girl presents with chronic otitis media and a draining ear.
- *Detailed history*—provider concentrates on the CC and obtains an extended HPI, but this time an extended ROS is conducted, and a relevant PFSH is taken. With a detailed history, the ROS might involve multiple organ systems.
  - *Example:* A 56-year-old man presents with a stasis ulcer of 3 months' duration.
- *Comprehensive history*—this is the most complex of the four levels of history taking. Besides the CC, the provider obtains an extended HPI, does a complete ROS, and takes a detailed PFSH.
  - *Example:* A 73-year-old man presents with chest pain and shortness of breath on exertion.

Cindy Carlson's examination would fall into the problem-focused history level.

Examination

The second component in determining the correct E/M level is the patient examination. As with history taking, there are four degrees, or detailed intensities, involved in a patient examination:

- *Problem focused*—limited to the affected body part or organ system identified in the CC. Considering the previous example of the infant with diaper rash, the examination would typically involve only the diaper area.
- *Expanded problem focused*—examination would involve the affected body area or organ system and any other related areas or organ systems. Considering the patient with otitis media (from the aforementioned example), the body areas and organ systems involved would be the ear, nose, and throat system and possibly the eyes.
- *Detailed*—extended examination is performed, which would include the affected body area and all related organ systems. Considering the previous example of the patient with a stasis ulcer, the examination typically would involve the lower extremities and possible various body systems.
- *Comprehensive*—a comprehensive examination— the most extensive type—is required for this level, encompassing all affected body areas and organ systems. For the 73-year-old man with chest pain and shortness of breath (see earlier example), the examination would need to be extensive because the physician must consider an impending cardiac episode.

Cindy Carlson's examination would be limited to the affected body part, resulting in the problem-focused category.

Medical Decision Making

The last of the three key components is medical decision making. The level of medical decision making is determined by weighing the complexity involved in the health care provider's assessment of and professional judgment regarding the patient's diagnosis and care. In determining the complexity of decision making, the health insurance professional must consider the following three elements:

1. How many diagnostic and treatment options were considered
2. The amount and complexity of data reviewed
3. The amount of risk for complications, morbidity, or mortality

The degree to which each of these three elements is considered determines the level of complexity in medical decision making. There are four medical decision making levels:

- *Straightforward*
  - Minimal number of (typically only one) diagnoses and management options to consider
  - Minimal or no data to be reviewed
  - Minimal risk of complications or death if the condition remains untreated
- *Low complexity*
  - Limited number of diagnoses or management options
  - Limited amount of data to be reviewed
  - Low risk of complications or death if the condition is left untreated
- *Moderate complexity*
  - Multiple diagnoses and management options to consider
  - Moderate amount of or complex data to be reviewed
  - Moderate risk of complications or death if problem is left untreated
- *High complexity*
  - Extensive diagnoses and management options
  - Extensive amount of complex data to be reviewed
  - High risk for complications or death if the condition remains untreated

Dr. Schubert's extent of medical decision making for his patient Cindy Carlson would be straightforward. There is a minimal number of (only one) diagnoses and management options to consider, minimal or no data to be reviewed, and minimal risk of complications or death if the condition remains untreated. For a new patient, three of the three criteria must be met or exceeded for that level code to be reported.

HPI, ROS, PFSH—Level 2
Examination—Level 2
Medical decision making—Level 2
The E/M code would be 99202

IMAGINE THIS!

Sarah Perez, a 55-year-old restaurant manager, was diagnosed with benign essential hypertension in June 2001. On doctor's orders, Sarah comes to Heartland Medical Clinic every week to have her blood pressure checked. Elizabeth Allen, a medical assistant at Heartland, takes and records Sarah's blood pressure reading in her health record. Sarah does not see a physician for these encounters. Francis Bentley, Heartland's health insurance professional, reports this encounter as 99211, or Level 1, in E/M coding. The visit is documented in the progress notes with the medical assistant's signature or initials, but no further documentation is needed.

Contributing Factors

In addition to the three key components in assigning an E/M code, contributing factors sometimes enter into the picture. Contributing factors help the health care provider determine the extent of the three key components (history, examination, and medical decision making) necessary to treat the patient effectively. These contributing factors are as follows:

1. **Counseling**—A service provided to the patient or his or her family that involves the following:
   - Impressions and recommended diagnostic studies
   - Discussion of diagnostic results
   - Prognosis
   - Risks and benefits of treatment
   - Instructions
2. **Coordination of care**—A health care provider often must arrange for other services to be provided to a patient, such as being admitted to a long-term care facility or home health care.
3. **Nature of presenting problem**—The presenting problem (CC) guides the health care provider in determining the level of care necessary to diagnose the problem accurately and treat the patient effectively. There are five types of presenting problems:

Minimal—Services typically are provided by a member of the medical staff other than the physician, but a physician must be on the premises at the time the service is rendered. This type may be used only if the patient does not see the physician.
   Example: A 10-year-old girl comes in for an injection based on charted orders by the physician. A medical assistant gives the injection.

Self-limiting—Problem runs a definite or prescribed course, is transient in nature, and is not likely to affect the health status of the patient permanently.
   Example: A patient with a sore throat is examined.

Low severity—Risk of morbidity is low, and there is little to no risk of mortality without treatment. The patient is expected to recover fully without functional impairment.
   Example: A 16-year-old boy comes in with a case of severe acne.

Moderate severity—There is moderate risk of morbidity or mortality without treatment, and an increased probability of prolonged functional impairment without treatment.
   Example: A 40-year-old woman with a 3-month history of severe, recurrent headaches undergoes an initial evaluation.

High severity—A patient has a high to extreme risk of morbidity or mortality without treatment and a high probability of severe, prolonged functional impairment without treatment.
   Example: A 10-year-old girl presents with severe coughing fits with wheezing that affect her sleep and other activities.

The health care provider should document the complexity of the patient's presenting problem in the health record. The health insurance professional must identify the words that correctly indicate the type of presenting problem.

4. **Time**—Time is measured in two ways in E/M coding:
   - **Face-to-face time**—This is the time the health care provider spends in direct contact with a patient during an office visit, which includes taking a history, performing an examination, and discussing results.
   - **Unit/floor time**—This includes time the physician spends on bedside care of the patient and reviewing the health record and writing orders.

Note: Time is not considered a factor unless 50% of the encounter is spent in counseling. Time is never a factor for emergency department visits.

Time typically is noted in the E/M section in statements such as the one located under code 99203 shown in Fig. 7-11.

99203	**Office or other outpatient visit** for the evaluation and management of a new patient, which requires these three key components:

■ a detailed history;

■ a detailed examination;

■ medical decision making of low complexity.

Counseling and/or coordination of care with other providers or agencies are provided consistent with the nature of the problem(s) and the patient's and/or family's needs.

Usually, the presenting problem(s) are of moderate severity. Physicians typically spend 30 minutes face-to-face with the patient and/or family.

Fig. 7-11 Example from E/M section showing how time is noted. (*From American Medical Association:* CPT 2007 Current procedural terminology, *2007, Standard Edition, Chicago, 2007, American Medical Association.*)

IMAGINE THIS!

Dr. Markov is asked to see a 56-year-old factory worker for dyspnea related to cirrhosis of the liver and ascites. Dr. Markov spends 60 minutes on the unit reviewing the chart and interviewing and examining the patient and an additional 20 minutes writing notes and conferring with the attending physician. Most (more than 50%) of Dr. Markov's interaction with the patient was related to eliciting his values and goals of care, clarifying his understanding of his diagnosis and prognosis, giving information, and counseling. There were some specific suggestions about the use of morphine to relieve the patient's dyspnea. For this initial consultation in the hospital that lasted 80 minutes, you would choose E/M code 99254.

WHAT DID YOU LEARN?

1. Explain the difference between a "new" and "established" patient.
2. How does an "outpatient" differ from an "inpatient"?
3. What are the three factors to consider before assigning an E/M code level?
4. Name the three key components in E/M coding.
5. What is "subjective" information?
6. Name the four "contributing factors" that assist the coder in assigning an E/M code.

Prolonged Services

When considering the applicable E/M coding level for a patient encounter, the health insurance professional looks at the history, examination, and medical decision making. Occasionally, the amount of time the health care provider spends face-to-face with the patient exceeds the usual length of service associated with the corresponding level in the inpatient or outpatient setting (Fig. 7-12). When this happens, this extra time is reported in addition to other physician services. The reason for the extra time spent must be documented.

Total Duration of Prolonged Services	Code(s)
less than 30 minutes (less than 1/2 hour)	Not reported separately
30-74 minutes (1/2 hr. - 1 hr. 14 min.)	99354 × 1
75-104 minutes (1 hr. 15 min. - 1 hr. 44 min.)	99354 × 1 AND 99355 × 1
105-134 minutes (1 hr. 45 min. - 2 hr. 14 min.)	99354 × 1 AND 99355 × 2
135-164 minutes (2 hr. 15 min. - 2 hr. 44 min.)	99354 × 1 AND 99355 × 3
165-194 minutes (2 hr. 45 min. - 3 hr. 14 min.)	99354 × 1 AND 99355 × 4

Fig. 7-12 Example of extra time scenario. *(From American Medical Association:* CPT 2007 Current procedural terminology, *2007, Standard Edition, Chicago, 2007, American Medical Association.)*

SUBHEADINGS OF THE MAIN E/M SECTION

Following the Office or Other Outpatient Services codes of the main E/M section are additional subheadings. The codes in these various subheadings are used to report services provided to patients who are admitted to a hospital or nursing facility as a result of an encounter in the physician's office or other ambulatory facility.

Office or Other Outpatient Services

The first subheading under the main E/M section deals with reporting professional services provided in the physician's office or in an outpatient or other ambulatory facility. (An individual is considered an outpatient unless he or she has been admitted to a hospital.) In this section, codes are differentiated between "new" and "established" patients. Codes for new patient services are 99201 through 99205, and codes for established patients are 99211 through 99215. As the codes increase numerically, the patient's problem becomes more complex or life-threatening or both. Also, for new patients, all three key components (history, examination, and medical decision making) must be met or exceeded; however, only two must be met for established patients (Table 7-3).

Hospital Observation Status

Observation is a classification for a patient who is not sick enough to qualify for the acute inpatient status, but requires hospitalization for a brief time. Patients typically are admitted for observation to determine what and how severe their problem or condition is. Codes in this category are used to report services provided to a patient designated as under "observation status" in a hospital.

1. **Initial observation care** (codes 99218 through 99220)—Use the codes from this category to report services for the first (or

TABLE 7-3 Elements Needed to Substantiate Code Choice

Levels of E/M Service	Problem Focused	Expanded Problem Focused	Detailed	Comprehensive
History	CC Brief HPI	CC Brief HPI Problem-focused ROS	CC Extended HPI Extended ROS Pertinent PFSH	CC Extended HPI Complete ROS Complete PFSH
Examination	Limited to affected body area or organ system	Limited to affected body area or organ system and related organ systems	Extended to all affected body areas and any related organ systems	Multisystem examination or examination of complete single organ system
Medical decision making	Straightforward	Low	Moderate	High
Diagnosis/management	0-1 element	2 elements	3 elements	>3 elements
Data	0-1 element	2 elements	3 elements	>3 elements
Risk	Minimal	Low	Moderate	High

additional) day of a multiple-day observation stay. The two higher level codes require a comprehensive history and physical examination. The lowest level code requires a detailed or comprehensive history and physical examination.

2. **Observation discharge care** (code 99217)—Report this service only for the final day of a multiple-day stay.

3. **Observation or inpatient care services** (codes 99234 through 99236)—Use codes to report observation or inpatient services when the patient is admitted and discharged on the same date of service. The two higher level codes require a comprehensive history and physical examination. The lowest level code requires a detailed or comprehensive history and physical examination.

When observation status services are initiated at another site, such as the emergency department, physician's office, or nursing facility, all E/M services provided by the supervising physician in conjunction with initiating the "observation status" are considered part of the initial observation care, if performed on the same day.

IMAGINE THIS!

Billy Marshall, a 6-year-old boy, was brought to the emergency department after a fall from a jungle gym at the school playground. Billy did not lose consciousness; however, he complained of headache, and his teacher reported an episode of vomiting. Billy was admitted for 24-hour observation to rule out head injury.

Hospital Inpatient Services

- *Initial hospital care*—The codes in this category are for reporting services provided only by the admitting physician. Other physicians providing initial inpatient E/M services should use consultation or subsequent hospital care codes, as appropriate.

- *Subsequent hospital care*—The codes in this category are for reporting inpatient E/M services provided after the first inpatient encounter (for the admitting physician) or for services (other than consultative) provided by a physician other than the admitting physician. A hospitalized patient may require more than one visit per day by the same physician. Group the visits together, and report the level of service based on the total encounters for the day. Third-party payers vary in their requirements for reporting this service.

- *Hospital discharge services*—Use these codes for reporting services provided on the final day of a multiple-day stay.

Time is the controlling factor for assigning the appropriate hospital discharge services code. Total duration of time spent by the physician (even if the time spent is not continuous) should be documented and reported. These codes include final examination, discussion of hospital stay, instructions to caregivers, preparation of discharge records, prescriptions, and referral forms, if applicable.

Consultations

By definition, a physician may not bill for a consultation unless another physician formally requests his or her opinion about the patient's present or future course of treatment. In addition, the consulting physician must communicate that opinion in either a letter or a dictated report. The patient's medical record should include the request by the physician who initiated the consultation and any information (letter, report, or dictation) that was communicated back to this physician.

If a specialist has a patient transferred to his or her care and is going to assume ongoing responsibility for a portion of the patient's care, this is a referral, and office visit or hospital visit codes should be used, not consultation codes. An example would be a referral from another oncologist for ongoing treatment because of patient choice or geographical transfer.

There are two consultation subheadings in E/M coding:

- Office or other outpatient
- Initial inpatient

These two subheadings define the location where the consultation was rendered—physician's office or other ambulatory facility, codes 99241 through 99245; or inpatient hospital, codes 99251 through 99255. Only one initial consultation is reported by a consultant for the patient on each separate admission. Any subsequent service is reported with applicable codes from Subsequent Hospital Care codes 99231 to 99233 or Subsequent Nursing Facility Care codes 99307 to 99310. A follow-up consultation includes monitoring the patient's progress, recommending management modifications, or advising on a new plan of care in response to the patient's status.

STOP AND THINK

Dr. Toledo, a family practitioner, has been treating patient Alma Cahill for a rash on her face; however, the medication she has prescribed is not helping the problem, and the rash is spreading to the neck. Dr. Toledo, with Alma's approval, makes an appointment with Dr. Farmer, a dermatologist, for continued treatment of the rash. Is this a consultation or a referral?

Emergency Department Services

E/M codes 99281 through 99288 are used for new and established patients who have been treated in an emergency department that is part of a hospital. To qualify, the facility must be available for immediate emergency care 24 hours a day for patients not on "observation status."

The "Other Emergency Services" subheading's single code, 99288, is used in physician-directed emergency care and advanced life support, when the physician is located in a hospital emergency or critical care department and is in two-way voice communication with ambulance or rescue personnel outside the hospital. The physician directs the performance of necessary medical procedures.

Pediatric critical care patient transport codes (99289 and 99290) are "time-based" codes used when a physician located in a hospital or other facility directs emergency treatment of a pediatric patient (24 months old or younger) to the transporting staff via two-way communication. Code 99289 is used for the first 30 to 74 minutes of hands-on care during transport. Code 99290 is used in addition to 99289 to report each additional 30 minutes of care.

Critical Care Services

- Critical care services can be provided in any setting.
- The physician must provide constant attendance or constant attention to a critically ill or injured patient. The physician need not be constantly at the bedside, per se, but is engaged in physician work directly related to the individual patient's care.
- Time is the controlling factor for assigning the appropriate critical care code. Total duration of time spent by the physician (even if the time spent is not continuous) should be documented and reported.
- Critical care codes should not be used for a duration of less than 30 minutes.
- Services in critical care units must meet CPT guidelines to be billed as critical care.

Neonatal Intensive Care Services

Services are provided to **neonates** (newborns 28 days old or younger) admitted to the intensive care unit. Infants older than 28 days who are admitted to an intensive care unit should be assigned the appropriate critical care or E/M codes. Neonatal codes are global 24-hour codes and not reported as hourly services. When the neonate is not critically ill and attains a body weight exceeding 1500 g, the initial hospital care codes (99221 through 99223) should be used. The same definitions for critical care services apply for adults, children, and neonates. Subsequent intensive care codes (99299 and 99300) were added in 2003. These per-day codes are used for the evaluation and management of recovering low-birth-weight infants with a present body weight of 1500 to 2500 g (99299) and 2501 to 5000 g (99300).

Additional Categories of the E/M Section

The categories that follow Neonatal and Pediatric Critical Care Services are as follows:

- Nursing Facility Services (99304 through 99318)
- Domiciliary, Rest Home (e.g., Boarding Home), or Custodial Care Services (99324 through 99337)
- Domiciliary, Rest Home (e.g., Assisted Living Facility), or Home Care Plan Oversight Services (99339 and 99340)
- Home Services (99341 through 99350)
- Prolonged Services (99354 through 99360)
- Case Management Services (99361 through 99373)
- Care Plan Oversight Services (99374 through 99380)
- Preventive Medicine Services (99381 through 99429)
- Newborn Care (99431 through 99440)
- Special Evaluation and Management Services (99450 through 99456)
- Other Evaluation and Management Services (99499)

Note: These categories and code ranges are based on the 2006 CPT-4 manual.

WHAT DID YOU LEARN?

1. What does "observation status" mean in E/M coding?
2. What is a "confirmatory consultation"?
3. Which of the four contributing factors has the most impact on critical care?
4. What is the term given to a newborn younger than 30 days old?

E/M MODIFIERS

Before assigning a final E/M code, it is important to check for potential modifiers that should be assigned to report an altered service or procedure (e.g., an unusual or special circumstance that affects the service or procedure). Attaching modifiers to codes provides additional information regarding the services performed. Leaving off a needed modifier can result in denial of payment. Following is a list of the modifiers used most often with the codes in the E/M section. (Appendix A in the CPT manual contains a complete list of modifiers.)

- Prolonged Evaluation and Management Services: Modifier -21 or 09921.
  - This modifier is used only with the highest level of each E/M category when the service provided is greater than that usually designated for that code.
  - Documentation should be provided to describe the circumstances.
  - This modifier does not affect reimbursement under Medicare's physician fee schedule.
- Unrelated Evaluation and Management Service by the Same Physician During a Postoperative Period: Modifier -24 or 09924
  - This modifier is used to differentiate between a related and unrelated service during the postoperative period. (Documentation must be submitted to the carrier when this modifier is assigned.) The ICD-9-CM code must substantiate that the care was provided for a condition unrelated to the condition that required surgery.
- Significant, Separately Identifiable Evaluation and Management Service by the Same Physician on the Same Day of a Procedure or Other Service: Modifier -25 or 09925
  - This modifier is used to differentiate services associated with global payment from services to be considered separately for payment. (Sending supporting documentation with the claim is not required when this modifier is applied.) This modifier should not be used to indicate that the visit or consultation resulted in the decision to perform major surgery.
- Mandated Services: Modifier -32 or 09932
  - This modifier is used to inform the third-party payer that the service is required or mandated (e.g., PRO, governmental, legislative, or regulatory requirement, or third-party payer).
- Reduced Services: Modifier -52 or 09952
  - In some instances, a service or procedure may be partially reduced or eliminated at the physician's discretion.
- Decision for Surgery: Modifier -57 or 09957
  - This modifier identifies an E/M service provided by the physician on the day before or the day of a surgery during which the initial decision to perform surgery was made.

WHAT DID YOU LEARN?

1. What is the function of a modifier?
2. Why is it important to attach a needed modifier to a code?
3. Where are modifiers found in the CPT manual?

IMPORTANCE OF DOCUMENTATION

Health record documentation is required to record pertinent facts, findings, and observations about a patient's health history, including past and present illnesses, examinations, tests, treatments, and outcomes. The health record chronologically documents the care of the patient and is an important element contributing to high-quality care. The appropriately documented health record facilitates the following:

- The ability of the physician and other health care professionals to evaluate and plan the patient's immediate treatment and to monitor his or her health care over time
- Communication and continuity of care among physicians and other health care professionals involved in the patient's care
- Accurate and timely claims review and payment
- Appropriate utilization review and quality of care evaluations
- Collection of data that may be useful for research and education

An appropriately documented health record can reduce many of the challenges associated with claims processing and may serve as a legal document to verify the care provided, if necessary. Fig. 7-13 is a list of the top 10 coding and billing errors.

E/M Documentation Guidelines: 1995 versus 1997

In addition to the guidelines found in the CPT manual, HCFA (now CMS) published two sets of documentation guidelines. The first set of guidelines became effective in 1995, and the second set became effective in 1997. The goal was to develop and refine a way to assign a "score" accurately for each level of medical services in the E/M categories. The guidelines specifically identify the elements that must be documented in the medical record to support a particular level or service and a workable method to determine the level of medical decision making.

1995 Guidelines

The history and medical decision-making criteria outlined in the 1997 guidelines are basically the same as the 1995 guidelines. The main difference in the two sets of guidelines is in the criteria needed for the examination component. The 1995 guidelines criteria required less information to be documented for the examination than the 1997 guidelines, but the examination criteria are vague and generally leave much to the opinion of an auditor, easily opening the door for differing opinions between auditor and physician.

1997 Guidelines

In the 1997 guidelines, the examination criteria are detailed and require more documentation. The advantage with this approach is that the 1997 guidelines criteria leave little room for an auditor to form an opinion different from that of the physician, and it becomes easier for auditors to verify that a higher level of service reported was correctly coded. Although the 1997 guidelines criteria may require a little more time to learn for some health insurance professionals, templates are available to make this task easier. Because of various problems encountered with the 1997 guidelines, mandatory implementation of this newer set of rules was postponed, and CMS currently allows either set of rules (1995 or 1997) to be used.

As mentioned previously, the principal difference between these two sets of rules is the examination portion. The 1997 guidelines have a series of detailed examinations with required items indicated by shaded areas or bullets, whereas the 1995 guidelines have a more general counting of body areas and systems. The health insurance professional may choose either the 1995 or the 1997 rules. Table 7-4 compares the 1995 versus 1997 guidelines.

Deciding Which Guidelines to Use

Although it is acceptable to use either the 1995 or the 1997 E/M documentation guidelines, it is unacceptable to use them interchangeably on the same document. An extended history may be documented under the 1997 guidelines by identifying three chronic or inactive conditions and the current status of those conditions. The 1995 guidelines do not permit this documentation practice. Under the

1. No documentation for services billed.
2. No signature or authentication of documentation.
3. Always assigning the same level of service.
4. Billing of consult vs. outpatient office visit.
5. Invalid codes billed due to old resources.
6. Unbundling of procedure codes.
7. Misinterpreted abbreviations.
8. No chief complaint listed for each visit.
9. Billing of service(s) included in global fee as a separate professional fee.
10. Inappropriate or no modifier used for accurate payment of claim.

Fig. 7-13   Top 10 coding and billing errors.

TABLE 7-4   Comparison of Physical Examination Guidelines

1995 Requirements	1997 Requirements
Problem-Focused Examination Limited to affected body area or organ system	**Problem-Focused Examination** One to five element(s) in ≥1 organ system(s) or body area(s)
Expanded Problem-Focused Examination Limited examination of affected body area or organ system and other symptomatic or related organ system(s) Two to seven body areas or organ systems	**Expanded Problem-Focused Examination** Six elements in ≥1 organ system(s) or body area(s)
Detailed Examination Extended examination of affected body area(s) and other symptomatic or related organ system(s) Two to seven body areas or organ systems	**Detailed Examination** At least six organ systems or body area(s) For each of the six organ systems or body areas, at least two elements identified by a bullet is expected; *or* At least 12 elements identified by a bullet in ≥2 organ systems or body areas
Comprehensive Examination General multisystem examination or complete examination of a single organ system* ≤Eight organ systems	**Comprehensive Examination** At least nine organ systems or body areas For each organ system/body area, *all* elements identified by a bullet should be performed For each organ system/body area, documentation of at least two elements identified by a bullet is expected

*1995 criteria do not define documentation elements for a single organ system examination.

1995 guidelines, an extended history requires documentation of at least four HPI elements. The HPI elements include *location, quality, severity, duration, timing, context, modifying factors,* and *associated signs/symptoms.*

WHAT DID YOU LEARN?

1. Name three ways a well-documented health record contributes to high-quality health care.
2. What is the principal difference between the 1995 E/M documentation guidelines compared with the guidelines published in 1997?
3. Which set of guidelines does CMS prefer that a medical office use?

≋ OVERVIEW OF THE HCPCS CODING SYSTEM

HCPCS is a coding system that is composed of Level I (CPT) codes, Level II (national) codes, and formerly Level III (local) codes. CPT codes are composed of five digits that describe procedures and tests. CPT codes are developed and maintained by the AMA with annual updates. Level II (national) codes are five-digit alphanumerical codes consisting of one alphabetical character (a letter between A and V) followed by four digits. HCFA created Level II codes to supplement CPT, which does not include codes for nonphysician procedures, such as ambulance services, durable medial equipment, specific supplies, and administration of injectable drugs. Level II codes are developed and maintained by CMS with quarterly updates. The following are examples of Level II codes:

A4646—Supply of low-osmolar contrast material (300 to 399 mg of iodine)
J0150—Injection, adenosine (Adenocard), 6 mg
J2250—Injection, midazolam hydrochloride (Versed), 1 mg

If a CPT code and HCPCS Level II code are available for the service provided, CMS requires that the HCPCS Level II code be used.

HCPCS Level II Format

HCPCS Level II codes are organized into 17 sections (Fig. 7-14). The D codes, which include dental procedure codes D0000 through D9999, represent a separate category of codes from the Current Dental Terminology (CDT-4) code set, which is copyrighted and updated by the American Dental Association.

Index of Main Terms

An index of main terms, arranged in alphabetical order similar to the Level I CPT-4 codes, follows the 17 alphabetized sections. Codes are located in the index using similar guidelines as CPT-4 codes: Locate the main term, turn to the alphanumeric listing, and find the applicable code (Fig. 7-15.)

- **A Codes:** Transportation Services Including
  - Ambulance
  - Medical and Surgical Supplies
  - Respiratory Durable Medical Equipment, Inexpensive and Routinely Purchased
  - Administrative, Miscellaneous and Investigational
- **B Codes:** Enteral and Parenteral Therapy
- **C Codes:** Hospital Outpatient Prospective Payment System (OPPS)
- **E Codes:** Durable Medical Equipment
- **G Codes:** Temporary Codes for Professional Services Procedures
- **H Codes:** Alcohol and/or Drug Services
- **J Codes:** Drugs Administered Other Than Oral Method
- **K Codes:** Temporary Codes for Durable Medical Equipment
- **L Codes:** Orthotic Procedures
- **M Codes:** Medical Services
- **P Codes:** Pathology and Laboratory Tests
- **Q Codes:** Temporary Codes
- **R Codes:** Domestic Radiology Services
- **S Codes:** Temporary National Codes
- **T Codes:** National Codes for State Medicaid Agencies
- **V Codes:** Vision/Hearing/Speech-Language Pathology Services

Fig. 7-14   Sections of HCPCS Level II (national) codes.

Table of Drugs

The Level II (national) code manual also contains a table of drugs, which the health insurance professional should use to locate appropriate drug names that correspond with the generic names listed in the J code subsection.

Modifiers

As with CPT-4, HCPCS Level II code sets contain modifiers. Modifiers in HCPCS Level II are alphabetical or alphanumerical. They are used to indicate that a service or procedure that has been performed has been altered by some specific circumstances but not changed in its definition or code. The HCPCS manual contains a complete listing of modifiers and their meaning.

WHAT DID YOU LEARN?

1. How are HCPCS Level II codes structured?
2. What do "J" codes represent in HCPCS coding?
3. What is the function of a HCPCS Level II code modifier?

HIPAA AND HCPCS CODING

CMS has taken steps to prepare for the full implementation of HIPAA. HIPAA requires that there be standardized procedure coding. For CMS to meet this requirement, they have produced an instructional guide to assist the health insurance professional in eliminating local procedure and modifier codes from their system. Official HCPCS Level III

HCPCS 2004 INDEX / Hair analysis

H

Hair analysis (excluding arsenic), P2031
Hallux-Valgus dynamic splint, L3100
Hallux prosthetic implant, L8642
Haloperidol, J1630
   decanoate, J1631
Halo procedures, L0810–L0860
Halter, cervical head, E0942
Hand finger orthosis, prefabricated, L3923
Hand restoration, L6900–L6915
   partial prosthesis, L6000–L6020
   orthosis (WHFO), E1805, E1825, L3800–L3805, L3900–L3954
   rims, wheelchair, E0967
Handgrip (cane, crutch, walker), A4636

Hydrocollator, E0225, E0239
Hydrocolloid dressing, A6234–A6241
Hydrocortisone
   acetate, J1700
   sodium phosphate, J1710
   sodium succinate, J1720
Hydrogel dressing, A6242–A6248, A6231–A6233
Hydromorphone, J1170
Hydroxyzine HCl, J3410
Hyland G-F 20, J7320
Hyoscyamine Sulfate, J1980
Hyperbaric oxygen chamber, topical, A4575
Hypertonic saline solution, J7130

I

pump, heparin, dialysis, E1520
pump, implantable, E0782, E0783
pump, implantable, refill kit, A4220
pump, insulin, E0784
pump, mechanical, reusable, E0779, E0780
pump, uninterrupted infusion of Epi-prostenol, K0455
supplies, A4221, A4222, A4230–A4232
therapy, other than chemotherapeutic drugs, Q0081
Inhalation solution (*see also* drug name), J7608–J7699
Injections (*see also* drug name), J0120–J7320
   contrast material, during MRI, A4643
   supplies for self-administered, A4211
Insertion, indwelling catheter, G0002
Insertion tray, A4310–A4316

Fig. 7-15   Example page from HCPCS Index. (*Data from U.S. Department of Health and Human Services, Centers for Medicare and Medicaid Services.*)

procedure and modifier codes are defined as codes and descriptors developed by Medicare contractors for use by physicians, practitioners, providers, and suppliers on a local level for the completion of insurance claims. Level III codes that were approved by CMS through the official process were incorporated into the HCPCS manual. Unapproved local procedure and modifier codes that were not approved by CMS were dropped.

Elimination of Unapproved Local Codes and Modifiers

In anticipation of implementation of HIPAA, CMS has required medical offices to eliminate any unapproved local procedure or modifier codes (Level III) that they are currently using. To accomplish this, medical offices must do the following:

- Identify all unapproved local procedure and modifier codes that were established or that are being used
- "Crosswalk" any unapproved local procedure and modifier codes to a temporary or permanent national code
- Submit any unapproved local procedure or modifier codes that the medical facility believes should be retained, along with a request for a temporary national code with a justification, to the regional office representative by April 1, 2002
- Delete all other unapproved local procedure and modifier codes by October 16, 2002

HIPAA TIP

Payers and providers must go over the HCPCS codes they use and determine how best to replace their "local" HCPCS codes with the new national codes.

What Is a Crosswalk?

A **crosswalk** is a procedure by which codes used for data in one database are translated into the codes of another database, making it possible to relate information between or among databases. In coding, a crosswalk is a "link" that refers to a relationship between a medical procedure (CPT code) and a diagnosis (ICD code). Medicare uses CPT/ICD crosswalks to validate or substantiate medical necessity under LCD/LMRP (Local Medicare Review Policy). Third-party payers also establish crosswalk tables for validating and auditing medical claims. In brief, physicians dealing in Medicare Part B claims are paid by CPT procedure code, not diagnosis. To

validate proper coding (e.g., the reason for the procedure), providers must specify a diagnosis. If the diagnosis does not support the procedure, the claim may not get paid.

WHAT DID YOU LEARN?

1. What does HIPAA require of HCPCS coding?
2. Which level of HCPCS codes did HIPAA eliminate?
3. What is a "crosswalk"?

CURRENT PROCEDURAL TERMINOLOGY, FIFTH EDITION (CPT-5)

The AMA is in the process of developing the next generation of *Physicians' Current Procedural Terminology,* **Fifth Edition** (CPT-5). Ideally, this updated version will improve existing CPT features and correct deficiencies. CPT-5 is structured to respond to challenges presented by emerging user needs and HIPAA. Changes to CPT have been oriented toward the need to preserve the core of CPT, while encouraging progress. Transition into the changes proposed for CPT-5 will be gradual, and all enhancements and modifications will occur through the traditional CPT Editorial process. To avoid disruption in medical offices, it is planned that changes will be phased in over several years.

The AMA states that CPT-5 "is intended to preserve the core elements that define CPT as *the language to communicate clinical information for administrative and financial purposes.*" CPT-5 will continue to include the following:

- Descriptions of clinically recognized and generally accepted health care services
- Five-character core codes (five digits for regular CPT codes for the foreseeable future) with concept extenders (modifiers)
- Professional responsibility for a mechanism for periodic review and updating

The AMA further states that "CPT-5 encourages progress so that CPT *evolves with changes in health care delivery and services to accommodate the needs of users.*" To stimulate change, CPT will continue to do the following:

- Maximize user input, while continuing to maintain an editorially rigorous update process
- Provide accurate and up-to-date communication of clinical services
- Respond to the requirements of health care professionals, payers, and researchers for tools to support evidence-based clinical practice

SUMMARY CHECK POINTS

☑ The *purpose* of CPT is to provide a uniform language accurately describing medical, surgical, and diagnostic services, serving as an effective means for reliable communication among physicians, third-party payers, and patients nationwide.

☑ CPT was developed and published by the AMA in 1966. Originally, it contained mainly surgical procedures, with limited sections on medicine, radiology, and laboratory procedures. The second edition, published in 1970, expanded codes to designate diagnostic and therapeutic procedures in surgery, medicine, and other specialties. In 1970, the five-digit system was introduced, replacing the former four-digit codes, and internal medicine procedures were added.

☑ In 1983, CPT was adopted as part of HCPCS. HCFA (now CMS) mandated the use of HCPCS to report services for the Medicare Part B Program. In 1986, HCFA required state Medicaid agencies to use HCPCS. In 1987, as part of the Omnibus Budget Reconciliation Act, HCFA mandated the use of CPT for reporting outpatient hospital surgical procedures.

☑ Today, CPT is the preferred system of coding and describing health care services.

☑ The CPT manual begins with an introduction, followed by six sections in the main body of the manual. Category III Codes follow the main section, after which there are 12 appendixes—A through L. The CPT Index of main terms appears at the back of the manual.

☑ A bullet (•) before a code means the code is "new" to the CPT book for that particular edition.

☑ A triangle (▲) means the description for the code has been "changed or modified" since the previous edition of the CPT book.

☑ Horizontal triangles (►◄) placed at the beginning and end of new or revised guidelines indicates changes in wording.

☑ Add-on codes are annotated by a + sign.

☑ The ⊘ symbol is used to identify codes that are exempt from the use of modifier -51.

☑ The semicolon is used to separate main and subordinate clauses in the CPT code descriptions. The complete description listed *before* the semicolon applies to that code plus any additional succeeding, indented codes. The complete description *after* the semicolon applies only to that code.

☑ The basic steps for CPT coding are as follows:
- *Step 1*—identify the procedure, service, or supply to be coded.
- *Step 2*—determine the main term.
- *Step 3*—locate the main term in the alphabetical index, and note the code.
- *Step 4*—cross-reference the single code, multiple codes, or the code range numerically in the tabular section of the manual.
- *Step 5*—read and follow any notes, special instructions, or conventions associated with the code.
- *Step 6*—determine and assign the appropriate code.

☑ A new patient is someone who is new to the practice, regardless of location of service, or one who has not received any medical treatment by the health care provider or any other provider in that same office *within the past 3 years*.

☑ An established patient is an individual who has been treated previously by the health care provider, regardless of location of service, within the past 3 years. If the provider saw the patient for the first time in a hospital, and that individual comes to the office for a follow-up visit after discharge, the patient is considered an established patient to the practice because health record documentation was generated from the hospital visit.

☑ The three key components that establish the level in E/M coding are as follows:
- *History*—subjective information based on four elements: CC (in the patient's own words), HPI, ROS, and PFSH. There are four levels of history: (1) problem focused, (2) expanded problem focused, (3) detailed, and (4) comprehensive.
- *Examination*—deals with the degree to which the health care provider examines various body areas and organ systems that are affected by the CC. There are four levels of examination: (1) problem focused, (2) expanded problem focused, (3) detailed, and (4) comprehensive.

- *Medical decision making*—this component is determined by weighing the complexity involved in the health care provider's assessment of and the professional judgment made regarding the patient's diagnosis and care. The three elements considered are how many diagnostic and treatment options are considered; the amount and complexity of data reviewed; and the amount of risk for complications, morbidity, or mortality. There are four levels in medical decision making: (1) straightforward, (2) low complexity, (3) moderate complexity, and (4) high complexity.

- Besides the above-mentioned three key components, the four contributing factors that may affect the level of E/M coding are as follows:
  - Counseling
  - Coordination of care
  - Nature of presenting problem—minimal, self-limiting, low severity, high severity
  - Time

- Time can be measured two ways in E/M coding:
  - *Face-to-face time*—time the physician spends in direct contact with the patient during an office visit, which includes taking a history, performing an examination, and discussing results.
  - *Unit/floor time*—time the physician spends on patient bedside care and reviewing the health record and writing orders.

- The history and medical decision-making criteria outlined in the 1995 guidelines are the same as the 1997 guidelines. The main difference in the two sets of guidelines is the criteria for the examination. The 1995 guidelines criteria require less information to be documented for the examination than the 1997 guidelines. The

1997 guidelines have a series of detailed examinations with required items indicated by shaded areas or bullets, whereas the 1995 rules have a more general counting of body areas and systems.

- The HCPCS is a coding system that is composed of Level I (CPT) codes, Level II (national) codes, and formerly Level III (local) codes. CPT codes are composed of five digits that describe procedures and tests. Level II (national) codes are five-digit alphanumerical codes that describe pharmaceuticals, supplies, procedures, tests, and services. HCFA created Level II codes to supplement CPT, which does not include codes for nonphysician procedures, such as ambulance services, durable medical equipment, specific supplies, and administration of injectable drugs. If there are a CPT code and HCPCS Level II code for the service provided, CMS requires that the HCPCS Level II code be used.

- HIPAA requires that there be standardized procedure coding. In anticipation of implementation of HIPAA, CMS has required medical offices to eliminate any unapproved local procedure or modifier codes that they are currently using. To accomplish this, medical offices must do the following:
  - Identify all unapproved local procedure and modifier codes that were established or that are being used.
  - "Crosswalk" any unapproved local procedure and modifier codes to a temporary or permanent national code.
  - Submit any unapproved local procedure or modifier codes that the medical facility believe should be retained, along with a request for a temporary national code with a justification, to the regional office representative by April 1, 2002.
  - Delete all other unapproved local procedure and modifier codes by October 16, 2002.

Closing Scenario

Park and Melanie have finished the chapter on CPT coding. Although they agree it was more challenging than the chapter on ICD-9 coding (particularly the E/M coding), Melanie believes that Park's help was extremely beneficial. She is now convinced that she will finish the course on time and with an acceptable grade. Meanwhile, Park still believes that coding is the right career move for him.

He has researched the websites at the end of the chapter to learn all he can about coding. He has even located a website bulletin board where practicing coders write in questions and answers on coding issues. After he finishes the medical insurance course, Park plans to take a coding course over the Internet. He is looking forward to continuing his pursuit of a career in coding.

WEBSITES TO EXPLORE

- AMA at
  http://www.ama-assn.org

- Medicare Learning Network (Medlearn) at
  http://www.cms.hhs.gov/medlearn

- CMS at
  http://www.cms.hhs.gov

- U.S. Department of Health & Human Services at
  http://www.hhs.gov

References

American Medical Association, *Current procedural terminology, CPT* (2007) Standard Edition, Chicago, 2007, AMA Press

American Medical Association: HCPCS, 2005, Chicago, 2005, AMA Press.

Buck CJ: Step-by-Step Medical Coding, ed 5, Philadelphia, 2004, Saunders.

Covell A: *Coding workbook for the physician's office*, Clifton Park, NY, 2003, Delmar/Thomson Learning.

Davis JB: *CPT and HCPCS coding made easy! A comprehensive guide to CPT and HCPCS coding for health care professionals*, Downer's Grove, Ill, 2000, PMIC.

Fordney MT: Insurance Handbook for the Medical Office, 7th ed. Philadelphia, 2002, Saunders.

Rowell JC, Green MA: *Understanding health insurance, a guide to professional billing*, ed 7, Clifton Park, NY, 2004, Delmar/Thomson Learning.

Chapter Review

Assessment

Multiple Choice

Directions: *In the following questions/statements, choose the response that **best** answers/completes the stem, and circle the letter that precedes it.*

1. The manual containing codes used in reporting medical services and procedures performed and supplies used by health care providers in the care and treatment of patients is the _____.
   A. HCPCS Level II
   B. ICD-9-CM
   C. CPT-4
   D. all of the above

2. CPT codes were developed by _____.
   A. the World Health Organization (WHO)
   B. the AMA
   C. HCFA
   D. the Department of Health and Human Services (HHS)

3. The CPT manual is published by _____.
   A. the AMA
   B. HCFA
   C. the WHO
   D. the HHS

4. A new CPT manual is published _____.
   A. annually
   B. semiannually
   C. biannually
   D. every 5 years

5. The first CPT was developed and published in _____.
   A. 1955
   B. 1966
   C. 1970
   D. 1977

6. The five-digit coding system replaced the four-digit system in the CPT edition published in _____.
   A. 1955
   B. 1966
   C. 1970
   D. 1977

7. The main body of the CPT manual is organized in _____.
   A. four sections
   B. six sections
   C. 10 sections
   D. 12 sections

8. The five-digit CPT codes may be defined further by two additional digits to help explain an unusual circumstance associated with a service or procedure, which are called _____.
   A. modifiers
   B. amendments
   C. appendixes
   D. CPT codes cannot have more than 5 digits

9. As with the ICD-9-CM, the CPT index is organized by _____.
   A. disease process
   B. anatomic sites
   C. main terms
   D. symptoms

10. A main term can stand alone, or it can be followed by up to _____ modifying term(s).
   A. one
   B. two
   C. three
   D. four

11. To help determine the appropriateness and medical necessity of a service or procedure, a _____ should accompany the claim.
   A. copy of the patient's health record
   B. letter of explanation
   C. special report
   D. diagram

12. The narrative describing a procedure/service that contains the full description of the procedure without additional explanation is referred to as a(an) _____.
   A. complete code
   B. unmodified code
   C. descriptive code
   D. stand-alone code

13. Procedures that do not contain the entire written description and refer to the common portion of the procedure listed in the preceding entry are coded with a(an) _____.
   A. modified code
   B. indented code
   C. unfinished code
   D. incomplete code

14. CPT uses _____ to separate main and subordinate clauses in the code descriptions _____.
   A. a bullet
   B. parentheses
   C. a triangle
   D. a semicolon

15. The reason the patient is seeing the physician—usually stated in the patient's own words—is referred to as the _____.
   A. chief complaint (CC)
   B. history of present illness (HPI)
   C. review of systems (ROS)
   D. past, family, and social history (PFSH)

16. The series of questions the provider asks the patient to identify what body parts or body systems are involved is referred to as the _____.
   A. chief complaint (CC)
   B. history of present illness (HPI)
   C. review of systems (ROS)
   D. past, family, and social history (PFSH)

17. The amount of time the physician spends on bedside care of the hospitalized patient and reviewing the health record and writing orders is called _____.
   A. face-to-face time
   B. unit/floor time
   C. counseling time
   D. treatment time

18. The classification for a patient who is not sick enough to qualify for acute inpatient status, but requires hospitalization for a brief time is referred to as _____.
  A. outpatient status
  B. observation status
  C. unit/floor time
  D. nonemergency status

19. A procedure by which codes used for data in one database are translated into the codes of another database, allowing information to be shared among databases, is called _____.
  A. a crosswalk
  B. database sharing
  C. intervention
  D. electronic recognition

20. HCPCS Level II codes are organized into _____ sections.
  A. 5
  B. 8
  C. 12
  D. 17

True/False

Directions: *Place a "T" in the blank preceding each of the following statements if it is true; place an "F" if it is false.*

_____ 1. Today, most managed care and other insurance companies base their reimbursements on the values established by the CMS.

_____ 2. If the correct CPT code is not known, a narrative description of the procedure/service rendered can be used in Block 24d of the CMS-1500 form.

_____ 3. Modifiers are listed in Appendix A at the back of the CPT manual.

_____ 4. Missing or incorrect modifiers are a common reason for claim denial.

_____ 5. If a Category I code is available and accurately describes the service provided, it should be used instead of a Category III code.

_____ 6. Modifier -99 can be used if the coder cannot find a five-digit CPT code that adequately describes the procedure performed.

_____ 7. There are two types of CPT codes: stand-alone and indented.

_____ 8. Every office visit, regardless of location, must include at least two of these three components—history, examination, and medical decision making.

_____ 9. The key to reimbursement for office/outpatient visits is being able to prove the level of complexity of the services performed.

_____ 10. Coding E/M services is based on the amount of time spent with the patient or his or her family.

_____ 11. Time is not considered a factor unless 75% of the encounter is spent in counseling.

_____ 12. Time is never a factor for emergency department visits.

_____ 13. All three key components (history, examination, and medical decision making) must be met or exceeded for new patients; only two must be met for established patients.

_____ 14. Hospital Discharge Services codes are used for reporting services provided on the final day of a multiple-day stay.

_____ 15. To qualify for the use of E/M codes 99281 to 99288, the facility must be available for immediate emergency care 24 hours a day for patients on "observation status."

_____ 16. Critical Care Services can be provided only if the facility has an emergency department that operates 24 hours a day.

_____ 17. To use the Critical Care Services codes properly, the physician must be constantly at the patient's bedside.

_____ 18. Time is the controlling factor for assigning the appropriate critical care code.

_____ 19. Modifiers are never used in E/M coding.

_____ 20. HCPCS Level II (national) codes are five-digit alphanumerical codes consisting of one alphabetical character (a letter between A and V), followed by three digits.

_____ 21. If there are CPT and HCPCS Level II codes for the service provided, the CMS requires that the HCPCS Level II code be used.

_____ 22. As with CPT-4, HCPCS Level II code sets contain modifiers; however, modifiers in HCPCS Level II are either alphabetical or alphanumerical.

_____ 23. HIPAA requires that procedure coding be standardized.

_____ 24. With the implementation of HIPAA, the CMS has required medical offices to eliminate any unapproved local procedure or modifier codes (Level III codes).

_____ 25. The AMA is in the process of developing CPT-5, which will totally change the procedural coding process.

Short Answer/Fill-in-the-Blank

1. What is the purpose of CPT coding?

_____

_____

_____

2. List the four things accomplished by the first CPT edition.

_____

_____

_____

3. List and discuss the three levels of procedural coding.

_____

_____

_____

4. The health record must contain adequate documentation to support the use of _____.

5. Each main section of the CPT is preceded by _____ specific to that section.

6. What is the purpose of Category III codes?

_____

_____

_____

7. List the 12 appendixes found in CPT and describe what each contains.

_____

_____

_____

8. Name and give an example of each of the four primary classes of main term entries.

_____

_____

_____

9. What are the three ways a CPT code can be displayed? Include examples of each.

_____

_____

_____

10. If a "special report" accompanies a claim to explain unusual circumstances, list what should be included in this document.

_____

_____

_____

11. Explain the use and importance of a semicolon (;) in assigning a CPT code.

_____

_____

_____

12. Codes in the tabular section of CPT are formatted using four classifications. List and explain each of these.

_____

_____

_____

13. List the six basic steps of CPT coding discussed in the textbook.

_____

_____

_____

14. Distinguish between a "new" patient and an "established" patient.

_____

_____

_____

15. The range of codes for office or other outpatient services is _____ to _____

_____ for new patients and _____ to _____ for established patients.

16. List the three factors that direct the health insurance professional to the proper category in the E/M coding section of CPT.

_____

_____

_____

17. In addition to determining each of the three factors listed in question 16, the health insurance professional must establish what level of service the patient received. Levels of service are based on three key components, which are as follows:

_____

_____

_____

18. In addition to the three key components listed in question 17, there may be four contributing factors that affect the E/M coding level reported. These contributing factors include the following:

_____

_____

_____

19. The first element to consider in assigning an E/M code is the level of patient history. Name the four elements of history taking.

_____

_____

_____

20. The second component in determining the correct E/M level is the patient examination. As with history taking, there are four degrees, or detailed intensities, involved in a patient examination. Name these four degrees of patient examination.

_____

_____

_____

21. The last of the three key components is medical decision making. In determining the complexity of decision making, the health insurance professional must consider what three elements?

_____

_____

_____

22. Discuss the importance of thorough and accurate documentation in a health record.

_____

_____

_____

23. Explain the main differences between the 1995 and the 1997 guideline criteria for assigning E/M codes.

_____

_____

_____

24. Explain in what ways, if any, CPT-5 differs from CPT-4.

_____

_____

_____

Matching

Directions: *Place the letter identifying the correct symbol in the blank in front of the numbered statements.* (**Note:** *Not all symbols are used.*)

_____ 1. Code is new to the CPT book

_____ 2. Description has been changed/modified

_____ 3. Identifies changes in wording of new or revised codes

_____ 4. Add-on code

_____ 5. Codes that are modifier-exempt

_____ 6. Modifier 51 exempt

A. *

B. •

C. –

D. ▲

E. +

F. ►◄

G. ⊘

H. ⊙

Critical Thinking Activities

A. In the following scenarios, determine if each patient is "new" or "established."

   1. Jessica Sidwell has an appointment at Broadmoor Medical Clinic today. She is new to the area, having recently moved to Milton from another state.
   2. Elwood Camp was seen at the hospital for a consultation 2 weeks ago. He is coming to the office today for a follow-up appointment.
   3. While Dr. Jones was attending a seminar in another city, Dr. Lucero treated Barbara Farris for acute sinusitis.
   4. Robert Fuller, who was seen by Dr. Jones 2 years ago for an eye infection, has an appointment today with Dr. Lucero. Robert has just returned from an 18-month tour of duty in Afghanistan.
   5. Martha Gibbs, who has a 10 a.m. appointment today, saw Dr. Lucero 5 years ago when she was a resident at Columbia University Clinic in Missouri.
   6. Jill Bennet has an appointment with Dr. Jones tomorrow for a consultation. She has not been seen at Broadmoor Medical Clinic before, but her primary care provider has forwarded her complete health record.

B. In the following scenarios, determine if the procedure/service would classify as a "consultation" or a "referral."

   1. Dr. Jones has been treating Sylvia Potter for a skin condition. He has prescribed several medications, but the problem persists. Dr. Jones instructs Mrs. Potter to make an appointment with Dr. Fontaine, a renowned dermatologist at the University Clinic, for his opinion of the condition.
   2. Dr. Lucero has asked you to make an appointment for Zebulon Porter with a cardiologist for diagnostic tests to pinpoint the cause of Mr. Porter's cardiac symptoms.
   3. Ellen Tyson is being seen at Broadmoor Medical Clinic for gastrointestinal problems that do not respond to treatment. Dr. Lucero asks Dr. Benson, a psychiatrist, to evaluate Ms. Tyson to see if her symptoms might be psychosomatic.
   4. The emergency department physician on duty telephones Dr. Jones to evaluate a patient who has sustained a back injury as a result of an automobile accident. After Dr. Jones examines the patient, the patient is rushed to the operating room for immediate surgery.
   5. Dr. Lucero's patient, Lucas Bonnet, asks for an appointment with ophthalmologist Vincent Carter for a second opinion before eye surgery.

C. Underline the main terms in the following procedures:

Intertrochanteric femoral fracture (closed treatment)
Removal of gallbladder calculi
Lung, bullae excision
Closed treatment of wrist dislocation
Dilation of cervix
Placement of upper gastrointestinal feeding tube
Radiograph and fluoroscope of chest, four views
Magnetic resonance imaging, lower spine
Darrach procedure
Manual CBC
Electrosurgical removal, five skin tags

Case Studies

In the Critical Thinking Activities for this workbook chapter, six scenarios were presented for which you had to determine whether the patient was new or established. Now, study these same six scenarios and code the procedures/services listed in each.

1. Jessica Sidwell has an appointment at Broadmoor Medical Clinic today. She is new to the area, having recently moved to Milton from another state.

   Initial new patient office visit Level II
   Intramuscular antibiotic injection

2. Elwood Camp was seen at the hospital for a consultation 2 weeks ago. He is coming to the office today for a follow-up appointment.

   Postoperative follow-up visit

3. While Dr. Jones was attending a seminar in another city, Dr. Lucero treated Barbara Farris for acute sinusitis.

   Established patient office visit Level II
   Removal of nasal polyp, simple

4. Robert Fuller, who was seen by Dr. Jones 2 years ago for an eye infection, has an appointment today with Dr. Lucero. Robert has just returned from an 18-month tour of duty in Afghanistan. Because it had been 2 years since Robert had been to the office, Dr. Lucero performed a complete physical examination.

   Established patient office visit Level III
   Comprehensive eye examination
   Removal of foreign body from right eye (external/superficial)

5. Martha Gibbs, who has a 10 a.m. appointment today, saw Dr. Lucero 5 years ago when she was a resident at Columbia University Clinic in Missouri.

> New patient office visit Level III
> Pap smear
> Lipid panel
> Electrocardiogram (12 leads)
> Occult blood fecal test

6. Jill Bennet has an appointment with Dr. Jones tomorrow for a consultation. She has not been seen at Broadmoor Medical Clinic before, but her primary care provider has forwarded her complete health record. Jill has been experiencing problems with her periods (heavy bleeding, bleeding between periods, and severe cramping).

> Initial visit new patient Level III
> Transvaginal ultrasound
> Vaginal colposcopy with biopsy

Internet Exploration

A. Log on to and peruse the AMA website's page on CPT coding at **http://www.ama-assn.org/ama/pub/category/3113.html.**

B. The following are just a few of many websites that provide information for further education if you are interested in becoming a certified coder:

- **http://www.aapc.com**
- **http://www.ahima.org/certification**
- **http://www.physicianswebsites.com/medical-coding-education.htm**
- **http://www.cms.hhs.gov/medlearn/ncci.asp?**

C. Log on to the website **http://www.medicarenhic.com/cal_prov/med_review/coding.htm#one** and read through some of the pertinent questions and answers regarding typical coding questions.

Additional Coding Exercises

Using the guidelines given in the text and the most current CPT manual, code the following procedures/services/supplies.

Exercise 1

Procedure: Surgery Section

_____ Removal of 25 skin tags

_____ Partial removal of the spleen

_____ Radical cervical lymphadenectomy

_____ Excision of benign tumor of the mediastinum

_____ Incision and drainage of a simple lymph node abscess

_____ Flexible sigmoidoscopy with three biopsies

_____ Colonoscopy with removal of polyp by a snare

_____ Exploratory laparotomy with cholecystectomy

_____ Repair of an initial incarcerated inguinal hernia in a 5½-year-old

_____ Complete vasectomy

_____ Reversal of urethral anastomosis

_____ Anterior segment of the left eyes, emboli removal

_____ Removal of left eye, muscles attached to implant

_____ Destruction of 0.4-cm malignant lesion of the neck

_____ Suture of sciatic nerve

Exercise 2

Procedure: Radiology, Pathology, and Laboratory Sections

_____ Bilateral mammography

_____ Radiologic examination of mastoids, two views

_____ Chest x-ray single view, frontal

_____ Complete hip x-ray study, two views

_____ Ultrasound of the chest using B-scan

_____ Fetal profile, biophysical

_____ Teletherapy, isodose plan, simple

_____ Automated urinalysis without microscopy

_____ Gases, blood pH only

Code the following using one of the six surgical pathology codes in the CPT manual:

_____ The specimen is a uterus, tubes, and ovaries. The procedure was an abdominal hysterectomy for ovarian cancer.

_____ The specimen is a portion of the lung. The procedure was a left lower lobe wedge resection (Level VI).

_____ The specimen is the prostate. The procedure was a transurethral resection of the prostate (Level IV).

Exercise 3

Procedure: Medicine Section

_____ Routine electrocardiogram with 12 leads, with interpretation and report

_____ Cardiac catheterization on the right side of the heart

_____ Pulmonary stress test, simple

_____ Direct nasal mucous membrane test

_____ Awake and drowsy electroencephalogram and photic stimulation in clinic

_____ Range of motion measurement and report on both legs

_____ Chemotherapy administered subcutaneously

_____ Initial psychiatric interview examination

_____ Acid reflux test of the esophagus with nasal catheter pH electrode placement, recording, analysis, and interpretation

_____ Fitting of contact lens for treatment of cataract, including the lens

_____ Nasopharyngoscopy with evaluation

_____ Hemodialysis with a single physician evaluation

_____ Oral polio vaccine

Exercise 4

Procedure: Integumentary System

_____ Destruction, flat wart

_____ Layer closure of skin wound, >30 cm, trunk

_____ Repair nail bed

_____ Mastectomy, partial

Procedure: Musculoskeletal System

_____ Injection, ganglion cyst

_____ Treatment of closed patella dislocation without anesthesia

_____ Injection of small joint bursa

_____ Biopsy, bone, trocar, or needle superficial

Procedure: Hemic/Lymphatic/Diaphragm (38100-39599)

_____ Repair, esophageal/diaphragmatic hernia

_____ Partial splenectomy

_____ Excision, two deep cervical nodes

Procedure: Radiology/Pathology

_____ Upper gastrointestinal x-ray study with films and KUB

_____ Ultrasound, pregnant uterus after first trimester

_____ Routine urinalysis with microscopy

_____ Colorimetric hemoglobin

OBJECTIVES

After completion of this chapter, the student should be able to:

1. Describe TRICARE's role in military insurance.
2. List and explain TRICARE's three choices for health care.
3. Distinguish eligibility criteria among the three TRICARE plans.
4. Define a nonavailability statement, and advise when it must be used.
5. Compare TRICARE participating providers and nonparticipating providers as they relate to claims processing.
6. Explain CHAMPVA's role in military insurance.
7. List the criteria necessary for CHAMPVA eligibility.
8. Discuss the CHAMPVA-Medicare connection.
9. List the important steps for filing military claims.
10. Explain how to use the Internet to find addresses for military claims submission.
11. State the deadlines for filing military claims.
12. Discuss what the Department of Defense has done to implement HIPAA's privacy rules.

MILITARY CARRIERS: TRICARE AND CHAMPVA

KEY TERMS

accepting assignment
beneficiaries
catastrophic cap (cat cap)
CHAMPUS Maximum Allowable Charge
CHAMPVA for Life (CFL)
Civilian Health and Medical Program of
   the Department of Veterans Affairs
   (CHAMPVA)
Civilian Health and Medical Program of
   the Uniformed Services (CHAMPUS)
claims processor

covered charges
Defense Enrollment Eligibility Reporting
   System (DEERS)
Military Health System
military treatment facility (MTF)
nonavailability statement (NAS)
other health insurance (OHI)
primary care manager (PCM)
regional director
remote assignment
reserve components (RCs)

sponsor
TRICARE
TRICARE Extra
TRICARE for Life (TFL)
TRICARE Management Activity
TRICARE Prime
TRICARE Prime Remote
TRICARE Standard
TRICARE Standard Supplemental Insurance
TRICARE's allowable charge
XPressClaim

Opening Scenario

Sally Curtis is looking forward to the chapter on military insurers. She comes from a long line of military people. Both her parents are in the Army Reserves, her uncle is currently a Marine stationed in Iraq, her maternal grandfather was a Green Beret, and her great-grandfather was stationed in England during World War II. Until now, Sally was not even aware that the military had its own insurance. During a family discussion, a lot of questions were raised about TRICARE and CHAMPVA that Sally could not answer.

Sally's Aunt Betty said she was aware that there were three plans available to spouses and dependents of active service members, but she did not know which was the best plan for her. The health insurance professional from whom Aunt Betty received her health care was of little help because she did not know much about military insurance either, and Aunt Betty wonders if her claims were handled properly. "She calls it CHAMPUS," Aunt Betty said, "not TRICARE. What's the difference?" Sally promised her family members that she would be able to give them the answers they were looking for after she has completed Chapter 8.

MILITARY HEALTH PROGRAMS

The federal government has provided health care for the military from the earliest years of U.S. history. In 1884, Congress requested that Army medical officers and surgeons should attend to the families of the officers and soldiers free of charge whenever possible. During World War II, Congress authorized the creation of the Emergency Maternal and Infant Care Program, which provided maternity care and care of infants up to 1 year of age for wives and children of service members. During the Korean War in 1956, the Dependents Medical Care Act became law. The 1966 amendments to this law initiated what later became the **Civilian Health and Medical Program of the Uniformed Services (CHAMPUS)**, a military health care program that existed for more than 30 years until it was replaced with TRICARE in 1998.

TRICARE

TRICARE developed from the CHAMPUS Reform Initiative, which began in 1988. It was a demonstration program for CHAMPUS-eligible individuals in California and Hawaii. TRICARE is a regionally based managed health care program for active duty and retired members of the uniformed services, their families, and survivors. **TRICARE Standard** has basically the same benefits and cost-sharing structure as the original CHAMPUS program.

To use TRICARE, an individual must be listed in DEERS as being eligible for military health care

benefits. TRICARE-eligible individuals include the following:

- Active duty service members (enrollment not required)
- Spouses and unmarried children of active duty service members
- Uniformed service retirees, their spouses, and unmarried children

TRICARE is a health benefit program for all seven uniformed services: the Army, Navy, Marine Corps, Air Force, Coast Guard, Public Health Service, and National Oceanic and Atmospheric Administration. It provides members of these uniformed services with networks of civilian health care professionals, which offers them better access to health care and high-quality service while maintaining the capability to support military operations. TRICARE's main objectives are *accessibility* and *affordability*, which serve as ways to

- improve overall access to health care for **beneficiaries** (recipients of insurance benefits);
- provide faster, more convenient access to civilian health care;
- create a more efficient way to receive health care;
- offer enhanced health care services, including preventive care;
- provide choices for health care; and
- control escalating health care costs.

TRICARE is administered on a regional basis. Until 2005, TRICARE had 11 regions; however, these 11 regions have since merged to form just three—

the West region, North region, and South region. Additionally, there are three regions outside the United States—TRICARE Europe, Canada/Latin America, and Puerto Rico/Virgin Islands (Fig. 8-1). Each region is headed by a **regional director,** who is responsible for oversight of all health care delivery activities within his or her region. Regional directors provide oversight of regional operations and health plan administration along with management of the health care support contracts. These directors also are responsible for providing support to the military treatment facility commanders in the region, sustaining quality care and improving customer satisfaction across the health care delivery system.

Military Health System is the name for the total health care system of the U.S. uniformed services. The Military Health System includes **military treatment facilities (MTFs)** and various programs in the civilian health care market, such as TRICARE. An MTF is a clinic or hospital operated by the Department of Defense located on a military base that provides care to military personnel, their dependents, and military retirees and their dependents. The Military Health System provides health care to roughly 9 million beneficiaries, including active duty military personnel and their dependents, retired military personnel and their dependents, and survivors of military personnel.

The Department of Defense established the **TRICARE Management Activity**, which began operations in 1998, to oversee the TRICARE managed health care program. TRICARE Management Activity has headquarters in the Washington, D.C., area and in Aurora, Colorado, the location of the former TRICARE Support Office. The main purpose of TRICARE Management Activity is to enhance the performance of TRICARE worldwide. An initial task of TRICARE Management Activity was to conduct a survey of approximately 10,000 beneficiaries, which gathered information about beneficiary information needs, preferred sources, and information-seeking strategies. Results of this survey are to be used to develop a new national compilation of beneficiary education products and services.

There are three basic plans under TRICARE—TRICARE Standard, TRICARE Extra, and TRICARE Prime. To use TRICARE Extra or TRICARE Prime, the individual receiving care must live in an area where these options are available, and a civilian provider network has been established to support these plans.

Who Is Eligible for TRICARE

Similar to recipients of Medicaid and Medicare, TRICARE-eligible individuals are referred to as *beneficiaries.* The service member, whether in active duty, retired, or deceased, is called the **sponsor.** The sponsor's relationship to the beneficiary (spouse, child, parent) creates eligibility under TRICARE.

After eligibility has been established, the individual must be listed in the Department of Defense's **Defense Enrollment Eligibility Reporting System (DEERS)**. DEERS is a computerized data bank that lists all active and retired military service members. Active and retired service members are listed automatically, but it is the sponsor's responsibility to list dependents and report any changes to family members' status (e.g., marriage, divorce,

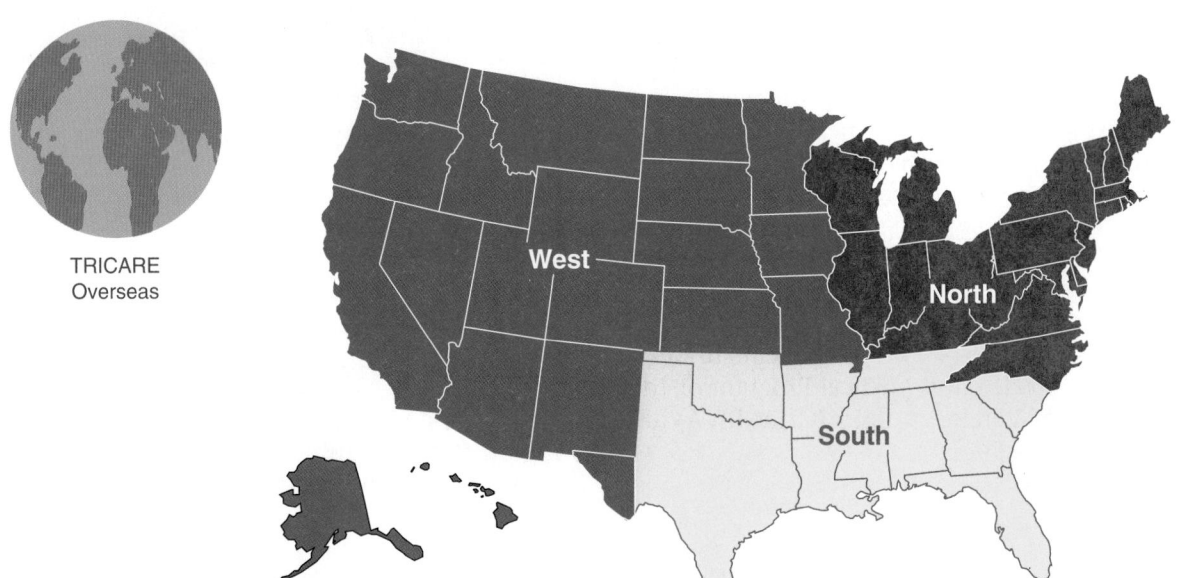

Fig. 8-1 TRICARE health care service regional map. *(Source: U.S. Department of Defense, TRICARE Management Activity.)*

birth of a child, adoption) or changes in mailing addresses. TRICARE contractors (TRICARE's term for fiscal intermediaries) check DEERS before processing claims to ensure patients are eligible for TRICARE benefits.

TRICARE-eligible individuals include the following main categories:

- Active duty service members (enrollment not required)
- Spouses and unmarried children of active duty service members
- Uniformed service retirees, their spouses, and unmarried children

For a more detailed list of TRICARE-eligible categories, go to the TRICARE Eligibility website at http://www.military.com/benefits/tricare/tricare-eligibility.

IMAGINE THIS!

Alan Workman is a Marine serving on active duty in Iraq. He has a wife and two children (2 and 7 years old) at home in the United States. In this scenario, TRICARE considers Alan the sponsor, and his wife and two children are the beneficiaries.

Who Is Not Eligible for TRICARE

Categories of individuals *not* eligible for TRICARE benefits include the following:

- Most individuals who are 65 years old and eligible for Medicare (except active duty family members) are not TRICARE-eligible. Individuals younger than 65 who are Medicare-eligible because of a disability or end-stage renal disease may retain TRICARE eligibility until age 65, but they must be enrolled in Medicare Part B.
- Parents and parents-in-law of active duty service members or uniformed services retirees, or of deceased active duty members or retirees, are not TRICARE-eligible. They may be able to receive treatment in military medical facilities if space permits, however.
- Individuals who are eligible for benefits under the Civilian Health and Medical Program of the Department of Veterans Affairs (CHAMPVA) are not TRICARE-eligible.

What TRICARE Pays

Similar to most insurers, TRICARE pays for only their *allowed* services, supplies, and procedures, which they refer to as **covered charges**. TRICARE's covered charges include medical and psychological services and supplies that are considered appropriate care and are generally accepted by qualified professionals to be reasonable and adequate for the diagnosis and treatment of illness, injury, pregnancy, mental disorders, and well-child care.

TRICARE's allowable charge, also known as the **CHAMPUS Maximum Allowable Charge**, is the amount on which TRICARE figures a beneficiary's cost share (co-insurance) for covered charges. TRICARE calculates this allowable charge by looking at all professional (noninstitutional) providers' fees for the same or similar services nationwide over the past year, with adjustments for specific localities. If the health insurance professional does not know what the allowable charge is for a particular service or supply, he or she can telephone the regional claims processor for this information or consult the TRICARE handbook. It is advisable to keep a current copy of the TRICARE handbook on file for information regarding TRICARE billing and claims submission guidelines.

HIPAA TIP

TRICARE/CHAMPVA beneficiaries and providers of care benefit from HIPAA in the following ways:
- Improves uniformity and efficiency of communication among providers
- Increases protection of patients' private, personal health information
- Makes transferring enrollment between plans easier

WHAT DID YOU LEARN?

1. List TRICARE's two main health care objectives.
2. What category of individuals are TRICARE sponsors?
3. Name the three categories of individuals eligible for TRICARE benefits.

TRICARE's Three Choices for Health Care

As mentioned earlier, TRICARE typically (depending on the geographical area) offers eligible beneficiaries three different health care plans from which to choose.

TRICARE Standard

TRICARE Standard is a fee-for-service option that has basically the same benefits as the original

CHAMPUS program. Under this plan, eligible enrollees can see the authorized provider of their choice. In some locations, TRICARE Standard may be the only option available.

ELIGIBILITY.   Anyone who is CHAMPUS-eligible may use TRICARE Standard. (Active duty personnel are not CHAMPUS-eligible and are automatically enrolled in TRICARE Prime.) Family members of military service personnel in the Army Reserves and National Guard, called **reserve components (RCs)**, are eligible for TRICARE Standard only if the RC is ordered to active duty for more than 30 consecutive days or if the orders are for an indefinite period. The RC is entitled to TRICARE Prime benefits as soon as he or she goes into active duty.

ADVANTAGES
- Broadest choice of providers
- Widely available
- No enrollment fee
- Eligible members also may use TRICARE Extra

DISADVANTAGES
- No primary care manager (PCM)
- Patient pays deductible and co-payment
- Patient pays 15% over and above allowable charge for nonparticipating providers (nonPARs)
- Beneficiaries may have to do their own paperwork and file their own claims if provider is nonPAR

SUMMARY
- Greatest flexibility in choosing health care providers
- Most convenient when away from home
- Potentially most expensive of all options
- Enrollment not required
- Allow for space-available care in military hospitals, but at low priority

TRICARE Extra
TRICARE Extra is a preferred provider option (PPO). The enrollee chooses a physician, hospital, or other medical provider listed in the TRICARE Provider Directory. With TRICARE Extra, there are no enrollment criteria to meet, and enrollees do not pay an annual fee. There is, however, an annual deductible and cost sharing for outpatient care. In the TRICARE Extra program, when an enrollee receives care from a TRICARE Extra network provider, he or she gets a discount on cost sharing, and patients do not have to file their own claims. TRICARE Extra may be used on a case-by-case basis just by choosing a provider within the network. TRICARE Extra is unavailable overseas or to active duty service members.

TRICARE Standard, Extra, and Prime have an annual **catastrophic cap (cat cap)**, which is a maximum cost limit placed on out-of-pocket expenses for covered medical bills. The limit that a family of an active duty member has to pay in any given year is $1000. For all others (other than Active Duty Families) using TRICARE Standard or Extra, there is a $3000 cat cap per fiscal year (October 1 to September 30) that is applied to out-of-pocket expenses for TRICARE-covered benefits (2006-2007 fiscal year figures). For more details on the cat cap, the health insurance professional should check with the nearest TRICARE Service Center. Also, see the websites listed in Websites to Explore at the end of this chapter.

ELIGIBILITY.   Anyone who is CHAMPUS-eligible may use TRICARE Extra. (Active duty personnel are not CHAMPUS-eligible and are automatically enrolled in TRICARE Prime.)

ADVANTAGES
- Co-payment 5% less than TRICARE Standard
- No balance billing
- No enrollment fee
- No deductible when using retail pharmacy network
- Patient not responsible for filing forms
- Enrollees also may use TRICARE Standard

DISADVANTAGES
- No PCM
- Provider choice is limited
- Patient must pay deductible and cost share
- Nonavailability statement (NAS) may be required for civilian inpatient care for areas surrounding MTFs
- Not available everywhere

SUMMARY
- Patients can choose any provider in the TRICARE Extra network
- Less expensive than TRICARE Standard
- Enrollment not required
- Eligible for space-available care in MTF, but at low priority

TRICARE Prime
TRICARE Prime is a health maintenance organization (HMO) type of managed care option in which MTFs are the principal source of health care. When eligible beneficiaries enroll in TRICARE Prime, they are assigned to a **primary care manager (PCM)**, which is a health care provider or a team of health care providers that the enrollee must see first for all routine medical care, similar to a primary care pro-

vider or gatekeeper in civilian managed care plans. The PCM is responsible for the following:

- Provides or coordinates all health care
- Maintains patient health records
- Arranges referrals to specialists if necessary (to be covered, specialty care must be arranged and approved by the PCM)

Similar to most managed health care plans, TRICARE Prime emphasizes preventive health care, including health risk assessments, screening tests (e.g., cholesterol, hypertension, mammogram, Pap and prostate screening), advice on nutrition, and smoking cessation classes designed to guide the enrollee to a healthy lifestyle. Retired military beneficiaries and their eligible family members also can enroll in TRICARE Prime. There is an annual enrollment fee for retired military beneficiaries, whereas active duty family members pay no enrollment fee.

When active duty service members are automatically enrolled in TRICARE Prime, they are assigned to a PCM, generally at an MTF. For all other eligible individuals, including family members, enrollment in TRICARE Prime is voluntary and can be done any time of the year. None of the three TRICARE options—Standard, Extra, or Prime—has preexisting condition limitations.

If the beneficiary lives in an area where TRICARE Prime is offered, he or she can call the regional TRICARE contractor and ask for an enrollment packet by mail. Enrollment must be in writing; enrollment by telephone is not an option. Health care usually is provided at an MTF, but civilian clinics may be used in some cases.

The point-of-service option under TRICARE Prime allows enrollees the freedom to seek and receive nonemergency health care services from any TRICARE-authorized civilian provider, in or out of the network, without requesting a referral from their PCM.

ELIGIBILITY.   There is no enrollment fee for TRICARE Prime, but there is a registration process. Besides active service members' automatic enrollment, the following categories of individuals may enroll in TRICARE prime:

- Dependent family members and survivors of active duty personnel
- Retirees and their family members and survivors younger than age 65
- RCs and their family members called to active duty for 179 days or more

RCs and their family members may enroll in TRICARE Prime or may be eligible for TRICARE

Prime Remote. Enrollment forms must be completed, and MTFs or TRICARE Prime network providers must be used.

TRICARE Prime Remote provides health care coverage through civilian networks or TRICARE-authorized providers for uniformed service members and their families who are on **remote assignment**, which is 50 miles or more from an MTF. TRICARE Prime Remote for Active Duty Family Members (TPRADFM) is the TRICARE Prime Remote plan for family members with similar benefits and program requirements. TRICARE Prime Remote/TPRADFM is offered in the 50 United States only, and both programs require enrollment.

The cat cap on most medical expenses (other than active duty enrollees) for TRICARE Prime managed care plan is $3000 per 12-month enrollment period. This means that for 1 year (beginning with the date of enrollment), TRICARE Prime enrollees pay a maximum of $3000 for enrollment fees, inpatient and outpatient cost shares, and co-payments for professional services and supplies. After the $3000 maximum is reached, enrollees pay nothing more for care received through the TRICARE Prime network of providers until a new enrollment period begins.

RE-ENROLLMENT AND DISENROLLMENT.   Enrollment in TRICARE Prime is continuous. Individuals may choose to disenroll or may be disenrolled because of a move to a non TRICARE Prime service area or for nonpayment of enrollment fees. If the individual chooses to disenroll from TRICARE Prime before his or her annual enrollment renewal date or is disenrolled for nonpayment, the individual may be subject to a 1-year lockout. The lockout provision does not apply to active duty family members of E-1 through E-4. Any change in status (e.g., active duty to retired or demobilization) causes a disenrollment from TRICARE Prime. When there is a status change, the individual must re-enroll in TRICARE Prime to maintain coverage.

ADVANTAGES
- No enrollment fee for active duty service members and their families
- Pay only a small fee per visit to civilian providers (no fee for active duty members)
- No balance billing
- Guaranteed appointments (access standards)
- PCM supervises and coordinates care
- Away-from-home emergency coverage
- Point-of-service option

DISADVANTAGES
- Enrollment fee for retirees and their families
- Provider choice limited to providers belonging to network

- Specialty care by referral only
- Not available outside the 50 United States

SUMMARY

- Guaranteed access to timely medical care
- Priority for care at military hospitals and clinics
- PCM provides and coordinates health care delivery
- Lowest cost for treatment among three options
- Requires enrollment for 1 year
- Retirees pay enrollment fee
- Very expensive to receive care outside TRICARE Prime (point-of-service option)
- Not available everywhere

It can be a challenge to decide which TRICARE option—Prime, Extra, or Standard—to choose (Fig. 8-2). As stated, active duty personnel are automatically enrolled in TRICARE Prime and pay no fees. Active duty family members pay no enrollment fees, but they have to choose a TRICARE option, and they must apply for enrollment if they choose TRICARE Prime.

Nonavailability Statement

As discussed previously, military personnel and their TRICARE-eligible dependents typically receive health care at an MTF. If treatment is unavailable at an MTF, the individual sometimes must obtain a **nonavailability statement (NAS)** (Figs. 8-3 and 8-4) indicating that care is unavailable from the MTF. An NAS is certification from the MTF that says it cannot provide the specific health care the benefi-

ciary needs at that facility. The statements must be entered electronically in the Department of Defense's DEERS computer files by the MTF.

As of December 2002, individuals covered by TRICARE Standard no longer need approval from their MTF to seek inpatient care at civilian hospitals. A requirement still exists, however, for TRICARE Standard beneficiaries to get an NAS before seeking *nonemergency inpatient mental health care services*. This requirement applies only to beneficiaries who use TRICARE Standard or Extra, who are not Medicare-eligible, and who have no other health insurance that is primary to TRICARE. Preauthorization for TRICARE beneficiary inpatient mental health care is not needed when Medicare is the primary payer.

With this change in policy, beneficiaries have the freedom to choose an MTF or a civilian facility without this extra paperwork. Nevertheless, TRICARE beneficiaries are urged to consider the Military Health System as their first choice for health care (Table 8-1).

> **HIPAA TIP**
>
> HIPAA privacy applies to individually identifiable health information, including paper, electronic, or oral communications. This includes information that identifies the patient and relates to his or her past, present, or future health condition.

Topic	TRICARE Prime	TRICARE Extra	TRICARE Standard
Definition	TRICARE Prime is a managed care option similar to a health maintenance organization (HMO).	TRICARE Extra is similar to a preferred provider organization (PPO) where the beneficiary selects from a network of providers.	TRICARE Standard has the same benefits and cost shares as the former CHAMPUS.
Cost vs. Choice	Least out-of-pocket costs with some restrictions on freedom of choice.	Co-payment 5% less than TRICARE Standard and no deductible when using the retail network pharmacy.	Highest out-of-pocket costs with the greatest degree of freedom to choose health care providers.

Fig. 8-2 TRICARE's three options. *(Source: U.S. Department of Defense, TRICARE Management Activity.)*

TRICARE POLICY MANUAL 6010.47-M, MARCH 15, 2002

CHAPTER 11, SECTION 2.1
NONAVAILABILITY STATEMENT (DD FORM 1251) FOR INPATIENT CARE

ENCLOSURE 1   DD 1251 (SAMPLE)

UNIFORMED SERVICES MEDICAL TREATMENT FACILITY NONAVAILABILITY STATEMENT (NAS)	REPORT CONTROL SYMBOL

Privacy Act Statement

AUTHORITY: 44 USC 3101, 41 CFR 101 et seq., 10 USC 1066 and 1079, and EO 9397, November 1943 (SSN).

PRINCIPAL PURPOSE: To evaluate eligibility for civilian health benefits authorized by 10 USC, Chapter 55, and to issue payment upon establishment of eligibility and determination that the medical care received is authorized by law. The information is subject to verification with the appropriate Uniformed Service.

ROUTINE USE: CHAMPUS and its contractors use the information to control and process medical claims for payment; for control and approval of medical treatments and interface with providers of medical care; to control and accomplish reviews of utilization; for review of claims related to possible third party liability cases and initiation of recovery actions; and for referral to Peer Review Committees or similar professional review organizations to control and review providers' medical care.

DISCLOSURE: Voluntary; however, failure to provide information will result in denial of, or delay in payment of, the claim.

1. NAS NUMBER *(Facility) (Yr-Julian) (Seq. No.)*	2. PRIMARY REASON FOR ISSUANCE *(X one)*	
	a.	PROPER FACILITIES ARE TEMPORARILY NOT AVAILABLE IN A SAFE OR TIMELY MANNER
3. MAJOR DIAGNOSTIC CATEGORY FOR WHICH NAS IS ISSUED *(Use code from reverse)*	b.	PROFESSIONAL CAPABILITY IS TEMPORARILY NOT AVAILABLE IN A SAFE OR TIMELY MANNER
	c.	PROPER FACILITIES OR PROFESSIONAL CAPABILITY ARE PERMANENTLY NOT AVAILABLE AT THIS FACILITY
	d.	IT WOULD BE MEDICALLY INAPPROPRIATE TO REQUIRE THE BENEFICIARY TO USE THE MPT *(Explain in Remarks)*

4. PATIENT DATA

a. NAME *(Last, First, Middle Initial)*	b. DATE OF BIRTH *(YYMMDD)*	c. SEX	
d. ADDRESS *(Street, City, State, and ZIP Code)*	e. PATIENT CATEGORY *(X one)*	f. OTHER NON CHAMPUS HEALTH INSURANCE *(X one)*	
	(1) Dependent of Active Duty	(1) Yes, but only CHAMPUS Supplemental	
	(2) Dependent of Retiree		
	(3) Retiree		
	(4) Survivor	(2) Yes *(List in Remarks)*	
	(5) Former Spouse	(3) No	

5. SPONSOR DATA *(if you marked 4e(3) Retiree above, print "Same" in 5a.)*

a. NAME *(Last, First, Middle Initial)*	b. SPONSOR'S OR RETIREE'S SOCIAL SECURITY NO.

6. ISSUING OFFICIAL DATA

a. NAME *(Last, First, Middle Initial)*	b. TITLE	
c. SIGNATURE	d. PAY GRADE	e. DATE ISSUED *(YYMMDD)*

7. REMARKS *(Indicate block number to which the answer applies.)*

DD Form 1251, JUL 91

Outside the United States and Puerto Rico, previous editions may be used until exhausted
Inside the United States and Puerto Rico, previous editions are obsolete

Fig. 8-3   Sample nonavailability statement for inpatient care. *(Source: U.S. Department of Defense, TRICARE Management Activity.)*

Application For Nonavailability Statement	Date:

TO: Health Benefits Advisor, Managed Care Division, DeWitt Army Community Hospital, Fort Belvoir 22060-5901

A Nonavailability Statement (DD Form 1251) is required when nonemergency inpatient care and certain outpatient care is to be provided to dependents of active duty personnel residing with, or apart from sponsor retirees and their dependents and dependents of deceased/former spouses residing within a ZIP Code Catchment area of this hospital. The following is required to evaluate a request for issuance of DD Form 1251:

Patient Name (Last, First, MI):		Status (wife, son, etc.)

Home Address (street, city, state, ZIP):	Home Telephone:
	Work Telephone:

Date of Birth:	Sponsor's Name:	Rank:

Sponsor's Category: (active duty, retired, deceased, former spouse). If active duty his/her unit/organization and BRANCH OF SERVICE (Army, Navy, Marines, Air Force or other)

Other Primary Health Insurance (yes or no) If you have private health insurance that pays first for the cost of medical services, you do not need a nonavailability statement from the local MTF.

All retroactive requests for nonavailability statements require summary of hospitalization or history and physical examination. If maternity care, name of hospital where delivery will take place, date of first civilian prenatal visit and delivery date. All other requests require name of civilian hospital and date of hospitalization. MEDICARE, ACTIVE DUTY, DEPENDENT PARENTS AND PARENTS-IN-LAW ARE NOT ELIGIBLE FOR CHAMPUS.

Reason for Request

Submit

Fig. 8-4 Application form for a nonavailability statement. *(Source: U.S. Department of Defense, TRICARE Management Activity.)*

IMAGINE THIS!

In February 2003, Kim Sun Hwa, a TRICARE Standard enrollee, sought care for a serious cardiac condition at the MTF near the town where she lived. The MTF did not have the facilities to perform the needed quadruple bypass surgery and referred her to Genesis Cardiac and Rehabilitation Center 150 miles away. The MTF filed a nonavailability statement with DEERS; however, the health insurance professional at Genesis advised Kim that an NAS was no longer necessary for beneficiaries enrolled in TRICARE Standard. After the surgery, Kim experienced postsurgical depression and returned to Genesis for outpatient psychotherapy. Because she did not need an NAS from the MTF for her surgery, Kim assumed she would not need an NAS for the treatment of her mental health condition; however, without it, TRICARE refused the second claim.

TABLE 8-1	TRICARE Comparison Chart (2006-2007)		
	TRICARE Prime	**TRICARE Extra**	**TRICARE Standard**
Active Duty Family Members			
Annual deductible	None	$150/individual or $300/family for E-5 and above; $50/$100 for E-4 and below	$150/individual or $300/family for E-5 and above; $50/$100 for E-4 and below
Annual enrollment fee	None	None	None
Civilian outpatient visit	No cost	15% of negotiated fee	20% of allowed charges for covered service
Civilian inpatient admission	No cost	Greater of $25 or $14.35/day	Greater of $25 or $14.35/day
Civilian inpatient mental health	No cost	Greater of $20/day or $25/admission	Greater of $20/day or $25/admission
Civilian inpatient skilled nursing facility care	$0 per diem charge per admission No separate cost share for separately billed professional charges	$11/day ($25 minimum) charge per admission	$11/day ($25 minimum) charge per admission
Retirees, Their Family Members, and Others			
Annual deductible	None	$150/individual or $300/family	$150/individual or $300/family
Annual enrollment fee	$230/individual or $460/family	None	None
Civilian cost shares	—	20% of negotiated fee	25% of allowed charges for covered service
Outpatient	$12	—	—
Emergency care	$30	—	—
Mental health visit	$25; $17 for group visit	—	—
Civilian inpatient cost share	Greater of $11/day or $25/admission; no separate co-payment for separately billed professional charges	Lesser of $250/day or 25% of negotiated charges plus 20% of negotiated professional fees	Lesser of $535/day or 25% of billed charges plus 25% of allowed professional fees
Civilian inpatient skilled nursing facility care	$11/day ($25 minimum) charge per admission	$250 per diem cost share or 20% cost share of total charges (whichever is less), institutional services, plus 20% cost share of separately billed professional charges	25% cost share of allowed charges for institutional services, plus 25% cost share of allowable for separately billed professional charges
Civilian inpatient behavioral health	$40/day; no charge for separately billed professional charges	20% of total charge plus 20% of the allowable charge for separately billed professional services	High-volume hospitals—25% hospital specific per diem, plus 25% of the allowable charge for separately billed professional services; low-volume hospitals—$175/day or 25% of the billed charges (whichever is lower) plus 25% of the allowable charge for separately billed services

Other Health Insurance

If a TRICARE-eligible beneficiary has other health care coverage besides TRICARE Standard, Extra, or Prime through an employer, an association, or a private insurer, or if a student in the family has a health care plan obtained through his or her school, TRICARE considers this **other health insurance (OHI).** It also may be called double coverage or coordination of benefits. OHI does not include TRICARE supplemental insurance or Medicaid.

WHAT DID YOU LEARN?

1. List TRICARE's three options for health care.
2. Into which option are active service members automatically enrolled?
3. How does TRICARE determine the allowable charge for a service?
4. List three advantages and three disadvantages of each of the three TRICARE options.
5. When is it necessary for TRICARE beneficiaries to obtain a nonavailability statement?

TRICARE Standard Supplemental Insurance

TRICARE Standard Supplemental Insurance policies, similar to Medicare supplemental insurance policies, are health benefit plans that are designed specifically to supplement TRICARE Standard benefits. These plans are frequently available from military associations or other private organizations and firms. They generally pay most or all of whatever is left after TRICARE Standard has paid its share of the cost of covered health care services and supplies. Such policies are not specifically for retirees and may be useful for other TRICARE-eligible families as well.

TRICARE for Life

TRICARE for Life (TFL) is a comprehensive health benefits program established by the National Defense Authorization Act. This program is available to uniformed services retirees, their spouses, and their survivors who are age 65 or older, are Medicare-eligible, are enrolled in Medicare Part A, and have purchased Medicare Part B coverage. TFL has no monthly premium cost and is a permanent health care benefit for all uniformed service branches.

Who Is Eligible for TRICARE for Life

The following individuals are eligible for TFL:

- All Medicare-eligible military retirees, regardless of age (retirees are individuals who had more than 20 years of active duty service)
- Spouses and survivors, regardless of age, who are eligible for Medicare Part A and who are enrolled in Medicare Part B
- Certain qualifying former spouses
- Reservists, including guardsmen, drawing reserve retired pay, their spouses, and other eligible family members become eligible for TFL when they turn 65
- Medal of Honor winners who left the service before retirement plus their spouses and survivors

In addition to the qualifying members of the uniformed service branches listed, individuals belonging to or employed by Public Health Service groups and the National Oceanic and Atmospheric Administration may enroll in TFL if they meet the eligibility criteria.

How TRICARE for Life Works to Supplement Medicare

TFL functions similar to Medicare supplemental insurance; TFL enrollees do not need a Medicare supplement policy. For individuals who are eligible for Medicare TFL and Medicare, the following applies:

- Eligible individuals pay no premium to be enrolled in TFL.
- Medicare automatically crosses claims over to TRICARE.
- TRICARE pays Medicare deductibles and co-insurance or co-payment amounts up to 115% of Medicare-allowable charges.

For procedures *not covered* by Medicare (e.g., chiropractic care), beneficiaries are responsible for TRICARE deductibles and co-payment amounts. When the annual out-of-pocket limit has been reached, TRICARE pays 100% of TRICARE-allowed charges for the remainder of the year. When a claim is submitted for a Medicare/TFL beneficiary, TRICARE pays last. Medicare/TFL beneficiaries have the same coverage for prescription drugs as that provided under Medicare Prescription Drug Coverage (Part D). For information on TFL, the TRICARE for Life website (http://www.tricare.mil/tfl/tflcostmatrix_b.html) has a table that explains what services are covered and who pays.

IMAGINE THIS!

Benjamin Hudson, a dual-eligible enrollee under TRICARE and Medicare, visited Dr. Alton Simmons, an ophthalmologist, for vision problems. Benjamin subsequently opted to receive laser surgery to correct his myopia. When he received a statement for the entire fee, he telephoned the health insurance professional in Dr. Simmons' office stating that because he had Medicare and TRICARE coverage, one or the other should pay. Under the impression that an error had been made, Benjamin insisted that the claim be resubmitted; however, the health insurance professional informed him that because laser surgery was a noncovered expense under Medicare, TRICARE would not pay it either. Mr. Hudson refused to pay the bill on the grounds that the health insurance professional should have informed him that this was a noncovered service before the procedure. Dr. Simmons ultimately adjusted the charge off Benjamin's account.

Verifying Eligibility

When a patient comes to the office for an appointment and informs the health insurance professional that he or she is eligible for benefits under one of the military's health care programs, it should be verified immediately. Box 8-1 lists some suggestions for verification. Fig. 8-5 shows sample ID cards.

TRICARE Participating Providers

Health care providers who participate in TRICARE (participating providers [PAR]), also referred to as **accepting assignment**, agree to accept the TRICARE allowable charge (including the cost share and deductible, if any) as payment in full for the health care services provided and cannot balance bill. Individual providers who do not accept assignment on all claims (nonPARs) can participate in TRICARE on a case-by-case basis. PARs and nonPARs who accept assignment must file the claim for the patient, and TRICARE sends the payment (if any) directly to the provider. Hospitals that participate in Medicare, by law, also must participate in TRICARE Standard for inpatient care. For outpatient care, hospitals may choose whether to participate.

TRICARE Claims Processing

The facility that handles TRICARE claims for health care received within a state or region is called a **claims processor**. In some regions, they are called TRICARE contractors or fiscal intermediaries. All

BOX 8-1   Suggestions for Verifying Eligibility

- Ask to see a Uniformed Services ID card or a family member's Uniformed Services ID card. Anyone 10 years old or older should have a personal ID card.
- Check the back of the card for TRICARE/CHAMPUS eligibility and the expiration date.
- Prime enrollees must show their Uniformed Services ID card and their TRICARE Prime ID card. The Prime ID card does not specify the beneficiary's period of eligibility, so the health insurance professional needs to verify the current eligibility status by calling the beneficiary services hotline. Failure to verify eligibility may result in claim denial.
- The Prime sponsor's Social Security number is included in the 11-digit number on the Prime ID card. Verify the Prime sponsor's Social Security number with the patient. It should match the final nine digits of the number given on the TRICARE Prime ID card.
- If you are the patient's PCM, you also should verify that you are the PCM listed on the Prime card, and note the effective date of the coverage.
- In most cases, active duty personnel must seek nonemergency health care from their host MTF. Under certain circumstances, such as nonavailability of needed services at the MTF, active duty personnel may obtain Prime benefits from civilian providers under the Supplemental Healthcare Program. Because active duty personnel are not issued Prime ID cards, they must show their green (active duty) ID cards to verify eligibility.
- Make a copy of the front and back of all ID cards for your records.

claims processors (fiscal intermediaries) have toll-free telephone numbers to handle questions that a health insurance professional might have regarding TRICARE claims. The health insurance professional should have the latest TRICARE handbook on file or log onto the TRICARE website for an electronic version of the handbook. In addition to the handbook, a file should be kept that has an up-to-date list of telephone numbers and addresses to facilitate claims processing.

Submitting Paper Claims

Providers submitting paper claims should use the standard CMS-1500 claim form. Patients who file their own claims must use Form 2692 (CHAMPUS Claim Patient Request for Medical Payment), which can be downloaded from the TRICARE website. If

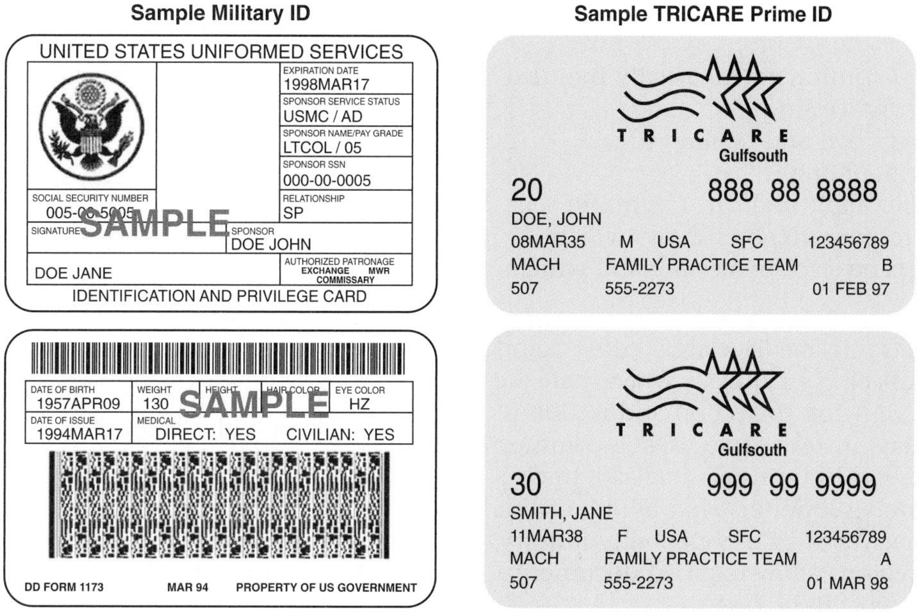

Sample Military ID

Sample TRICARE Prime ID

Fig. 8-5   Examples of military ID cards. *(Source: U.S. Department of Defense, TRICARE Management Activity.)*

the patient files his or her own claim, the provider's detailed itemized statement and an NAS (if necessary) must be attached. Completed claims are sent to the TRICARE claims processor in the region in which the enrollee resides. For information on where to file paper claims, the TRICARE website (http://www.tricare.osd.mil) lists the names and addresses of claims processors by region. At the TRICARE home page, click on "site map," choose "claims," and select the region of choice to access the chart of pertinent information.

Who Submits Claims

If the patient is enrolled in TRICARE Prime and goes to a Prime provider, the provider submits the claims. After the claims are submitted, the beneficiary and provider receive an explanation of benefits (EOB) from the claims processor showing the services performed and the adjudication.

Patients using TRICARE Standard are usually responsible for submitting their own claims to the appropriate *claims processor*. If the patient has access to the Internet, these forms can be downloaded from the TRICARE website. They are in Portable Document Format (PDF). PDF is a universal file format that preserves the fonts, images, graphics, and layout of any source document, regardless of the application and platform used to create it. PDF files are compact and complete and can be shared, viewed, and printed by anyone with free Adobe Reader software. It may be necessary first to download the Adobe Reader software. Instructions for downloading and installing the software are available at the download site.

In the case of nonPARs, TRICARE Standard patients must file their own claims. In this case, the reimbursement check would be sent to the patient, and it is his or her responsibility to ensure that the provider's bill is paid. If the claims processor needs additional information, whoever filed the claim is contacted. This additional information must be sent to the processor within 35 days of the date of the letter or phone call, or the claim may be denied.

STOP AND THINK

Ruth Carson is a 36-year-old teacher and a TRICARE Standard beneficiary. On March 30, she visits her family physician, Dr. Bennett, for a routine yearly examination. As Dr. Bennett's health insurance professional, you must advise Ruth that Dr. Bennett does not accept assignment on TRICARE claims and that Ruth will have to file her own claim. Ruth asks you how to file the claim. What are your instructions?

Electronic Claims Submission

As with other third-party payers, TRICARE claims can be filed electronically, and providers are encouraged to do so. The numerous advantages to electronic claims filing include the following:

- Saves time by sending claims directly into the TRICARE processing system
- Saves money with no-cost or low-cost claims filing options

- Improves cash flow with faster payment turnaround
- Expedites claim confirmation—usually the next day with batch processing
- Reduces postage costs and mailing time
- Reduces paper handling
- Provides a better audit trail (the electronic media claims response reports shows which claims were accepted for processing and which were denied)

Front-end electronic media claims edits claims and provides feedback more quickly when there are claim problems, allowing correction and resubmission in hours or days instead of weeks, as is common with paper claims. Software also is available to electronic media claims submitters that allows online claims status inquiry and DEERS eligibility inquiry. Some TRICARE regions allow required documentation for claim support to be faxed.

XPressClaim is a secure, streamlined World Wide Web–based system that allows providers to submit TRICARE claims electronically and, in most cases, receive instant results. XPressClaim is the fastest way available to get TRICARE claims processed, and it is free. Filing a TRICARE claim with XPressClaim is straightforward. If the provider is already a member of *myTRICARE claims for Providers,* all the health insurance professional has to do is sign on and click the XPressClaim tab on the top left. To submit the claim, the health insurance professional

1. selects the location where the patient received care, the physician who provided it, and the patient who received it;
2. enters the services and charges for claim;
3. clicks "Submit"; and
4. makes any necessary online corrections.

In most cases, providers receive immediate claim results. Fig. 8-6 illustrates the process that TRICARE paper claims undergo.

Deadline for Submitting Claims

TRICARE claims should be submitted within 30 days from the date services were rendered or as soon as possible after the care is rendered. No payment is made for incomplete claims or claims submitted *more than 1 year* after services are rendered for PARs and nonPARs. In addition, PARs are required to participate in Medicare (accept assignment) and submit claims on behalf of TRICARE beneficiaries and Medicare beneficiaries. It is important for TRICARE

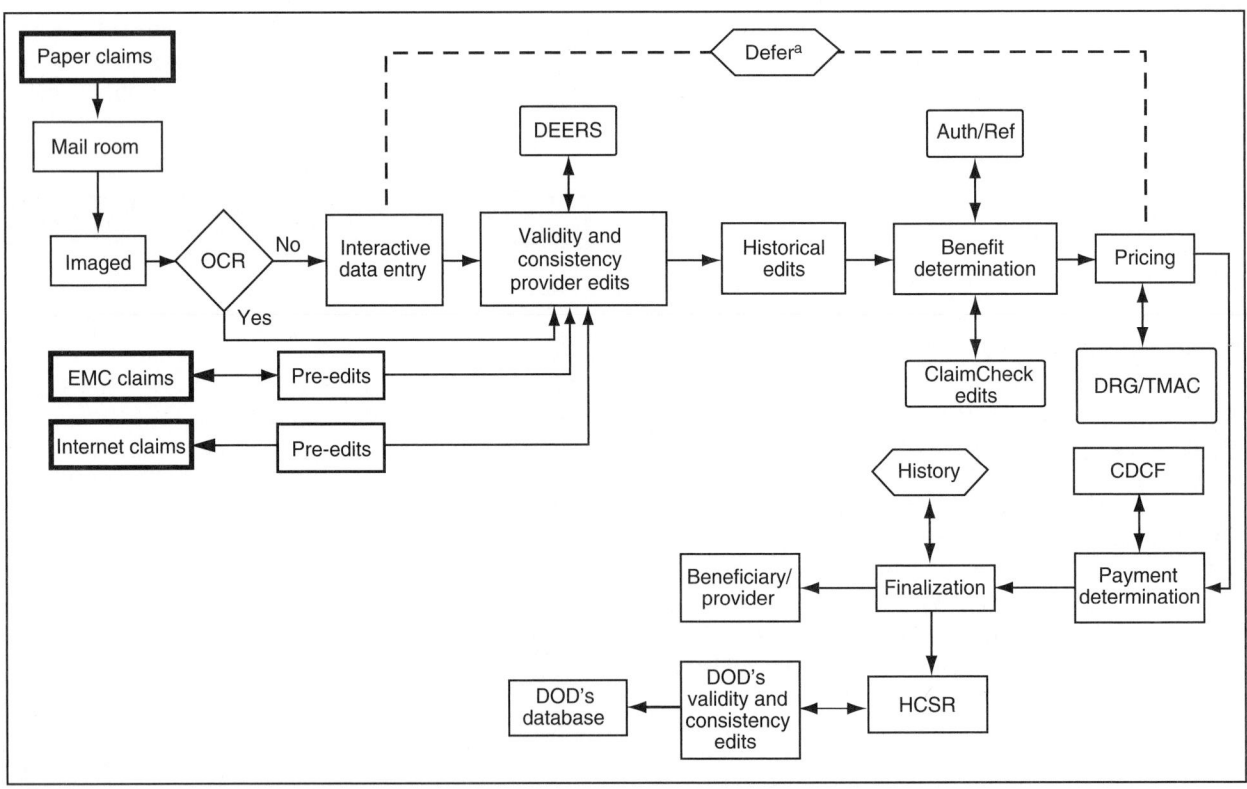

Source: GAO.

Fig. 8-6 TRICARE claims flow chart. At any point between Interactive Data Entry and Pricing, processing can be deferred, and the claim can loop back to obtain additional information, usually requiring manual intervention. *(Source: U.S. Department of Defense, TRICARE Management Activity.)*

providers to adhere to specific guidelines in claims preparation to ensure smooth and timely processing and payment of claims.

The sooner the TRICARE contractor gets the claim forms and other papers, the sooner the claim is paid. As mentioned, the contractor must receive claims within 1 year of the date the service was received or, in the case of inpatient care, within 1 year of the date of an inpatient's discharge. If the claim covers several different medical services or supplies that were provided at different times, the aforementioned 1-year deadline applies to each item on the claim. When a claim is submitted on time, but the claims contractor returns it for more information, the claim must be resubmitted, along with the requested information, so that it is received by the contractor no later than 1 year after the medical services or supplies were provided or 90 days from the date the claim was returned, whichever is later.

TRICARE Explanation of Benefits

If there are no problems with the claim, the contractor should send whoever filed the claim a written notice, known as an EOB, in about 1 month. The EOB shows the following (Fig. 8-7):

- What the provider billed
- The TRICARE allowable charge at the time of care
- How much of the patient's annual deductible has been met
- How much the patient has paid toward the annual cost cap
- The patient's cost share for the care
- How much TRICARE paid
- Any reasons for denying services on a claim

WHAT DID YOU LEARN?

1. What types of third-party coverage does TRICARE consider OHI?
2. When a beneficiary has TRICARE and Medicare, which pays first?
3. Define a dual-eligible beneficiary under TRICARE.
4. Under what circumstances do beneficiaries have to submit their own claims?
5. List six items of information contained on a TRICARE EOB.

CHAMPVA

The **Civilian Health and Medical Program of the Department of Veterans Affairs** **(CHAMPVA)** is a health care benefits program for dependents of veterans who

1. have been rated by the Department of Veterans Affairs (VA) as having a total and permanent service-connected disability;
2. are survivors of veterans who died from VA-rated service–connected conditions or who, at the time of death, were rated permanently and totally disabled from a VA-rated service–connected condition; and
3. survivors of individuals who died in the line of duty that was not due to misconduct and who are not otherwise entitled to TRICARE benefits.

Under CHAMPVA, the VA shares the cost of covered health care services and supplies with eligible beneficiaries. CHAMPVA is managed by the VA's Health Administration Center in Denver, Colorado. There is no cost to CHAMPVA beneficiaries when they receive health care treatment at a VA facility.

HIPAA TIP

TRICARE and MTFs are required to give health information about any individual to the Department of Health and Human Services for use in an investigation of a complaint.

Eligibility

The precise eligibility criteria of individuals who are entitled to CHAMPVA benefits are as follows:

- *The spouse or dependent child* of a veteran who has been rated by a VA regional office as having a permanent and total service-connected condition/disability
- *The surviving spouse or dependent child* of a veteran who died as a result of a VA-rated service–connected condition or who, at the time of death, was rated permanently and totally disabled from a VA-rated service–connected condition
- *The surviving spouse or dependent child* of an individual who died in the line of duty, and the death was not due to misconduct

CHAMPVA eligibility can be lost if certain demographic changes occur, such as a widow (younger than 55 years old) remarrying, divorcing the sponsor, or becoming eligible for Medicare or TRICARE. Dependent children lose their eligibility on reaching age 18 years. This age is extended to 23 years if they are attending an accredited college full-time (a

TRICARE Explanation of Benefits

TRICARE EXPLANATION OF BENEFITS

PGBA or WPS
TRICARE Claims Administrator for Your Region

This is a statement of the action taken on your TRICARE Claim.
Keep this notice for your records.

1*

3*

2*

4*

5*

Date of Notice:	August 02, 2000
Sponsor SSN:	000-00-0000
Sponsor Name:	NAME OF SPONSOR
Beneficiary Name:	NAME OF BENEFICIARY

7*   Benefits were payable to:

6*
PATIENT, PARENT/GUARDIAN
ADDRESS
CITY STATE ZIP CODE

PROVIDER OF MEDICAL CARE
ADDRESS
CITY STATE ZIP CODE

8*
Claim Number: 919533693-00-00

Services Provided By Date of Services	Services Provided	Amount Billed	TRICARE Approved	See Remarks
9*	10*	11*	12*	13*
PROVIDER OF MEDICAL CARE				
07/08/2000 1	Office/outpatient visit, est (99213)	$ 45.00	$ 38.92	1
07/08/2000 1	Comprehen metabolic panel (88054)	20.00	19.33	1
07/08/2000 1	Automated hemogram (85025)	12.00	12.00	1
Totals:		**$ 77.00**	**$ 70.25**	

Claim Summary	Beneficiary Liability Summary	Benefit Period Summary
	15*	16*

Fiscal Year Beginning:
October 01, 1999

Amount billed:	77.00	Deductible	0.00		Individual	Family
TRICARE Approved:	70.25	Copayment:	0.00			
Non-Covered: 14*	6.75	Cost Share	17.56	Deductible:	150.00	150.00
Paid by Beneficiary:	0.00			Catastrophic Cap:		
Other Insurance:	0.00			**Enrollment Year Beginning:**		
Paid to Provider:	52.69			December 01, 1999		
Paid to Beneficiary:	0.00				Individual	Family
Check Number:		POS Deductible:			300.00	600.00
		Prime Cap:				856.32

Remarks 17*

1 – CHARGES ARE MORE THAN ALLOWABLE AMOUNT

1-888-XXX-XXXX 18*

THIS IS NOT A BILL
If you have questions regarding this notice, please call or write us at the telephone number/address listed above.

1.   PGBA or WPS processes all TRICARE claims depending on the region where you live.

2.   Prime Contractor: The name and logo of the company that provides managed care support for the region where you live will appear here.

3.   Date of Notice: PGBA or WPS prepared your TRICARE Explanation of Benefits (TEOB) on this date.

4.   Sponsor SSN/Sponsor Name: Your claim is processed using the Social Security Number of the military service member (active duty, retired or deceased) who is your TRICARE sponsor.

5.   Beneficiary Name: The patient who received medical care and for whom this claim was filed.

Fig. 8-7   Example of TRICARE explanation of benefits. (*Source: U.S. Department of Defense, TRICARE Management Activity.*)

TRICARE Explanation of Benefits

6. Mail To Name and Address: We mail the TRICARE Explanation of Benefits (TEOB) directly to the patient (or patient's parent or guardian) at the address given on the claim. (HINT: Be sure your doctor has updated your records with your current address.)

7. Benefits Were Payable To: This field will appear only if your doctor accepts assignment. This means the doctor accepts the TRICARE Maximum Allowable Charge (TMAC) as payment in full for the services you received.

8. Claim Number: Each claim is assigned a unique number. This helps PGBA or WPS keep track of the claim as it is processed. It also helps them find the claim quickly whenever you call or write us with questions or concerns.

9. Service Provided By/Date of Services: This section lists who provided your medical care, the number of services and the procedure codes, as well as the date you received the care.

10. Services Provided: This section describes the medical services you received and how many services are itemized on your claim. It also lists the specific procedure codes that doctors, hospitals and labs use to identify the specific medical services you received.

11. Amount Billed: Your doctor, hospital or lab charged this fee for the medical services you received.

12. TRICARE Approved: This is the amount TRICARE approves for the services you received.

13. See Remarks: If you see a code or a number here, look at the Remarks section (17) for more information about your claim.

14. Claim Summary: A detailed explanation of the action taken by PGBA or WPS taken on your claim is given here. You will find the following totals: amount billed, amount approved by TRICARE, non-covered amount, amount (if any) that you have already paid to the provider, amount your primary health insurance paid (if TRICARE is your secondary insurance), benefits we have paid to the provider, and benefits paid to the beneficiary by PGBA or WPS. A Check Number will appear here only if a check accompanies your TEOB.

15. Beneficiary Liability Summary: You may be responsible for a portion of the fee your doctor has charged. If so, you'll see that amount itemized here. It will include any charges that we have applied to your annual deductible and any cost-share or copayment you must pay.

16. Benefit Period Summary: This section shows how much of the individual and family annual deductible and maximum out-of-pocket expense you have met to date. If you are a TRICARE Standard or Extra beneficiary, PGBA or WPS calculates your annual deductible and maximum out-of-pocket expense by fiscal year. See the Fiscal Year Beginning date in this section for the first date of the fiscal year. If you are a TRICARE Prime beneficiary, we calculate your maximum out-of-pocket expense by enrollment and fiscal year. See Enrollment Year Beginning date in this section for the first date of your enrollment year. (Note: the Enrollment Year Beginning will appear on your TEOB only if you are enrolled in TRICARE Prime.)

17. Remarks Explanations of the codes or numbers listed in See Remarks will appear here.

18. Toll-Free Telephone Number: Questions about your TRICARE Explanation of Benefits? Please call PGBA or WPS at this toll-free number. Their customer service representatives will assist you.

Fig. 8-7, cont'd

minimum of 12 credit hours). CHAMPVA recipients should report any changes in status to CHAMPVA immediately.

IMAGINE THIS!

Scott Talbott was an Army corporal stationed in Haiti in 2004 during its civil war. One evening, Scott and two other enlisted men went to a local bar. After an evening of drinking, they got into a brawl with a group of civilian townsmen. During the altercation, Scott sustained a knife wound to the chest and subsequently died of his injuries. Jenny Talbott, his widow, was informed that she and her three children were not eligible for CHAMPVA benefits because Scott's death was due to "misconduct." Jenny appealed but lost.

STOP AND THINK

Harold and Patsy Yates were divorced 12 years ago. Harold, a double-amputee Vietnam veteran, was rated by the regional VA office as having a permanent and total service-connected disability. Harold and Patsy are CHAMPVA-eligible; however, Patsy plans to remarry. How, if at all, would this affect her eligibility?

STOP AND THINK

Suppose that Harold Yates had been killed in Vietnam, rather than disabled, and he and Patsy were married at the time of his death, which makes her eligible for CHAMPVA benefits. In this scenario, if Patsy remarries, how would this affect her eligibility?

CHAMPVA Benefits

Generally, CHAMPVA covers most health care services and supplies that are medically and psychologically necessary. Prescription medications are free; however, over-the-counter medications are not covered. CHAMPVA benefits do not normally include dental or most eye care. Exceptions are limited to services directly related to treatment of certain medical conditions of the eyes or mouth. CHAMPVA-eligibles may see any provider of their choice as long as the provider is properly licensed.

On confirmation of eligibility, applicants receive program materials that specifically address covered and noncovered services and supplies. Pre-authorization is required for certain types of services, as follows:

- Dental care (other than the exceptions mentioned previously)
- Durable medical equipment with a total purchase price or total rental price of more than $300
- Hospice services
- Mental health/substance abuse services
- Organ and bone marrow transplants

Failure to acquire pre-authorization results in denial of the claim. Pre-authorization for visits to specialists or diagnostic tests is unnecessary.

What CHAMPVA Pays

CHAMPVA pays the allowable amount of covered services generally equivalent to the TRICARE and Medicare rates for same or similar services. In fiscal year 2006-2007, CHAMPVA had an outpatient deductible of $50 per person up to $100 per family per year and a cost share (co-insurance) of 25% up to the cat cap. If the patient has OHI, CHAMPVA pays the lesser of 75% of the allowable amount after the $50 calendar year deductible is met or the remainder of the charges. The beneficiary normally has no cost share. CHAMPVA also covers any medical expenses incurred overseas.

It is advised that the health insurance professional collect the 25% of the charges at the time services are rendered, unless the patient has a supplemental policy or OHI. If the beneficiary has OHI, such as group health insurance, the OHI is primary to CHAMPVA and must be billed first. After the OHI has paid, the EOB should be filed with the CHAMPVA claim.

The cat cap for CHAMPVA is $3000 per year. The cat cap time period begins on January 1 of each year and runs through December 31. When the beneficiary has met his or her cat cap, cost sharing for covered services for the remaining calendar year is

waived, and CHAMPVA pays 100% of the *allowable* amount.

CHAMPVA offers a more cost-effective prescription drug benefit than Medicare Part D and has no monthly premium. Under CHAMPVA, the prescription plan is considered "credible coverage," and beneficiaries typically do not have to sign up for a Medicare Part D prescription drug plan. If CHAMPVA beneficiaries get their maintenance medications through the CHAMPVA Meds by Mail program and do not routinely use a local pharmacy, they will continue to have those prescriptions provided free of charge and delivered directly to their home.

If there is any question as to whether a particular service is payable under CHAMPVA guidelines, the health insurance professional should consult the CHAMPVA handbook or contact the VA Health Administration Center using their toll-free phone line or e-mail at HAC.INQ@MED.VA (Table 8-2).

STOP AND THINK

Elaine Porter is employed by Harper Products, Inc. She has single coverage under her employer's group health care plan. Elaine's husband, a helicopter pilot, was killed when his Chinook helicopter was shot down by an air-to-ground missile during Desert Storm. Because Elaine also is covered under CHAMPVA, which payer in this case would be primary?

CHAMPVA-TRICARE Connection

CHAMPVA and TRICARE are federal programs; however, an individual who is eligible for TRICARE is not eligible for CHAMPVA. Although similar, TRICARE should not be confused with CHAMPVA. TRICARE provides coverage to the families of active duty service members, families of service members who died while on active duty, and retirees and their families, whether or not the veteran is disabled. CHAMPVA provides benefits to eligible family members of veterans who have been declared 100% permanently disabled from service-connected conditions, survivors of veterans who died from service-connected conditions, and survivors of service members who died in the line of duty who are not otherwise entitled to TRICARE benefits.

CHAMPVA-Medicare Connection

CHAMPVA and Medicare are federal programs; however, CHAMPVA is the last payer after all other third-party payers have met their obligations except for Medicaid and CHAMPVA supplemental

TABLE 8-2 CHAMPVA Costs/Patient Summary (2006-2007)

Benefits	Deductible?	Beneficiary Pays	CHAMPVA Pays
Ambulatory surgery facility services	No	25% of CHAMPVA allowable	75% of CHAMPVA allowable
Professional services	Yes	25% of CHAMPVA allowable after deductible	75% of CHAMPVA allowable
Durable medical equipment: non-VA source	Yes	25% of CHAMPVA allowable after deductible	75% of CHAMPVA allowable
Inpatient services: DRG-based	No	Lesser of (1) per day amount × number of inpatient days, (2) 25% of billed amount, or (3) DRG rate	CHAMPVA allowable less beneficiary cost share
Inpatient services: non–DRG-based	No	25% of CHAMPVA allowable	75% of CHAMPVA allowable
Mental health: high volume/residential treatment center	No	25% of CHAMPVA allowable	75% of CHAMPVA allowable
Mental health: low volume	No	Lesser of (1) per day amount × number of inpatient days or (2) 25% of billed amount	CHAMPVA allowable less beneficiary cost share
Outpatient services (i.e., physician visits, laboratory/radiology, home health, skilled nursing visits, ambulance)	Yes	25% of CHAMPVA allowable after deductible	75% of CHAMPVA allowable
Pharmacy services	Yes	25% of CHAMPVA allowable after deductible	75% of CHAMPVA allowable
VA source (durable medical equipment, Meds by Mail, CHAMPVA In-house Treatment Initiative)	No	Nothing	100% of VA cost
Part B—Outpatient			
Outpatient medical care to include: Office visits (physician) Durable medical equipment Cancer screenings Mammograms PAP smears Immunizations (including flu shots) Diabetes supplies (e.g., test strips, monitors) Diabetes self-management training Bone mass measurements	80% of Medicare allowable amount	In most cases, CHAMPVA allowable covers the Medicare co-pay and a portion of the beneficiary's Medicare outpatient deductible	In most cases, $0
Clinical laboratory	100% of Medicare allowable	CHAMPVA allowable less Medicare's payment	$0*
Mental health visit	50% of Medicare allowable	CHAMPVA allowable less Medicare's payment	In most cases, $0
Hospice	100% of Medicare allowable	CHAMPVA allowable less Medicare's payment	$0*
Outpatient medications	All but $5 per prescription		
Respite care	95% of Medicare allowable		
Pharmacy	$0 (with a few exceptions)	Retail, 75% of allowable amount; Meds by Mail, 100%	Retail, 25% of CHAMPVA allowable amount; by mail: $0

*Where Medicare has paid 100% of the allowable representing payment in full, in most cases there is no out-of-pocket expense for beneficiary.

insurance. Another exception to third-party payer priority is when a CHAMPVA-eligible beneficiary resides or travels overseas. When this is the case, if all eligibility criteria are met, CHAMPVA is the primary payer (unless there is OHI) until the individual returns to the United States.

When a beneficiary is eligible for health care benefits under Medicare and CHAMPVA, Medicare is the primary payer. For health care services covered under both plans, there are often no out-of-pocket expenses for covered services. It is important for the beneficiary to be aware that if he or she has Medicare and CHAMPVA, Medicare's rules and procedures must be followed for covered services. Failure to do so means the service would not be covered under CHAMPVA. If Medicare determines that the service is not medically necessary or appropriate, CHAMPVA also would deny coverage. If the beneficiary or the provider disagrees with the Medicare decision, an appeal should be made with Medicare, rather than with CHAMPVA.

CHAMPVA and Health Maintenance Organization Coverage

If a CHAMPVA-eligible beneficiary has an HMO plan, CHAMPVA would pay any co-payments under the HMO. When medical services are available through the HMO, and the patient chooses to seek care outside the HMO (e.g., the patient seeks care from a physician who is not associated with the HMO or does not follow the rules and procedures of the HMO to obtain the care), CHAMPVA would not pay for that medical care. When submitting the OHI Certification (Form 8-7959c), the patient or health insurance professional should include a copy of the HMO co-payment information or schedule of benefits.

CHAMPVA Providers

Health care providers may elect to participate in CHAMPVA simply by agreeing to see the beneficiary and submitting a claim to CHAMPVA on the beneficiary's behalf. Providers who accept CHAMPVA patients also must accept the CHAMPVA allowable rate as payment in full and cannot balance bill. Providers may choose not to participate; in this case, patients typically pay the entire bill and submit their own claims to CHAMPVA for personal reimbursement of the allowable amount. Even in the case of nonPARs, providers must accept the allowable rate and cannot balance bill. Under the CHAMPVA program, however, the patient is responsible for paying the CHAMPVA cost share and any charges for noncovered services.

CHAMPVA for Life

The **CHAMPVA for Life (CFL)** program became effective October 1, 2001. This relatively new benefit is designed for spouses or dependents of veterans who are age 65 or older. They must be family members of veterans and meet one of the following conditions:

- The veteran has a permanent and total service-connected disability.
- The veteran died of a service-connected condition.
- The veteran was totally disabled from a service-connected condition at the time of death.
- The spouses and dependents must have Medicare coverage.

Similar to TFL, CFL pays benefits for covered medical services to eligible beneficiaries who are age 65 or older and enrolled in Medicare Parts A and B. The CFL benefit is payable after Medicare pays its share. If the beneficiary has a Medigap-type insurance policy, CHAMPVA becomes third in line for payment. If a beneficiary is eligible for TFL, he or she is not eligible for CHAMPVA because TFL is for military retirees and their dependents. CFL combined with Medicare gives the beneficiary extensive coverage that covers most health care needs. There are exceptions, however. If a particular procedure is not covered by Medicare, it probably would not be covered by CHAMPVA (e.g., eye glasses, dental care). CHAMPVA would not pay Medicare Part B premiums, but it does pay Medicare's first-day hospital deductible. CFL beneficiaries cannot use a VA medical center.

Filing CHAMPVA Claims

As with TRICARE, providers accepting assignment for CHAMPVA claims must submit the claim for the beneficiary. Beneficiaries who receive treatment from nonPARs usually are required to submit their own claims. All CHAMPVA claims, whether electronic or paper, should be sent to the following address:

VA Health Administration Center
CHAMPVA
PO Box 65024
Denver, CO 80206-9024

As stated earlier, if the beneficiary has OHI, claims should be sent to the OHI first. The EOB from the OHI should be attached to the claim and submitted to CHAMPVA. By law, CHAMPVA is always secondary payer except to Medicaid and CHAMPVA supplemental policies.

CHAMPVA Claims Filing Deadlines

CHAMPVA claims follow the same filing deadline specifications as TRICARE with the exception that all CHAMPVA claims are sent to the VA Health Administration Center in Denver, Colorado. A TRICARE contractor can grant exemptions from the filing deadlines under certain circumstances. Box 8-2 lists circumstances that qualify for a timely filing exemption.

BOX 8-2 Circumstances for Exemptions to the Claims Deadline Date

1. If CHAMPUS headquarters or a CHAMPUS/TRICARE contractor made a mistake that resulted in a claim being improperly denied for lack of timely filing.
2. If mental incompetency of the patient (or of a guardian or sponsor, in the case of a minor child) resulted in a claim not being filed in a timely manner. The incompetency may include an inability to communicate, even if the inability is the result of a physical disability. It must be documented by a physician.
3. If the provider agreed to participate in CHAMPUS (also known as accepting assignment) on the claim, and to bill CHAMPUS/TRICARE directly, but failed to do so.
4. If delays by other health insurance plans (health plans that must pay first, before a claim for the care may be filed with CHAMPUS/TRICARE) in making their payment determinations cause the person or organization filing the claim to miss the deadline. Delays must not be the fault of the CHAMPUS/TRICARE-eligible patient.
5. If billings are made directly by participating providers, and they request an exception to the deadline.
6. If a patient is found to have been CHAMPUS/TRICARE-eligible after the care was received, but claims were not filed with the contractor in time to meet the deadline because of the delay in determining eligibility. Individuals who want to request an exception to the claim-filing deadline may submit a request to the CHAMPUS/TRICARE contractor for the state or region in which the medical services or supplies were provided. Such requests must include a complete explanation of the circumstances of the late filing, together with all available documentation supporting the request, along with the claim denied for late filing.

INSTRUCTIONS FOR COMPLETING TRICARE/CHAMPVA CLAIM FORMS

All professional charges must be submitted on a CMS-1500 claim form according to TRICARE guidelines. Guidelines are provided in Table 8-3. When completing the claim, the "sponsor" is the member or was active duty military. The sponsor's dependent (spouse or child) is the "patient" or "beneficiary" (these terms are often used interchangeably). The instructions in Table 8-3 are generic and may not be exactly the same as required by the claims processor in each area. The health insurance professional should obtain complete, detailed, and up-to-date claims completion guidelines from the TRICARE claims processor in his or her area to ensure the CMS-1500 forms are completed correctly to expedite reimbursement.

Claims Filing Summary

The following are important points to consider when filing claims:

TABLE 8-3   **Instructions for Filing TRICARE/CHAMPVA Paper Claims**

Block 1	Required. Place an "X" in the TRICARE CHAMPUS box for TRICARE claims; place an "X" in the CHAMPVA for CHAMPVA claims
Block 1a	Required. Enter the sponsor's Social Security number (not the beneficiary's unless they are one and the same). If the beneficiary is a NATO beneficiary, enter "NATO" here
Block 2	Required. Enter the patient's last name, first name, and middle initial (if any) *exactly* as shown on the TRICARE or CHAMPVA ID card
Block 3	Required. Enter the patient's eight-digit birth date (MM DD YYYY) as shown on the ID card, and place an "X" in the appropriate box indicating sex
Block 4	Required. Enter the sponsor's last name, first name, and middle initial, or if the sponsor and the patient are one and the same, enter the word "SAME"
Block 5	Required. Enter the complete address of the patient's place of residence at the time of service and the telephone number. Do not use PO Box numbers. For rural addresses, indicate the box number and rural route or 911E number
Block 6	Required. If the beneficiary is the sponsor, indicate "SELF" or provide the relationship to the sponsor. If "other" is checked, indicate how the beneficiary is related to the sponsor (e.g., former spouse) *Note*: Parents, parents-in-law, stepparents, and any grandchildren who are not adopted are not eligible for TRICARE despite the fact that they may have a military ID card. Be sure to check the back of the dependent beneficiary's ID card to ensure it indicates authorization for civilian/ TRICARE benefits
Block 7	Required. Enter the address of the active duty sponsor's duty station or the retiree's mailing address. If the address is the same as the beneficiary's, enter "SAME." If "SAME" is entered in Block 4, leave this block blank. If the sponsor resides overseas, enter the APO/FPO address
Block 8	Required. Check the appropriate box for the patient's marital status and whether employed or a student
Block 9	Enter the name of the insured if different from that shown in Block 2. If the beneficiary is covered by a spouse's insurance, Blocks 11a-d should be used to show other health insurance held by the beneficiary *Note*: Block 11d should be completed before determining the need for completing Blocks 9a-d. If Block 11d is checked "yes," Blocks 9a-d must be completed before claims processing as follows:
Block 9a	Provide the policy number/group number of the insured's policy
Block 9b	Enter the other insured's date of birth, and check the appropriate box for sex
Block 9c	Enter the name of the employer or name of the school
Block 9d	Enter the name of the insurance plan or the program name where the individual has OHI coverage. If the other coverage is truly supplemental to TRICARE (Medicaid or a plan specifically stating it is supplemental to TRICARE), enter the name and the word "SUPPLEMENTAL" in this block
Blocks 10a-c	Required. Check "YES" or "NO" to indicate whether employment, auto liability, or other accident involvement applies to one or more of the services described in Block 24. Provide information concerning potential third-party liability. The claims processor will send a DD form 2527, "Statement of Personal Injury—Possible Third Party Liability," to the beneficiary if the diagnosis code(s) fall within the 800-999 range
Block 10d	Conditionally required. Use this block to indicate that other health insurance is attached, if this is the case
Block 11	Conditionally required. If the beneficiary has OHI, enter the policy/group number here. Indicate if the beneficiary is covered by Medicare. Blocks 9a-d should be used to report other primary coverage held by family members that includes coverage of the beneficiary
Block 11a	Conditionally required. If the beneficiary has OHI, enter the date of birth and sex if different from Block 3
Block 11b	Conditionally required. Enter the employer or school name, if applicable
Block 11c	Conditionally required. Enter the OHI plan or program name. If the beneficiary is covered by a supplemental policy (Medicaid or a policy specifically stating it is supplemental to TRICARE), indicate "SUPPLEMENTAL"

TABLE 8-3	**Instructions for Filing TRICARE/CHAMPVA Paper Claims—cont'd**
Block 11d	Required. Indicate if there is or is not another health benefit plan that is primary to TRICARE. The beneficiary may be covered under a plan held by a spouse, a parent, or some other person. If this block is checked "yes," Blocks 9a-d must be completed
Block 12	Required. "SIGNATURE ON FILE" or "SOF" can be used here if the beneficiary's signature is on file in the provider's office (and on a document that includes a release of information statement). If not on file, the beneficiary must sign and date Block 12. If the patient is younger than 18 years old, either parent should sign the claim unless the services are confidential. If the patient is older than 18 years old but cannot sign the claim, the person who signs must be the legal guardian or, in the absence of a legal guardian, a spouse or parent of the patient. The signer should write the beneficiary's name in Block 12, followed by the word "by" and his or her own signature. A statement must be attached giving the signer's full name, address, relationship to the beneficiary, and the reason the signer is unable to sign. Also, documentation must be attached showing the signer's appointment as legal guardian or power of attorney
Block 13	Leave blank for TRICARE and CHAMPVA claims. Claims checks are forwarded to PAR and nonPAR accepting assignment. On nonPAR claims, benefit checks are mailed to the patient
Block 14	Conditionally required. Enter the eight-digit (MM DD YYYY) date of current illness, injury, or pregnancy, if it is documented in the health record
Block 15	Conditionally required. If it is documented in the health record that the patient has had the same or similar condition previously, enter that date here
Block 16	Conditionally required. If the patient is employed and unable to work in his or her current occupation, enter the eight-digit (MM DD YYYY) date when patient was unable to work. *Note*: An entry in this field may indicate employment-related insurance coverage
Block 17	Required. Enter the name and address of the entity that referred the patient to the provider of services identified on the claim. This is required for all charges for a consultation or the claims processor will have to pay the claim at the rate for the lowest category of office visit. If the beneficiary was referred from an MTF, enter the name of the MTF and attach a copy of the military referral form (DD 2161 or SF 513)
Block 17a-17b	Effective May 23, 2007, 17a is no longer reported, and the NPI of the provider entered in Block 17 must be reported in 17b
Block 18	Conditionally required. If the patient was hospitalized as an inpatient, enter the "from" and "to" dates here
Block 19	Not required. Leave blank
Block 20	Conditionally required. Indicate whether laboratory work was done outside of the provider's office, and if so, enter the total amount charged by the laboratory for work being reported on the claim
Block 21	Required. Enter the patient's diagnosis/condition using an ICD-9-CM code number
Block 22	Not required. Leave blank
Block 23	Conditionally required. Enter the prior authorization number if the services require pre-authorization/pre-admission review
Block 24a	Required. Enter the month, day, and year for each procedure/service or supply using the MM DD YYYY format. If "from" and "to" dates are shown here for a series of identical services, enter the total number of units in Block 24g
Block 24b	Required. Enter the appropriate two-digit numerical place of service (POS) code. See Table 8-4 for the list of applicable codes
Block 24c	This block is conditionally required. Enter an "X" or an "E" as appropriate for services performed as a result of a medical emergency
Block 24d	Required. Enter the appropriate CPT/HCPCS code for each service. If using one of the "not elsewhere classified" codes, you must supply a narrative description of the service/supply
Block 24e	Required. Enter the appropriate diagnosis reference code (1, 2, 3, and/or 4) as shown in Block 21 to relate to each service/procedure. If multiple services/procedures were performed, enter the diagnosis code reference number for each service/procedure
Block 24f	Required. Enter the charge for each listed service. Include the cents with dollar amounts. *For example, $24.00 should be entered as 24 00 rather than $24. Dashes, decimal points, or lines should not be used in this item*

Continued

TABLE 8-3	Instructions for Filing TRICARE/CHAMPVA Paper Claims—cont'd
Block 24g	Required. Provide the days or units for each line item. This block should be used for multiple visits for identical services, number of miles, units of supplies, or oxygen volume. If anesthesia, provide the beginning and end time of administration, time in minutes, or 15-minute units
Block 24h	Not required. Leave blank
Block 24i	Conditionally required. Enter the appropriate ID qualifier. Contact local TRICARE/CHAMPVA fiscal intermediary for this information
Block 24j	After May 23, 2007, enter the provider's NPI number in the lower, unshaded portion. In the case of a service provided incident to the service of a physician or nonphysician practitioner, when the person who ordered the service is not supervising, enter the PIN of the supervisor in the shaded portion
Block 25	Required. Enter the nine-digit federal tax ID (employer identification number) assigned to that provider (or group), and check the appropriate box. In the case of an unincorporated practice or a sole practitioner, the provider's Social Security number is typically used
Block 26	Conditionally required. Enter the patient's account number assigned by the provider of service's or supplier's accounting system
Block 27	Required. PARs and nonPARs accepting assignment should check this box "YES." Failure to complete this box or if the "X" is outside the box means assignment was not accepted. To accept assignment under TRICARE guidelines means that the provider will accept the TRICARE-determined allowed amount as payment in full for services. If a provider does not accept assignment, payment and the explanation of benefits (EOB) go to the beneficiary *only*. The provider would not be given any information on the claim other than receipt. On claims where assignment is not accepted, the provider may collect only up to 115% of the TRICARE-determined allowed amount for the services
Block 28	Required. Enter total charges for the services (i.e., total of all charges in Block 24f). Use the same formatting as that explained in Block 24f
Block 29	Required. Enter the amount received by the provider or supplier from OHI. If no payment was made by the primary payer, an EOB should be attached to the claim indicating why the primary payer made no payment. If the primary payer is Medicare or an HMO, an EOB should be attached whether payment was made or not. Any payment received from the beneficiary should not be included in this box
Block 30	Not required. Leave blank
Block 31	Required. This block must contain the signature of the provider and date or that of his or her authorized representative. If someone other than the provider of services signs on the provider's behalf, there should be a notarized statement on file with the claims processor indicating the provider's permission to accept someone else's signature. This "representative" should sign his or her name and title so as not to be confused with the actual provider
Block 32	Enter the name, address, and Zip Code of the service facility location
Block 32a	Enter the NPI of the service facility in Block 32a
Block 32b	After May 23, 2007, 32b is no longer reported. Follow the specific guidelines of the TRICARE fiscal intermediary
Block 33	Enter the name, complete address, and telephone number (including area code) where the provider's office is physically located
Block 33a	Effective May 23, 2007, the NPI of the billing provider must be reported here
Block 33b	Effective May 23, 2007, 33b is no longer reported

- Claims should be submitted as soon as services are rendered to expedite the claims process.
- Claims filing deadline is 1 year from the date of service or 1 year from the date of discharge for inpatient hospitalization.

- Copies should be kept of all information submitted to the TRICARE claims processor or CHAMPVA.
- It is not beneficial to hold multiple claims over a period of time and submit them all at once. If

TABLE 8-4 POS Codes

Place-of-Service Codes (for Use in Block 24B of CMS-1500 Form)

11 Office
12 Home
21 Inpatient
22 Outpatient, hospital
23 Emergency department—hospital
24 Ambulatory surgical center
25 Birthing center
26 Military treatment facility
31 Skilled nursing facility
33 Custodial care facility
34 Hospice
41 Ambulance, land
42 Ambulance, air or water
51 Inpatient psychiatric facility
52 Psychiatric facility (partial hospitalization)
53 Community mental health center
54 Intermediate care facility (mentally handicapped)
55 Residential substance abuse treatment facility
56 Psychiatric residential treatment facility
61 Comprehensive outpatient rehabilitation facility
71 State or local public health clinic
72 Rural health clinic
81 Independent laboratory
99 Other, unlisted facility

numerous claims are submitted, and there is a problem with one, it could delay the processing of all claims.

CHAMPVA Explanation of Benefits

On completion of the processing of a CHAMPVA claim, an EOB form is sent to the beneficiary and to the provider, if the claim was filed by the provider. The EOB is a summary of the action taken on the claim and contains the following information (Fig. 8-8):

- Provider name
- Date of service
- Description of service
- Amount billed by the provider
- CHAMPVA-allowed amount
- Amount not covered
- Amount paid by OHI
- Amount applied to the beneficiary's annual deductible requirement

- Beneficiary and family deductible accrual
- CHAMPVA payment
- Annual cat cap accrual
- Remarks

Claims Appeals and Reconsiderations

In the event a provider or beneficiary disagrees with the manner in which a claim was processed and considers it necessary to file a claims appeal or have the processing of a claim reconsidered, such an appeal must be filed within 90 days of the receipt of the EOB. The EOB contains the pertinent information on the procedures for filing an appeal. All appeals must be submitted in writing. On receipt of the written appeal, all claims for the entire course of treatment are reviewed. Health insurance professionals should contact the claims processor in their region or the CHAMPVA office in Denver for details on how to submit an appeal.

IMAGINE THIS!

Dr. Serjio Manya, a psychiatrist, provided psychiatric treatment to Samuel Fortune, a Gulf War veteran, for clinical depression. Samuel, who was determined to be CHAMPVA-eligible after his diagnosis, subsequently was admitted to the Trenton Mental Healthcare Facility because of a suicide attempt, where he remained for 15 months. Because Dr. Manya was nonPAR and Samuel's mental condition rendered him incompetent, the claim was not filed within the time limit. Because Samuel's illness was documented by Dr. Manya, however, Samuel was able to get a filing extension and ultimately received CHAMPVA benefits.

WHAT DID YOU LEARN?

1. In which block on the claim form should the "sponsor's" name appear?
2. List at least five items of information shown on the CHAMPVA EOB.
3. What is the deadline for filing a CHAMPVA appeal?

≋ HIPAA AND MILITARY INSURERS

All military medical facilities have implemented the privacy rules of the Health Insurance Portability

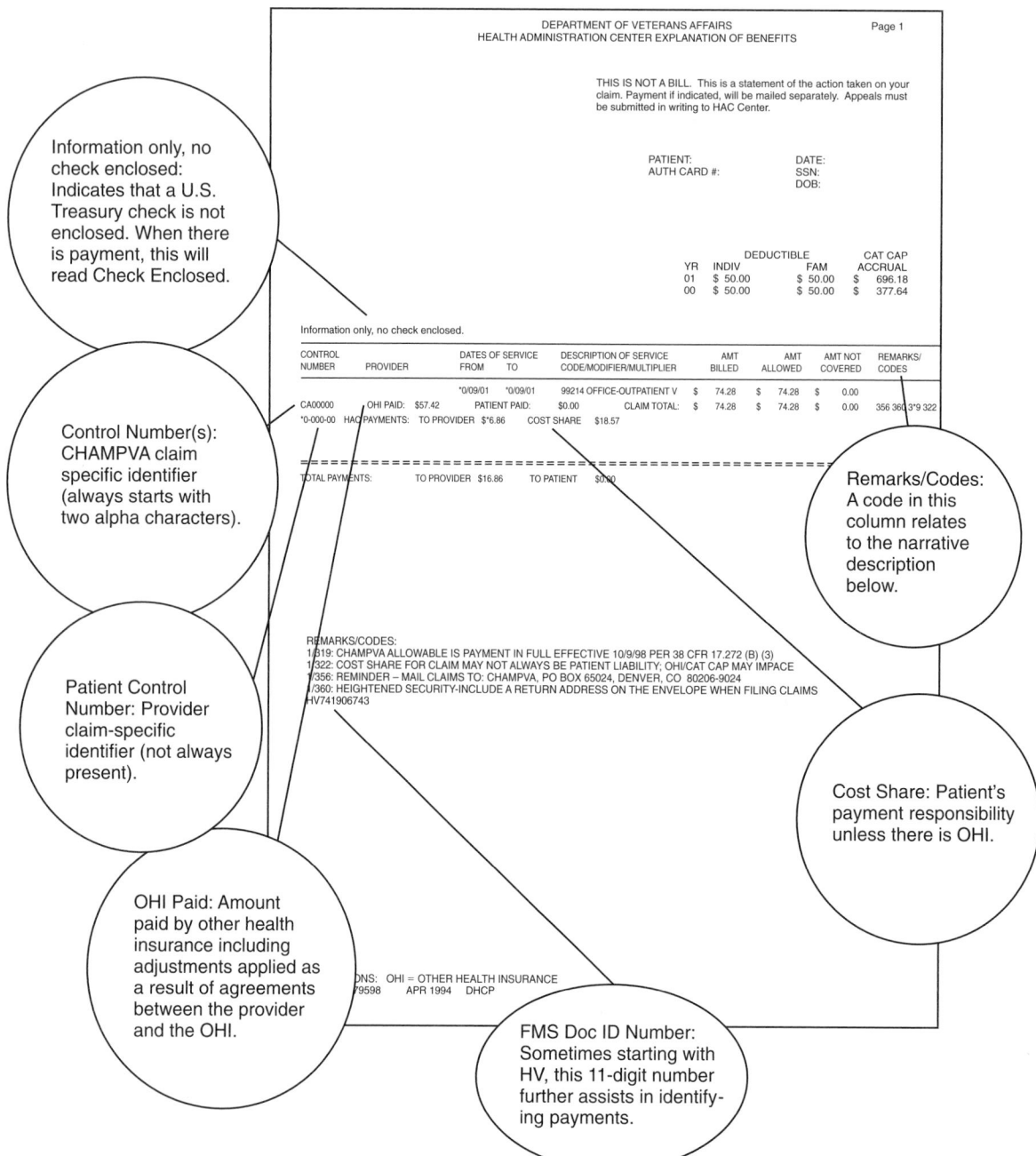

Fig. 8-8 Sample CHAMPVA explanation of benefits. *(Source: U.S. Department of Veterans Affairs, Health Administration Center.)*

and Accountability Act of 1996 (HIPAA). The Military Health System always has had privacy standards in place to limit unauthorized access and disclosure of personal health information. The new HIPAA rules heighten awareness, raise the level of oversight, and provide a standard set of guidelines to protect the privacy of all patients.

HIPAA TIP

HIPAA requires all employees, contractors, and volunteers of health care provider organizations, health care insurers, and health care clearinghouses, including those associated with TRICARE and CHAMPVA, who come in contact with Protected Health Information to be trained annually in the areas of privacy and security.

In preparation to become HIPAA compliant by the required date, the Department of Defense mailed approximately 5 million MTF notices of privacy practices—one to each beneficiary enrolled in DEERS. Each MTF has an assigned, trained privacy officer available to respond to any questions or concerns that beneficiaries may have regarding the new privacy rules. The privacy officers also serve as patient advocates ensuring that personal health information maintained by the MTF remains protected yet accessible to beneficiaries and their providers. A copy of the notice to privacy practice is available on the TRICARE website for sponsors and family members to download; copies also are available for distribution at each Department of Defense MTF.

WHAT DID YOU LEARN?

1. What steps did CHAMPVA take to become HIPAA compliant?
2. What is the role of the privacy officer?

SUMMARY CHECK POINTS

☑ Through its main objectives of accessibility and affordability, TRICARE brings together the health care resources of the Army, Navy, and Air Force and supplements them with networks of civilian health care professionals to provide better access to health care and high-quality service, while maintaining the capability to support military operations.

☑ TRICARE's three choices for health care are as follows:
- *TRICARE Standard*—the standard fee-for-service (indemnity) option, formerly called CHAMPUS. This program provides greater personal choice in the selection of health care providers, although it requires higher individual out-of-pocket costs than a managed care plan.
- *TRICARE Extra*—a preferred provider option through which, rather than an annual fee, a yearly deductible is charged. Health care is delivered through a network of civilian health care providers who accept payments from TRICARE and provide services at negotiated, discounted rates.
- *TRICARE Prime*—an HMO-type plan in which enrollees receive health care through an MTF PCM or a supporting network of civilian providers.

☑ Eligibility under TRICARE's three plans is as follows:
- *TRICARE Standard eligibles* include spouses and dependents of active service members, military retirees and their eligible family members, and survivors of all uniformed services who are not eligible for Medicare. Dependents of military service members in the Army and National Guard Reserves, known as RCs, also are eligible for TRICARE Standard, if the RC is ordered to active duty for more than 30 consecutive days, or if the orders are for an indefinite period. All TRICARE eligibles must be listed in DEERS.
- *TRICARE Extra eligibles* include any individual who is eligible for TRICARE Standard.
- *TRICARE Prime eligibles* include retired military beneficiaries and their eligible family members. Active military members are automatically enrolled in TRICARE Prime.

☑ An NAS is a document of certification from the MTF that says it cannot provide the specific health care the beneficiary needs. The statements must be entered electronically in the Defense Department's DEERS computer files by the MTF. An NAS is no longer needed for TRICARE Standard beneficiaries except for non-emergency mental health services.

☑ TRICARE PARs agree to accept the TRICARE allowable charge on all claims as payment in full for the health care services provided and not balance bill. NonPARs can participate in TRICARE on a case-by-case basis. PARs and nonPARs who accept assignment must file the claim for the patient, and TRICARE sends the payment (if any) directly to the provider.

☑ CHAMPVA is a health care benefits program for qualifying dependents and survivors of veterans. Under CHAMPVA, the VA shares the cost of covered health care services and supplies with eligible beneficiaries. CHAMPVA is managed by the VA's Health Administration Center in Denver, Colorado.

☑ Individuals who are entitled to CHAMPVA benefits include
- *the spouse or dependent child* of a veteran who has been rated by a VA regional office as having a permanent and total service-connected condition/disability;
- *the surviving spouse or dependent child* of a veteran who died as a result of a VA-rated

☑ service–connected condition or who, at the time of death, was rated permanently and totally disabled from a VA-rated service–connected condition; and
- *the surviving spouse or dependent child* of an individual who died in the line of duty, and the death was not due to misconduct.

☑ A qualifying beneficiary can be eligible for health care benefits under Medicare and CHAMPVA. For health care services covered under both plans, there are often no out-of-pocket expenses for covered services. The beneficiary should know that if he or she has Medicare and CHAMPVA, Medicare's rules and procedures must be followed for covered services. If the beneficiary fails to do so, the service is not covered under CHAMPVA. Also, if Medicare finds the service is not medically necessary or appropriate, CHAMPVA does not provide coverage either. Medicare is primary to CHAMPVA.

☑ Providers filing claims should
- use the standard CMS-1500 claim form,
- follow the TRICARE guidelines for completing the form,
- ensure the information is complete and accurate,
- affix the required signature format,
- date the claim form,
- make and keep a copy of all paper claims, and
- send completed claims (electronic or paper) to the TRICARE claims processor in the region in which the enrollee resides.

☑ Patients who file their own claims must
- use Form 2692 (CHAMPUS Claim Patient Request for Medical Payment) and
- attach the provider's detailed itemized statement and an NAS (if necessary).

☑ All CHAMPVA claims, whether electronic or paper, should be sent to VA Health Administration Center, CHAMPVA, PO Box 65024, Denver, CO 80206–9024.

☑ For information regarding where to file paper claims, the TRICARE website lists the names and addresses of claims processors by region. At the TRICARE home page, click on "Site Map," choose "Claims," and select the region of choice to access the chart of pertinent information.

☑ The deadline for submitting all military claims is 1 year from the date of service. If the service was rendered on August 30, 2003, the claim must be in the hands of the claims processor by the end of the working day on August 30, 2004. For inpatient hospital claims, the deadline is 1 year from the date of discharge.

☑ In preparation to become HIPAA compliant, the Department of Defense mailed notices of privacy practices to all MTFs and to every beneficiary enrolled in DEERS. In addition, each MTF has an assigned, trained privacy officer available to respond to any questions or concerns that beneficiaries may have regarding the new privacy rules. A copy of the notice of privacy practices also is available on the TRICARE website for sponsors and family members to download; copies also are available for distribution at each Department of Defense MTF.

Closing Scenario

After completing the chapter on military carriers, Sally thinks she is ready to answer her Aunt Betty's questions. She agrees with her aunt that the various plans available under TRICARE can be confusing, and it may be difficult to decide which plan best suits a military spouse's or dependent's needs. First, Sally explained that CHAMPUS was the former name, and it was now called TRICARE (TRI because it offers three plans). Next, Sally outlined the three plans along with the advantages and disadvantages of each. She gave her aunt several Internet websites from which to get further details regarding TRICARE and

suggested that she sit down with the health insurance professional at the medical clinic to resolve some of the confusion over claims.

Sally also discovered that her grandfather was eligible to receive his prescription medicine by mail through the VA. This would be a tremendous cost savings for him because he was on seven different medications. It gave Sally a good feeling to know that she was able to help her family. Now, she looked forward to helping others through her career as a health insurance professional.

Websites to Explore

- To find the nearest uniformed services personnel office, log on to
  http://www.dmdc.osd.mil/rsl

- For detailed information on TRICARE, log on to
  http://www.tricare.osd.mil/hipaa

- To view the TRICARE handbook, log on to
  http://www.tricare.osd.mil/tricarehandbook

- For details regarding the cat cap in a particular area, log on to
  http://tricare.mil/contactus

- To view the CHAMPVA handbook, log on to
  http://www.va.gov/hac/forbeneficiaries/champva/handbook.asp

- Additional information on HIPAA, TRICARE, and the new privacy standards is available on the TRICARE website at
  http://www.tricare.osd.mil/hipaa

- To report fraud, waste, or abuse in federal programs, log on to
  www.gao.gov/fraudnet/fraudnet.htm

Chapter Review

Assessment

Multiple Choice

Directions: *In the questions/statements presented, choose the response that **best** answers/completes the stem, and circle the letter that precedes it.*

1. TRICARE's two main objectives are _____.
   A. health and welfare
   B. accessibility and affordability
   C. manageability and cost-effectiveness
   D. supply health care during war and peace

2. TRICARE is administered regionally, serving _____ separate regions.
   A. 3
   B. 5
   C. 7
   D. 12

3. Each region is headed by an individual who is responsible for oversight of all health care delivery activities within his or her region and is called a _____.
   A. claims review officer
   B. fiscal intermediary
   C. regional carrier
   D. regional director

4. The name of the total health care system of the U.S. uniformed services is _____.
   A. Military Health System
   B. U.S. Military Insurance Program
   C. Federal Uniformed Services Program
   D. National Military Health Care System

5. TRICARE is administered by _____.
   A. the Department of Defense
   B. the Centers for Medicare and Medicaid Services (CMS) (formerly the Health Care Financing Administration)
   C. the VA
   D. individual state governments

6. The main purpose of the TRICARE Management Activity (TMA) is to _____.
   A. keep TRICARE premiums low
   B. adjudicate TRICARE claims
   C. coordinate TRICARE benefits with other health insurance (OHI)
   D. enhance the performance of TRICARE worldwide

7. The computerized data bank that lists all active and retired military service members is called _____.
   A. TMA
   B. FEMA
   C. DEERS
   D. COBRA

8. Similar to Medicaid and Medicare, TRICARE-eligible individuals are referred to as _____.
   A. enrollees
   B. plan members
   C. beneficiaries
   D. covered employees

9. The fee-for-service option offer by TRICARE, which has basically the same benefits as the original CHAMPUS program, is _____.
   A. TRICARE Standard
   B. TRICARE Extra
   C. TRICARE Prime
   D. TRICARE for Life

10. The TRICARE option similar to preferred provider organization–type managed care is _____.
    A. TRICARE Standard
    B. TRICARE Extra
    C. TRICARE Prime
    D. TRICARE for Life

11. CHAMPVA is managed by _____.
    A. the Social Security Administration
    B. the CMS
    C. the VA's HAC
    D. individual state governments

12. CHAMPVA eligibility can be lost if certain demographic changes occur, such as _____.
    A. a widow remarrying
    B. divorcing the sponsor
    C. becoming eligible for Medicare
    D. all of the above

13. CHAMPVA is the last payer after all other third-party payers have met their obligations except for _____.
    A. Medicaid
    B. CHAMPVA supplemental insurance
    C. OHI
    D. A and B are correct

14. The deadline for filing military claims is _____.
    A. 60 days
    B. 90 days
    C. 1 year
    D. 2 years

15. The annual catastrophic (cat) cap for CHAMPVA is _____.
    A. $1000
    B. $3000
    C. $5000
    D. $10,000

True/False

Directions: *Place a "T" in the blank preceding the sentence if it is true; place an "F" if it is false.*

____ 1. The sponsor's relationship to the beneficiary creates eligibility under TRICARE.

____ 2. Military retirees and their family members are not eligible for TRICARE.

____ 3. TRICARE pays for only their allowed services, supplies, and procedures.

____ 4. There is no "cost sharing" under TRICARE regulations.

____ 5. Active duty personnel are not CHAMPUS-eligible and are automatically enrolled in TRICARE Standard.

____ 6. TRICARE Prime is a health maintenance organization–type managed care option in which MTFs are the principal source of health care.

____ 7. Under TRICARE Prime's point of service (POS) option, enrollees are allowed to receive health care services only from providers within the POS network.

____ 8. Under TRICARE for Life, TRICARE pays Medicare deductibles and co-insurance or co-payment amounts up to 115% of Medicare-allowable charges.

____ 9. Eligibility for patients claiming TRICARE and CHAMPVA coverage should be verified immediately.

____ 10. TRICARE participating providers (PARs) must accept the TRICARE allowable charge as payment in full for the health care services provided and cannot balance bill.

____ 11. Patients using TRICARE Standard are usually responsible for submitting their own claims.

____ 12. In the case of nonparticipating providers (nonPARs), TRICARE Standard patients must file their own claims; however, the reimbursement check is sent to the provider.

____ 13. Even though electronic claims submission is preferred by most major carriers, military carriers still prefer paper claims.

____ 14. The deadline for submitting military claims varies from region to region.

Short Answer/Fill-in-the-Blank

1. List the three basic plans available under the TRICARE program.

_____

_____

_____

2. The service member, whether in active duty, retired, or deceased, is called the _____.

3. List the various categories of TRICARE-eligible individuals.

_____

_____

_____

4. List three advantages of TRICARE Standard.

_____

_____

_____

5. List three responsibilities of a primary care manager.

_____

_____

_____

6. List the categories of individuals who are eligible for TRICARE Prime Remote.

_____

_____

_____

7. Explain the purpose of a nonavailability statement.

_____

_____

8. What are the eligibility criteria for TRICARE for Life?

_____

_____

_____

9. How might the health insurance professional verify eligibility for benefits under one of the military's health care programs?

_____

_____

_____

10. List the categories of individuals who are eligible for CHAMPVA.

_____

_____

_____

_____

11. List four types of medical services for which pre-authorization may be required for CHAMPVA beneficiaries.

_____

_____

_____

_____

Critical Thinking Activities

A. Patient Betsy Froman has been referred to you, the health insurance professional at Broadmoor Clinic, with the following question: "I am currently participating in TRICARE Prime. Do I need to re-enroll in TRICARE Prime on a yearly basis?" What should you tell Ms. Froman?

B. Assume that the Broadmoor providers are nonPARs for military claims and require patients to file their own claims. Patient Arnold Chessworth, a CHAMPVA-eligible patient, asks you for help in getting claims filing information. Generate an instruction sheet for military patients on where to find this information; include online sources and toll-free telephone numbers.

Case Studies

Refer to Tables 8-5 and 8-6 for help with the following case studies.

TABLE 8-5   TRICARE Cost Comparison Chart: Active Duty Family Members

	TRICARE Prime	TRICARE Extra	TRICARE Standard
Annual Deductible	None	$150/individual or $300/family for E-5 and above; $50/$100 for E-4 and below	$150/individual or $300/family for E-5 and above; $50/$100 for E-4 and below
Annual Enrollment Fee	None	None	None
Civilian Outpatient Visit	No cost	15% of negotiated fee	20% of negotiated fee
Civilian Inpatient Admission	No cost	Greater of $25 or $13.32/day	Greater of $25 or $13.32/day
Civilian Inpatient Mental Health	No cost	$20/day	$20/day
Civilian Inpatient Skilled Nursing Facility Care	$0 per diem charge per admission; no separate co-payments/cost share for separately billed professional charges		

| TABLE 8-6 | TRICARE Cost Comparison Chart: Retirees, Their Families, and Others |

	TRICARE Prime	TRICARE Extra	TRICARE Standard
Annual Deductible	None	$150/individual or $300/family	$150/individual or $300/family
Annual Enrollment Fee	$230/individual or $460/family	None	None
Civilian Co-pays	$12	20% of negotiated fee	25% of allowed charges for covered service
Emergency Care	$30		
Mental Health Visit	$25; $17 for group visit		
Civilian Inpatient Cost Share	Greater of $11/day or $25 per admission; no separate co-payment for separately billed professional fees	Lesser of $250/day or 25% of negotiated charges plus 20% of negotiated fees	Lesser of $535/day or 25% of billed charges plus 25% of allowed professional fees
Civilian Inpatient Skilled Nursing Facility Care	Greater of $11/day or $25 per admission; no separate co-payment for separately billed professional fees	$250 per diem cost share or 20% cost share of total charges, whichever is less; institutional services, plus 20% cost share of separately billed professional charges	25% cost share of allowed charges for institutional services, plus 25% cost share of allowable for separately billed professional charges
Civilian Inpatient Behavorial Health	$40/day; no charge for separately billed professional charges	20% of total charge. Plus, 20% of the allowable charge for separately billed professional services	**High volume hospitals:** 25% hospital specific per diem, plus 25% of the allowable charge for separately billed professional services **Low volume hospitals:** $175 per day or 25% of the billed charges, whichever is lower, plus 25% of the allowable charge for separately billed services

A. Christine Moss comes to Broadmoor Medical Clinic complaining of upper gastrointestinal pain. She subsequently is admitted to Broadmoor Medical Center on an outpatient basis for endoscopy. The following are the procedures performed on Mrs. Moss along with the charges:

Date of Service	CPT Code	Procedure/Service	TRICARE-Approved Charge
11/29/20XX	99244	Office consultation	$166.00
11/30/20XX	43239	Upper GI endoscopy with biopsy*	$625.00
11/30/20XX	43453-78	Dilate esophagus*	$670.00

*Outpatient procedure.

Aaron Moss, her husband, is currently on active duty in Afghanistan with an E-4 ranking. They have no children, so Mrs. Moss has "individual" coverage.

1. If Mrs. Moss is covered under TRICARE Prime, what is her annual deductible?
2. If she had TRICARE Extra, what would her annual (individual) deductible be?
3. Would Mrs. Moss' deductible be greater if she had enrolled in TRICARE Standard? If so, how much?
4. Assuming that Mrs. Moss has TRICARE Standard and she has met her deductible for the year, what would her co-pay be for (a) the office consultation and (b) the outpatient procedures? Assume that the charges listed are the same as TRICARE's "allowable charges."
5. If Mrs. Moss was enrolled in TRICARE Extra, what would be the total amount she would have to pay out-of-pocket for the procedures and services rendered on 11/29/20XX and 11/30/20XX (a) if she had not yet met her annual deductible, and (b) if she had met her annual deductible?

B. Patrick Olson is a retired colonel of the U.S. Army. He is admitted as an inpatient to Broadmoor Medical Center for a knee replacement. The colonel only has to pay the individual deductible of $150. Other family members pay the balance. The orthopedic surgeon's bill for Col. Olson's hospitalization for $8825 is broken down as follows:

Date of Service	Procedure/Service	TRICARE-Approved Charge
11/29/20XX	Initial hospital visit	$150.00
11/30/20XX	Surgery (total knee replacement)	$8000.00
12/01/20XX through 12/05/20XX	Subsequent hospital visits × 5	$550.00
12/06/20XX	Discharge visit	$125.00

1. Assuming this patient has a family policy and has met any required annual deductibles, what would be the total out-of-pocket amount Col. Olson would have to pay for just the professional service listed (not including the enrollment fee) if he was enrolled in (a) TRICARE Prime, (b) TRICARE Extra, or (c) TRICARE Standard? Assume that the fees charged are the same as the "allowed fees."
2. Assuming this patient had not met his annual deductible, what would be the total out-of-pocket amount Col. Olson would have to pay if he was enrolled in (a) TRICARE Prime, (b) TRICARE Extra, or (c) TRICARE Standard?
3. In this scenario, after Col. Olson was discharged from Broadmoor Medical Center, he was transferred to a civilian inpatient skilled nursing facility (SNF) for a 10-day stay. If the SNF charges $180/day, how much did this stage of his rehabilitative care cost him if he was enrolled in (a) TRICARE Prime, (b) TRICARE Extra, or (c) TRICARE Standard?

Internet Exploration

A. The health insurance professional should have ready access to the latest handbooks available for guidance in submitting claims. Log on to the following websites and peruse the electronic versions of the handbooks.

1. TRICARE website: **http://www.tricare.osd.mil/tricarehandbook**
2. CHAMPVA website: **http://www.va.gov/hac/forbeneficiaries/champva/handbook.asp**

B. Create a list of addresses where the various military claims (TRICARE and CHAMPVA) should be sent and a list of telephone numbers to call for questions and claims processing assistance.

C. The website **http://www.tricare.mil/faqs** provides extensive information and answers to frequently asked questions regarding TRICARE. Log on to this website and search for information that may be helpful to a health insurance professional.

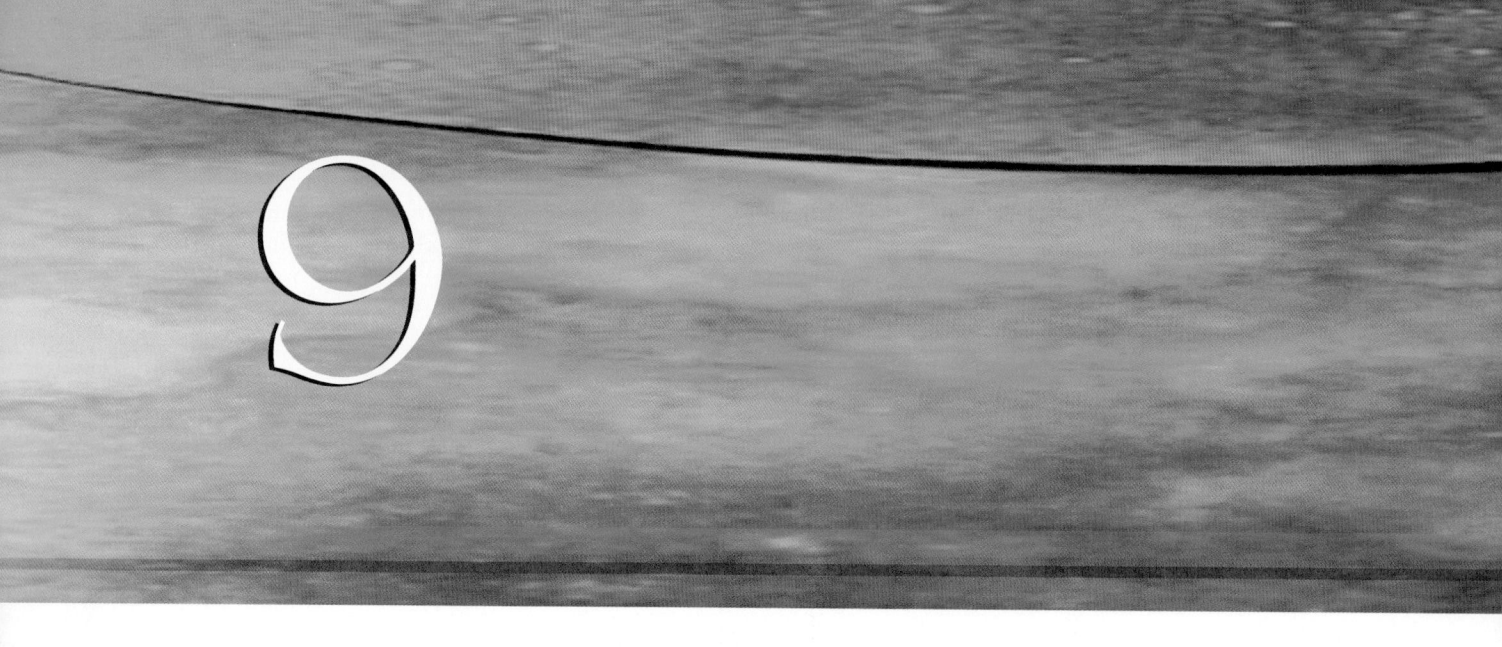

OBJECTIVES

After completion of this chapter, the student should be able to:

1. Explain the purpose of workers' compensation.
2. Discuss workers' compensation eligibility requirements, exemptions, and benefits.
3. Understand the reporting requirements of workers' compensation claims.
4. Describe how disability is determined in workers' compensation cases.
5. Explain the purpose of disability income insurance.
6. Differentiate between Social Security Disability Insurance and Supplemental Security Income.
7. Summarize the Centers for Disease Control and Prevention's Disability and Health Team Activities.
8. Explain the Ticket to Work Program.
9. Discuss the process for filing Social Security Disability Insurance and Supplemental Security Income claims.
10. List the health insurance professional's responsibilities that can facilitate disability claims processing.

MISCELLANEOUS CARRIERS: WORKERS' COMPENSATION AND DISABILITY INSURANCE

KEY TERMS

activities of daily living
Americans with Disabilities Act (ADA)
benefit cap
Black Lung Benefits Act
casual employee
coming and going rule
Disability and Health Team
disability income insurance
earned income
egregious
employment network
exemption
Federal Employment Compensation Act (FECA)
Federal Employment Liability Act (FELA)

financial means test
instrumental activities of daily living
interstate commerce
job deconditioning
Longshore and Harbor Workers' Compensation Act
long-term disability
Merchant Marine Act (Jones Act)
modified own-occupation policy
no-fault insurance
occupational therapy
ombudsman
own-occupation policy
permanent and stationary
permanent disability

permanent partial disability
permanent total disability
progress or supplemental report
protected health information
short-term disability
Social Security Disability Insurance (SSDI)
Supplemental Security Income (SSI)
temporarily disabled
temporary disability
temporary partial disability
temporary total disability
Ticket to Work Program
treating source
vocational rehabilitation
workers' compensation

Opening Scenario

The terms "workers' compensation" and "disability insurance" were familiar to Jim Lightfoot. His father had been a construction worker on a high-rise apartment building and had fallen to his death 6 years earlier. Even though Jim was young at the time, he remembers the monthly benefit checks his mother received, which were so vital in helping pay living expenses for the family. Now, Jim was anxious to learn as much as he could about the various types of disability listed in the chapter outline.

Tammy Hansen, a classmate, did not share Jim's enthusiasm for the subject at first, but her uncle was an insurance salesman. The day before Jim and Tammy were to begin the chapter on workers' compensation and disability insurance, Uncle Niles stopped by her house, and Tammy overhead her father and uncle discussing disability income insurance. "I can't afford to have disability insurance," her father stated, to which her uncle replied: "With your growing family, you can't afford not to!" The tone of her uncle's voice made Tammy sit up and listen. Why, she wondered, did her uncle believe that disability income insurance was important? Perhaps this chapter might be more informative and interesting than she first thought.

WORKERS' COMPENSATION

Workers' compensation is a type of insurance regulated by state laws that pays medical expenses and partial loss of wages for workers who are injured on the job or become ill as a result of job-related circumstances. If death results, benefits are payable to the surviving spouse and dependents as defined by law. Most U.S. workers are covered by the Workers' Compensation Law. In many states, the employer, not the employee, pays the premiums. Each state sets up its own workers' compensation laws and regulations; however, they are basically the same from state to state.

History

Workers' compensation began in Germany in the 1800s when it was determined that something needed to be done to take care of injured workers to limit their physical and financial suffering from injuries or illnesses resulting from their jobs. Workers' compensation became common in the United States in the 1930s and 1940s, and it exists today in all 50 states and territories.

When workers' compensation was first proposed, U.S. companies were hesitant to accept full responsibility for paying the premiums. Their argument was that on top of the premium expense, they still could be financially liable in a worker-initiated lawsuit. A compromise was reached between businesses and workers: Companies would pay the premiums for the insurance that protected workers, and the workers would give up the right to sue the employer for damages resulting from a job-related illness or injury. This principle continues essentially intact today. Workers' compensation is not considered a "benefit"; rather, it is a legally mandated right of the worker.

Companies that meet specific state requirements must provide workers' compensation for all employees. There are fines and sometimes other penalties for businesses that do not provide coverage as required by law. Workers' compensation can be purchased from several possible sources—private insurance companies, state funds, insurance pools, and self-insurance programs. Most states require employers to purchase workers' compensation insurance in the state in which their business operates. State statutes establish the framework and set up the laws for most workers' compensation insurance. As we learned earlier, these laws provide benefits not only for workers but also for dependents of workers who are killed or die as a result of job-related accidents or illnesses. Many state laws also protect employers and their fellow workers by limiting the amount an injured employee can recover from an employer and by eliminating the liability of co-workers in most accidents.

Federal Legislation and Workers' Compensation

Workers' compensation programs are offered at the state level. In addition, there are several categories of federal programs for workers who do not fall under the umbrella of covered employees under state laws.

The **Federal Employment Compensation Act (FECA)** provides workers' compensation for nonmilitary federal employees. Many of the provisions are similar to state workers' compensation laws; however, awards are limited to disability or death incurred while in the performance of the employee's duties but not caused willfully by the employee or by intoxication or other illegal acts. FECA covers medical expenses resulting from the disability and can require the employee to undergo job retraining. Under this act, a disabled employee receives two thirds of his or her normal monthly salary during the disability period and may receive more for permanent physical injuries or if he or she has dependents. FECA provides compensation for survivors of employees who are killed while on the job or die from a job-related illness or condition. FECA is administered by the Office of Workers' Compensation Programs.

The **Federal Employment Liability Act (FELA)**, although not a workers' compensation statute, states that companies in which railroads are engaged in **interstate commerce** (trade that involves more than one state) are liable for injuries to their employees if they have been negligent. The **Merchant Marine Act (Jones Act)** provides seamen (individuals involved in transporting goods by water between U.S. ports) with the same protection from employer negligence that FELA provides railroad workers.

Congress enacted the **Longshore and Harbor Workers' Compensation Act** to provide workers' compensation to specified employees of private maritime employers. The Office of Workers' Compensation Programs administers the act.

The **Black Lung Benefits Act** provides compensation for miners with *black lung* (pneumoconiosis; also called anthracosis). The Black Lung Benefits Act requires liable mine operators to award disability payments and establishes a fund administered by the Secretary of Labor providing disability payments to miners when the mine operator is unknown or unable to pay. The Office of Workers' Compensation Programs regulates the administration of the act.

Eligibility

In the United States, any employee who injures himself or herself on the job or develops an employ-ment-related illness that prevents the employee from working is likely to be eligible to collect workers' compensation benefits. The same applies to the spouse and dependents of a family member who dies because of a job-related accident or illness. If the disability is permanent, or the employee has dependents, benefits include a specific percentage (often two thirds) of regular wages or salary.

As with many rules and regulations, there are exceptions. Benefits are awarded only for disability or death occurring while the employee was in the process of performing lawful duties. If any horseplay, drunken stumbling, or illegal drugs are involved, workers' compensation usually does not pay. The same applies for self-inflicted injuries and for injuries incurred while a worker is off the job, committing a crime, or violating company policy.

Exemptions

Not all business organizations are required to purchase workers' compensation insurance for their employees. **Exemption** criteria vary, however, from state to state. The following list presents various exemption classifications (keep in mind that these classifications are not nationwide but vary from state to state):

- Employers with a minimum number of full-time employees (fewer than three and up to five, depending on the state)
- Executive officers
- Individuals who are business partners (coverage is optional)
- Sole proprietors (most states allow optional coverage)
- "Casual" employees. A **casual employee** is one who is not entitled to paid holiday or sick leave, has no expectation of ongoing employment, and for whom each engagement with the employer constitutes a separate contract of employment. Casual employees often receive a higher rate of pay to compensate for a lack of job security and benefits
- Volunteers
- Part-time domestic employees, agricultural workers, and emergency relief workers. These categories of employees are typically excluded, but employees can obtain workers' compensation and employers' liability insurance coverage by agreement between their employer and an insurance carrier

Benefits

Workers' compensation insurance is **no-fault insurance**. Benefits are paid to the injured (or ill) worker regardless of who is to blame for the accident or injury barring the exceptions mentioned previously. There are four major benefit components to workers' compensation:

1. *Medical expense*—pays the expenses involved for hospitalization, physicians' visits, and any necessary medical treatment
2. *Disability pay*—can be temporary or permanent if it is determined that the worker will never fully recover
3. *Vocational rehabilitation*—if the injury or illness results in the worker being unable to perform the usual duties of his or her occupation, retraining may be necessary for the worker to enter into a new trade or business; also, physical therapy may be needed
4. *Death benefits*—paid to surviving dependents

Because workers' compensation imposes strict liability without inquiry into fault, an employer could be penalized if the cause of injury or illness was **egregious**, meaning the employer was conspicuously negligent, such as violating federal or state safety standards, failing to correct known defects, or other such careless conduct.

Most state workers' compensation laws exclude coverage for injuries sustained while an employee is commuting to and from work. This is referred to as the **coming and going rule**. There are exceptions to this rule, however, such as when the scope of the employee's duties includes travel or when the employee is running an errand for the employer during the commute. Inquiry as to whether the coming and going rule applies to a particular situation should be made before simply ruling out the possibility of coverage for an accident that occurred during a worker's commute to or from work. If an employee is injured during a lunch period, it is usually considered outside the scope of the employment relationship. In the case of an automobile accident, however, workers' compensation might deny the claim, indicating that the automobile insurance carrier of the at-fault party is the primary payer.

STOP AND THINK

Carol Brown, bookkeeper at the Memorial Health Clinic, drops off the bank deposit each evening on her way home from work. One evening, as she is in the process of making the deposit, she slams her hand in the depository door, sustaining a laceration to her middle and index finger. Several weeks later, as Carol is on her way to the bank to make the daily deposit, she stops at a convenience store for a cup of coffee and a donut. In her haste, she spills the coffee, sustaining second-degree burns to her torso. Does either of these scenarios represent a legitimate workers' compensation claim?

HIPAA TIP

HIPAA requirements do not apply to certain types of benefit plans known as excepted benefits, which include coverage only for accidents (including accidental death or dismemberment) or certain categories of disability income insurance.

Denial of Benefits and Appeals

Employees who believe they have been wrongly denied workers' compensation benefits can appeal or resort to litigation. Some states have an **ombudsman**, who is an individual responsible for investigating and resolving workers' complaints against the employer or insurance company that is denying the benefits.

Most work injuries result in granted benefits because it is usually obvious when an injury is work-related. In these cases, if the claim was filed in a timely manner and according to a company's work rules, benefits would be awarded. Various situations, however, may justify an employer or the insurer contesting a claim for workers' compensation benefits. It may be believed that an injury or resulting disability does not meet one or more of the legal requirements for entitlement to benefits. In these cases, a notice that the claim has been denied, containing reasons for the denial, must be issued promptly to the worker by the employer or by the employer's workers' compensation insurance company.

IMAGINE THIS!

Louise Carson has been a teacher at Harrison Junior High School for 10 years. At her yearly physical examination, her health care provider informs her that she is dangerously hypertensive. Louise attributes her hypertension to stress from her teaching responsibilities plus increasing pressure from her supervisor to maintain better discipline in the classroom. Louise's blood pressure does not respond to conventional antihypertensive medication, so her physician suggests a 6-week leave of absence from her job. Louise files a workers' compensation claim with the Harrison City School District; however, the claim is denied. The reason for denial, TEL-Abbot, Harrison's insurer informs her, is that high stress is a normal part of the teaching profession.

STOP AND THINK

Benjamin Abbott, owner of Abbott Manufacturing, holds an annual Christmas party every year in the company cafeteria. Attendance to the party is optional, but Mr. Abbott uses this occasion to hand out the employee Christmas bonuses. Night shift foreman Ken Carter sustains a back injury while doing the limbo at the party. Abbott's insurer denies the claim stating that even though, technically, the injury occurred at work, it was not during regular work hours, and the employee was not engaged in his usual work duties. Can Ken appeal this decision?

The appeal process differs from state to state. In many states, if the employee disagrees with the decision to deny the claim, he or she may appeal, but it must be done within a specific time, depending on state statutes. The appeal process can be started by contacting the appropriate state agency or by hiring an attorney. If all attempts at appeal do not reverse the decision, and the denial becomes final, the worker is responsible for payment of all medical bills. If the individual has other health insurance, a claim can be submitted to that insurer. Most health insurance companies ask that a copy of the workers' compensation claim denial be included with the claim.

Time Limits

Each state has rules established under which an employee is required to file a claim within a certain time limit. Usually, traumatic claims must be brought within a time frame that runs from the date of the accident, date of last medical treatment, or date of the last payment of benefits. In cases wherein a job-related disease does not manifest immediately (i.e., lung cancer, toxic disease, or mesothelioma [a type of lung disease caused by asbestos exposure]), the time limit may extend from the date of the last exposure, date of the first symptoms of the disease, or date the diagnosis was determined. The time limits for filing claims and issuing appeals are established by individual state statutes and vary from state to state; the health insurance professional needs to become familiar with the workers' compensation regulations in the state in which he or she is employed.

Workers' Compensation Claims Process

The workers' compensation claims process can be long and arduous. Various steps must be followed, and report forms must be completed. This process can be facilitated, however, if the individual steps are adhered to carefully and the forms are completed correctly and in a timely manner. The following sections discuss the steps for successful workers' compensation claim processing.

First Report of Injury

Employees who are injured, suspect they have been injured, or have contracted a disease they believe is related to their job should take immediate steps to protect their rights and to ensure that their claim is processed properly. Failure to seek timely medical treatment within the workers' compensation network may cause a delay in claim processing and perhaps denial of benefits. Injured workers should be transported to a medical treatment facility without delay in the case of an emergency. For nonemergency situations, the employee should take the following steps:

- The injured or ill worker should notify a supervisor of the incident immediately and provide the names of witnesses, if any.
- The injured or ill worker should complete the initial accident report or necessary paperwork. It does not matter whether the injury is severe or minor; it *must* be documented. The employer should supply the necessary forms (Fig. 9-1).
- The employer should report the incident to his or her workers' compensation carrier.
- The injured or ill worker should be sent to a medical facility for treatment or diagnosis, if not already done.

The procedure for reporting injuries and filing claims may vary from state to state. Contact the workers' compensation department in the state in which you reside and request specific guidelines for your state.

Physician's Role

Physicians have two distinct roles in the workers' compensation process:

1. To diagnose and treat work-related injuries and illnesses
2. To provide claims administrators opinions in response to specific medical and legal questions about work-related injuries or illnesses, including the following:
   - Was the injury or illness caused by the employee's work?
   - Is the condition **permanent and stationary**, meaning has the employee reached a state of maximal medical improvement?
   - If an employee is permanent and stationary, has the injury caused permanent disability that limits the ability to compete in the open labor market?
   - Can the employee return to his or her usual and customary work assignment? If not, does he or she need some type of accommodations because of work

WORKERS COMPENSATION - FIRST REPORT OF INJURY OR ILLNESS

| Employer (Name & Address with Zip Code) | Carrier/Administrator Claim Number | Report Purpose Code |
| | Jurisdiction | Jurisdiction Claim Number |

Insured Report Number

| SIC Code | Employer Fein | Employer's Location Address (If different) | Location #: |
| | | | Phone # |

CARRIER/CLAIMS ADMINISTRATOR

Carrier (Name, Address & Phone No)	Policy Period	Claims Administrator (Name, Address & Phone Number)
	To	
	Check if Appropriate	
	☐ Self-Insurance	

| Carrier Fein | Policy/Self-Insured Number | Administration Fein |

Agent Name & Code Number

EMPLOYEE / WAGE

Name (Last, First, Middle)	Birth Date	Social Security Number	Hire Date	State of Hire
Address (include Zip Code)	Sex	Marital Status	Occupation/Job Title
			Employment Status
			NCCI Class Code
Phone	# Dependents		

| Rate　Per　☐ Day　☐ Month | # Days Worked/Week | Full Pay for Day of Injury?　☐ Yes　☐ No |
| ☐ Week　☐ Other: | | Did Salary Continue?　☐ Yes　☐ No |

OCCURANCE/TREATMENT

| Time Employee Began Work | Date of Injury/Illness | Time of Occurrence | Late Work Date | Date Employer Notified | Date Disability Began |
| | | AM PM | | | |

| Contact Number/Phone Number | Type of Injury/Illness | Part of Body Affected |

| Did Injury/Illness Exposure Occur on Employer's Premises?　Yes ☐　No ☐ | Type of Injury/Illness Code | Part of Body Affected Code |

| Department or Location Where Accident or Illness Exposure Occurred | All Equipment, Materials, or Chemicals Employee Was Using When Accident or Illness Exposure Occurred |

| Specific Activity the Employee was Engaged in When the Accident or Illness Exposure Occurred | Work Process the Employee Was Engaged in When Accident or Illness Exposure Occurred |

| How Injury or Illness/Abnormal Health Condition Occurred. Describe the Sequence of Events and Include Any Objects or substances that Directly Injured the Employee or Made the Employee ILL | Cause of Injury Code |

| Date Return(ed) To Work | If Fatal, Give Date of Death | Were Safeguards or Safety Equipment Provided?　☐ Yes　☐ No |
| | | Were They Used　☐ Yes　☐ No |

| Physician/Health Care Provider (Name & Address) | Hospital (Name & Address) | Initial Treatment |

Witness (Name & Phone #)

| Date Administrator Notified | Date Prepared | Preparer's Name & Title | Phone Number |

Fig. 9-1　Sample workers' compensation first report of injury form.

Employer's Instructions
DO NOT ENTER DATA IN SHADED FIELDS

Preferred Formats for Date and Time: Dates should be entered as MM/DD/YYYY, and times as HH:MM a (am) / p (pm)

SIC Code: This is the code which represents the nature of the employer's business which is contained in the Standard Industrial Classification Manual published by the Federal Office of Management and Budget.

Carrier: The licensed business entity issuing a contract of insurance and assuming financial responsibility on behalf of the employer of the claimant.

Claims Administrator: Enter the name of the carrier, third party administrator, state fund, or self-insured responsible for administering the claim.

Agent Name & Code Number: Enter the name of your insurance agent and his/her code number if known. This information can be found on your insurance policy.

Employee/Wage Section: When filling in Social Security Number, do **NOT** include dashes.

Occupation/Job Title: This is the primary occupation of the claimant at the time of the accident or exposure.

Employment Status: Indicate the employee's work status. The valid choices are:

Apprenticeship Full-Time	Apprenticeship Part-Time	Disabled	Full-Time
Not Employed	On Strike	Part-Time	Piece Worker
Retired	Seasonal	Unknown	Volunteer

Date Disability Began: The first day on which the claimant originally lost time from work due to the occupation injury or disease or otherwise deigned by statute.

Contact Name/Phone Number: Enter the name of the individual at the employer's premises to be contacted for additional information.

Type of Injury/Illness: Briefly describe the nature of the injury or illness (e.g. Lacerations to the forearm).

Part of Body Affected: Indicate the part of body affected by the injury/illness (e.g. Right forearm, lower back). Part of Body Affected Code does not allow multiple body parts to be selected. Please choose the most dominant body part affected from the list.

Department or Location Where Accident or Illness Exposure Occurred: (e.g. Maintenance Dept or Client's Office at (address). If the accident or illness exposure did not occur on the employer's premises, enter address or location. Be specific.

All Equipment, Material or Chemicals Employee Was Using When Accident or Illness Exposure Occurred: (e.g. Acetylene cutting torch, metal plate). List of all the equipment, materials, and/or chemicals the employee was using, applying, handlings or operating when the injury or illness occurred. Be specific, for example: decorator's scaffolding, electric sander, paintbrush, and paint. Enter "NA" for not applicable if no equipment, materials, or chemicals were being used. NOTE: The items listed do not have to be directly involved in the employee's injury or illness.

Specific Activity the Employee Was Engaged in When the Accident or Illness Exposure Occurred: (e.g. Cutting metal plate for flooring). Describe the specific activity the employee was engaged in when the accident or illness exposure occurred, such as sanding ceiling woodwork in preparation for painting.

Work Process the Employee Was Engaged in When Accident or Illness Exposure Occurred:
Describe the work process the employee was engaged in when the accident or illness exposure occurred, such as building maintenance. Enter "NA" for not applicable if employee was not engaged in a work process (e.g. walking along a hallway).

How Injury or Illness/Abnormal Health Condition Occurred. Describe the Sequence of Events and Include Any Objects or Substances That Directly Injured the Employee or Made the Employee Ill:
(Worker stepped back to inspect work and slipped on some scrap metal. As worker fell, worker brushed against the hot metal.) Describe how the injury or illness/abnormal health condition occurred. Include the sequence of events and name any objects of substance that directly injured the employee or made the employee ill. For example: Worker stepped to the edge of the scaffolding to inspect work, lost balance and fell six feet to the floor. The worker's right wrist was broken in the fall.

Date Return(ed) To Work: Enter the date following the most recent disability period on which the employee returned to work.

Fig. 9-1, cont'd

restrictions, or does the employee need to be retrained for a new job?
- Will the employee who has attained permanent and stationary status require access to future medical treatment for the condition?

Usually, a single physician fills both roles in workers' compensation cases; however, an independent medical evaluator commonly addresses the specific medical and legal questions. When an injured or ill employee visits the medical facility, the attending physician should

- obtain a complete history of the condition, including preexisting conditions or disability;
- obtain a thorough work history, including any exposures as they pertain to the chief complaint;
- perform a physical examination, focusing on the system or systems involved;
- consider restrictions (e.g., no typing for more than 1 hour) before taking the patient off work to prevent **job deconditioning** (i.e., the patient psychologically or physically loses his or her ability to perform normal job duties at the previous level of expertise as a result of being absent from work);
- make a diagnostic evaluation; and
- complete all paperwork promptly because the patient may have no source of income if the paperwork is delayed (Fig. 9-2).

Determining Disability

When an injured or ill worker visits the health care facility for treatment, the provider completes an attending physician statement (as discussed in the previous section), which should indicate any physical or mental impairments resulting from the incident. The classification of workers' compensation disability cases, mandated by federal law, is as follows:

- *Medical treatment only*—this category comprises minor injuries or illnesses that are resolved quickly, resulting in a minimal loss of work time with no residual limitations. Compensation is made for medical expenses rendered that are necessary to cure and relieve the effects of the injury or illness.
- **Temporary disability**—benefits in this category are paid so long as the physician's opinion concurs with that claim of status. Temporary disability includes two subcategories:
  - **Temporary total disability**—the worker's ability to perform his or her job responsibilities is totally lost but on a temporary basis.

- **Temporary partial disability**—an injury or illness impairs an employee's ability to work for a limited time. The impairment is such that the individual is able to perform limited employment duties and is expected to recover fully.
- **Permanent disability**—the ill or injured employee's condition is such that it is impossible to return to work. Compensation is awarded to the worker for the loss of value of his or her skills in the open labor market. As with temporary disability, permanent disability has two classifications:
  - **Permanent partial disability**—prevents the individual from performing one or more occupational functions but does not impair his or her capability of performing less demanding employment.
  - **Permanent total disability**—the employee's ability to work at any occupation is totally and permanently lost.

STOP AND THINK

George Meade makes his living as a concert pianist. To relax between concerts, George takes up woodworking and inadvertently severs his right index finger, preventing him from performing. What classification would George's disability fall into?

Vocational Rehabilitation

When employees cannot return to their previous job because of a workers' compensation injury or illness, they often are entitled to **vocational rehabilitation** services if it is reasonable to assume that these individuals can be trained for some alternative type of employment. The goal of vocational rehabilitation is to return the injured worker to some sort of suitable, gainful employment that he or she can reasonably achieve and that offers an opportunity to restore the injured worker to maximum self-support as soon as practical and as near as possible to what it was before the incident.

Waiting Periods

Workers' compensation benefits normally do not begin immediately. Table 9-1 lists waiting periods for several states. For a complete list of waiting periods for all states, log on to http://www.dol.gov/esa/regs/statutes/owcp/stwclaw/stwclaw.htm and click on Table 14. Most states allow for retroactive compensation when disability continues for a certain period from the date of injury or illness.

Occupational therapy is different from vocational rehabilitation. Occupational therapy is a

Health Care Provider Report

See Instructions on Reverse Side
(WHEN COMPLETED RETURN TO REQUESTER)

H C 0 1

DO NOT USE THIS SPACE

Please PRINT or TYPE your responses.
Enter dates in MM/DD/YYYY format.

SOCIAL SECURITY NUMBER	DATE OF INJURY
EMPLOYEE	EMPLOYER
INSURER/SELF-INSURER/TPA	INSURER CLAIM NUMBER
INSURER ADDRESS	
CITY	STATE ZIP CODE

REQUESTER must specify all items to be completed by health care provider. ☐ Items: _____   ☐ MMI (#9)   ☐ PPD (#10)

HEALTH CARE PROVIDER TO COMPLETE ITEMS REQUESTED ABOVE

1. Date of first examination for this injury by this office: _____ (date)

2. Diagnosis (include all ICD-9-CM codes):

3. History of injury or disease given by employee:

4. In your opinion (as substantiated by the history and physical examination) was the injury or disease caused, aggravated or accelerated by the employee's alleged employment activity or environment?   ☐ No   ☐ Yes

5. Is there evidence of pre-existing or other conditions that affect this disability?   ☐ No   ☐ Yes   If yes, describe:

6. Is further treatment of this injury or referral to another doctor planned?   ☐ No   ☐ Yes   If yes, describe:

7. Has surgery been performed?   ☐ No   ☐ Yes   If yes, date and describe: _____ (date)

8. Attach the most recent Report of Work Ability. Date of report: _____ (date)

9. **Has the employee reached maximum medical improvement?**   ☐ No   ☐ Yes   Date reached: _____
   (If yes, complete item #10) (See definition on back)

10. **Has the employee sustained any permanent partial disability from the injury?**   ☐ No   ☐ Yes   ☐ Too early to determine
    The permanent partial disability is _____ % of the whole body. This rating is based on Minn. Rules:

5223.	%	5223.	%
5223.	%	5223.	%

NAME (Type or Print)	SIGNATURE		DEGREE
ADDRESS	STATE	LICENSE #/REGISTRATION #	
CITY STATE ZIP CODE	AREA CODE TELEPHONE #	DATE SIGNED	

MN HC01 (7/01)

Fig. 9-2 Sample health care provider report.

Continued

NOTICE TO EMPLOYEE: SERVICE OF THIS REPORT OF MAXIMUM MEDICAL IMPROVEMENT (SEE DEFINITION IN INSTRUCTIONS FOR ITEM 9) MAY HAVE AN IMPACT ON YOUR TEMPORARY TOTAL DISABILITY WAGE LOSS BENEFITS. IF THE INSURER PROPOSES TO STOP YOUR BENEFITS, A NOTICE OF INTENTION TO DISCONTINUE BENEFITS SHOULD BE SENT TO YOU. IF YOU HAVE ANY QUESTIONS CONCERNING YOUR BENEFITS OR MAXIMUM MEDICAL IMPROVEMENT, YOU MAY CALL THE CLAIM REPRESENTATIVE OR THE DEPARTMENT OF LABOR AND INDUSTRY, WORKERS' COMPENSATION DIVISION.

INSTRUCTIONS TO THE INSURER AND HEALTH CARE PROVIDER

Within ten (10) calendar days of receipt of a request for information on the Health Care Provider Report from an employer, insurer, or the commissioner, a health care provider must respond on the report form or in a narrative report that contains the same information. (Minn. Rules 5221.0410, subp. 2)

A. **The employer, insurer, or Commissioner may request required medical information on the Health Care Provider Report form.**

- The requester must complete the general information identifying the employee, employer, and insurer.

- The requester must specify all items to be answered by the health care provider.

- For those injuries that are required to be reported to the Division, the self-insured employer or insurer must file reports with the Division. (M.S. § 176.231, subd. 1 and Minn. Rules 5221.0410, subp. 5 and subp. 8)

- The self-insured employer or insurer must serve the report of maximum medical improvement (MMI) on the employee. (M.S. §176.101, subd. 1(j) and Minn. Rules 5221.0410, subp. 3)

B. **Instructions to the Health Care Provider for completing the Health Care Provider Report:**

- Items 1 - 5: Fill in all information as required.

- Item 6: Indicate if further treatment or referral is planned. Describe the treatment plan (e.g., continue medication, refer to physical therapy, refer to a specialist, perform surgery).

- Item 7: State if surgery has been performed. If yes, fill in the date performed and describe the procedure.

- Item 8: Attach the most recent Report of Work Ability. (Minn. Rules 5221.0410, subp. 6)

- Item 9: Indicate if the employee has reached MMI. If yes, fill in the date MMI was reached. At MMI, permanent partial disability (PPD) must be reported (item 10). (M.S. § 176.011, subd. 25 and Minn. Rules 5221.0410, subp. 3)

  MAXIMUM MEDICAL IMPROVEMENT means "The date after which no further significant recovery from or significant lasting improvement to a personal injury can reasonably be anticipated, based upon reasonable medical probability, irrespective and regardless of subjective complaints of pain."

- Item 10: The health care provider must render an opinion of PPD when ascertainable, but no later than the date of MMI. (M.S. §176.011, subd. 25 and Minn. Rules 5221.0410, subp. 4)

  Indicate if the employee sustained PPD from this injury. Check one of the three boxes (too early to determine, no, yes). If yes, specify any applicable category of the PPD schedule in effect for the employee's date of injury. Report any zero ratings.

- Identify the health care provider completing the report by name, professional degree, license or registration number, address, and phone number.

- The health care provider must sign and date the report.

This material can be made available in different forms, such as large print, Braille or on a tape.

ANY PERSON WHO, WITH INTENT TO DEFRAUD, RECEIVES WORKERS' COMPENSATION BENEFITS TO WHICH THE PERSON IS NOT ENTITLED BY KNOWINGLY MISREPRESENTING, MISSTATING, OR FAILING TO DISCLOSE ANY MATERIAL FACT IS GUILTY OF THEFT AND SHALL BE SENTENCED PURSUANT TO SECTION 609.52, SUBDIVISION 3.

Fig. 9-2, cont'd

treatment that focuses on helping individuals achieve independence in all areas of their lives. The occupational therapist works with individuals with varying disabilities and provides treatment for these individuals to relearn physical skills lost as a result of an illness or accident, ideally so that they can return to some form of gainful employment or an independent, productive life.

Claim Forms

In contrast to most major third-party payer claims, there is no universal form to use when filing a workers' compensation claim. Some states (e.g., Iowa) allow workers' compensation claims to be submitted on the CMS-1500 form. Private insurance carriers typically have their own forms. The health insurance professional should determine if it is

TABLE 9-1	Partial List of States Showing Waiting Periods

State	Waiting Period
Alabama	21 days
Alaska	>28 days
California	14 days (also retroactive if person is hospitalized)
Colorado	>2 wk
Connecticut	7 days
Delaware*	7 days, including date of injury
District of Columbia	>14 days
Hawaii[†]	None
Illinois[†]	>14 days
Iowa[†]	>14 days
Maryland	>14 days
Minnesota[†]	10 days
Missouri	>14 days
New Hampshire	>14 days
Oklahoma	None
Oregon[†]	14 days (inpatient in hospital receive compensation from date of incapacity)

*No waiting period in the case of amputation of an extremity, or a part thereof, or when the injury results in hospitalization of the employee.
[†]Temporary total disability only.

acceptable to submit a workers' compensation claim on the CMS-1500 form; if not, the health insurance professional should ask the patient to request the required form from his or her employer or insurer.

IMAGINE THIS!

Frank Turner sustains a serious cut to his right hand while operating a band saw at work. Frank's injury qualifies him for workers' compensation benefits, which start 1 week after the incident occurred. Larry Boggs, a co-worker in the millroom with Frank, becomes ill the same week. Thinking he was just suffering from a minor cold, Larry does not file for workers' compensation; however, 2 weeks later, his cold is no better. Larry returns to his physician, who determines he has pneumonia. Larry subsequently is hospitalized for 1 week, during which time further tests reveal that Larry's condition is caused by breathing minute particles of sawdust. When Larry is discharged from the hospital, he files a workers' compensation claim. The claim is approved, but Larry's benefits do not begin until 4 weeks after his illness began.

Normally, multiple copies of all workers' compensation reports are essential for proper distribution as follows:

1. Original form to the insurance carrier
2. One copy to the appropriate state agency
3. One copy to the patient's employer
4. One copy to be retained in the health care provider's files

When special claim forms should be used, instructions usually are provided—often on the back side of the form. If instructions do not come with the form, the health insurance professional should ask the patient to obtain detailed guidelines from the employer or insurer.

Because there are thousands of different forms used for workers' compensation claims in the United States, to avoid confusion, instructions for completing the standard CMS-1500 claim form are used in this chapter. These instructions are generic, and the health insurance professional should obtain exact guidelines from the employer, the insurer, or the particular state the claim occurs in to prevent delays or rejections.

Before completing the blocks, the health insurance professional should determine the name and address of the insurer to whom the claim will be sent. This information should appear in the upper right-hand corner of the claim form. Table 9-2 provides step-by-step instructions for completing the CMS-1500 form for a workers' compensation claim.

Progress Reports

Keeping the employer and insurance carrier apprised of the patient's treatment plan, progress, and status is a priority in workers' compensation cases. The health insurance professional should be well versed in the particulars of workers' compensation reporting so that written communications meet all accepted legal standards. After the initial visit to the physician has occurred, and the attending physician report has been filed, unless the employee has returned to work full-time, periodic reports have to be filed. These are referred to as **progress or supplemental reports** (Fig. 9-3). Often, there are no special printed forms for progress reports; copies of clinical notes from the patient's health record or a letter from the attending physician giving a detailed account of the patient's progress are acceptable. When the patient's disability ends, and he or she is able to return to work, the physician submits a final report.

Special Billing Notes

Most states have a fee schedule that providers must use when billing a workers' compensation claim,

TABLE 9-2 Step-by-Step Guidelines for Workers' Compensation Claims

Block 1	"Other" should be checked for workers' compensation claims, unless the claim is for patients who are receiving Black Lung benefits
Block 1a	Enter the claim number if one has been assigned (check your state's requirements for this block if no claim number has been assigned, or use the patient's Social Security number)
Block 2	Use the same guidelines as with all other carriers
Block 3	Indicate the patient's eight-digit birth date and sex
Block 4	The *employer's name* is entered here as the "insured"
Block 5	Use the same guidelines as with all other carriers
Block 6	Check "OTHER"
Block 7	Enter the address of the insuring company/corporation
Block 8	Check "employed." Consult your local state guidelines as to whether it is necessary to indicate marital status
Block 9	For most claims, leave blank. If there is a question as to whether or not the injury/illness falls under workers' compensation, enter the applicable information for the patient's other insurance
Blocks 9a-d	Leave blank
Block 10a	Check "YES" to indicate that the injury occurred while the patient was on the job
Blocks 10b-c	Check "NO"
Block 10d	Leave blank
Blocks 11-11c	Leave blank
Block 11d	Normally, this is left blank; however, if the workers' compensation case is pending, check with your local state agency's guidelines as to whether or not this box would be checked "YES"
Blocks 12-13	No signature is required
Block 14	Enter the date that the injury occurred or the date on which the illness first was noticed by the patient (this date must coincide with the employer's First Report of Injury and the provider's First Report of Treatment)
Block 15	If a date is documented in the patient's record, indicate it in this block; otherwise, leave blank
Block 16	Enter the first full day patient was unable to perform his or her job duties to the first day the patient is back to work (this should be documented in the provider's First Report of Treatment)
Block 17	Enter the name (first, middle initial, last name) and credentials of the professional who referred, ordered, or supervised the service(s) or supply(s) on the claim. Do not use periods or commas within the name. A hyphen can be used for hyphenated names. For laboratory and x-ray claims, enter the name of the physician who ordered the diagnostic services
Blocks 17a-b	If the name of a health care professional was reported in 17b, enter his/her NPI in 17b. Block 17a is not to be reported after May 23, 2007, unless the payer's or state agency's guidelines say differently
Block 18	Use the same guidelines as with all other carriers
Block 19	Leave blank
Block 20	Use the same guidelines as with all other carriers
Block 21	Use the same guidelines as with all other carriers
Blocks 22-23	Leave blank
Blocks 24a-j	Use the same guidelines as with all other carriers, or consult the appropriate state agency's guidelines
Block 25	Use the same guidelines as with all other carriers
Block 26	Use the same guidelines as with all other carriers
Block 27	Leave blank; not applicable because all workers' compensation payments go to the provider
Block 28	Use the same guidelines as with all other carriers
Block 29-30	Leave blank
Block 31	Use the same guidelines as with all other carriers
Block 32	Key the name and address of the location where services were provided
Block 32a	Enter the NPI of the service facility in Block 32
Block 32b	Block 32b is no longer reported after May 23, 2007. Follow the specific guidelines of the applicable workers' compensation carrier
Block 33	Enter the name, address, Zip Code, and telephone number of the billing provider
Block 33a	Effective May 23, 2007, the NPI of the billing provider or group must be reported here
Block 33b	Effective May 23, 2007, Block 33b is no longer reported. Follow the specific guidelines of the applicable workers' compensation carrier

**Workers' Compensation
Medical Progress Report**

Claim Number	Health Care Provider

Employee Last Name	First Name

Mailing Address (include zip code)	Telephone (include area code)

Occupation	Date of Birth	Sex

Description of injury/illness	Date of Exam	Social Security Number

Employer	Employer Contact Person

Employer Address	Phone #

Insurer Name	Claim Representative

Insurer Address	Phone #

Current Work Ability: ☐ Fit for regular work duties   ☐ Unfit for regular work duties

Start date for return to regular work duties (dd/mm/yy)

Duration of modified duties: ☐ 1-7 days   ☐ 8-14 days   ☐ 15-21 days   ☐ More

Start date for modified duties (dd/mm/yy)

Subjective Information

Objective Information

Past diseases/injuries

Diagnostics (Lab/x-rays, CT, etc.)	ICD Code:

Prescribed treatment/advice/referrals

Please give details for the following questions when the answer is Yes

Has worker been hospitalized?   ☐ Yes   ☐ No   Dates:_____ to_____

Has an operation been performed?   ☐ Yes   ☐ No   Date(s):

Any factors delaying recovery?   ☐ Yes   ☐ No   Explain:

Is permanent disability probable?   ☐ Yes   ☐ No

Would you suggest an examination by a WC doctor?   ☐ Yes   ☐ No

Will worker be seen again?   ☐ Yes   ☐ No   Date:

I hereby certify that the above is a correct statement of services personally rendered by me.

Health Care Professional Signature _____ Date _____

Name of Physician	EIN #
Address	NPI #

Fig. 9-3   Sample workers' compensation medical progress report.

and as long as a workers' compensation claim is pending, the provider cannot bill the patient. Additionally, balance billing is not allowed on workers' compensation claims. If the claim has been denied, and all efforts for appeal have been exhausted, the health insurance professional should issue a letter of reply immediately, after which direct billing to the patient or the patient's private insurance company for the services rendered is allowed. The workers' compensation fee schedule does not apply to denied claims; instead, the provider's usual and customary fees apply. Workers' compensation claims are handled differently in each state, and the health insurance professional must follow the guidelines set forth by the law in his or her state.

IMAGINE THIS!

Sandra Cotter was injured at work when a filing cabinet fell on her foot. The human relations officer advised Sandra to see her own physician because the company did not have a specific workers' compensation physician. Sandra was treated at the Heartland Medical Clinic, which billed her health insurer, Blue Cross and Blue Shield. Blue Cross and Blue Shield refused payment, so Heartland billed Sandra. Sandra refused to pay the bill, stating that it was a workers' compensation case. Heartland argued that they had not received a call from Sandra's employer authorizing treatment. Still, Sandra refused to pay. After sending Sandra statements for 6 months, Heartland sent her a certified letter stating they were refusing all future medical treatment at the clinic. Sandra filed a complaint with the State Workers' Comp Board, and the case eventually was resolved; however, Heartland still refused to see Sandra for subsequent visits.

HIPAA and Workers' Compensation

The Health Insurance Portability and Accountability Act (HIPAA) Privacy Rule does not apply to workers' compensation insurers, workers' compensation administrative agencies, or employers. The Privacy Rule recognizes the legitimate need for insurers and other entities involved in the workers' compensation system to have access to an injured worker's **protected health information** as authorized by state or other law. Workers' compensation patients may or may not be required to sign a release of information form for a claim form to be filed. Additionally, employers and claims adjusters retain the right of access to workers' compensation files. If the health insurance professional encounters a workers' compensation case for an established

patient who already has a health record in that office, a separate record should be created and kept separate from that individual's regular health record. Some medical offices color code or flag workers' compensation records or file them in a separate area to avoid confusion. The health insurance professional should check the regulations in his or her state regarding protected health information regulations.

Workers' Compensation Fraud

As with any type of insurance, fraud occurs in workers' compensation cases. Most states require workers' compensation insurers, self-insured employers, and third-party administrators to report fraud to the State Insurance Commissioner's office or to the local District Attorney's Office or both. Anyone can report workers' compensation fraud, however. When fraud is suspected, a report should be made within a reasonable time frame, usually within 30 days from the time the individual reporting knows or reasonably believes he or she knows the identity of a person or entity that has committed workers' compensation fraud or has knowledge that such fraud has been committed. This report often can be accomplished by a telephone call to the either of the aforementioned offices.

WHAT DID YOU LEARN?

1. How did workers' compensation originate?
2. Who is eligible for workers' compensation benefits?
3. List four exemption classifications.
4. What is "no-fault" insurance?
5. What does an ombudsman do?

PRIVATE AND EMPLOYER-SPONSORED DISABILITY INCOME INSURANCE

Most people think about insurance coverage as it relates to health, life, home, or auto, but the most crucial aspect of personal and family finances is **earned income**—income from employment. If an illness or injury occurred, and this income stopped, most people would quickly find it difficult or impossible to maintain a home and provide for their family. **Disability income insurance** replaces a *portion* of earned income when an individual is unable to perform the requirements of his or her job because of injury or illness (that is not work-related).

IMAGINE THIS!

Paul Graham, a self-employed auto mechanic, purchased private disability income insurance from Excel Coverage Experts. When he became disabled because of a shoulder injury, his monthly disability benefits paid his house and car payments. Stanley Morgan, Paul's neighbor, fell from a ladder while fixing his roof, resulting in multiple fractures in both legs. Stanley did not have disability income insurance. Stanley was disabled for 6 months, during which time the bank foreclosed on his house because he could not pay the mortgage.

Disability insurance can be purchased privately through a commercial insurance company, or it is sometimes furnished by the employer. There are two major types of disability coverage:

1. **Short-term disability**, which provides an income for the early part of a disability—typically 2 weeks to 2 years
2. **Long-term disability**, which helps replace income for a longer time—5 years or until the disabled individual turns 65

Defining Disability

Disability is commonly defined one of two ways:

1. An individual is unable to perform in the occupation or job that he or she was doing before the disability occurred. This definition of disability is covered in what is referred to as **own-occupation policies**. A variation is the **modified own-occupation policy**, which covers workers for their own occupation as long as they are not gainfully employed elsewhere.
2. An individual is unable to perform any occupation for which he or she is suited by education and experience.

The distinction between these two definitions can be crucial. If a surgeon loses a hand, he or she may not be able to perform surgery. In the case of an *own-occupation policy,* the surgeon would be able to recover, even though he or she was able to work as a physician in a nonsurgical field. With the inability to perform *any occupation,* there would be no recovery, even if the surgeon could work as a tour guide.

Short-Term Disability

Short-term disability pays a percentage of an individual's wages or salary if he or she becomes **tem-porarily disabled**, meaning that the individual is unable to work for a short time because of sickness or injury (excluding job-related illnesses or injuries). A typical short-term disability policy pays one half to two thirds percent for a specific number of weeks, depending on the policy. Most short-term disability policies have a **benefit cap**, meaning there is a maximum benefit amount paid per month.

A worker generally begins receiving money from a short-term disability policy within 1 to 14 days after becoming sick or disabled. The actual time elapsed before payments begin depends on the stipulations in the policy. Often, if the individual sustains an injury, benefits begin immediately. An illness usually takes longer because there needs to be enough time to show that the illness is severe enough to be disabling. If the disability insurance is furnished by the employer, there may be additional restrictions as to when the short-term disability benefits begin. The employer may require all sick days to be used up before the employee begins receiving disability payments. Typically, if the condition worsens over time, the individual would receive disability pay retroactive to the first sick day.

Long-Term Disability

As with short-term disability, a long-term disability insurance policy protects an individual from the loss of ability to earn an income because of an illness or injury that is not work-related. It pays a monthly amount to help cover expenses when an individual is unable to perform his or her job or function in a chosen occupation or profession.

There are two major types of individual long-term disability insurance: no cancelable and guaranteed renewable. In the case of no cancelable or guaranteed renewable policies, the insurer cannot cancel or refuse to renew the policy as long as the required premiums are paid on time. The key difference between the two major types of policies is that under a no cancelable contract, the individual has the extra security that premiums can never be increased above those shown in the policy as long as the required premiums are paid. With a guaranteed renewable policy, the premiums can be increased but only if the change affects an entire class of policyholders. For this reason, initial premiums for guaranteed renewable policies can be less expensive than no cancelable policies.

Disability Claims Process

As with workers' compensation, there are several steps to the disability claims process. There are certain responsibilities to which the employee and the employer must attend to allow this process to work efficiently and effectively.

Employee's Responsibilities

First, the worker must notify the proper party that he or she intends to file a disability claim. To do this, the individual first needs to submit a claim request. If disability insurance is provided through the employer, a claim form may be obtained from the company's human resources department. Some insurers allow telephone submission of claims. In this case, the human resources department should provide a toll-free number and specific instructions for calling in the claim. In the case of an individual or private disability policy, a claim form may be obtained from the insurance company where the policy was purchased. The claim request should include everything needed to process the claim, including the following:

1. Information the employee provides (Fig. 9-4)
2. Information the employer provides (Fig. 9-5)
3. The attending physician statement (Fig. 9-6)
4. An authorization release form that enables the insurer to gather additional information as it becomes necessary (Fig. 9-7)

Employer's Responsibilities

If the disability insurance is provided by the employer, a statement that helps identify the benefits available should accompany the claim. The employer also must provide detailed information as to the type of coverage, policy number, division/class number, and division/class description.

Attending Physician's Statement

It is important that the injured or ill worker be examined by a physician as soon as possible after the disability has occurred and within the time limit allowed by the insurer. The physician must determine that the individual is disabled as defined by the policy. To accomplish this, an attending physician's statement must be completed, which typically includes information such as

- the diagnosis,
- the first day the individual was unable to work,
- whether or not the illness or injury was work-related,
- the nature of the treatment or suggested treatment, and
- restrictions and limitations.

> ### HIPAA TIP
>
> HIPAA mandates that, if an employer provides insurance to its employees and their dependents, all employees and dependents must be covered regardless of medical condition.

Health Insurance Professional's Role

Frequently, disability claim handling gets tied up in time-consuming tasks, such as document processing, record keeping, written correspondence, telephone inquiries, photocopying, and sending faxes. The process involves a lot of human interaction, which complicates the process, especially if all phases are not properly documented and monitored. Everyone involved can become quickly frustrated and impatient. It is the health insurance professional's responsibility to see that everything possible is done to facilitate the claims process for the benefit of the medical practice and the disabled patient. This can be accomplished by seeing to it that claim forms and statements are completed correctly and submitted promptly, and all necessary documentation is included.

The health insurance professional's role also might be to educate the patient regarding disability benefits. With disability insurance, the insurer does not reimburse the patient strictly according to the fees charged for medical services rendered by the attending physician. Disability insurance benefits are paid to compensate for loss of income from wages. Periodic payments (typically monthly) are made directly to the patient to use for expenses as he or she sees fit. Ideally, the patient has a separate health insurance policy to pay the cost of needed health care.

> ### WHAT DID YOU LEARN?
>
> 1. What do disability income insurance benefits pay?
> 2. What items should a typical claim request include?
> 3. List five things the attending physician's statement should address.
> 4. What is the health insurance professional's role in the disability claims process?

FEDERAL DISABILITY PROGRAMS

Federal disability programs provide services such as cash support, health care coverage, and direct supportive services to eligible individuals with disabili-

EMPLOYEE'S CLAIM FOR COMPENSATION

ANSWER ALL QUESTIONS
FULLY - PRINT OR TYPE
CLEARLY

IMPORTANT: Your Social Security Number Must Be Entered:

IMPORTANTE: El Numero de su Seguro Social Debe Ser Indicado:

WCB Case No. (If known)_____   Carrier Case No. (if known)_____

A.
Injured
person
	1. Name..
	         First Name Middle Name Last Name
	2. Mailing Address...
	         Number and Street (include Apartment No.) City State Zip Code.
	3. Sex ☐ Male ☐ Female Date of Birth...Telephone No. ( )................................
	4. Do you speak English? ☐ Yes ☐ No If no, what language do you speak?..
	5. Name of union and local number, if member...
	6. State what your regular work/occupation was..
	7. Wages or average earnings per day, including overtime, board, rent and other allowances...................
	8. Were you paid full wages for the day of injury? ☐ Yes ☐ No
	9. Your work week at time of injury was: ☐ Five day ☐ Six day ☐ Seven day ☐ Other....................

B. Employer(s)	1. Employer..Telephone No. ( ).................... 2. Employer's Address... 3. Were you employed by any other employer or employers at the time of your injury/illness? ☐ Yes ☐ No 4. If yes, did you lose time from work at this other employment as a result of your injury/illness? ☐ Yes ☐ No
C. Place/Time	1. Address where injury occurred...County.......................... 2. Date of Injury.......................................at.................o'clock, ☐ AM ☐ PM
D. The Injury	1. How did injury/illness occur?... ....
E. Nature and Extent of Injury/ Illness	1. State fully the nature of your injury/illness, including all parts of body injured........................ .... 2. Date you stopped work because of this injury/illness?.. 3. Have you returned to work? ☐ Yes ☐ No If yes, on what date?.................................... 4. Does injury/illness keep you from work? ☐ Yes ☐ No 5. Have you done any work during period of disability? ☐ Yes ☐ No 6. Have you received any wages since your injury/illness? ☐ Yes ☐ No

F.
Medical
Benefits
	1. Did you receive or are you now receiving medical care? ☐ Yes ☐ No
	2. Are you now in need of medical care? ☐ Yes ☐ No
	3. Name of attending doctor..
	   Doctor's address..
	4. If you were in a hospital, give the dates hospitalized..
	   Name of hospital..
	   Hospital's address...

G. Comp. Payments	1. Have you received or are you now receiving workers' compensation payments for the injury reported above? ☐ Yes ☐ No 2. Do you claim further workers' compensation payments? ☐ Yes ☐ No
H. Notice	1. Have you given your employer (or supervisor) notice of injury? ☐ Yes ☐ No 2. If yes, notice was given ☐ orally ☐ in writing, on... to ....

ANY PERSON WHO KNOWINGLY AND WITH INTENT TO DEFRAUD PRESENTS, CAUSES TO BE PRESENTED, OR PREPARES WITH KNOWLEDGE OR BELIEF THAT IT WILL BE PRESENTED TO, OR BY AN INSURER, OR SELF INSURER, ANY INFORMATION CONTAINING ANY FALSE MATERIAL STATEMENT OR CONCEALS ANY MATERIAL FACT SHALL BE GUILTY OF A CRIME AND SUBJECT TO SUBSTANTIAL FINES AND IMPRISONMENT.

Signed by..Dated................................
                    (Claimant)

C-3 (2-04)

Fig. 9-4 Employee's statement form.

ties. These programs typically are limited to individuals younger than age 65. There are nine major federal disability programs that include sizable proportions of individuals age 50 to 64, as follows:

1. Social Security Disability Insurance (SSDI)
2. Supplemental Security Income (SSI)
3. Medicare
4. Medicaid
5. Workers' compensation

EMPLOYER'S REPORT OF NON-WORK-RELATED ACCIDENT/OCCUPATIONAL DISEASE

Send this notice directly to the Chair, Workers' Compensation Board at the address shown on the reverse side within ten (10) days after an accident occurs. ANSWER ALL QUESTIONS FULLY. A copy should also be provided to or retained by your workers' compensation insurance carrier.

Any employer who fails to timely file Form C-2, as required by Section 110 of the Workers' Compensation Law, is subject to a fine of not more than $1,000. In addition, the Board or Chair may impose a penalty of up to $2,500.

TYPEWRITER PREPARATION IS STRONGLY RECOMMENDED - INCLUDE ZIP CODE IN ALL ADDRESSES-EMPLOYEE'S S.S.NO. MUST BE ENTERED BELOW ↓

WCB CASE NO.(If Known)	CARRIER CASE NO.	CARRIER CODE NO.	WC POLICY NO.	DATE OF ACCIDENT	EMPLOYEE'S S.S. NO.
		W		m m d d y y	

1.(a) EMPLOYER'S NAME | (b) EMPLOYER'S MAILING ADDRESS | (c) OSHA CASE/FILE NO.

(d) LOCATION (If Different From Mailing Address) | (e) NATURE OF BUSINESS (Principal Products, Services, etc.) | (f) NY UI EMPLOYER REG. NO. | (g) FEIN - if UI Emp. Reg. No. Unknown

2.(a) INSURANCE CARRIER | (b) CARRIER'S ADDRESS

3.(a) INJURED EMPLOYEE (First, M.I., Last) | (b) ADDRESS (Includes No. & Street, City, State, Zip & Apt. No.)

ACCIDENT

4. (a) ADDRESS WHERE ACCIDENT OCCURRED | (b) COUNTY | (c) WAS ACCIDENT ON EMPLOYER'S PREMISES? ☐ Yes ☐ No

5. HOUR EMP. BEGAN WORK h h : m m ☐ AM ☐ PM | 6. TIME OF ACCIDENT h h : m m ☐ AM ☐ PM | 7. DEPT. WHERE REGULARLY EMPLOYED | 8.(a) DATE STOPPED WORK BECAUSE OF THIS INJURY/ILLNESS m m d d y y | (b) WAS EMPLOYEE PAID IN FULL FOR DAY? ☐ Yes ☐ No

INJURED ON

9. SEX ☐ Male ☐ Female | 10. DATE OF BIRTH m m d d y y | 11. OCCUPATION (Specific job title at which employed) | 12. DATE HIRED m m d d y y

13.(a) AVERAGE EARNINGS PER WEEK? $. 0 0 | (b) TOTAL EARNINGS PAID DURING 52 WEEKS PRIOR TO DATE OF ACCIDENT (Include bonuses, overtime, value of lodging, etc.) $, . 0 0 | 14. (a) EMPLOYEE IS: ☐ Full Time ☐ Part Time | (b) INJURED EMPLOYEE'S WORK WEEK (Check days usually worked.) Mon ☐ Tue ☐ Wed ☐ Thu ☐ Fri ☐ Sat ☐ Sun ☐

NATURE OF INJURY

15. NATURE OF INJURY AND PART(S) OF BODY AFFECTED | 16. (a) DID YOU PROVIDE MEDICAL CARE? ☐ Yes ☐ No | (b) IF YES, WHEN?

17. WAS EMPLOYEE TREATED IN AN EMERGENCY ROOM? ☐ Yes ☐ No | 18. WAS EMPLOYEE HOSPITALIZED OVERNIGHT AS AN IN-PATIENT? ☐ Yes ☐ No

19. (a) NAME AND ADDRESS OF DOCTOR | (b) NAME AND ADDRESS OF HOSPITAL

20. (a) HAS EMPLOYEE RETURNED TO WORK? ☐ Yes ☐ No | (b) IF YES, GIVE DATE: m m d d y y | (c) AT WHAT WEEKLY WAGE? $, . 0 0

NOTE: FORM C-11 MUST BE FILED EACH TIME THERE IS A CHANGE IN EMPLOYMENT STATUS

CAUSE OF ACCIDENT

21. WHAT WAS EMPLOYEE DOING WHEN INJURED? (Please be specific. Identify tools, equipment or material the employee was using.)

22. HOW DID THE ACCIDENT OR EXPOSURE OCCUR? (Please describe fully the events that resulted in injury or occupational disease. Tell what happened and how it happened. Please use separate sheet if necessary.)

23. OBJECT OR SUBSTANCE THAT DIRECTLY INJURED EMPLOYEE. e.g., the machine employee struck against or which struck him/her, the vapor or poison inhaled or swallowed, the chemical that irritated his/her skin. In cases of strains, the thing (s)he was lifting, pulling, etc.

FATAL CASES

24. (a) DATE OF DEATH m m d d y y | (b) NAME AND ADDRESS OF NEAREST RELATIVE | (c) RELATIONSHIP

PREPARATION

DATE EMPLOYER/SUPERVISOR FIRST KNEW OF INJURY m m d d y y | DATE OF THIS REPORT m m d d y y | IF FORM IS SUBMITTED BY EMPLOYER, COMPLETE A & B BELOW. IF FORM IS SUBMITTED BY THIRD PARTY, COMPLETE A,B,C & D BELOW.

A. EMPLOYEE PREPARING FORM OR SUPPLYING INFORMATION TO THIRD PARTY | B. TITLE | TELEPHONE NUMBER & EXTENSION

C. IF REPORT PREPARED BY THIRD PARTY, COMPANY NAME AND ADDRESS

D. THIRD PARTY CONTACT NAME | TELEPHONE NUMBER & EXTENSION

Fig. 9-5 Sample employer's statement form.

Health Care Provider Report
See Instructions on Reverse Side
(WHEN COMPLETED RETURN TO REQUESTER)

Please PRINT or TYPE your responses.
Enter dates in MM/DD/YYYY format.

SOCIAL SECURITY NUMBER	DATE OF INJURY
EMPLOYEE	EMPLOYER
INSURER/SELF-INSURER/TPA	INSURER CLAIM NUMBER
INSURER ADDRESS	
CITY	STATE ZIP CODE

REQUESTER must specify all items to be completed by health care provider. ☐ Items: _____ ☐ MMI (#9) ☐ PPD (#10)

HEALTH CARE PROVIDER TO COMPLETE ITEMS REQUESTED ABOVE

1. Date of first examination for this injury by this office: _____ (date)

2. Diagnosis (include all ICD-9-CM codes):

3. History of injury or disease given by employee:

4. In your opinion (as substantiated by the history and physical examination) was the injury or disease caused, aggravated or accelerated by the employee's alleged employment activity or environment? ☐ No ☐ Yes

5. Is there evidence of pre-existing or other conditions that affect this disability? ☐ No ☐ Yes   If yes, describe:

6. Is further treatment of this injury or referral to another doctor planned? ☐ No ☐ Yes   If yes, describe:

7. Has surgery been performed? ☐ No ☐ Yes   If yes, date and describe: _____ (date)

8. Attach the most recent Report of Work Ability. Date of report: _____ (date)

9. **Has the employee reached maximum medical improvement?** ☐ No ☐ Yes   Date reached: _____
   (If yes, complete item #10) (See definition on back)

10. **Has the employee sustained any permanent partial disability from the injury?** ☐ No ☐ Yes ☐ Too early to determine
    The permanent partial disability is _____ % of the whole body. This rating is based on Minn. Rules:

5223.	%	5223.	%
5223.	%	5223.	%

NAME (Type or Print)	SIGNATURE		DEGREE
ADDRESS	STATE	LICENSE #/REGISTRATION #	
CITY STATE ZIP CODE	AREA CODE	TELEPHONE #	DATE SIGNED

MN HC01 (7/01)

Fig. 9-6 Attending physician statement form.

CLAIMANT'S AUTHORIZATION TO DISCLOSE HEALTH INFORMATION
(Pursuant to HIPAA)

INSTRUCTIONS
To the Claimant: The Health Insurance Portability and Accountability Act of 1996 (HIPAA) set standards for guaranteeing the privacy of individually identifiable health information and the confidentiality of patient medical records. By completing and signing this form, you authorize your health care provider to file medical reports with the parties that you choose (such as the Workers' Compensation Board, your employer's insurance carrier, your attorney or representative, etc.) by checking the appropriate boxes below.

You have the right to refuse to sign this Authorization. If you sign, you have the right to revoke this Authorization at any time by mailing a request to revoke to the health care provider. You have the right to receive a copy of this Authorization.

IMPORTANT: Failure to execute this authorization may interfere with your ability to obtain workers' compensation benefits.

CLAIMANT'S NAME	CLAIMANT'S SOCIAL SECURITY NUMBER	CLAIMANT'S DATE OF BIRTH

LIST ALL WCB CASE NUMBER(S) AND CORRESPONDING DATE(S) OF ACCIDENT FOR WHICH YOU ARE GRANTING AUTHORIZATION

I, _____, hereby authorize my treating health provider,
_____Claimant's Name_____

_____, to disclose the following described health information:
_____Health Provider's Name_____

_____

_____

_____

This information can be disclosed to the following parties: *(check all that apply; give names and addresses, if known)*

☐ New York State Workers' Compensation Board

☐ My current/former employer _____

☐ Workers' compensation insurance carrier(s) _____

☐ Third-party administrator _____

☐ My attorney/licensed representative _____

☐ The Uninsured Employer's Fund (this fund is responsible for paying the medical bills and lost wage benefits when an employer is uninsured.)

☐ Special Funds Conservation Committee (for cases under Section 25-a or 15-8 of the Workers' Compensation Law)

   Section 25-a: If your claim is being reopened after being previously closed, the Special Fund for Reopened Cases may be responsible for paying your medical bills and lost wage benefits.

   Section 15-8: If you had a medical condition that existed prior to this injury, the Special Fund for Second Injuries may be responsible for reimbursing your employer's insurance carrier after a period of time has elapsed.

Redisclosure: I understand that once the above-referenced health care provider discloses health information based on this Authorization, that health information is no longer protected by HIPAA and the Privacy Rule.
Expiration Date: This Authorization expires upon the final closing of the workers' compensation claim(s) for which it is executed.

I have had the opportunity to review and understand the content of this Authorization. By signing this Authorization, I confirm that it accurately reflects my wishes.

Printed Name of Claimant or Legal Representative	Signature of Claimant or Legal Representative	Date

If Authorization signed by a legal representative on behalf of claimant, state relationship to claimant_____and basis for authority (e.g. claimant is a minor; patient is deceased and representative is the claimant in a workers' compensation proceeding or represents the estate) _____

TO THE HEALTH PROVIDER: Keep the original of this Authorization on file. A copy must be given to the patient/claimant upon request.

Fig. 9-7 Authorization release form.

6. Black Lung
7. Department of Veterans Affairs (VA) Disability Compensation Program
8. VA Pension Programs
9. VA Health Services Program

An individual may receive benefits from more than one program if he or she meets all the eligibility requirements. Specific eligibility requirements typically vary, depending on the purpose of the program, and eligibility requirements may change over time, as the result of amendments to the law, new regulations, or court decisions that affect eligibility criteria.

Disability under the federal programs generally is defined as significant difficulty with or the inability to perform certain day-to-day functions as a result of a health condition or impairment. For adults age 18 through 64, these functions often involve working or keeping house. For individuals age 65 and older, the functions may involve the inability to carry out routine daily tasks. Some commonly used factors federal programs look at in assessing disability are the following:

- Sensory impairments—difficulty with or the inability to see, hear, or speak
- Cognitive/mental impairments—the presence of or resulting disabilities from cognitive/mental impairments (e.g., Alzheimer disease, mental illness, mental retardation)
- Functioning of specific body systems—capacity of specific body systems (e.g., climbing stairs, walking three blocks, lifting 10 lb)
- **Activities of daily living and instrumental activities of daily living**—difficulty with or the inability to perform without the help of another person or a device the activities of daily living, which typically include bathing, dressing, eating, toileting, getting in or out of a bed or chair, and walking, or the instrumental activities of daily living, which generally include using the telephone, shopping, preparing meals, keeping house, doing laundry, doing yard work, managing personal finances, and managing medications
- Working—inability to work; limitations in the amount or kind of work; or ability to work only occasionally, irregularly, or part-time

Americans with Disabilities Act

The intent of the Americans with Disabilities Act (ADA) of 1990 is to protect the civil rights of individuals with disabilities. Equal opportunity provisions pertain to employment, public accommodation, transportation, state and local government services, and telecommunications. Disability is present for purposes of the ADA if an individual meets one of the following three criteria:

1. There is a physical or mental impairment that substantially limits one or more major life activities.
2. There is a record of such an impairment.
3. The individual is regarded as having an impairment.

Social Security Disability Insurance

Social Security Disability Insurance (SSDI) is the primary federal insurance program that protects workers from loss of income as a result of disability. SSDI provides monthly cash benefits to disabled workers younger than age 65 and to certain of their dependents. SSDI is intended for workers who retire before age 65 because of a disability.

History of the Social Security Disability Insurance Program
The 1935 Social Security Act established the federal Social Security system to provide old-age benefits for retired workers. The SSDI program was enacted in 1956 to provide benefits to workers age 50 through 64 who retired early because of a disability. Subsequent amendments broadened SSDI coverage to include certain dependents and workers younger than age 50.

Administration and Funding
SSDI is federally administered by the Social Security Administration. Funding is provided through the disability insurance (SSDI) portion of the Social Security payroll tax on wages. As of 2007, the payroll tax was 7.65% of earnings, of which 5.6% was for the Old-Age and Survivors Insurance portion of Social Security, 0.62% for the SSDI portion, and 1.45% for the hospital insurance portion of Medicare. A matching 7.65% tax is contributed by employers. Self-employed individuals must contribute the entire 15.3% because they pay the employer and employee shares. As of 2007, the wage base limits for Social Security (Old-Age and Survivors Insurance and disability insurance parts) was $97,500. There is no wage base limit for the Medicare (hospital insurance) payroll tax.

Eligibility
To become eligible for SSDI, individuals must meet two criteria:

1. They must have worked enough Social Security–covered work quarters.

2. They must have a severe impairment that makes them unable to do their previous work or any other kind of substantial financially gainful activity.

Social Security–covered work quarters are credited annually for the years during which an individual works, is covered by Social Security, and earns a specified amount, which is adjusted upward each year. No more than four quarters can be credited per year. Workers must be fully insured (based on Social Security contributions) and (except for individuals who are blind or who are more than 31 years old) must have at least 20 quarters of coverage during the 40-quarter period up to the time of disability to receive SSDI. Individuals who are fully insured under Social Security have at least one quarter of coverage for every four quarters up to the time of disability. Individuals who have 40 quarters are fully insured for life. Workers younger than age 31 and individuals who are blind need fewer quarters, but a minimum of six quarters is required. Disability for SSDI is defined as the inability to do any substantial gainful activity by reason of any medically determinable physical or mental impairment that can be expected to result in death or that has lasted or can be expected to last for a continuous period of not less than 12 months.

After it has been established that the applicant has enough quarters and is not earning more than the "substantial gainful activity amount," a State Disability Determination unit examines medical evidence to determine if the applicant's mental or physical impairment is severe enough to have more than a minimal effect on the applicant's ability to work. If so, the applicant's medical condition is compared with a Social Security Administration listing of more than 100 impairments (e.g., loss of two limbs; fracture of vertebra with spinal cord involvement, substantiated by appropriate sensory and motor loss; vision of 20/200 or less after correction).

Applicants whose medical conditions are at least as severe as the conditions in the Social Security Administration listing are considered disabled. Applicants who are not found disabled at this point are evaluated two additional steps. First, a determination is made regarding whether the applicant can do his or her past work. This decision is based on assessments of factors such as physical abilities (e.g., strength, walking, standing) or mental abilities (e.g., the ability to carry out and remember instructions or to respond appropriately in work settings).

For applicants who cannot perform past work, an assessment is done to determine their ability to perform other jobs that exist in the national economy. This assessment is based on the individual's functional capacity, age, education, and work experience. Generally, individuals younger than age 50 are considered to be able to adapt to new work situations.

Dependent coverage and survivor benefits are offered through SSDI to certain qualifying individuals. Disabled individuals can receive SSDI in three ways:

1. On their own as disabled workers (described previously)
2. As widows or widowers (who are age 50 to 59) of insured individuals
3. As adults age 18 through 64 who became disabled in childhood whose parents receive SSDI, are Social Security retirees, or who are deceased (but had been insured under Social Security)

IMAGINE THIS!

After teacher Louise Carson had her workers' compensation claim denied, she quit her job and filed for SSDI. SSDI found Louise to be disabled at her teaching position; however, they determined that she could perform at a "new work" situation that was less stressful and suggested that Louise use her education and training to work in a library or become a private tutor.

Supplemental Security Income

The **Supplemental Security Income (SSI)** program provides monthly cash payments to low-income aged, blind, and disabled individuals. The SSI program was established by the 1972 amendments to the Social Security Act, which replaced earlier federal grants to the states for old-age assistance, aid to the blind, and aid to the permanently disabled.

Administration and Funding

The SSI program is administered by the Social Security Administration. Funding comes from general federal revenues. Many states have chosen the option to supplement federal SSI payments with their own funds.

Eligibility

In contrast to SSDI, individuals receiving SSI because of blindness or disability have no work requirements but must meet a **financial means test**, a detailed and comprehensive questionnaire that establishes financial need. The SSI means test depends on income and resources. Individuals younger than age 65 must meet disability and financial criteria, whereas individuals age 65 or older need to meet only the financial means test. Individuals may receive SSI payments either as individuals or as couples. Both members of a couple must be aged, blind, or disabled and must meet the financial means test to collect payments. Other than these provisions for couples, there are no dependent or survivor benefits in SSI.

The determination of disability under SSI for adults is identical to the one used in the SSDI program. For children younger than age 18, the determination of disability is based on a standard of comparable severity. Their methods of counting various types of income and resources are complex, but generally the maximum unearned monthly income in 2007 for individuals applying for SSI was $623 and $934 for couples if they received only Social Security and $1326 for individuals and $1948 for couples if their income was only from wages. Countable resources are limited to $2000 for individuals and $3000 for couples (Table 9-3).

HIPAA TIP

As a "covered entity" under HIPAA, the Social Security Administration, which oversees the federal disability programs such as SSDI and SDI, must comply with HIPAA's medical information standards.

State Disability Programs

A few states (California, Hawaii, New Jersey, New York, and Rhode Island) and Puerto Rico currently have disability programs that provide short-term benefits for employees. These state programs are set up to supplement Social Security disability benefits. Because Social Security disability benefits do not cover the first 6 months of the disability, these state plans provide benefits to qualifying disabled individuals until Social Security payments begin. The funds are financed by a combination of the employees' payroll deductions and employer contributions. An employee's contributions are based on his or her earnings and are withheld from wages by the employer and transferred to the state fund. There are severe penalties for failing to withhold the contributions. With the exception of Rhode Island, an employer can opt out of the state plan and put the employee's contributions into a private plan. Private plans must meet state requirements regarding coverage, eligibility, contribution amounts, and employee approval.

Centers for Disease Control and Prevention Disability and Health Team

The **Disability and Health Team** is part of the new National Center on Birth Defects and Developmental Disabilities at the Centers for Disease Control and Prevention (CDC) in Atlanta, Georgia. The team's focus is promoting the health of individuals who are living with disabilities. The CDC Disability and Health Team activities include the following:

- Assessing and monitoring disability prevalence
- Assessing the health status and quality of life for individuals with disabilities
- Describing risk factors and costs associated with secondary conditions and poor health
- Developing health promotion interventions to reduce secondary conditions and evaluate intervention effectiveness and costs
- Offering training to health care professionals interested in the field of disability and public health
- Supporting conferences to facilitate and encourage discussion, circulate and exchange information, establish research and policy priorities, and outline and undertake further action

To learn more about the Disability and Health Team, log on to the following Web page: http://www.cdc.gov/ncbddd/dh.

Ticket to Work Program

The **Ticket to Work program** was created with passage of the federal Ticket to Work and Work Incentives Improvement Act of 1999. Ticket to Work is a *voluntary* program that gives certain individuals with disabilities greater choice in selecting the service providers and rehabilitation services they need to help them keep working or get back to work.

Purpose

Ticket to Work was created to help individuals who receive SSDI or SSI benefits find and keep employment by offering them more options for services and supports. Many individuals receiving SSDI or SSI choose not to work because they are concerned about losing their benefits. Ticket to Work gives these individuals an opportunity to choose services to meet their unique needs and obtain benefits-planning assistance so that they can make informed choices about employment. Individuals receiving SSDI or SSI disability benefits may participate in Ticket to Work.

TABLE 9-3	SSI and SSDI Similarities and Differences	
	SSI	**SSDI**
Also Known as:	Supplemental Security Income	Social Security Disability Insurance
Eligibility Criteria	Needs-based—must have little or no income and resources	Insured status as a worker, or a child, widow, or widower of an insured worker No resource limits, no limits on *unearned* income
Monthly Benefit Amounts	Federal Benefit Rate (FBR) of $637 (2008) Check amount depends on: (1) living situation, (2) earnings, and (3) unearned income Some states supplement the federal amount for some or all living situations	Either eligible for a full benefit check or ineligible and receive no benefits Amount based on: (1) earnings history of wage earner, (2) age when benefits begin, and (3) number of people in addition to the wage earner who are receiving benefits If benefit amount is less than SSI FBR ($637 in 2008), also may be eligible for SSI
When Checks Arrive	First day of the month; if the 1st is a holiday or weekend, the check arrives on the business day before the 1st	People who qualified for SSDI before May 1997: arrives 3rd of the month Qualified after May 1997 and birthday between: (1) 1st-10th: arrives 2nd Wednesday (2) 11th-20th: arrives 3rd Wednesday (3) 21st-31st: arrives 4th Wednesday
Funding Source	Annual Congressional appropriation from "General Fund"	Social Security Trust Fund, FICA taxes
Laws and Regulations	*Title XVI* (16) of the Social Security Act (Title 42 US Code, The Public Health and Welfare, Chapter 7, Subchapter XVI) Regulations in 20 CFR; Part 416	*Title II* (2) of the Social Security Act (Title 42 US Code, The Public Health and Welfare, Chapter 7, Subchapter II) Regulations in 20 CFR, Parts 400-499
Medical Benefits	*Medicaid* eligible in 32 states In other states, must apply separately for Medicaid Eligible the month of SSI application and possibly 3 mo retroactively	*Medicare* eligible (Parts A and B), 24 months after person qualifies for SSDI
Monthly Cost (Premium)	None	SSDI recipients with yearly incomes <$82,000 have $96.40 (2008) deducted from their check each month. If SSDI recipient also receives SSI, Medicaid pays the monthly Medicare premium
Deductible	None, but there may be "cost sharing" instituted by states for various services	Yes—in 2008, the Part B deductible is $135/yr. If person also receives SSI, Medicaid pays the deductible
Co-pay	Possibly none; however, states may elect to have small co-pays for medications, services, and hospitalization	20% of costs deemed allowable by Medicare; 100% of costs not deemed allowable by Medicare. If person also receives SSI, Medicaid pays all co-pays

Available at: http://ruralinstitute.umt.edu/training/publications/fact_sheets/ssi_ssdi.asp.

TABLE 9-3	SSI and SSDI Similarities and Differences—cont'd	
	SSI	**SSDI**
Range of Coverage	Very comprehensive. Generally covers physician visits, prescriptions, dentures, glasses, hospital, hospice care, home help services/personal care, and other costs. Pays Medicare premium for concurrent recipients. Pays premiums for private insurance when cost-effective. Coverage may vary from state to state	Hospital costs primarily. Some home health care and durable medical equipment. Usually does *not* cover glasses, dentures, day-to-day medical costs, and physician visits. Owing to recent changes, however, Medicare pays for comprehensive care at select clinics, and since 2006 there is a Part D prescription benefit that pays substantial costs for most people
Proof of Coverage	Card comes monthly. Lists person covered, recipient ID number for billing, Managed Care Provider, and contract number of any other insurance (e.g., Medicare) to be billed first	Permanent wallet-sized card, white with red and blue stripe. Names the person covered, the coverage, and the date that coverage began

How the Program Works

Ticket to Work participants receive a paper document or "ticket" that explains the program and includes some personal information about them. They can take their ticket to an approved employment network to receive the services they want. An **employment network** can be a public agency or private organization that has agreed to provide services under the Ticket to Work program guidelines.

Filing Supplemental Security Income and Social Security Disability Insurance Disability Claims

Patient's Role

The patient initiates the SSI or SSDI claim. The best way to begin the process is to file a Social Security disability claim at the nearest Social Security office in person. An alternative method is to contact Social Security by telephone and arrange for a telephone interview to file the claim.

A claim for Social Security disability benefits may be filed on the same day that an individual becomes disabled. There is no reason to file a Social Security disability claim for a minor illness or one that is unlikely to last 1 year or more. An individual who has a serious illness or injury and expects to be out of work for 1 year or more should not delay in filing a claim for Social Security disability benefits.

Unless the disability is catastrophic (e.g., terminal cancer, a serious heart condition requiring transplant, total paralysis of both legs), there is no easy way to tell whether an individual would be found disabled by Social Security. Individuals should make the decision about whether to file for Social Security disability on the basis of their own belief regarding their condition. If the individual believes that he or she is truly disabled and is not going to be able to return to work in the near future, that individual should file for Social Security disability benefits.

After a Social Security disability claim is filed, the case is sent to a disability examiner at the Disability Determination Agency in that state, who works with a physician to make the initial decision on the claim on the basis of a thorough clinical examination and interviews. If the claim is denied and the individual requests reconsideration, the case is sent to a second disability examiner at the Disability Determination Agency, where it goes through a similar process. If a claim is denied at reconsideration, the individual may request a hearing. At this point, the case is sent to an administrative law judge who works for Social Security. The administrative law judge makes an independent decision on the claim, which is usually final.

An individual can hire an attorney to represent him or her on Social Security disability claim denials. The National Organization of Social Security Claimants' Representatives offers a referral service at 1-800-431-2804 during regular Eastern Standard Time business hours.

Applicants for SSI or SSDI benefits should get the free booklet *Social Security Disability Benefits* (Social Security Administration Publication No. 05-10029). This booklet suggests ways to help shorten the process by knowing what documents to include when applying for benefits.

Role of the Health Care Provider

The disability determination process relies on the participation of the medical community in many ways. One of the most important ways is as a **treating source** that provides the long-term medical information (called medical evidence of record), which is normally required in every claim for disability benefits. In addition to providing treating source evidence, the medical community can assist the disability programs in the following ways:

- As a member of the state Disability Determination Services disability evaluation team that makes the initial or continuing disability determination
- As a reviewer of the state decision
- As a consultative examiner for the Disability Determination Services
- As a medical expert for an administrative law judge

Health care providers who serve as medical experts may be asked to give verbal testimony or provide answers to questions on claim reviews. Frequently, the final decision to allow or deny a Social Security disability claim rests on the advice and medical opinions provided by these medical experts.

HIPAA TIP

HIPAA protects against gaps in insurance coverage, allowing the freedom to move from one job to another or the freedom to move from SSI or SSDI status to the ranks of the employed.

Role of the Health Insurance Professional

The health insurance professional needs to know the Social Security regulations so that he or she is able to provide the exact information needed for evaluation of an individual's disability. There are many steps in the application process, which can be time-consuming and confusing, and knowledgeable health care team members should do all they can to facilitate this process.

Similar to workers' compensation claims, there is no standard form for billing disability claims. When a patient comes to the medical facility for the purpose of getting the physician's medical opinion regarding disability, the health insurance professional should advise the patient to bring the necessary forms provided by the Social Security office.

Additional responsibilities of the health insurance professional include the following:

- Procuring the patient's authorization to release information
- Acquiring the necessary information for claims processing
- Ensuring that the attending physician forms are complete and signed
- Photocopying all forms for the patient's health record
- Maintaining a well-documented health record
- Answering the patient's questions

STOP AND THINK

Amy Turner, a health insurance professional for Dr. Laura Nelson, wants to be able to help patients through the often complicated process of filing for SSI/SSDI benefits. What would you suggest Amy do to become knowledgeable in this area?

WHAT DID YOU LEARN?

1. List six federal disability programs.
2. How do federal programs define disability?
3. ADA considers disability present if an individual meets what three criteria?
4. What is the difference between SSI and SSDI?
5. List the five states that provide short-term disability benefits.

SUMMARY CHECK POINTS

- ☑ Workers' compensation is a type of insurance regulated by state laws that pays medical expenses and partial loss of wages for workers who are injured on the job or become ill as a result of job-related circumstances.

- ☑ Any employee who injures himself or herself on the job or develops an employment-related illness that prevents the individual from working is usually eligible to receive workers' compensation benefits. A spouse and dependents of an employee who dies or gets killed because of a job-related accident or illness also are eligible for benefits.

- ☑ Most employers must purchase workers' compensation insurance coverage for their workers; however, there are certain classifications of exemptions, depending on state statutes.

Common types of exemptions include the following:
- Employers with a *minimum* number of full-time employees (individual states determine this number)
- Executive officers
- Individuals who are business partners
- Sole proprietors
- Casual employees

☑ The four major benefit components to workers' compensation are as follows:
- *Medical expense*—pays expenses involved for hospitalization, physicians' visits, and any necessary medical treatment
- *Disability pay*—can be temporary or permanent if it is determined that the worker will never fully recover
- *Vocational rehabilitation*—if the injury or illness results in the worker being unable to perform the usual duties of his or her occupation, retraining may be necessary for the worker to enter into a new trade or business; also, physical therapy may be needed
- *Death benefits*—paid to surviving dependents

☑ The reporting requirements for filing a workers' compensation claim include the following steps:
- Employee notifies a supervisor of the incident immediately and provides the names of any witnesses.
- Employee completes a detailed accident report on a form furnished by the employer.
- Employer reports the incident to the company's workers' compensation carrier.
- Employee is sent to a medical facility for treatment or diagnosis. (In emergencies, this should be the first step.)
- Attending physician completes statement and distributes copies.
- Follow-up progress reports are submitted until the employee returns to work, after which a final report is filed.

☑ When the injured or ill worker visits the health care facility for treatment, the attending physician takes a history, performs an examination, makes a diagnosis, and completes a statement indicating any physical or mental impairments resulting from the incident. Disability is determined on the basis of these reports.

☑ The purpose of disability income insurance is to replace a portion of salary or wages earned income when an individual is unable to perform the requirements of his or her job because of injury or illness that is not work related.

☑ SSDI is a federal insurance program that pays monthly cash benefits to disabled workers younger than age 65 and to certain dependents who have lost their income because of disability. Individuals applying for SSDI must meet two criteria:
- They must have worked a specific number of Social Security–covered work quarters.
- They must have a severe impairment that makes them unable to perform their previous work or any other kind of financially gainful activity.

☑ SSI provides monthly cash payments to low-income aged, blind, and disabled individuals. There are no work requirements for SSI, but individuals must answer a detailed and comprehensive questionnaire that establishes financial need, called a financial means test. Disability determination for adults is the same under SSDI and SSI.

☑ The CDC Disability and Health Team activities include the following:
- Assessing and monitoring the occurrence of disabilities
- Assessing the health status and quality of life for individuals with disabilities
- Describing risk factors and costs associated with secondary conditions and poor health
- Developing and evaluating effectiveness of health promotion interventions
- Offering training to interested health professionals
- Supporting conferences to facilitate and encourage team activities

☑ Ticket to Work was created to help SSDI/SSI recipients find and keep employment by offering them more options. The program gives individuals an opportunity to choose services to meet their unique needs and obtain benefits-planning assistance so that they can make informed choices about employment. Participants receive a paper document (ticket) that explains the program and includes some personal information about them. They can take their ticket to an approved employment network to receive the desired services.

☑ The patient initiates an SSI/SSDI claim by going to the nearest Social Security office in person or by telephoning and arranging for a telephone interview to file the claim. After the claim is filed, the case is sent to a disability examiner who works with a physician to make the initial decision on the claim on the basis of a thorough clinical examination and interviews.

☑ The health insurance professional's responsibilities for facilitating disability claims processing include the following:
- Obtaining the patient's authorization to release information
- Acquiring the necessary information and forms for claims processing
- Ensuring that the attending physician reports are complete and signed
- Photocopying all forms and correspondence for the patient's health record
- Maintaining a well-documented health record
- Answering the patient's questions

Closing Scenario

Jim and Tammy had discussed their individual areas of interest before beginning the chapter. Tammy visited with her Uncle Niles on several occasions to learn all she could about disability income insurance, and she shared what she learned with Jim. Meanwhile, Jim researched the workers' compensation websites available on the Internet. By the end of the chapter, the two students thought that they had acquired a good knowledge base for workers' compensation and private and federal disability income insurance. Jim now has a better understanding of the payment system that kept his family going after his father's death.

Jim and Tammy realize that acquiring a solid foundation in all areas of insurance is a benefit not only to health insurance professionals but also to the entire health care team. By becoming well informed, health insurance professionals can help educate patients to alleviate the cumbersome task of filing and maintaining all of the documents necessary for workers' compensation and disability insurance.

WEBSITES TO EXPLORE

- To find out about the workers' compensations laws in your state, log on to http://www.workerscompensation.com

- For an overview of state workers' compensation laws, the U.S. Department of Labor provides one in PDF (Portable Document Format) at http://www.dol.gov
(*Note*: You must download and install a *free Adobe Acrobat Reader* to view and print PDF files)

- To keep aware of changes in the SSDI and SSI programs, log on to http://www.ssa.gov

- For more information on the CDC Disability and Health Team Program, log on to the CDC website at http://www.cdc.gov

Chapter Review

Assessment

Multiple Choice

Directions: *In the questions/statements presented, choose the response that **best** answers/completes the stem, and circle the letter that precedes it.*

1. Workers' compensation got its start in the 1800s in ____.
   A. the United States
   B. England
   C. Germany
   D. Japan

2. In workers' compensation insurance, the premiums are paid by ____.
   A. the employee
   B. the employer
   C. split equally between employer and employee
   D. there are no premiums with workers' compensation

3. The federal program that establishes workers' compensation for nonmilitary federal government employees is known by the acronym ____.
   A. OSHA
   B. FEMA
   C. FECA
   D. FELA

4. The federal program that establishes workers' compensation for railroad workers engaged in interstate commerce is known by the acronym ____.
   A. OSHA
   B. FEMA
   C. FECA
   D. FELA

5. An individual responsible for investigating and resolving workers' complaints against the employer or insurance company that is denying the benefits is called a(an) ____.
   A. ombudsman
   B. lead agent
   C. fiscal intermediary
   D. claims investigator

6. The time limit for filing a workers' compensation claim is established by ____.
   A. the employer
   B. the federal government
   C. individual state statutes
   D. the insurance company that issues the policy

7. An injury or illness that is job related typically must be reported to the employer ____.
   A. within 24 hours
   B. within 2 days
   C. there are no time limits
   D. time limits vary from state to state

8. A patient's inability to perform normal job duties at the previous level of expertise as a result of being absent from work is called ____.
   A. acquiescing
   B. noncompliance
   C. job deconditioning
   D. job reclassification

9. After the initial attending physician report has been filed, periodic updates must be provided to the employer/insurer, called ____.
   A. progress reports
   B. supplemental reports
   C. period update reports
   D. A and B

10. The type of insurance that replaces a portion of earned income when an individual is unable to perform the requirements of his or her job because of non–job-related injury or illness is called ____.
    A. SSDI
    B. workers' compensation
    C. indemnity insurance
    D. disability insurance

11. The maximum amount of benefits that can be received in a specific time period is called ____.
    A. a benefit cap
    B. liability limit
    C. payment closure
    D. a catastrophic cap

12. The federal act established in 1990 that protects the civil rights of individuals with disabilities is called the ____.
    A. Consolidated Omnibus Budget Reconciliation Act (COBRA)
    B. Occupational Health and Safety Administration (OSHA) Act
    C. Social Security Disability Insurance (SSDI)
    D. Americans with Disabilities Act (ADA)

13. The examining body that determines if an applicant qualifies for SSDI is the ____.
    A. State Disability Determination unit
    B. Social Security Administration
    C. Centers for Medicare and Medicaid Services (CMS)
    D. Department of Health and Human Services

14. The method of determining whether an individual is eligible for SSI benefits is through a(an) ____.
    A. activities of daily living evaluation
    B. financial means test
    C. spend-down process
    D. patient/provider interview

15. The program that provides greater choice in selecting the providers and rehabilitation services disabled individuals need to help them keep working or return to work is called ____.
    A. SSI
    B. SSDI
    C. Ticket to Work
    D. CDC Disability and Health

True/False

Directions: *Place a "T" in the blank preceding the numbered statement if it is true; place an "F" if it is false.*

_____ 1. Employers must purchase workers' compensation policies from the state in which their business operates.

_____ 2. In the United States, any employee who is injured on the job or develops an employment-related illness that prevents the individual from working is likely to be eligible to collect workers' compensation benefits.

_____ 3. If an employee is injured on the job, the employer can be penalized if the cause of injury or illness was due to the employer being conspicuously negligent.

_____ 4. Most state workers' compensation laws include coverage for injuries sustained while an employee is commuting to and from work.

_____ 5. If a workers' compensation claim is denied, the worker may file a claim with his or her health insurance carrier only after all workers' compensation appeals have been exhausted.

_____ 6. The first thing an injured employee must do is call his or her family physician.

_____ 7. Workers' compensation claims must be submitted on the universal CMS-1500 claim form.

_____ 8. As long as a workers' compensation claim is pending, the provider cannot bill the patient.

_____ 9. Workers' compensation patients are not required to sign a release of information form for a claim form to be filed.

_____ 10. An individual may receive benefits from only one federal disability program even if he or she meets all the eligibility requirements for several.

_____ 11. The SSI program provides monthly cash payments to low-income aged, blind, and disabled individuals.

_____ 12. The CDC Disability and Health Team's focus is promoting safe workplace procedures.

Short Answer

Directions: *Answer each question fully in the space provided.*

1. List four work-related incidents in which injury occurs that would be exceptions to the employee drawing workers' compensation benefits.

_____

_____

_____

_____

2. List five classifications of businesses that do not have to provide workers' compensation for their employees.

_____

_____

_____

_____

_____

3. Workers' compensation insurance is **no-fault insurance**. Explain what this means.

_____

4. List the four major benefit components to workers' compensation.

_____

_____

_____

_____

5. List the physician's two distinct roles in workers' compensation claims.

_____

_____

6. List and explain the various classifications of workers' compensation disability cases, as mandated by federal law.

_____

_____

_____

7. List and explain the two major classifications of disability coverage.

_____

_____

8. List five pertinent items the attending physician's statement must include when filing a disability claim.

_____

_____

_____

_____

_____

9. List the nine federal disability programs.

_____

_____

_____

_____

_____

_____

_____

_____

_____

10. Name at least four of the commonly used factors federal programs look at in assessing disability.

_____

_____

_____

_____

11. Name the two criteria an individual must meet to become eligible for SSDI.

_____

_____

12. List the three ways disabled individuals can receive SSDI.

_____

_____

_____

13. Discuss the health insurance professional's role in the disability claims process.

_____

_____

_____

Critical Thinking Activities

A. Casey Belmont, a 33-year-old established patient, comes to Broadmoor Medical Clinic for treatment of a back injury. Casey, who is employed by National Parcel Delivery Service, claims he was injured at work while lifting a heavy box onto a conveyor. When Casey's chart arrives in your office for claims processing, you notice that the clinical notes from this visit are added to his ongoing health record. Is this appropriate? Why or why not?

B. You also note from Casey's chart that his employer has not notified Broadmoor Medical Clinic of this alleged work-related injury. How does this affect the case? Can you telephone Casey's employer to confirm or disaffirm this injury without jeopardizing patient confidentiality?

C. On the Patient Information Form, Casey has listed his primary health insurance carrier as Fortune Health through National Parcel. There is no completed "First Report of Injury" form; is it okay to go ahead and file a claim with Fortune Health?

D. During a telephone conversation with the Human Resources Department at National Parcel, they inform you that they do not consider Casey Belmont's claim valid because he did not attend the mandatory safety meetings the company provides periodically, and he did not follow the instructions in the company's safety manual for proper procedure in lifting heavy containers. How does this affect the case?

Case Studies

Determine the amount each workers' compensation patient can be billed in the following scenarios and briefly explain your answer.

1. Brett Swanson, a constructor worker, was treated in your office for a fractured leg sustained in a fall into a footing excavation. Total charges were $1875, and workers' compensation paid $1400.

   Patient can be billed: _____

2. Part-time worker Effie Brockett was treated for a cut above her right eye sustained during an altercation with a fellow worker. Total charges were $256.50. Workers' compensation denied the claim. She has no health care coverage.

   Patient can be billed: _____

3. John Stevens underwent surgery for carpal tunnel syndrome caused by repetitive motion from assembly line work. Total charges were $7345. Workers' compensation paid $3500, and his group health insurance paid $2500.

   Patient can be billed: _____

4. Antonio Estabon was treated for a dislocated shoulder sustained while performing his duties as a county roads engineer. Total charges were $3900. Workers' compensation case is pending.

   Patient can be billed: _____

5. Salid Mufazi was treated for an acute case of bronchitis, which he claims was caused by breathing dust while cleaning a grain elevator at his jobsite. Charges totaled $730. Workers' compensation denied the claim, and Mr. Mufazi informs you that he is appealing the decision.

   Patient can be billed: _____

6. Sally Forsythe was treated in the office for injuries sustained in an automobile accident while delivering flowers for Elegant Arrangements. Total charges were $1600. Workers' compensation–allowed charges in your state for the services and procedures provided to Sally are $1195; however, the claim was denied.

   Patient can be billed: _____

Internet Exploration

A. Explore the Internet websites on workers' compensation. Determine the following:
   1. Specific rules and regulations for filing claims in your state
   2. Your state's approved claim form

B. Explore the Ticket to Work program website at **http://www.yourtickettowork.com**.

C. Using search worlds such as "state disability programs," log on to the Internet and see if you can determine what programs, if any, your state provides to disabled workers, and what the eligibility requirements are.

D. Explore the Internet using search words such as "disability" and "HIPAA." Determine how HIPAA affects workers' compensation and disability claims.

10

Objectives

After completion of this chapter, the student should be able to:

1. List and discuss various patient expectations.
2. Name two future trends in the patient-practice relationship.
3. Explain what a "HIPAA covered entity" is.
4. Define "identifiable information," and list the various elements that make it so.
5. Explain how personal health information can be "de-identified."
6. List the elements that a HIPAA-approved release of information must contain.
7. Discuss two methods of accounting used in today's health care facilities.
8. Describe how a health care practice can increase its financial success.
9. List the five federal laws that affect collections.
10. Outline the steps involved in the small claims litigation process.

THE PATIENT

KEY TERMS

accounts receivable
alternate billing cycle
assignment of benefits
billing cycle
collection agency
collection ratio
daily journal
defendant
de-identified

disbursements journal
Equal Credit Opportunity Act
Fair Credit Billing Act
Fair Credit Reporting Act
Fair Debt Collection Practices Act
general journal
general ledger
HIPAA-covered entities
identifiable health information

"one-write" systems
patient information form
patient ledger
payroll journal
plaintiff
self-pay patient
small claims litigation
surrogates
Truth in Lending Act

Opening Scenario

Callie Foster enrolled in the health insurance program not only because it offered interesting and challenging career opportunities but also because of an incident she had recently experienced. Callie had had ear pain for several days, so she called for an appointment at ENT Dr. Susan Dayton's office. Callie took time off work to drive the 30 miles to the ENT clinic. When she arrived and signed in at the front desk, the medical receptionist asked for her insurance card; however, after searching in vain through

her pockets and purse, Callie said she must have left it at home. "Then," said the receptionist brusquely, "you will have to reschedule. Dr. Dayton does not see patients who do not have insurance." Before Callie could confirm the fact that she had coverage through her employer, the receptionist turned away, ignoring her protests. Callie ended up in the emergency department later that day with a ruptured eardrum.

This experience was very upsetting, and Callie wants to find out what patients typically expect when they visit a health care office. She firmly believes that all members of the health care team should learn how to empathize and listen to what patients have to say. Callie was convinced that there is no excuse for impolite behavior and harsh treatment in a health care office.

Scott Tanner is a classmate of Callie Foster. Scott's interests lay not only in the patient side of medical insurance but also in credit law and collections. Scott wants to learn about the small claims process; his parents own rental units and occasionally experience problems collecting rents. Scott and Callie look forward to having their questions answered in Chapter 10.

PATIENT EXPECTATIONS

When patients visit a health care practice, they bring something with them that may not be obvious to the health care team. Besides their sore throats, broken legs, or heart palpitations, they bring with them a set of expectations. These expectations were created by previous experiences with other health care providers, the media, and the opinions of their friends and family. If the health care provider and health care office staff members are oblivious to those expectations, the entire practice risks being perceived as cold and unfeeling. If the health care office staff is successful in meeting or exceeding these expectations, the patient likely will be pleased with the care he or she receives.

The first step in creating a good patient-staff relationship begins when the individual telephones for an appointment. How this encounter is handled can create a lasting impression of how the patient perceives the entire practice, including the health care providers. If the rapport between the physicians and the medical team is strained and uneasy, patients sense this, and they are likely to feel tension also. The bottom line: Overlooking patients' needs and expectations can be costly to the practice. Without patients, there is no practice.

It also is important to be up-front with office policies and procedures. When patients are sick or hurting, they usually do not feel up to questioning the medical staff about their policies or procedures. They usually are reacting from their physical symptoms, and their lack of questions or interest is caused by the fear of the unknown. Some conditions can be very frightening, such as a burning chest pain or a breast lump. It is the responsibility of the medical staff to find out what their patients' expectations are by asking questions. Being open with patients, anticipating their concerns, and helping create an atmosphere where patients feel they can discuss their needs safely are comforting and affirming.

Patient expectations vary from office to office. The following are some issues to consider when evaluating new patient protocol.

Professional Office Setting

When individuals walk into a hardware or clothing store, they are looking for physical items—tangible things they can pick up, examine, and put into their shopping cart. If they are unhappy with the hammer or sweater purchased, they can voice a complaint or return the item for a refund. The services offered by a health care facility are intangible—individuals cannot see or feel them. When individuals buy intangible services, they compensate by looking for **surrogates**—or substitutes to put their mind at ease. Surrogates that patients look for in a health care office may be the office location, size and layout, and staff enthusiasm; even the color of the walls can affect a new patient's initial judgment about the quality of care that particular office provides. A shabby reception room suggests shabby care.

Relevant Paperwork and Questions

A good deal of paperwork must be completed and many questions need to be answered when seeing a health care provider for the first time. Besides being brief and of high quality, paperwork should seem relevant to the reason the patient is there. Personal questions, such as whether a patient smokes or drinks, how many pregnancies a (female) patient has had, whether a patient is divorced or widowed, and whether a patient has some form of sexual dysfunction, should be asked privately out of hearing from office staff members and other patients. It also might be necessary to explain how these forms and questions relate to the individual's care and treatment.

Honoring Appointment Times

Time is a valuable commodity in today's fast-paced lifestyle in the United States, and staying on schedule communicates respect for the patient's time. Because the encounter may be a new experience for some patients, when a patient phones for an appointment, time-management experts recommend that the medical receptionist explain approximately how long an initial visit will take and what to expect. If the health care provider gets behind schedule, as is often the case, patients can become annoyed, glancing at their watches, shifting in their seats, and looking at the receptionist expectantly for explanations. The receptionist should keep the patient advised as to the length of delay and the reason for the delay. The patient might be told, "Dr. Miller has been delayed because of an emergency, so you may have to wait another 10 or 15 minutes." The patient should be kept apprised of the anticipated time he or she will be seen: "Dr. Miller has just left the hospital and will be here in approximately 10 minutes." If it looks like the wait is going to be lengthy, the receptionist should offer to reschedule the patient's appointment or ask if the patient has a brief errand to run. Many individuals today believe that their time is equally as valuable as the physician's, especially if they have taken time off work for their appointment.

IMAGINE THIS!

Jennifer Cooper had a 2 p.m. appointment with Dr. Shirley Bennet, a gynecologist. She arrived about 10 minutes early, as the receptionist recommended when she made the appointment. After completing all the necessary new patient forms, the receptionist advised Jennifer that Dr. Bennet had been called out on an emergency cesarean section and that she would be about a half hour late. The staff gave Jennifer the options of waiting or rescheduling. Jennifer, already having waited nearly 2 weeks for an opening in Dr. Bennet's schedule, chose to stay. Dr. Bennet kept the reception staff informed periodically as to how things were progressing, and this information was quickly and quietly passed on to Jennifer. Additionally, she was offered a choice of coffee or a cold soda. The reception room atmosphere was comfortable with pleasant background music and had an assortment of recent issues of magazines to browse through. Although Jennifer ended up waiting nearly 45 minutes for her appointment with Dr. Bennet, she did not become irritated or impatient because she was kept apprised of Dr. Bennet's schedule and was treated courteously by the staff.

IMAGINE THIS!

Lurvis Burke, a civil engineer with a consulting engineering firm, took time out of his busy schedule to visit a cardiologist for a routine stress test, recommended by his family physician. Lurvis had a 9 a.m. appointment with Dr. Harlan Solomon and arrived shortly before his appointment time, filled out the new patient paperwork, and sat down to wait. Two hours later, his name was called and a member of the medical staff ushered him to an examination room without a word. When Dr. Solomon entered the examination room where Lurvis was waiting, he found an angry patient who informed him that he did not appreciate the long wait, and that he considered his time just as important as the physician's. Lurvis vowed not to return to Dr. Solomon's office in the future. Compare this patient's experience with that of Jennifer Cooper.

STOP AND THINK

Reread the "Imagine This!" scenario featuring Lurvis Burke. Do you think Mr. Burke is justified in his decision not to return to this office? How would you have handled this situation if you were the front desk receptionist?

Patient Load

A new patient often draws conclusions about the competency of the health care provider and the entire health care team by observing how many others are waiting in the reception area. If the reception area is empty when the patient enters, he or she may think, "Why aren't there more people here? Maybe this doctor isn't very good." To avoid this negative reaction, some practices schedule new patients during their busiest times. This can be a workable solution as long as it does not result in a longer wait for established patients.

IMAGINE THIS!

Juanita Lindo, the medical receptionist for Anthony Park, a neurosurgeon, informed new patients when scheduling appointments that Dr. Park preferred reserving an ample amount of time for the encounter. The physician allowed a half hour before the examination, an hour for the examination, and a half hour after to answer all questions and ensure that the patient and family members were comfortable and well informed as to their options before leaving his office. When a patient arrived for an appointment, he or she was already aware of how long the encounter would take, explaining the absence of a reception room full of waiting patients.

Getting Comfortable with the Health Care Provider

It is human nature for patients to want to like their physicians as much as respect them. Perceptive patients expect their physicians to reveal enough information about themselves so that they can "identify" with them. That does not mean the physician and staff members need to discuss their personal lives with patients, but sharing of personal information does promote a good provider-patient relationship and often tends to relieve anxiety if the physician and staff members compare a personal experience that is relevant to what the patient is experiencing.

IMAGINE THIS!

Dottie Shrike visited Dr. Forrest Carpenter, her family practitioner, for treatment of an episode of anxiety and mild depression after being fired from her job as a teacher's aide. Dr. Carpenter, attempting to alleviate some of Dottie's angst, related a story about an experience he had had before becoming a physician. He was working for a trucking firm and had lost his job

because of noncompliance with company policy. He was young then, like Dottie, and the experience left him feeling humiliated and vulnerable. Relating this story to Dottie allowed her to feel as if he really understood her problem, reinforcing the provider-patient relationship.

Privacy and Confidentiality

If the medical professional wants patients to reveal their most personal health-related secrets, patients must feel confident that this information will be kept private and confidential. If patients who are waiting in the reception room hear the front desk staff talking about other patients, it can lead them to believe that their own information will be treated casually, too. The office staff must make every effort possible to assure patients that any personal information they divulge will be held in the strictest confidence. When making and receiving telephone calls, staff members should speak quietly or close the glass partition (which is recommended by Health Insurance Portability and Accountability Act [HIPAA] regulations) so that conversations do not carry out into the reception area. Also, the entire medical staff should be cautioned when talking among themselves or to patients in examining rooms. Walls are often thin, allowing voices to carry into adjacent rooms.

Financial Issues

Most patients have an idea of what their medical care and treatment should cost before they make an appointment. Some even do some "comparison shopping." Although many patients may be embarrassed or uneasy discussing fees, especially ahead of time, it is good business practice to discuss the financial ramifications of the health care encounter. Most physicians prefer to leave the subject of fees to their reception staff. When a new patient telephones for an appointment and explains his or her condition or symptoms that prompted the call, giving the individual a range of what the initial fee would be is considered appropriate. Today's health care consumers expect the cost of their health care to be addressed up-front.

STOP AND THINK

Mary Ellen Brown calls Dr. Bennet's office for an appointment. She explains that she is new in the area and is looking for a "good" OB-GYN because she thinks she may be pregnant. What kind of information might the medical receptionist give Mrs. Brown?

WHAT DID YOU LEARN?

1. Besides their health problems, what do patients bring with them to the health care office?
2. List four "issues" that affect patient expectations.
3. Why is a clean, well-kept reception room important?
4. What is the rationale of explaining policies and fees up-front to patients?

FUTURE TRENDS

Most health care experts agree that today's health care bears little resemblance to that of a decade ago. The United States is faced with a rapidly changing health care environment, and individuals who are involved in the health care field must identify and anticipate future trends—from new technology to changing directions and demographics.

Aging Population

Over the next 30 years, as the baby boomer generation ages, the number of Americans older than age 65 will double. Health care facilities will need to be prepared to handle an increasing volume of elderly patients. Dealing with the geriatric population can be quite different from dealing with younger groups. Health care staff members should be aware of, or even specially trained in, the particular skills for interacting with this demographic faction. Many local medical organizations or community colleges offer continuing education courses in the care and treatment of elderly patients.

The Internet as a Health Care Tool

Individuals have found that the Internet offers access to a lot of relevant, quality health care information. Websites are delivering large amounts of health care knowledge to consumers, allowing them to form their own opinions and expectations. Individuals are involved in the relatively new process of self-education not possible before the advent of the Internet. Websites help individuals find physicians and hospitals that offer certain procedures, and other websites offer lifestyle advice plus educational details and references for a multitude of health conditions.

Internet tools that can be used to reach today's computer-oriented consumer can help health care facilities serve patients better. Some successful online patient-centered topics include the following:

- Physician-patient communication
- Online scheduling (e.g., examinations, procedures)
- Online billing services
- Physician biographies
- Procedural information

It is predicted that future patients will rely more and more on the Internet, and health care providers will have to adapt their practices to meet these state-of-the-art electronic requirements.

IMAGINE THIS!

Greg Manning was diagnosed with prostate cancer, and the options his physician gave him held a high probability of impotence, which was unacceptable to Greg. He logged onto the Internet and began an extensive search for possible alternatives. He found a clinic in another state where the medical staff offered a relatively new, noninvasive procedure that was highly successful in patients with similar malignancies. Greg traveled to the clinic and met with the staff physicians to discuss the procedure. Greg was very happy with the alternative they presented and subsequently underwent the new procedure successfully.

Patients as Consumers

As shown by the increase in medical news on television and in advertising, radio broadcasts, periodicals, and Internet sites, the health care industry must acknowledge a new type of patient—one who is more educated, more aware of choices, and more likely to take an active part in his or her own health care decisions. Experts say that today's patients should be considered "consumers" rather than "patients." Today, Americans are exposed to an enormous amount of medical information on a daily basis. Some of this information can be misleading and confusing. Whether or not patients are correctly informed, however, health care providers are expected to take the time to satisfy patients' questions about diagnosis, treatment, and therapy options.

A new set of health care consumer essentials has been developed that experts believe should become mandatory for any health care facility that endeavors to provide patient-centered service. These essentials include the following:

- Choice
- Control (self-care, self-management)
- Shared medical decision making
- Customer service
- Information

Today's patients, similar to other types of consumers, are likely to switch health care plans or health care providers if they believe they are not getting the quality service they desire.

WHAT DID YOU LEARN?

1. List three things that affect future trends in the health care office.
2. How might the Internet change the future of health care?
3. Name three medical services that currently are being offered over the Internet.
4. List four health care consumer "imperatives" that experts claim should be mandatory for "patient-centered" services.

≋ HIPAA REQUIREMENTS

HIPAA has had a big impact on health care, particularly where confidentiality is concerned. What is contained in a patient's health record has always been confidential—dating back to the wording of the Hippocratic oath. HIPAA has refined the rules of confidentiality for covered entities, however, in a much more comprehensive way.

Authorization to Release Information

The release of any information contained in a patient's health record to a third party, with certain exceptions, is prohibited by law. Civil and criminal penalties exist for the unauthorized release of such information. A health care provider can be allowed to release confidential information from an individual's health records only with the consent of the individual or the person authorized to give consent for that individual.

HIPAA and Covered Entities

HIPAA is a federal law designed to protect the privacy of individuals' health information. A major component of HIPAA addresses this privacy by establishing a nationwide federal standard concerning the privacy of health information and how health information can be used and disclosed. This federal standard generally preempts all state privacy laws except for laws that establish stronger protections. HIPAA privacy laws became effective April 14, 2003.

HIPAA-covered entities consist of health care providers, health plans (including employer-sponsored plans), and health care clearing houses (including billing agents). These covered entities must comply with HIPAA rules for any health information of identifiable individuals. Protected health information under HIPAA is referred to as individually **identifiable health information**. *Identifiable health information* not only refers to data that are explicitly linked to a particular individual but also includes health information with data items that reasonably could be expected to allow individual identification. Identifiable medical information includes medical records, medical billing records, any clinical or research databases, and tissue bank samples. Covered entities generally are unable to communicate or transfer protected health information to noncovered entities (who do not come under HIPAA rules) without violating HIPAA.

Potential identifiers that can link information to a particular individual include obvious ones, such as name and Social Security number, and the following:

- All geographic subdivisions smaller than a state, including street address, city, county, precinct, ZIP Code (under certain circumstances, the initial three digits of a ZIP Code can be used)
- All elements of dates (except year) directly related to an individual, including birth date, admission date, discharge date, and date of death
- Voice and fax telephone numbers
- E-mail addresses
- Medical record numbers, health plan beneficiary numbers, or other health plan account numbers
- Certificate/license numbers
- Vehicle identifiers and serial numbers, including license plate numbers
- Device identifiers and serial numbers
- Internet Protocol (IP) address numbers and Universal Resource Locators (URLs)
- Biometric identifiers, including fingerprints and voice prints
- Full-face photographic images and any comparable images
- Any other unique identifying number, characteristic, or code

Note: The *covered entity* may assign a code or other means of identification to allow de-identified information, if it later may become necessary to re-identify the information. When the above-listed identifiable elements are removed, the information is, under most circumstances, considered **de-identified**.

Covered entities, such as health plans, health care providers, and claims clearinghouses, must comply with HIPAA rules. Other businesses may comply voluntarily with the standards, but the law does not require them to do so.

HIPAA Requirements for Covered Entities

Essentially, a HIPAA-covered entity cannot use or disclose protected health information (PHI) for any purpose other than treatment, payment, or health care operations without either the authorization of the individual or an exception in the HIPAA regulations. In addition to limiting the use and disclosure of protected health information, HIPAA gives patients the right to access their medical information and to know who the covered entity has disclosed this information to (including investigative research files). It also restricts most disclosures to the minimum amount possible to accomplish the intended purpose and establishes criminal and civil penalties and fines for improper use and disclosure by HIPAA-covered entities.

HIPAA requires covered entities to do the following:

- Institute a required level of security for health information, including limiting disclosures of information to the minimum required for the activity
- Designate a privacy officer and contact person
- Establish privacy and disclosure policies to comply with HIPAA
- Train all staff members on privacy policies
- Establish sanctions for staff members who violate privacy policies
- Establish administrative systems in relation to the health information that can respond to complaints, respond to requests for corrections of health information by a patient, accept requests not to disclose for certain purposes, and track disclosures of health information
- Issue a privacy notice to patients concerning the use and disclosure of their protected health information
- Establish a process through an international review or privacy board for a HIPAA review of research protocols
- Include consent for disclosures for treatment, payment, and health care operations in treatment consent form (optional)

HIPAA provides a limited public policy exception for protected health information disclosure involving public health issues, judicial and administrative proceedings, law enforcement purposes, and others as required by law.

Patient's Right of Access and Correction

A patient has the right to inspect or obtain copies of his or her protected health information from a health care provider or health plan but not from clearinghouses. In contrast to other rules, exceptions to the right of access are limited. The primary exceptions are for circumstances considered reasonably likely to endanger the life or physical safety of that individual or another person (emotional health is excluded) and for clinical research.

The privacy rules introduce a new concept—the patient's right to correct or amend his or her medical record. This reflects an idea that has long been controversial: patient ownership of the medical record. Although under the new HIPAA rules, this right is limited by reasonable protections for the covered entity who controls the protected information, for the first time a patient has a right to ask for corrections or amendments to his or her medical record and to place an explanation into the record if that request is denied. The privacy notice that a medical practice gives to patients must specify how they should make requests to amend their records (e.g., in writing). The practice may refuse such a request for several reasons, including that the patient's record is accurate and complete. The patient has the right to appeal, however. If the practice agrees to amend the patient's record, it must notify the individual and others to whom the information was provided that the record has been amended. The rules do not include, however, a requirement that incorrect information be removed from the record; rather, it should be labeled as corrected, and the correction should be appended.

Basic patient rights under HIPAA include the following:
1. Right to notice of privacy practices (NOPP)
2. Right to access to personal health information (PHI)
3. Right to an accounting of how PHI has been disclosed outside normal patient care channels
4. Right to request an amendment/correction to PHI

Accessing Information Through Patient Authorization

HIPAA states that when an authorization to release information (Fig. 10-1) is required from a patient, it must include the following elements:

Standard Authorization to Use or Disclose Protected Health Information (PHI)

Section A: The individual for whom this authorization is being requested. Please complete the following:

Name: First _____   M _____   Last _____   Group # _____   Identification # _____

Social Security Number _____   Date of Birth _____

Address _____   City _____   State _____   ZIP _____

Area Code & Telephone Number _____   E-mail Address (if available) _____

Section B: Please place an "X" in the box next to each category of specific Protected Health Information to disclose. (You may mark as many boxes as appropriate.)

☐ Any and All Information about my CHIP Coverage   ☐ Claims   ☐ Premium Payment/Billing History

☐ Eligibility and Enrollment   ☐ Other (describe): _____

Section C: Describe the reason for the release or request of information.

☐ At my request   ☐ Other (describe): _____

Section D: Who will provide this information?	**Section E: Who will receive this information?**
Name CHIP and its Plan Administrator	Name _____
Address 400 W. Monroe, Suite 202	Address _____
Anytown, IL 08095	_____
Relationship Health Plan	Relationship _____

Section F: Please place an "X" in the box next to the date or event that describes when your authorization will expire. (Please mark only one box.)

☐ Upon Revocation   ☐ 1 year after my death   ☐ 1 year after my CHIP coverage ends
☐ A specific date: _____   ☐ Other (describe): _____
        Month   Day   Year

Section G: I understand that:

- This authorization will expire on the date or event listed in Section F above.
- This authorization is voluntary.
- Payment, enrollment or eligibility for benefits for my health care will not be affected if I do not sign this form.
- I may revoke this authorization at any time by notifying in writing the company/individual listed in Section D from providing the PHI identified in this authorization, but if I do revoke this authorization, it won't have any affect on any actions the Comprehensive Health Insurance Plan took before they received the revocation.
- Information disclosed as a result of this authorization may no longer be protected by federal privacy laws and may be disclosed by the company or individual receiving the information.
- I should retain as my copy one of the duplicate authorization forms I received.

Section H: Signature.

I hereby authorize the use or disclosure of the Protected Health Information as described in Section B pertaining to the Individual listed in Section A.

Signature of Individual or Individual's Personal Representative _____   Date: month/day/year _____

Section I: If Section H is signed by a Personal Representative, please complete the information below:

Personal Representative's Name _____   Relationship to Individual _____

Personal Representative's Address _____   City _____   State _____   ZIP _____

Personal Representative's Area Code & Telephone Number _____   Personal Representative's E-mail Address (if available) _____

TPAuth Rev 6.03   Page 1 of 1 (See Instructions on Next Page)   Standard Authorization – CHIP

Fig. 10-1 HIPAA-approved release of information form.

- A description that identifies the information in a specific and meaningful fashion
- The name of the person authorized to make the requested use or disclosure
- The name of the person to whom the covered entity may make the requested use or disclosure

- A description of each purpose of the requested use or disclosure
- An expiration date or event that relates to the purpose of the use or disclosure
- A statement of the individual's right to revoke the authorization in writing and the exceptions

to the right to revoke, together with a description of how the individual may revoke the authorization
- A statement that information used may be subject to re-disclosure by the recipient and no longer be protected by this rule
- Signature of the individual and date signed
- A description of a representative's authority to act for an individual if the authorization is signed by a personal representative of the individual.

HIPAA TIP

Uses and disclosures not requiring patient consent include the following:
1. To carry out treatment, payment, or health care operations
2. For public health, health oversight, judicial/administrative proceedings, coroners/medical examiners, and law enforcement

Accessing Information Through De-Identification

Covered entities can release de-identified health information without patient authorization. Protected health information can be de-identified through a general deletion of the identifiers listed in the section titled "HIPAA and Covered Entities." To release the information without patient authorization, the covered entity cannot have actual information that could be used alone or in combination with other information to identify an individual.

STOP AND THINK

What information in the following documentation should be removed to "de-identify" this patient?
Frasier, Eric
DOB 1/13/1977
Patient #12112
6/10/2004
History: Eric presents to the clinic today for chief complaint of an abrasion on the right knee following a fall yesterday. According to the patient, he has had this soft tissue lesion for some time, and when he fell, he basically abraded the lower half of the lesion. He is here for re-evaluation and possible excision of the lesion.
Pain assessment: Scale 0 to 10, 1
Allergies: Meperidine (Demerol)
Current medications: None

Physical examination: NAD; ambulatory; appears well
Vital signs: Blood pressure, 120/74 mm Hg; weight 150 lb
Right knee examination: The patient has a tibial prominence, and just above that, there is what appears to be a 1.5-cm epidermal inclusion cyst with an abraded area inferiorly. There is mild erythema and serous drainage, but no purulence. There is no appreciable edema. Just lateral to the lesion is a small superficial abrasion. The knee examination was normal.
IMP: Epidermal inclusion cyst measuring 1.5 to 2 cm of the right knee, traumatized with abrasion
Plan: The patient was empirically started on cephalexin (Keflex) 500 mg 1 p.o. b.i.d. He was given instructions on home care and is to follow up this week for excision of the lesion. Routine follow-up as noted. Return as needed.
Frederick Mahoney, MD
Friendly Family Clinic

WHAT DID YOU LEARN?

1. What are the three "entities" that are covered under HIPAA?
2. List at least six elements that make a patient health record "identifiable."
3. How does a patient health record become "de-identifiable"?
4. Name three exceptions to the confidentiality rule.

BILLING POLICIES AND PRACTICES

Although specific billing policies and procedures differ from one practice to another, the goals are similar. Many health care facilities anticipate that the patient will pay for services or procedures the same day they are rendered. If the patient has insurance, most offices accept a partial payment or co–pay—typically 10% to 25% of the fee. Medical facilities are in business to make a profit; procedures and policies should be in place to protect the financial success of the practice.

Assignment of Benefits

An **assignment of benefits** is an arrangement by which a patient requests that his or her health insurance benefit payments be made directly to a designated person or facility, such as a physician or hospital. When new patients come to the health care office, they are typically asked to fill out a form providing name, address, employer, and health insurance information. Usually at the bottom of the page is a place for the patient's signature or, in the case of a minor or mentally handicapped individual, the signature of a parent or legal guardian. This form is commonly referred to as the **patient information form**.

On many patient information forms, in addition to the authorization to release information, there is nomenclature above the patient's signature that provides for the assignment of benefits, authorizing this transfer of payment from the insured to the health care provider. Some health care providers do not see a patient unless this assignment of benefits is signed or unless payment is made up-front.

Many health care providers today participate in a health maintenance organization, a preferred provider organization, or some similar organization. These practitioners are referred to as *participating providers*. When a provider is a participating provider, assigning benefits on the CMS-1500 form or on the patient information form is unnecessary because there is a contractual agreement between the provider and the third-party carrier that payment automatically is sent directly to the provider. That is one of the benefits to becoming a participating provider.

Keeping Patients Informed

It is important that patients understand the health care practice's patient accounting policies and procedures, such as

- approximately how much the medical service or procedure will cost,
- when they are expected to pay for it, and
- what the practice is willing to do as far as claims submission to their insurance carrier.

Discussing professional fees with patients is an important step requiring a sensitive and balanced approach by the health insurance professional. The health insurance professional should not intimidate or offend patients when discussing fees and payment policies; however, he or she should ensure that patients are clear about their responsibilities. Most patients appreciate having billing information presented clearly and matter-of-factly, yet always in a pleasant and courteous manner. The health care office staff should encourage patients to ask questions about their bills or the payment/insurance process. Many offices have printed materials available, such as an informational brochure, for stating or reinforcing the practice's financial policies and procedures. This written information can be helpful in collecting fees.

Establishing sound billing practices is important in a health care office. Although health care practitioners are dedicated to the health and well-being of their patients, they are ultimately running a business for the purpose of making a profit. Keeping accurate financial records is equally as important as keeping accurate patient health records.

The ultimate goal in health care office billing is reimbursement or payment for the medical services provided to patients. A satisfactory **collection ratio** (the total amount collected divided by the total amount charged) can be challenging at times. Some health care offices display a sign that payment for services rendered is expected on the day services are provided. In other words, patients are expected to pay as they go, just as retail stores expect customers to pay for a tube of toothpaste or a can of soup at the time of purchase.

The receptionist should request payment on the day of the visit, either before or after the encounter is concluded. Experts consider this the most effective payment policy. Patients who put off paying for their services are historically more difficult to collect from. It is common practice for the receptionist to ask for a particular percentage—often 20%—of the current charge; 20% is a common co-insurance amount.

STOP AND THINK

The accounts receivable total of Dr. David Barclay's office was $231,500 for the first quarter of 2004. If $173,625 of this amount was successfully collected, what would be Dr. Barclay's collection ratio for this quarter?

Accounting Methods

There is a good chance that the office where the health insurance professional finds employment uses a computerized medical accounting system for financial records. This is not always the case, however, and the health insurance professional should be aware of how paper accounting records are generated and maintained. A typical paper method of accounting includes a series of journals and ledgers, such as the following:

A **daily journal** (or day sheet) (Fig. 10-2) is a chronological record of all patient transactions, including previous balances, charges, payments, and current balances for that day.

A **disbursements journal** (Fig. 10-3) is a listing of all expenses paid out to vendors, such as building rent, office supplies, and salaries. Some

		DATE	PROFESSIONAL SERVICE	FEE	PAYMENT	ADJUST-MENT	NEW BALANCE	OLD BALANCE	PATIENT'S NAME
1									
2									
3									
4									
5									
6									
7									
8									
9									
10									
11									
12									
13									
14									
15									
16									Totals this page
17									Totals previous page
18									Totals to date

JOURNAL OF DAILY CHARGES, PAYMENTS & DEPOSITS

PLACE FIRST PEG HERE

COLUMN A   COLUMN B   COLUMN C   COLUMN D   COLUMN E

MEMO _____

DAILY - FROM LINE 31
ARITHMETIC POSTING PROOF

Column E	$
Plus Column A	
Sub-Total	
Minus Column B	
Sub-Total	
Minus Column C	
Equals Column D	

MONTH - FROM LINE 31
ACCOUNTS RECEIVABLE PROOF

Accts. Receivable Previous Day	$
Plus Column A	
Sub-Total	
Minus Column B	
Sub-Total	
Minus Column C	
Accts. Receivable End of Day	

Fig. 10-2 Example of a day sheet.

offices maintain a separate **payroll journal** (Fig. 10-4) for wages and salaries.
A **general journal**, the most basic of journals, is a chronological listing of transactions. It has a specific format for recording each transaction. Each transaction is recorded separately and consists of the following:
- A date
- All accounts that receive a debit entry (these are typically listed first with an amount in the appropriate column)
- All accounts that receive a credit entry (these are indented and listed next with an amount in the appropriate column)
- A clear description of each transaction
A **general ledger** is the core of the practice's financial records. The general ledger constitutes the central "books" of an accounting system, and every transaction flows through the general ledger. These records remain as permanent tracking of the history of all financial transactions from day 1 of the life of a practice.

FEBRUARY 2006

DATE	DESCRIPTION	CHECK NUMBER	AMOUNT	PER CAPITA	RENT	PHONE	OFFICE SUPPLIES	POSTAGE	OFFICERS' EXPENSE	NEWS LETTER
1-FEB	ABC Realty	291	475.00		475.00					
1-FEB	AFT	292	2,301.60	2,301.60						
1-FEB	State Fed	293	1,288.60	1,288.60						
1-FEB	Central Labor Council	294	75.60	75.60						
1-FEB	Bell Telephone	295	131.00			131.00				
7-FEB	State Fed	296	1,828.60	1,828.60						
21-FEB	Sue Smith, Sec'y	297	50.00						50.00	
28-FEB	Mary Jones, Petty Cash	298	18.50				16.00	2.50		
			6,168.90	5,494.40	475.00	131.00	16.00	2.50	50.00	0.00

Fig. 10-3   Sample cash disbursements journal.

Date	Employee	Hourly Rate	Regular Hours	Overtime Hours	Net Pay	Check Number	Federal Withholding	OASI	Insurance	Retirement	Other	Gross Pay	Fund	Account

Fig. 10-4   Payroll journal.

The general ledger can be used to prepare a range of periodic financial statements, such as income statements and balance sheets.

A **patient ledger** (Fig. 10-5) is a chronological accounting of a particular patient's (or family's) activities, including all charges and payments. The entire group of patient ledgers is referred to as the **accounts receivable**.

"One-Write" or Pegboard Accounting System

Paper accounting systems, such as "one-write" or "write-it-once" systems, have been widely used in physicians' offices over the years. **"One-write" systems** (Fig. 10-6) (also known as the pegboard system) are a useful method of accounting for small practices. A one-write system captures information at the time the transaction occurs. These systems are efficient because they eliminate the need for recopying the data, and many are compatible with electronic data processing if the office decides to computerize. Many small businesses rely totally on the one-write system for simplicity and versatility. One-write systems are popular for several reasons, including the following:

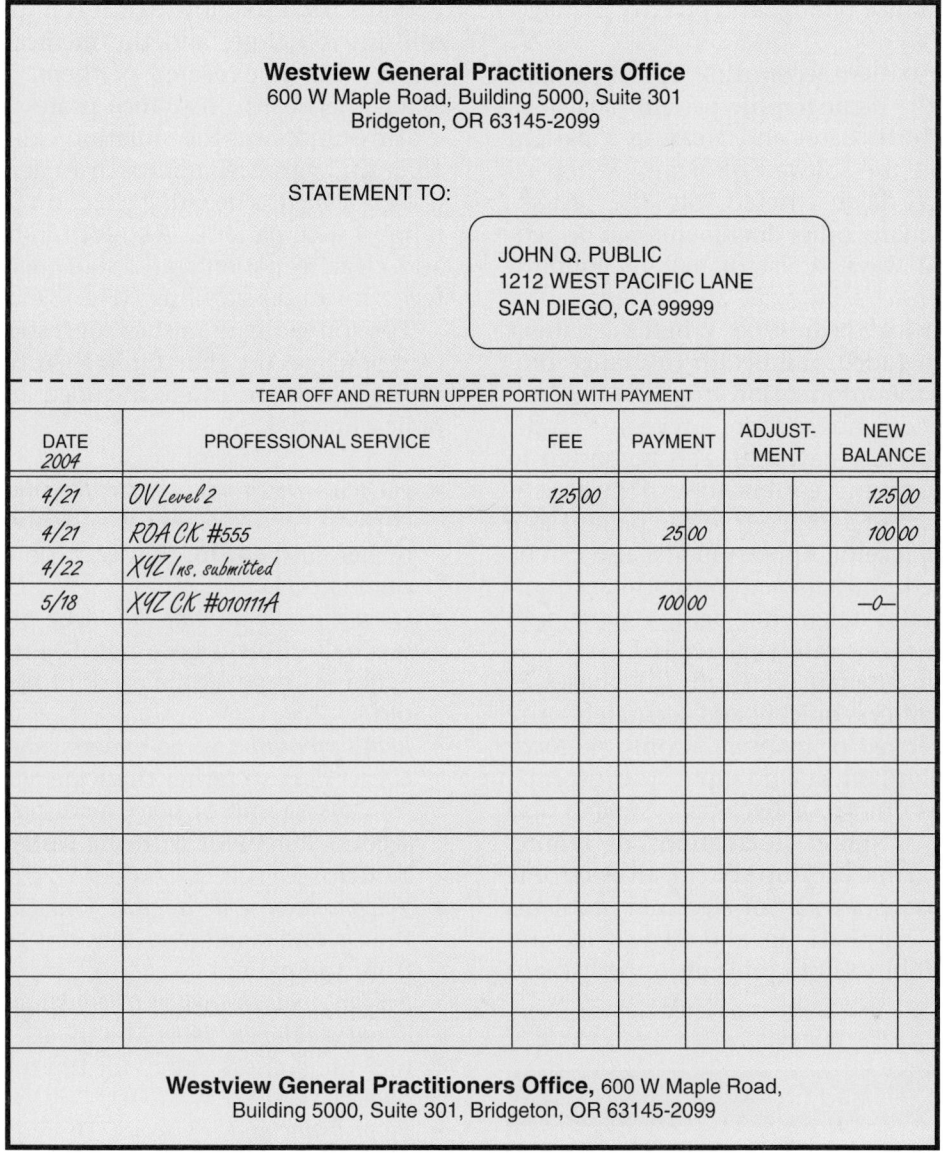

Westview General Practitioners Office
600 W Maple Road, Building 5000, Suite 301
Bridgeton, OR 63145-2099

STATEMENT TO:

JOHN Q. PUBLIC
1212 WEST PACIFIC LANE
SAN DIEGO, CA 99999

- -
TEAR OFF AND RETURN UPPER PORTION WITH PAYMENT

DATE 2004	PROFESSIONAL SERVICE	FEE	PAYMENT	ADJUST-MENT	NEW BALANCE
4/21	OV Level 2	125 00			125 00
4/21	ROA CK #555		25 00		100 00
4/22	XYZ Ins. submitted				
5/18	XYZ CK #010111A		100 00		—0—

Westview General Practitioners Office, 600 W Maple Road,
Building 5000, Suite 301, Bridgeton, OR 63145-2099

Fig. 10-5 Sample patient ledger card.

- Accurate
- Relatively inexpensive
- Easy to learn
- Use a write-it-once process for recording daily office transactions

Electronic Patient Accounting Software

Increasingly, health care offices are using electronic patient accounting software programs, and most health care practices are computerized to some extent. Previous barriers to computerization have been largely overcome by the introduction of effective and user-friendly systems for the management of clinical records and appointments. Computerized patient billing software typically includes accounts receivable, appointment

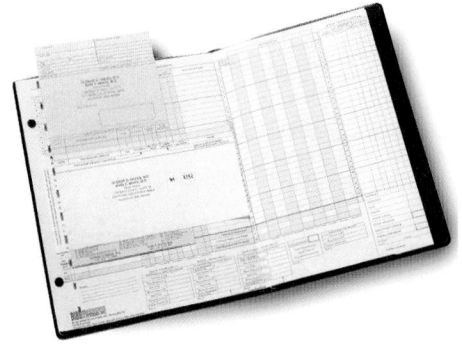

Fig. 10-6 Front office "one-write" (pegboard) billing example. *(Courtesy Bibbero Systems, Inc., Petaluma Calif., [800] 242-2376; Fax [800] 242-9330; www.bibbero.com.)*

scheduling, insurance billing, and practice management modules.

Computerized patient accounting typically begins with inputting the demographic patient data (e.g., name, address, birth date) and creating a patient "account" within the software program. When all patient data have been entered into the system, patient lists and many other documents can be generated in several ways. A list of patient appointments by day and by provider and an encounter form for each one can be printed. When the patient encounter is concluded, the health insurance professional inputs the information from the encounter form—date, diagnosis code, procedure code, and charges. Also, any payments can be posted to the computer program. A current copy of the patient ledger can be printed and given to the patient as a statement or as a receipt. Appointments also can be scheduled, deleted, and adjusted within the accounting system. Periodic statements, aging reports, and CMS-1500 claim forms can be generated.

The computer program performs all phases of the accounting process quickly and accurately. Any system, computerized or manual, is only as good, however, as the individual who inputs the information. Accuracy is crucial. A back-up system is also crucial in case of power fluctuations or failure. Without a dependable back-up system, all electronic data could be lost as a result of electrical problems or human error. Daily back-ups should be made and stored in a fireproof vault to prevent loss of patient records.

WHAT DID YOU LEARN?

1. What is an "assignment of benefits"?
2. Name three things that are important for patients to know about a health care practice.
3. What are the four elements that must be included in each transaction in a general journal?
4. Name three advantages to the "one-write" pegboard accounting system.
5. A computerized patient accounting system can generate many kinds of documents. Name four.

≋ BILLING AND COLLECTION

Individuals who work in health care offices claim that collecting past due accounts is one of the least pleasant aspects of the job. Health care practices that maintain a high collection ratio say that the most effective way to collect money is to establish a formal financial policy that is clear to patients, and that the health care staff members enforce it.

Patients need to know that it is important to pay in full and on time, and the medical staff needs to know what is expected of them. There are times when the health insurance professional must take a firm stand, and the situation can get uncomfortable. An aggressive approach to account collection does not have a negative effect on developing good rapport with patients. A collection policy that is fair and clear to patients and staff members results in fewer misunderstandings (Fig. 10-7).

The following is a list of suggestions some health care practices use that aid in their financial success. These items are often included in the practice's policy manual.

- *Have a written payment/credit policy.* Give a copy to each patient, discuss it with him or her, and ensure that each point is understood.
- *Do not ignore overdue bills.* The older the bill, the less collectible it becomes. Begin a plan of action as soon as the account becomes 30 days old.
- *Rebill promptly.* Some experts suggest rebilling every 15 days rather than the traditional 30 days. Stamp or place a sticker on the second statement with the words "Second Notice."
- *Telephone or write a letter.* This can be effective if the second statement does not get a response from the patient.
- *Do not apologize when telephoning or writing about delinquent bills.* Simply ask the customer to write a check today for the full amount owed.
- *Be pleasant and courteous.* There is never a reason to get into an argument, even if the patient becomes hostile. Listen patiently to what the patient has to say without interrupting; try to be understanding.
- *Ask for the full amount, not just a partial payment.* If a patient owes $500, ask for the full $500. If the patient says he or she will send a partial payment, ask what the exact amount will be and exactly what date the payment will be sent. Avoid vagueness, such as, "I'll send you something in a couple of days."
- *Negotiate the terms, but not the amount.* If you believe the patient truly has a problem paying, offer to work out a payment plan, but do not make this offer right away, only as a last resort. Also, always adhere to the office policy when negotiating terms.
- *Use the services of a small claims court.* If patient promises are not kept, or if the account ages past a certain time period (e.g., 60 days, depending on office policy), small claims litigation is an alternative.

Payment Policy

Thank you for choosing our practice! We are committed to the success of your medical treatment and care. Please understand that payment of your bill is part of this treatment and care.

For your convenience, we have answered a variety of commonly-asked financial policy questions below. If you need further information about any of these policies, please ask to speak with a Billing Specialist or the Practice Manager.

How May I Pay?
We accept payment by cash, check, VISA, MasterCard, American Express, and Discover.

Do I Need A Referral?
If you have an HMO plan with which we are contracted, you need a referral authorization from your primary care physician. If we have not received an authorization prior to your arrival at the office, we have a telephone available for you to call your primary care physician to obtain it. If you are unable to obtain the referral at that time, you will be rescheduled.

Which Plans Do You Contract With?
Please see attached list.

What Is My Financial Responsibility for Services?
Your financial responsibility depends on a variety of factors, explained below.

Office Visits and Office Services

If you have:	You are Responsible for:	Our staff will:
Commercial Insurance Also known as indemnity, "regular" insurance, or "80%/20% coverage."	Payment of the patient responsibility for all office visit, x-ray, injection, and other charges at the time of office visit.	Call your insurance company ahead of time to determine deductibles and coinsurance. File an insurance claim as a courtesy to you.
Medicare HMO	All applicable copays and deductibles at the time of the office visit.	File the claim on your behalf, as well as any claims to your secondary insurance.
Workers' Compensation	If we have verified the claim with your carrier No payment is necessary at the time of the visit. If we are not able to verify your claim Payment in full is requested at the time of the visit.	Call your carrier ahead of time to verify the accident date, claim number, primary care physician, employer information, and referral procedures.
Workers' Compensation (Out of State)	Payment in full is requested at the time of the visit.	Provide you a receipt so you can file the claim with your carrier.
Occupational Injury	Payment in full is requested at the time of the visit.	Provide you a receipt so you can file the claim with your carrier.
No Insurance	Payment in full at the time of the visit.	Work with you to settle your account. Please ask to speak with our staff if you need assistance.

Fig. 10-7 Payment policy. *(Courtesy Karen Zupko & Associates.)*

STOP AND THINK

You notice that Theodore Simpson's account balance is $365, and he has not made a payment for 45 days. Office policy is to telephone patients 15 days after the last statement has been sent. How will you handle this? Create a telephone "scenario" of your conversation with Mr. Simpson.

Billing Cycle

Sending statements to patients on a regular basis is necessary to maintain cash flow for the practice and an acceptable collection ratio. Every health care office has its own routine for sending statements. Typically, statements are mailed periodically—usually every 30 days. This process is called a **billing cycle**. In large practices, one 30-day mass billing for all patients is a cumbersome task. Large health care offices often use an **alternate billing cycle**—a billing system that incorporates the mailing of a partial group of statements at spaced intervals during the month. With an alternate billing cycle, the breakdown of accounts frequently is determined by an alphabetical list of last names or by account numbers. Patients with last names ending in A through F would be sent statements on the first of the month; patients with last names ending with G through L would receive statements on the 10th day of the month. One advantage to an alternate billing cycle is that cash flow is distributed throughout the entire month, whereas billing only once a month generates a large amount of receipts at one time during the month. No one specific method is considered best for all health care practices. Each practice must establish its own system that works well.

Arranging Credit or Payment Plans

The cost of some medical treatments or procedures can be thousands of dollars, and the patient might not have adequate insurance coverage (or may have no insurance at all) to pay the medical fees. Many health care facilities offer patient/client financing plans, which allow patients to get the treatment or procedures they need and want and pay for it in periodic installments—similar to purchasing a car. A comprehensive range of plan options is available in health care facilities across the United States that offer low, or at least manageable, monthly payments to fit almost every budget.

Self-Pay Patients
Some patients may have inadequate health insurance coverage or no insurance at all. These are referred to as **self-pay patients**. Just because patients are self-pay does not mean they would deliberately try to avoid paying their bills. Some individuals who do not carry health insurance still are able to pay their medical bills in a timely manner.

As mentioned previously, the patient should be provided with the policies and expectations of the health care practice early on in the encounter. Under most state laws, full payment for medical services is due and payable at the time the service is provided. Health care providers often take the initiative, however, to temper this mandate as they see fit.

When a patient completes the patient information form, and there is no insurance listed, the health insurance professional should inquire about the reason. It is possible that the insurance section was overlooked. If the patient has no insurance, it is prudent to inquire tactfully as to how he or she intends to pay for the service. Some health care offices ask the patient whether he or she has insurance when the appointment is made, and if not, the patient must make at least a partial payment in advance.

Ideally, the practice should have an established credit plan for self-pays because it is mandatory that every patient be treated equally. Equally as important, the health care office cannot refuse to see an established patient because of an outstanding debt. There is a procedure, however, whereby (if carried out within the confines of the law) a health care provider can terminate the patient-provider relationship. This procedure involves sending a certified letter to the patient, with a return receipt to confirm the patient received the letter, communicating the fact that the patient can no longer be treated (for whatever reason spelled out in the letter), and giving the patient a specified amount of time to find alternative care. Following this structured method of notifying the patient that the practice will no longer accept him or her as a patient and spelling out the reason why limit the practice's liability in the event of legal action brought by the patient accusing the practice of "abandonment."

Establishing Credit
When patients cannot make payment in full, credit is sometimes arranged, and a payment plan is established (Fig. 10-8). Some medical facilities offer a credit arrangement whereby the patient can pay the fee, interest-free, in several installments. Other medical facilities allow more flexibility for self-paying patients by offering an installment plan with interest rates lower than those of most major credit cards.

It is important to keep in mind that an installment payment plan of more than four payments comes under the federal Truth in Lending Act of 1968, Regulation Z. Regulation Z applies to each individual or business that offers or extends consumer credit if the following four conditions are met:

1. The credit is offered to consumers.
2. Credit is offered on a regular basis.
3. The credit is subject to a finance charge (i.e., interest) or must be paid in more than four installments according to a written agreement.
4. The credit is primarily for personal, family, or household purposes.

The Truth in Lending Act of 1968 and Regulation Z are discussed in more detail later.

5 Financial Arrangements

Payment is expected at time of service.

For your convenience, we offer the following methods of payment.
Please check the option which you prefer.

_____ Cash

_____ Personal Check

_____ Credit Card   _____ VISA

_____ I wish to make arrangements with an office manager today.

Late Charges

I realize that failure to keep this account current may result in you being unable to provide additional services except for emergencies or where there is prepayment for additional services. In the case of default on payment of this account, I agree to pay collection costs and reasonable attorney fees incurred in attempting to collect on this amount or any future outstanding account balances.

Thank you for filling out this form completely.
The information you have provided will help us serve your healthcare needs more effectively and efficiently.
If you have any questions at any time, please ask – we are always happy to help.

Fig. 10-8 Sample of financial arrangement plan.

Problem Patients

There are times that the health insurance professional knows or has reason to believe that it may be difficult to collect fees from a particular patient. A policy should be in place for "problem" patients such as these or for patients who, for whatever reason, "send up a red flag." The following are some suggestions to maximize collection success from problem or questionable patients:

- Contact a local credit bureau to find out if the patient is creditworthy.
- Discuss the credit policy with the patient before the encounter, and establish a payment that is affordable for the patient.
- Have the patient sign a written agreement.
- Ask the patient to make a down payment of at least 20%.
- Arrange with the patient and his or her bank for automatic withdrawals if the patient has an account where that is a viable option.
- Charge interest (if that is practice policy) or a "carrying fee" to give the patient added incentive to make regular payments and pay off the balance promptly.
  Note: Even if the practice does not charge interest, if it is mutually agreed that the account will be paid off in more than four payments, the practice by law must provide the patient with a copy of the Truth in Lending Law.
- Arrange to have payments automatically deducted each month on a presigned credit card form.

- Do not allow the payments to extend past the treatment program, or 12 months, whichever is the lesser.
- Provide the patient with a self-addressed, stamped, return envelope in each bill.

Keep a copy of the signed agreement on file, so the office staff can refer to the agreement for specific monthly payments or fees for missed payments. Most health care offices keep these agreements in a separate file rather than in the patient's health record.

When setting up payment arrangements, be considerate but firm. The health insurance professional should explain the payment plan clearly, emphasizing that payments must not be missed and that the payment must be received on or before the due date.

Five Categories of Problem Debtors

It takes experience and intuition to know the difference between patients who will not or tell you they cannot pay but who have sufficient funds to do so and patients who genuinely cannot pay. Problem debtors fall into five categories:

- The *something-else-came-up debtors*—Unforeseen events cause delayed payments, a common occurrence in most health care practices. The patient had intended to pay the bill but has had an emergency and now is in a financial situation that prevents him or her from paying the bill on time.
- The *chronically slow debtors*—These patients have funds but simply do not pay their bills on time.

- The *can't pay debtors*—These patients are overextended; they have too many expenses and not enough income to pay them.
- The *forgetful debtors*—These patients simply need reminding.
- The *fraudulent debtors*—These patients never intended to pay. These are the "deadbeats." The good news is they compose only a small percentage of the population.

It may be a waste of time to call patients who fall into the last category. Efforts should be concentrated on recovering dollars from patients who can or want to pay—the something-else-came-up, the chronically slow, the can't-pay, and the forgetful debtors. These are the individuals who will pay, but they may need prodding to collect.

Collecting from Problem Debtors
A recommended procedure for collecting from problem debtors is as follows:

- Ask for full payment on the day services are rendered.
- If the patient cannot or will not pay in full, request at least 20% of the bill.
- Send the patient a statement after 30 days.
- Send a second statement 15 to 30 days later with a "second reminder" sticker or note.
- Telephone the patient 15 days after the second statement has gone out if a substantial payment has not been received.
- Turn the account for collection, or take the patient to small claims court.

WHAT DID YOU LEARN?

1. List five things a health care practice can do to aid in its financial success.
2. Explain how an "alternate billing cycle" can be used.
3. What is meant by a "self-pay" patient?
4. Name the four conditions that must be met under Regulation Z when a business extends credit.

LAWS AFFECTING CREDIT AND COLLECTION

Because health care offices typically extend credit to their patients/customers, they need to comply with federal consumer credit laws. Before we get too far into the collection process, it is important that the health insurance professional become acquainted with collection laws. The following is an introduction to the relevant federal laws dealing with consumer credit.

Truth in Lending Act

The **Truth in Lending Act** helps consumers of all kinds know what they are getting into. It requires the person or business entity to disclose the exact credit terms when extending credit to applicants and regulates how they advertise consumer credit. Among the items that must be disclosed to a consumer who buys on credit are the following:

- The monthly finance charge
- The annual interest rate
- When payments are due
- The total sale price (the cash price of the item or service, plus all other charges)
- The amount of any late payment charges and when they'll be imposed

Fair Credit Billing Act

The **Fair Credit Billing Act** tells the business entity, in this case, the health care practice, what to do if a customer claims you made a billing mistake. The customer must notify the practice within 60 days after the first statement containing the claimed error was mailed. The practice must respond within 30 days, unless the dispute already has been resolved. The practice also must conduct a reasonable investigation and, within 90 days of getting the customer's letter, explain why the bill is correct or else correct the error. If this procedure is not followed, the practice must give the customer a $50 credit toward the disputed amount—even if the statement was correct. Until the dispute is resolved, the practice cannot report to a credit bureau that the customer is delinquent.

State laws also may deal with billing disputes. Generally, if a state law on this subject conflicts with the federal statute, the federal statute would control, but there is one exception: A state law would prevail if it gives a consumer more time to notify a creditor about a billing error. As explained earlier, the federal law gives a consumer 60 days after receiving a bill to notify you of a billing error. If a state law gives a consumer 90 days to notify you, the consumer will be entitled to the extra 30 days. In addition to advising how to handle billing disputes, the Fair Credit Billing Act requires that the entity granting credit, in periodic mailings, must tell consumers what their rights are.

Equal Credit Opportunity Act

The **Equal Credit Opportunity Act** states that a business entity may not discriminate against a credit applicant on the basis of race, color, religion, national origin, age, sex, or marital status. The act does allow freedom to consider legitimate factors in granting credit, such as the applicant's financial status (earnings and savings) and credit record. Despite the prohibition on age discrimination, you can reject a consumer who has not reached the legal age for entering into contracts.

Fair Credit Reporting Act

The **Fair Credit Reporting Act** deals primarily with credit reports issued by credit reporting agencies. It is intended to protect consumers from having their eligibility for credit damaged by incomplete or misleading credit report information. The law gives consumers the right to a copy of their credit reports. If they see an inaccurate item, they can ask that it be corrected or removed. If the business entity reporting the credit problem does not agree to a change or deletion, or if the credit bureau refuses to make it, the consumer can add a 100-word statement to the file explaining his or her side of the story. This statement becomes a part of any future credit report.

Fair Debt Collection Practices Act

The **Fair Debt Collection Practices Act** addresses abusive methods used by third-party collectors—bill collectors hired to collect overdue bills. Small businesses are more directly affected by state laws that apply directly to collection methods used by a creditor. The Fair Debt Collection Practices Act states that unless a debtor consents or a court order permits, debt collectors may not call to collect a debt

- at any time or place that is unusual or known to be inconvenient to the consumer (8 a.m. to 9 p.m. is presumed to be convenient);
- when the creditor is aware that the patient/debtor is represented by an attorney with respect to the debt, unless the attorney fails to respond to the communication in a reasonable time period; and
- at work if the creditor is aware of the fact that the patient's employer prohibits such contacts.

WHAT DID YOU LEARN?

1. List the five federal laws that affect credit and collection.
2. Generally, if a state law allows more time for the debtor to notify the creditor about a billing error than does the federal statue, which prevails?
3. What does the Equal Credit Opportunity Act address?
4. Name the three telephone limitations upheld by the Fair Debt Collection Practices Act.

COLLECTION METHODS

No matter how careful, how cautious, or how capable the health insurance professional or collection manager is; no matter how experienced, how resourceful, or how persuasive the health insurance professional or collection manager is—there always will be some bad debts in a health care practice. Two common methods health care offices use for collecting bad debts are collection by telephone and collection by letter.

Collection by Telephone

Collecting overdue accounts by phone is a job that many health care office employees would prefer not to do. It is so much easier to write a collection letter than to call a patient about a delinquent account, but the collection call is considered far more effective because patients usually respond more readily to a friendly voice than they do to a letter. Many offices have found that the collection call, when done correctly, is an inexpensive and effective collection technique. It costs money to continue sending statements and letters.

Health care practices that have experienced success with telephone collections call patients approximately 15 days after a second statement has been mailed out. The practice identifies the remaining accounts to be called and prioritizes them according to amount owed, with the largest amount to be handled first. An alternative method is to work the accounts in alphabetical order, but if time runs out, the last half of the alphabet may not get called, which may include individuals who owe large amounts. Ideally, the most recent and largest accounts are called first.

Making collection calls throughout the day, with special emphasis from 5 p.m. to 8 p.m., is recommended whenever possible. Most offices report that more patients can be reached between 5 p.m. and 7 p.m. than at any other time during the day. The health insurance professional should be aware of the legal limits of telephone collection calls as spelled out in the Fair Debt Collection Practices Act. For more information on this act, see the listing in Websites to Explore.

Timetable for Calling

A workable telephoning timetable needs to be specific and must be followed consistently to get results. This may be one half of the list per week or per month, depending on the size of the practice. Random calling tends not to work as well.

Do not wait too long to get aggressive with collections. Many offices wait 4, 5, or 6 months before

Patient:	"The check is in the mail."
HIP:	"Thank you for mailing your check. What day did you mail it? What was the amount of the check and the check number?"
Patient:	"I don't pay the bills. Talk to my wife."
HIP:	"Mr. Hughes, you're our patient. That is why I'm calling you regarding the account."
Patient:	"I'll have to discuss it with my husband. He's at work right now."
HIP:	"May I call your husband at work and straighten this out? What is the phone number?"
Patient:	"I'll have to think about it and see if I can raise the money."
HIP:	"Mr. Hughes, credit was extended to you in good faith when it was needed. I'm sure you are a responsible person and want to meet your obligations."
Patient:	"I'm laid off work and can't pay anything now."
HIP:	"Mrs. Hughes, I'm sorry that you've been laid off. How long have you been out of work? Are you receiving unemployment compensation? Is your spouse working?"
Patient:	"But I can't pay all of it now."
HIP:	"We have a payment plan available, Mr. Williams, that will bring your account up-to-date without too much difficulty."

Fig. 10-9 Sample phone conversations. *HIP*, Health insurance professional.

making the first collection call—a policy that yields a very low return. Collection specialists claim that calling closer to the time of service results in greater payoffs. The longer an account is left without follow-up calls, the less chance there is of collecting the fees.

Selecting Which Patients to Call

The next step is to select which patients to call. Some offices believe that it is not cost-effective to call regarding accounts that are less than a certain amount—$30 to $45. A large practice with thousands of patient visits per month may not find it cost-effective to call regarding accounts less than $100. Fig. 10-9 shows examples of typical conversation scenarios and how the health insurance professional may handle the situation.

Collection by Letter

Collecting delinquent accounts by letter has been successful for some health care practices. The timing and wording of written communications with patients should be based on numerous factors, including the size of the balance owing, the payment history of the patient, and the philosophy and policy of the practice.

When composing collection letters, be careful with the wording used so as not to anger or upset the patient. Be matter-of-fact and nonthreatening. Adopt the attitude that the patient has simply overlooked the bill and will make a payment because of this reminder letter. Fig. 10-10 shows a series of example collection letters. These letters can be tailored to fit the particular needs of the practice and the patients. Additional letters or phone calls can

be added to extend the time between communications. The key is to stay in constant communication with overdue accounts rather than adopting a "wait until tomorrow" attitude or assuming that the account will have to be written off or turned over for collection.

WHAT DID YOU LEARN?

1. Why might a telephone call be more effective in collecting delinquent accounts than a letter?
2. When does the text suggest the health care practice make its first collection call?
3. What minimum amount does the text say warrants a telephone call?

BILLING SERVICES

Some health care practices "outsource" their medical billing by hiring a separate professional medical billing service. A reputable medical billing service can provide comprehensive, cost-effective, HIPAA-compliant medical billing solutions for health care professionals nationwide. Medical billing services typically are organized and run by medical billing professionals who design, implement, and manage the accounts receivable portion of the health care practice. A well-run medical billing service can help a health care practice run more efficiently by eliminating staffing issues, undisciplined medical billing and collection processes, outdated medical billing systems, and archaic reporting tools that result in poor collection ratios. Billing services can perform multiple functions for the health care practice, such as the following:

Example Letter 1: Send when the account is past 30 days.

Dear Mrs. Williams:

Your account balance of $340.50 is now overdue. Please send your payment to the above address at your earliest convenience.

If you have questions, you can reach our bookkeeper at xxx-xxxx between 8 a.m. and 5 p.m. weekdays.

Sincerely,

XYZ Family Clinic

Example Letter 2: Send 15 days after letter #1 if no payment is made.

Dear Mrs. Williams:

Despite several communications, we have not received payment for your overdue balance in the amount of $340.50. Your account is now seriously past due.

Please send your payment to the above address or contact our bookkeeper at xxx-xxxx if you have questions. We will contact you by telephone if we do not hear from you within 7 days.

Sincerely,

XYZ Family Practice

Example Letter 3: Send 15 days after letter #2 if no payment is made.

Dear Mrs. Williams:

We have made all reasonable attempts to work with you to reduce your seriously overdue balance with our clinic. You have not met the terms of the payment plan that we agreed upon.

Professional services have been provided to your family in good faith, and payment of your account will protect your status as a family in good standing.

We must hear from you within 15 days of the date of this letter.

Our bookkeeper is available on weekdays between the hours of 8 a.m. and 5 p.m.

Sincerely,

XYZ Family Clinic

Example Letter 4: Send 15 days after letter #3 if no payment is made.

CERTIFIED MAIL RETURN RECEIPT REQUESTED

Dear Mrs. Williams:

You have failed to pay or satisfactorily reduce your severely delinquent balance despite our many efforts to work with you. Therefore, XYZ Family Clinic will no longer be providing medical care for you and your children. You should place your family under the care of another physician as soon as possible. You may contact XYZ Family Clinic or the County Medical Society for a referral to a new physician.

When you have selected another physician, please send us a signed authorization so that we can provide a copy of your children's medical charts or a summary of its contents to your new physician.

XYZ Family Clinic will remain available to treat your children for a short time, which will be no more than 30 days from the date of this letter. Please make the transfer to a new physician as soon as possible within that period.

Sincerely,

XYZ Family Clinic

Fig. 10-10 Sample letter series for delinquent accounts.

- Preparing and submitting insurance claims
- Providing data entry of patient demographics, insurance information, charges, payments, and adjustments
- Tracking payments from patients and third-party payers
- Producing practice management reports
- Collecting delinquent accounts

Usually, a computer, modem, and Internet access are all that is needed to access a billing service's network, after which the medical facility can retrieve up-to-the-minute patient information and practice management reports at any time on a secure server.

Many billing services are available locally and nationwide. With the advent of the Internet, a health care office can interact with a professional billing service anywhere in the United States. Care should be taken, however, when choosing a billing service. The service should be thoroughly researched and references checked out with several of their current customers.

WHAT DID YOU LEARN?

1. What is a billing service?
2. List five functions of a billing service.

COLLECTION AGENCIES

A **collection agency** is an organization that obtains or arranges for payment of money owed to a third party—in this case, a health care office. Many health care practices use collection agencies to help collect delinquent accounts. Collection agencies provide a service to businesses that

- are too small to have a collection department of their own,
- lack the expertise to collect delinquent accounts themselves,
- think a collection agency would get faster results, or
- simply do not want to deal with the hassle of collections.

Most collection agencies request at least 50% of the money they collect. Experts suggest that delinquent bills should be turned over for collection only when it is obvious that payment by any other means is a dead issue. When to go to collection is a business decision made within each health care practice.

If the decision is made to turn delinquent accounts over to a collection agency, care should be taken when choosing the agency. Experts say that a credible collection agency should be a member of a national trade association, such as Consumer Data Industry Association, formerly Associated Credit Bureaus, and American Collectors Association. These organizations provide all-important standards and training. When choosing a collector, choose one that specializes in collecting medical accounts. Also, use standard business practices such as talking with associates; checking references, credentials, and local professional or trade memberships; and touching base with state or local licensing authorities and perhaps the Better Business Bureau. In addition to checking references and credentials, the health care practice should ensure that the agency chosen

- employs trained, certified collectors who understand and abide by the Fair Debt Collection Practices Act and follow the requirements of state laws;
- is insured, licensed, and bonded; and
- is able to collect in other states.

HIPAA TIP

The HIPAA Privacy Rule does not require consent from a patient before turning in his or her account for collection. Covered providers still must be cautious when using personal health information for collection purposes in determining just how much personal health information is needed to accomplish the specific goal of satisfying their account receivables.

WHAT DID YOU LEARN?

1. What is a collection agency?
2. List four reasons a health care practice might hire a collection agency.
3. What two trade organizations do experts suggest contacting when choosing a collection agency?
4. Name three things to look for in a reputable collection agency.

SMALL CLAIMS LITIGATION

Small claims litigation is an alternative to turning accounts over for collection. Filing a small claims suit can be effective for a health care practice to collect delinquent accounts. Before making the decision to take a delinquent patient to small claims court, however, the cost should be weighed against the monetary gain. The cost of generating a small claims lawsuit is typically $30 to $50, so the account ideally should total enough to offset this expense. The process is administered by the services at local county or district courts, but the individual initiating the small claims lawsuit must prepare the paperwork.

The small claims process is set up to make it easy for individuals or businesses to recover legitimate debts without using expensive legal advisors. The claim usually is heard by a judge in chambers (or, in some case, an appointed arbitrator), with the parties presenting their sides in person. The individual or business entity that initiates the legal process must pay the initial costs, such as filing and serving fees, but these fees usually can be recovered from the debtor. Small claims suits can be for any amount of money up to a limiting threshold, which varies by state, usually $3000 to $5000; however, there is ongoing legislation in many states to increase this limit to $10,000.

Who Can Use Small Claims

Generally, any person of legal age or any business entity can file a small claims lawsuit if there is a legitimate claim against someone who owes money and is refusing to pay. All that is needed is proof that the debt exists. In the case of a health care office, this is usually some sort of written evidence, such as a patient ledger. The important thing is that there is full and proper documentation. The most prolonged and expensive disputes generally result from inadequate paperwork and a lack of attention to detail.

Before a claim can proceed, the court expects the **plaintiff** (the party bringing the lawsuit) to have explored all other avenues of settlement. This means that the plaintiff should allow the other side (in this case, the patient) a "reasonable period of time" to make a payment before resorting to legal action.

How the Small Claims Process Works

The procedure starts with the plaintiff filling out a standard form, which outlines details about the claim and the various parties. The following information needs to appear on the form:

1. Name of the party being sued
2. Current address of that party
3. Amount of the plaintiff's claim
4. Basis, or proof, of the claim

The completed form is returned to the court office with the appropriate filing and serving fees. A copy of the form is "served" to the **defendant** (the party being sued), who may choose to pay the debt in full plus all accrued fees before the process goes any further. He or she also may dispute the claim in its entirety.

If the claim, or any part of it, is disputed, the matter goes to a court hearing, where the evidence is heard in informal surroundings, usually around the table in a judge's chambers. The plaintiff and defendant are given an opportunity to introduce evidence, ask questions, and explain to the judge (or arbitrator) why judgment should be entered in his or her favor. The judge usually makes an immediate decision, and the parties involved get a full and final result on the day of the hearing. The judgment of the court is an official statement in the court's records that the defendant owes the plaintiff a certain amount of money with interest. The judgment must be enforced out of the defendant's assets. More simply put, if the judgment is in favor of the plaintiff, the defendant must pay immediately. If the defendant does not pay after judgment, the plaintiff can "attach," or gain ownership of the defendant's assets, such as a paycheck, a bank account, or a car.

Small claims litigation can be successful, but it is time-consuming and can be costly if there are a lot of claims. If the health care practice has someone on staff who is able and willing to prepare all the proper documents and attend court hearings, this process can have positive results. Filing and serving fees can be far less than the typical 50% of the outstanding debt kept back by a collection agency.

WHAT DID YOU LEARN?

1. What was the initial intent of the small claims process?
2. What is a typical monetary threshold for a small claims suit?
3. What is the first step in initiating a small claims suit?
4. List the four elements of information that must appear on the small claims form.

SUMMARY CHECK POINTS

- Patients typically come to a health care office expecting certain things, such as the following:
  - A *professional office setting*—Because patients cannot see and touch an intangible service, such as health care, they look for substitutes to put their mind at ease. Substitutes include esthetics, such the office location, size and layout, carpet, and staff enthusiasm.
  - *Relevant paperwork and questions*—Patients prefer paperwork to be brief, of high quality, and relevant to the encounter. Personal questions should be asked privately, and patients should be given reasons why these forms and questions are important to their care and treatment.
  - *Honoring appointment times*—Time has become a valuable commodity in *everyone's* life; the medical receptionist should indicate approximately how long an initial visit will take and briefly explain what to expect when the patient phones for an appointment. If the schedule lags, the patient should be told the reason for the delay and offered alternatives to waiting.
  - *Patient load*—Negative conclusions about the competency of the entire health care team can be offset by explaining to the patient why the reception room has no or few patients waiting.
  - *Getting comfortable with the health care provider*—Sharing a relevant personal experience or information promotes a good provider-patient relationship and often tends to relieve an anxious patient.
  - *Privacy and confidentiality*—Patients must feel confident that any personal information

they divulge will be kept private and confidential. The staff should be discreet when talking to patients or among themselves because voices tend to carry.

- *Financial issues*—Discuss financial issues and practice policies up-front with patients so that they know what to expect.

☑ Future trends in the patient-practice relationship include the following:

- *An aging population*—Over the next 30 years, the number of Americans older than age 65 will double, and health care facilities will need to be prepared to handle an increasing volume of elderly patients.
- *Using the Internet as a health care tool*—Individuals are using websites to find physicians and hospitals that offer opportunities for certain procedures, lifestyle advice, and educational details and references for a multitude of health conditions. Future patients will rely more on the Internet, and health care providers will have to adapt their practices to meet these state-of-the-art electronic requirements.
- *Seeing patients as consumers*—Treating patients as "consumers," rather than "patients," is recommended. Today's patients, similar to other types of consumers, are likely to switch health care plans or health care providers or both if they think they are not getting quality service.

☑ Any individual or any business involved in transferring data or carrying out transactions related to patient protected health information is a HIPAA-covered entity. The law applies to three groups:

- *Health care providers*—Any provider of health care services or supplies who transmits any health information in electronic form in connection with a transaction for which standard requirements have been adopted
- *Health plans*—Any individual or group plan that provides or pays the cost of health care
- *Healthcare clearinghouses*—Any public or private entity that transforms health care transactions from one format to another.

☑ Personally identifiable information includes information about an individual collected by the covered entity that reasonably could be used to identify the individual, regardless of the source of such information or the medium in which it is recorded. Personally identifiable information includes, but is not limited to,

first and last name, residence or other physical address, electronic mail address, telephone number, birth date, credit card information, and Social Security number.

☑ When all identifiable elements are removed, the information is, under most circumstances, considered de-identified.

☑ A HIPAA-approved release of information must contain the following elements:

- A specific and meaningful description of the information sought
- The name of the person or persons authorized to make the request
- The name of the person or persons to whom the covered entity may make the request
- A description of each purpose of the requested use or disclosure
- An expiration date that relates to the purpose of the use or disclosure
- A statement of the right (and exceptions to this right) to revoke the authorization in writing and saying how this may be accomplished
- A statement that information used may be subject to re-disclosure by the recipient and no longer be protected by this rule
- Signature of the individual and date signed
- A description of the covered entity's authority to have a representative act for the individual (if applicable)

☑ Two common methods of accounting are used in today's health care facilities.

- *"One-write" pegboard accounting system*—This system, made up of several accounting forms and carbonized shingled receipts, captures information at the time the transaction occurs with a single writing and eliminates the need for recopying the data. One-write systems are popular because they are accurate, are easy to learn, and use a write-it-once process for recording daily office transactions.
- *Electronic patient accounting software*—A computer software program can perform all phases of the accounting process quickly and accurately. It allows the input of demographic data and creates a patient "account" from which many documents can be generated, such as a list of appointments by day and by provider and an encounter form for each one. A current copy of the patient ledger can be printed showing dates, diagnosis and procedure codes, charges, payments, and current balances. Appointments also

can be scheduled, deleted, and adjusted within the accounting system. Periodic statements, aging reports, and CMS-1500 claim forms can be generated.

 Some things a health care practice might do to increase its financial success include, but are not limited to, the following:
- Establish a written credit policy
- Discuss payment and practice policies upfront with patients
- Bill promptly
- Plan an action for bills more than 30 days old
- Telephone (or send a letter) after the second statement
- Use the services of a small claims court

Laws affecting credit and collection include the following:
- The Truth in Lending Act
- The Fair Credit Billing Act
- The Equal Credit Opportunity Act
- The Fair Credit Reporting Act
- The Fair Debt Collection Practices Act

 The steps involved in small claims litigation are as follows:
- Acquire the proper forms from the local county or district court, along with instructions on how to fill them out properly.
- Include the following information on the original form: (1) the name of the defendant, (2) the current address of the defendant, (3) the amount of the plaintiff's claim, and (4) the basis of the claim.
- Attach documentation that provides proof that the money is owed.
- Return the completed form (and the required number of copies) to the court office with the appropriate filing and serving fees.
- Appear in court on the date indicated to substantiate the case.

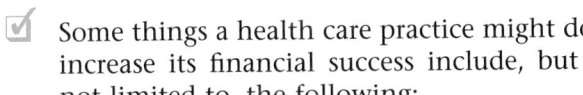

Closing Scenario

Before Callie Foster completed Chapter 10, her goal was to learn how to be considerate, patient, and empathetic to patients because of a recent negative incident she had experienced at a health care office. Her confrontation had been very upsetting, and she firmly believed that no one should be treated so rudely. Callie thought that what other patients expect when they come to a health care office is what she herself expected when she went to Dr. Dayton's office. It became obvious, however, as she progressed through the chapter, that although consideration, patience, and empathy are important during the actual patient-staff encounter; when it comes to collections, sometimes a fair but firm and pragmatic attitude is necessary.

Scott found the section on consumer credit laws especially interesting and informative. To him, the steps involved in the small claims litigation process were straightforward and manageable—a fair and economical way to collect outstanding accounts.

WEBSITES TO EXPLORE

- For information on HIPAA regulations, go to
  http://www.hipaadvisory.com/regs

- For more information on financial policies for health care offices, go to
  http://www.pcc.com/pub/pm/finpol.html

- For more information on laws regarding credit and collection, log on to the following:
  http://www.consumerlaw.com/debt.html
  http://www.fair-debt-collection.com

- For more information on the Consumer Data Industry Association, log on to
  http://www.cdiaonline.org/index.cfm

- For more information on the American Collectors Association, log on to
  http://www.debtmarketplace.com

- For more information on small claims procedures, log on to
  http://www.peopleslawyer.net/smallclaims

References and Resources

American Medical Association: How to "HIPAA"—top 10 Tips AMA, 2003. Available at: http://www.ama-assn.org/ama1/pub/upload/mm/435/hipaa10tips-opt.pdf.

Burton B: Quick guide to HIPAA for the physician's office, Philadelphia, 2004, Saunders.

Quinsey CA: Practice brief. A HIPAA security overview. J AHIMA 75:56A–56C, 2004.

Chapter Review

Assessment

Multiple Choice

Directions: *In the questions/statements presented, choose the response that* ***best*** *answers/completes the stem, and circle the letter that precedes it.*

1. Creating a good patient-staff relationship begins when __C__.
   A. the patient arrives at the medical facility
   B. the patient is in the examination room
   C. the patient telephones for an appointment
   D. the patient encounter has been completed

2. The health care staff can find out what their patients' expectations are by __B__.
   A. writing a letter
   B. asking questions
   C. having them fill out forms
   D. taking a survey

3. The services offered by a medical facility usually cannot be felt or seen, which means they __A__.
   A. are intangible
   B. are not important
   C. cannot be documented
   D. cannot be billed

4. Most physicians prefer to leave the subject of fees up to their __C__.
   A. nurse
   B. accountant
   C. reception staff
   D. health insurance professional

5. Experts predict that over the next 30 years, the number of Americans older than age 65 will __A__.
   A. double
   B. triple
   C. quadruple
   D. decrease by about 20%

6. Data that are explicitly linked to a particular individual (including data items that reasonably could be expected to allow individual identification) are referred to as __C__.
   A. protected health information
   B. HIPAA-explicit information
   C. individually identifiable health information
   D. A and C are correct

7. An arrangement by which a patient requests that his or her health insurance benefit payments be made directly to a physician or hospital is called a(an) __D__.
   A. release of information
   B. discharge of authority
   C. power of attorney
   D. assignment of benefits

8. Although health care practitioners are dedicated to the health and well-being of their patients, their ultimate goal is _B_.
   A. research
   B. making a profit
   C. keeping up on new medical technologies
   D. publishing articles in prestigious journals

9. The total amount of fees collected divided by the total amount charged provides the practice with a(an) _C_.
   A. profit
   B. billing ratio
   C. collection ratio
   D. accounts receivable balance

10. A patient's name, age, address, telephone number, Social Security number, and employer information are generally referred to as _D_.
    A. demographics
    B. vital statistics
    C. "de-identified" data
    D. all of the above

11. When a medical facility uses patient billing software, it is *crucial* to _A_.
    A. input data correctly
    B. keep the equipment clean
    C. make weekly backups
    D. use state-of-the-art electronic equipment

12. Most medical offices send out statements periodically, which is referred to as a _C_.
    A. collection practice
    B. statement control
    C. billing cycle
    D. mailing

13. Patients who have inadequate health insurance coverage or no insurance at all are called _A_.
    A. self-pay patients
    B. deadbeats
    C. indigent
    D. red-flaggers

14. When no insurance is listed on a patient information form, the health insurance professional should _D_.
    A. alert the physician
    B. ask the patient to leave
    C. ask the patient to pay up front
    D. inquire as to why no insurance is listed

15. An installment payment plan of more than four payments falls under _____.
    A. HIPAA regulations
    B. the Fair Credit Billing Act
    C. the Equal Credit Opportunity Act
    D. the Federal Truth in Lending Act of 1968, Regulation Z

16. The act that deals primarily with credit reports issued by credit reporting agencies is called _A_.
    A. the Fair Credit Reporting Act
    B. the Fair Credit Billing Act
    C. the Equal Credit Opportunity Act
    D. the Federal Truth in Lending Act of 1968, Regulation Z

17. An organization that obtains or arranges for payment of money owed to a third party is referred to as a _C_.
    A. legal aid society
    B. small claims association
    C. collection agency
    D. certified public account (CPA) group

18. The process available to individuals or businesses to recover legitimate debts without using expensive legal advisors is known as _B_.
    A. adjudication
    B. small claims litigation
    C. appellate court
    D. grievance

19. In a small claims suit, the party initiating the action is referred to as the _A_.
    A. plaintiff
    B. defendant
    C. bailiff
    D. attorney

20. The party being sued is the _B_.
    A. plaintiff
    B. defendant
    C. bailiff
    D. attorney

True/False

Directions: *Place a "T" in the blank preceding each of the following statements if it is true; place an "F" if it is false.*

_T_ 1. Patient expectations are the same from office to office.

_T_ 2. Besides being brief and of high quality, paperwork in a medical office should be relevant to the reason the patient is there.

____ 3. Patients need to be tolerant of long waits because the physician's time is worth more than their own.

_F_ 4. If the reception area is empty when the patient enters, he or she may think the health care provider is second-rate.

____ 5. Patients must realize and accept the fact that partition walls are thin in many medical facilities, and private conversations can be overheard.

_T_ 6. Most patients typically have no idea what their medical care and treatment should cost before they make an appointment.

_F_ 7. Today's health care consumers expect the cost of their health care to be addressed up-front.

_T_ 8. It is a trend in today's fast-paced world for people to believe that their time is just as valuable as their health care provider's time.

_F_ 9. Members of the health care team should discuss their personal lives with patients to promote good provider-patient relationships.

_F_ 10. Identifiable medical information includes medical records, medical billing records, any clinical or research databases, and tissue bank samples.

_F_ 11. "Covered entities" can transfer protected health information to noncovered entities (those who do not come under HIPAA rules) without violating HIPAA.

_T_ 12. HIPAA gives patients the right to access their medical information and to know to whom the covered entity has disclosed this information.

_F_ 13. Patients have the right to obtain copies of their protected health information from their physicians or health plans, unless the information is likely to endanger their lives or the lives of other people.

_T_ 14. Patients have the right to correct or amend their medical records.

____ 15. Covered entities can release "de-identified" health information without patient authorization.

_T_ 16. Most patients appreciate having fee and billing information presented clearly and matter-of-factly, but in a pleasant and courteous manner.

_F_ 17. Experts consider the most effective payment policy is for the front desk staff to request payment when the patient/provider encounter is concluded.

_F_ 18. Computerized patient billing software typically includes accounts receivable, insurance billing, and practice management modules.

_T_ 19. The most effective way to collect money is to establish a formal financial policy that is clear to patients and the medical staff and to enforce it.

_T_ 20. By law, medical facilities are not allowed to extend credit.

_T_ 21. Under most state laws, full payment for medical services is due and payable at the time the service is provided.

_T_ 22. Regarding collection and credit, it is mandatory that every patient be treated equally.

_T_ 23. It is often not cost-effective to use small claims litigation for past due accounts that are less than $30.

_F_ 24. To use the small claims process, the practice must retain an attorney.

_F_ 25. Professional collection agencies typically retain 50% of collected fees.

Short Answer/Fill-in-the-Blank

1. The text discussed "surrogates" that patients look for in a medical office. List at least four of these common surrogates.

STAFF ENTHUSIASM

LAYOUT

COLOR OF OFFICE

OFFICE SIZE

2. List some successful online patient-centered topics.

PROCEDURAL INFO

PHYSICAN BIOGRAPHIES

ONLINE SCHEDULING

3. It is the trend for patients to be viewed as "consumers" in today's health care world. Explain this phenomenon.

PEOPLE ARE MORE EDUCATED, AWARE OF CHOICES

& CAN NOW MAKE CONSCIOUS DECISIONS ABOUT THEIR

HEALTH.

4. The text lists five consumer essentials that experts believe should be mandatory for any medical facility wishing to provide patient-centered service. These are:

INFORMATION

CONTROL (SELF CARE)

CUSTOMER SERVICE

CHOICE

SHARED DECISION MAKING

5. HIPAA states that specific "covered entities" must comply with HIPAA rules for any health or medical information of identifiable individuals. Identify these covered entities.

HEALTH CARE PROVIDERS

HEALTH PLANS

CLEARING HOUSING

6. List the elements that a HIPAA-compliant release of information must include.

IDENTIFYING INFO, NAME OF AUTHORIZED PERSON, TO MAKE

REQUEST, NAME OF PERSON TO WHOM ENTITY MAY MAKE

REQUEST, DESCRIPTION OF PURPOSE

Matching

Directions: *Place the letter identifying the correct choice in the blank in front of the numbered statements.* (**Note:** *Not all choices are used.*)

_K_ 1. A chronological record of all patient transactions, including previous balances, charges, payments, and current daily balances

_G_ 2. A listing of all expenses paid out to vendors, such as building rent, office supplies, and salaries

_D_ 3. A separate record some offices keep for wages and salaries

_F_ 4. A chronological listing of all transactions, considered the most basic of all office records

_B_ 5. The "core" of a practice's financial records

_C_ 6. A chronological accounting of activities of a particular patient (or family), including all charges and payments

_A_ 7. The entire grouping of patient ledgers

A. Accounts receivable

B. General ledger

C. Patient ledger

D. Payroll journal

E. Accounts payable

F. General journal

G. Disbursements journal

H. Chronological journal

I. Core journal

J. Activities journal

K. Daily journal

Critical Thinking Activities

A. This statement recently appeared in the *Health Day News:* "Patients who have good relationships with their physicians tend to be more satisfied with their care and have better results." Write a critical thinking paragraph discussing whether you agree with this statement, and why or why not.

_____

_____

_____

_____

_____

B. Lindell Holmes, a former patient at Broadmoor Medical Clinic, has not made a payment on his outstanding account for more than 90 days. His account was turned over to the Milton County Collection Agency on 10/07/20XX. Two weeks later, Mr. Holmes comes to the Clinic and pays his bill in full with money order #003665UPS. Assuming that the collection agency keeps 50% of all collections, correctly post this payment on the ledger card in Fig. 10-11.

DOB:　03/22/51
Self-pay

STATEMENT

BROADMOOR MEDICAL CLINIC
4353 Pine Ridge Drive
Milton, XY 12345-0001
Telephone: 555-656-7890

LINDELL R. HOLMES
4216 WEST PINE AV
MILTON, XY 12345

| DATE 20XX | PROFESSIONAL SERVICE DESCRIPTION | CHARGE | CREDITS | | CURRENT BALANCE |
			PAYMENTS	ADJUSTMENTS	
6/09	99203 New Pt Exam	135 00			135 00
6/10	94620 ROA-CASH	185 00	132 00		188 00
7/10	Phone call				
8/10	Col. Letter-cert				

Due and payable within 10 days.　　　　Pay last amount in balance column ⇧

Fig. 10-11　Ledger card.

C. Assume that Broadmoor Medical Clinic does not use a collection agency for delinquent accounts but instead files small claims suits at the local county courthouse on 10/07/20XX. The filing fee is $30, and the Milton County Sheriff's Department charges $25 for serving the papers to Mr. Holmes on 10/09. Using the ledger card in Fig. 10-12, post these charges to Mr. Holmes' account.

DOB: 03/22/51
Self-pay

STATEMENT

BROADMOOR MEDICAL CLINIC
4353 Pine Ridge Drive
Milton, XY 12345-0001
Telephone: 555-656-7890

LINDELL R. HOLMES
4216 WEST PINE AV
MILTON, XY 12345

DATE 20XX	PROFESSIONAL SERVICE DESCRIPTION	CHARGE	PAYMENTS	ADJUSTMENTS	CURRENT BALANCE
6/09	99203 New Pt Exam	135 00			135 00
6/10	94620 ROA-CASH	185 00	132 00		188 00
7/10	Phone call				
8/10	Col. Letter-cert				

Due and payable within 10 days.   Pay last amount in balance column ⇧

Fig. 10-12   Ledger card.

Case Studies

A. When Emily Fortune's appointment is concluded on February 7, 20XX, you hand her an encounter form listing the fees, which total $265. Mrs. Fortune does have insurance, but her policy has a $2500 deductible; her carrier will pay nothing toward the fees generated on this date. She advises you that because her condition restricts her ability to perform her job, she cannot pay the entire bill right now, but she can pay $50 a month. Review the credit policy you created for Broadmoor's Policy Manual. Is Mrs. Fortune's monthly payment in line with this policy? If not, how should the payment plan be revised so that it meets the stipulations outlined in the Policy Manual?

B. LaDon Williams is a self-pay patient at Broadmoor. He has not paid on his outstanding balance ($300) for 2 months. During a telephone conversation, Mr. Williams agrees to come to the Clinic and discuss a credit plan. He informs the reception staff that he can afford to pay only $10 a month on his delinquent account. The reception staff refuses to accept the payment, informing Mr. Williams that the entire bill must be paid at once, or his account will be turned over for collection. Can this situation possibly create a problem for Broadmoor Medical Clinic? If so, explain.

Internet Exploration

A. Log on to the Internet. Using "find doctors," or similar search words, find how much information is available on the Web for today's health care consumers.

B. Using search words, such as "patients as consumers," explore the Internet in search of information and thoughts on this subject.

C. To learn more about how to maximize patient collections, search the Internet using the appropriate search words.

D. Search the Internet for information on how to file a small claims suit.

OBJECTIVES

After completion of this chapter, the student should be able to:

1. List and explain the six keys to successful claims.
2. List and explain the six steps of the adjudication process.
3. Discuss time limits for submitting insurance claims and appeals.
4. Outline the process for submitting secondary claims.
5. Discuss the process for appealing incorrect payments and denied claims.
6. Explain the Medicare multilevel appeals process.

THE CLAIM

KEY TERMS

adjudication
birthday rule
clean claim
coordination of benefits
correct code initiative

downcoding
employer identification number (EIN)
hearing on record
insurance claims register (log)
Medicare Secondary Payer claims

personal hearing
secondary claim
suspension file
telephone hearing

Opening Scenario

Zoey Edwards, confined to a wheelchair after an automobile accident at the age of 12, was looking for a career opportunity that would to allow her to work out of her home. She noticed an article in a flyer from a local community college about a health care billing and insurance program. The article listed the career possibilities for graduates of this program, along with testimonials from several former students who had established successful home-based businesses in health care billing and insurance. Zoey decided that a career in this field might meet her needs. Through a state-of-the-art communications network, and with the help of the student services staff at the college, Zoey was able to "attend class" in the comfort of her own home, traveling to campus only for major examinations.

Kristin Underwood also was looking for an opportunity to work at home and still care for her two preschool children. Kristin had a friend who worked as a health insurance professional in a local health care office, so she was aware of the challenges and rewards this career area offered. Kristin thought she had the personal traits and work ethic to make a home business successful, so she enrolled in a career school in her neighborhood and signed up for a health care insurance course.

GENERAL GUIDELINES FOR COMPLETING THE CMS-1500 FORM

In earlier chapters, we discussed the steps for completing the universal CMS-1500 claim form for generic commercial carriers and the major payers—Medicaid, Medicare, and TRICARE/CHAMPVA. As a review, Box 11-1 lists some general guidelines for preparing all paper claims. Earlier chapters also stressed the importance of strict adherence to payer-specific guidelines when preparing claims.

WHAT DID YOU LEARN?

1. List five important guidelines for submitting paper claims.

KEYS TO SUCCESSFUL CLAIMS

Claims processing involves many steps, and each step must be performed thoroughly and accurately to receive the maximum payment that the health record documentation substantiates. This process begins with the patient appointment and ends with the carrier's subsequent payment. Understanding how this process works allows the health insurance professional to file claims properly, resulting in full and timely reimbursement. Fig. 11-1 illustrates the six "keys" to successful claims processing.

First Key: Collect and Verify Patient Information

Unless a patient visits the health care facility on a regular basis (e.g., weekly allergy shots or blood pressure checks), the health insurance professional should verify the patient's information each time he or she visits the office. New patients must complete a patient information form on the first visit. Established patients should be required to update the form at least annually because within a year's time, the patient could have remarried; moved to a new address; changed jobs; or, most important, changed insurance companies. In addition to demographic data (e.g., name, address, age, gender), the patient information form should include basic items such as the insurance carrier's name, policy and group numbers (if applicable), the insured's name (if different from the patient), effective date of coverage, and any secondary insurance information. It is not unusual for some practices with a high volume of Medicare patients to have a separate information form for those patients.

After the patient information form is completed, the health insurance professional should check it over to ensure that the correct information has been entered in the required blanks and that all information is legible. One key to successful claims submission is to have the patient provide as much information as possible, and the health insurance professional should verify this information.

BOX 11-1 General Guidelines for Completing the CMS-1500 Form

- Use the preprinted red and white CMS-1500 claim form only.
- Follow OCR guidelines.
- Submit claims that are legible using computer-generated or typed entries.
- Submit only six line items per claim. Do not compress two lines of information on one line.
- Send paper claims unfolded in large envelopes.
- Use standard fonts (preferably Courier) in 10-point or 12-point size.
- Type within each block and not outside the block. Characters out of alignment would cause the claim to be returned as misaligned.
- Follow payer guidelines as to where to type the insurance carrier's name and address. Some carriers stipulate that the area to the right of the bar code be left blank.

- Do not submit a narrative description of the ICD-9 code in Item 21.
- Do not submit procedure codes with negative charges in Item 24d.
- Do not type a telephone number in the NPI(a) or NON-NPI(b) portion of the field in Item 33.
- Do not highlight information. Instead, underline information on attachments that you want to bring to the payer's attention.
- Remove pin-feed strips on pin-fed claims at the perforations only. Do not cut the strips because it may alter the document size.
- Do not tape, glue, or staple attachments to the CMS-1500 claim form. Do not tear, bend, or fold corners of the claim form with attachments.
- Attachments should be the same size as the paper claim form ($8\frac{1}{2} \times 11$ inches).

Fig. 11-1 Six keys to successful claims processing.

In some situations, more than one insurer is involved. Such cases might occur when the patient and his or her spouse are covered under separate employer group plans or when the parents of a minor patient are divorced, and each parent has his or her own insurance policy. In the case of the latter, if the primary carrier is not designated on the information form, the health insurance professional should obtain this information from the parent who accompanies the child to the office.

In addition to the standard demographic and insurance questions asked on the patient information form, many health care practices include a section (often positioned at the bottom of the form) for the patient to sign a release of information and an assignment of benefits. Other practices use separate forms for these functions. A signed and dated release of information is necessary before the health insurance professional can complete and submit an insurance claim. When a patient signs an assignment of benefits, he or she is authorizing the insurance carrier to send payment directly to the health care provider.

After obtaining a complete and accurate patient information form, the health insurance professional should make a photocopy of the patient's insurance card and place it in an easily accessible location in the patient's health record, such as inside the front cover. Many insurance identification (ID) cards also have information on the back. If this is the case, the health insurance professional should be sure to copy the back of the card also.

HIPAA TIP

Patients have certain rights and protections against the misuse or disclosure of their health records. All patients should receive a Notice of Privacy Practices that informs individuals of their rights and of the health care practice's legal duties with respect to protected health information.

IMAGINE THIS!

Shirley Gibson, a health insurance professional for Westlawn Family Medical Center, updates all demographic and insurance information when patients come to the office for an appointment. Additionally, she checks to ensure that the release of information is signed, dated, and current, as is the assignment of benefits. After the patient completes the new information form, Shirley checks it for accuracy and legibility. If two insurance companies are listed, she asks the patient which is primary. In some cases, Shirley has to call either the employer or the insurance carrier to verify which is the primary carrier. "It is important for smooth, efficient, and timely claims processing," Shirley says, "to have all information current and accurate before the claim is prepared for submission. It is surprising," she continues, "how much people move around, change jobs, and change insurers these days."

Second Key: Obtain the Necessary Pre-authorization and Precertification

The health insurance professional should be familiar with the rules regarding pre-authorization and precertification. Some third-party payers reject certain types of claims if they do not know about and approve the services beforehand. Services that most often require pre-authorization or precertification include inpatient hospitalizations, new or experimental procedures, and certain diagnostic studies. Emergency services typically do not need prior authorization, but they often require some type of follow-up with the insurance company—typically within 24 to 48 hours. Ultimately, it is the patient's responsibility to know when and how to notify the insurance company for pre-authorization or precertification; however, the health insurance professional should advise the patient when this process is necessary to avoid rejected claims. Also, if the patient is incapacitated in any way, the health insurance professional or a member of the health care staff should notify the patient's insurer to acquire the necessary pre-authorization. Telephone numbers for contacting the carrier are usually on the back of the patient's ID card. Fig. 11-2 shows the back of an insurance ID card with a toll-free number to call when precertification is needed. Some carriers issue a "prior authorization" number, which should be placed in Block 23 of the CMS-1500 form.

Reminder: Medicare (fee-for-service) does not need prior authorization to provide services.

STOP AND THINK

Helen Rigdon was admitted as an inpatient to Memorial East Hospital after a visit to the emergency department for a bleeding ulcer. After Helen was discharged, she received an EOB from her insurance carrier stating that they were denying the claim because there had been no pre-authorization for the hospital admission. In this case, whose responsibility was it to contact the insurance company to obtain the required pre-authorization?

Third Key: Documentation

It is the health care provider's responsibility to document the appropriate comments in the patient's health record. Each entry must indicate clearly the history, physical examination, and medical decision making for the patient. The provider also fills out an encounter form, indicating the proper procedure codes (CPT or HCPCS level II) and diagnosis

---

IMPORTANT PHONE NUMBER INFORMATION

For pre-admission certification, OB and emergency admissions call 1-800-558-xxxx.

To locate a participating provider call 1-800-810-xxxx or access BlueCard website @ www.bcbs.com.

Providers - Please submit all claims to your local Blue Cross and Blue Shield Plan.

Pharmacists - Pharmacy Benefits Manager (PBM) is AdvancePCS. For assistance call 1-800-600-xxxx.

Wellmark Blue Cross and Blue Shield of Iowa, an independent licensee of the Blue Cross and Blue Shield Association.

Fig. 11-2 Back of insurance ID card.

codes (ICD-9-CM) to describe the patient's condition and the services that were rendered. These codes should be checked before transferring to the claim because some practitioners when in a hurry may indicate the wrong ones. The health insurance professional places the appropriate diagnosis codes, procedure codes, charges, and any other pertinent information in the proper boxes on the claim. Claims may be in paper or electronic format. Each required field on the claim helps to determine if that claim is clean. Claims that are not clean are returned for more information or are denied. It is important that the claim show the exact diagnosis that is documented in the health record.

Fourth Key: Follow Payer Guidelines

As pointed out in previous chapters, some major payers (Medicaid, Medicare, Blue Cross and Blue Shield, TRICARE/CHAMPVA) have slightly differing guidelines for completing the CMS-1500 claim form. The health insurance professional must obtain the most recent guidelines from each of these major payers to complete the claim exactly to their specifications.

Fifth Key: Proofread Claim to Avoid Errors

Claims are commonly rejected or denied. Being aware of some common mistakes can help the health insurance professional avoid delays, denials, or rejections. It is good practice first to proofread the claim carefully when it is completed, paying particular attention to code entries and dollar amounts. Make sure the claim is dated, and the proper signature is affixed. When the claim is completed and signed, make a photocopy for the file. Box 11-2 lists some common errors that cause a claim to be rejected or denied.

BOX 11-2 Common Errors Made on Claims

- Patient's insurance ID number is incorrect.
- Patient information is incomplete.
- Patient/insured name and address do not match the insurer carrier's records.
- Physician's EIN, provider number, NPI, or Social Security number is incorrect or missing.
- There is little or no information regarding primary or secondary coverage.
- Physician's (or authorized person's) signature has been omitted.
- Dates of service are incorrect or do not correlate with information from other providers (e.g., hospital, nursing homes).
- The fee column is blank, not itemized, and not totaled.
- The CPT or ICD-9 codes are invalid, or the diagnostic codes are not linked to the correct services or procedures.
- The claim is illegible.
- Pre-authorization/precertification was not obtained before services rendered.

Sixth Key: Submit a Clean Claim

The most important document in the health care insurance process is the insurance claim form—the CMS-1500—and the most important thing about the CMS-1500 is that, when completed and submitted to the third-party insurer, it is a **clean claim**. A clean claim means that all of the information necessary for processing the claim has been entered on the claim form, and the information is correct. Clean claims are usually paid in a timely manner; paying careful attention to what should appear in each of the boxes helps produce clean claims.

STOP AND THINK

Silver River Medical Center has a higher than average number of rejected paper claims. The billing and insurance staff consists of four health insurance professionals, and each handles approximately 50 to 55 claims per day. Many of the claims are rejected or denied because of simple errors—transposed numbers, misspelled patient names, incorrect charges, or omission of the provider signature. What might the billing/insurance staff do to resolve this problem?

Rejected Claims versus Denied Claims

A claim that does not successfully pass through the adjudication process to the payment system is rejected. Examples of why a claim is rejected include provider not found, member not found, incorrect address was used, or more than one rendering provider submitted on a claim. A claim that is denied was passed through to a payment system, but was not payable for a number of reasons, including, but not limited to member ineligible, benefit not covered, or benefit maximum has been met. A rejected claim must be researched differently than a denied claim. Questions regarding rejected claims should be directed to the carrier or clearinghouse. Questions regarding denied claims should be directed to the carrier's customer service department.

HIPAA AND THE NATIONAL STANDARD EMPLOYER IDENTIFIER NUMBER

The Secretary of the Department of Health and Human Services proposed that the **employer identification number (EIN)** that is assigned by the Internal Revenue Service (IRS) be used as the employer identifier standard for all electronic health care transactions as required by HIPAA. The ruling requires the following:

- Health plans must accept the EIN on all electronic transactions that require an employer identifier.
- Health care clearinghouses must use the EIN on all electronic transactions that require an employer identifier.
- Health care providers must use the EIN on all transactions, wherever required, that are electronically transmitted.
- Employers must disclose their EIN when requested to do so by an entity that conducts standard electronic transactions requiring that employer's identifier.

An EIN consists of nine digits with the first two digits separated by a hyphen (e.g., 00-1234567). The IRS assigns EINs to employers, who can obtain an EIN by submitting IRS Form SS-4 (Application for Employer Identification Number). Business entities that pay wages to one or more employees are required to have an EIN as their taxpayer identifying number; most employers already have an EIN assigned to them.

In May 2002, the Department of Health and Human Services issued a final rule to standardize the identifying numbers assigned to employers in the health care industry by using the existing EIN (this EIN should appear in Block 25 of the CMS-1500 form with a space replacing the hyphen). Most covered entities were to have been in compliance with the EIN standard by July 30, 2004; however, small health plans were allowed an additional year to comply.

≋ CLAIM PROCESS

After a claim has been received by a third-party payer, it is reviewed, and the carrier makes payment decisions. This process is referred to as **adjudication**. If the claim is clean, it continues on through several more steps to the reimbursement process, and, ideally, the insurance carrier pays up to the allowed amount (according to the patient's policy) for the services that have been billed. The carrier can reduce payment, however, or deny the claim completely. If any information is missing, or if there are errors on the claim, the process is stopped, and the claim is returned to the health care office where it originated. Fig. 11-3 is a flow chart that illustrates how a paper claim progresses through the various steps after it is received at the payer's facility. The steps discussed in the following sections and listed in Fig. 11-4 are for a paper claim.

Step One: Claim Is Received

When the insurance carrier receives the claim, it is dated, and the claim is processed through an optical character recognition (OCR) scanner. If any attachments accompanied the claim, the practice name, provider/group number, address, and telephone number should appear on each attached document. This helps prevent claim denial in case the attachments get separated from the claim during the adjudication process. Box 11-3 lists the general guidelines for OCR scanning.

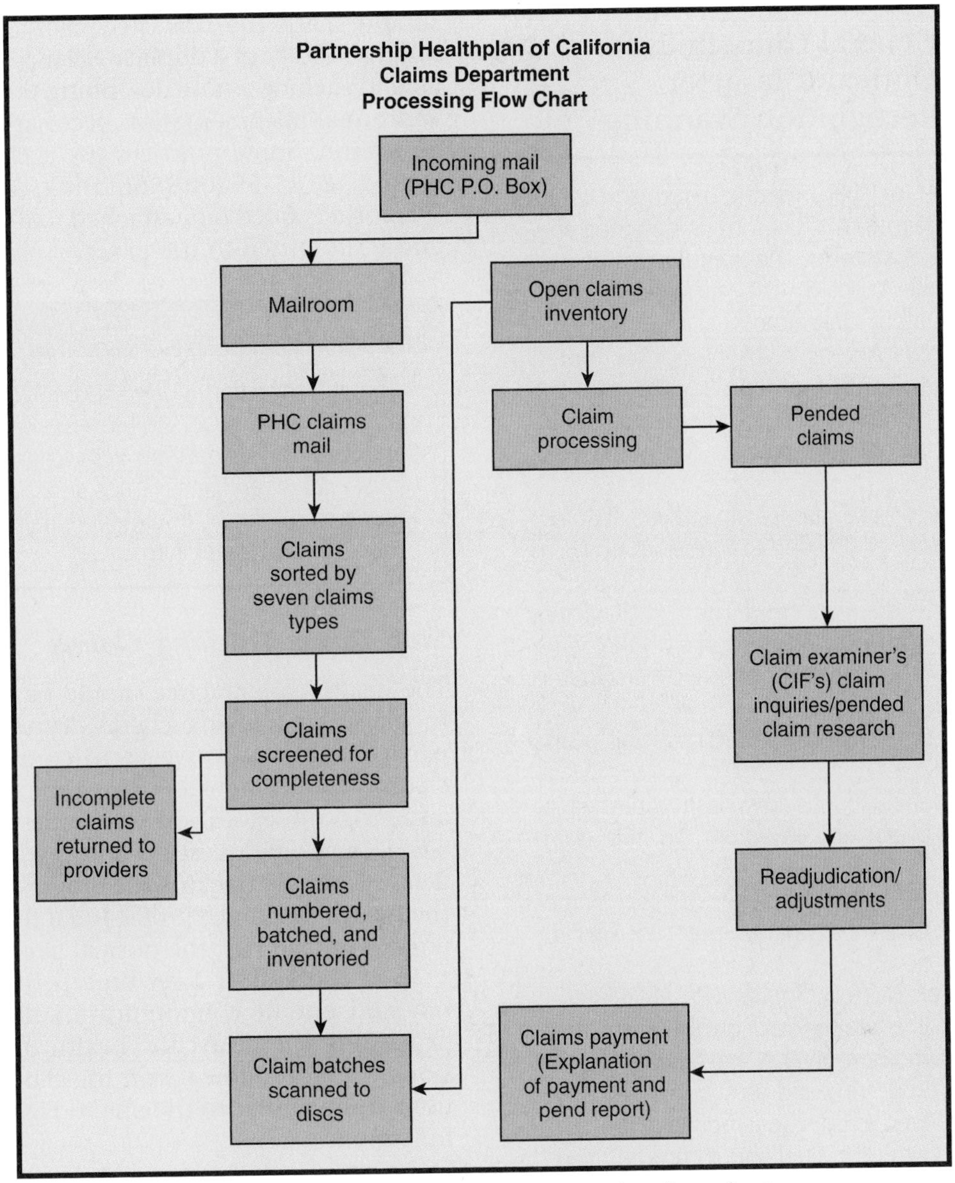

Partnership Healthplan of California
Claims Department
Processing Flow Chart
Incoming mail (PHC P.O. Box)
Mailroom
PHC claims mail
Claims sorted by seven claims types
Claims screened for completeness
Incomplete claims returned to providers
Claims numbered, batched, and inventoried
Claim batches scanned to discs
Open claims inventory
Claim processing
Pended claims
Claim examiner's (CIF's) claim inquiries/pended claim research
Readjudication/ adjustments
Claims payment (Explanation of payment and pend report)

Fig. 11-3 Claims department processing flow chart.

Step Six: Posting payments
Step Five: Interpreting EOBs
Step Four: Receiving payment
Step Three: Tracking a claim
Step Two: Claims adjudication
Step One: The claim is received
Health insurance professional
Insurance company

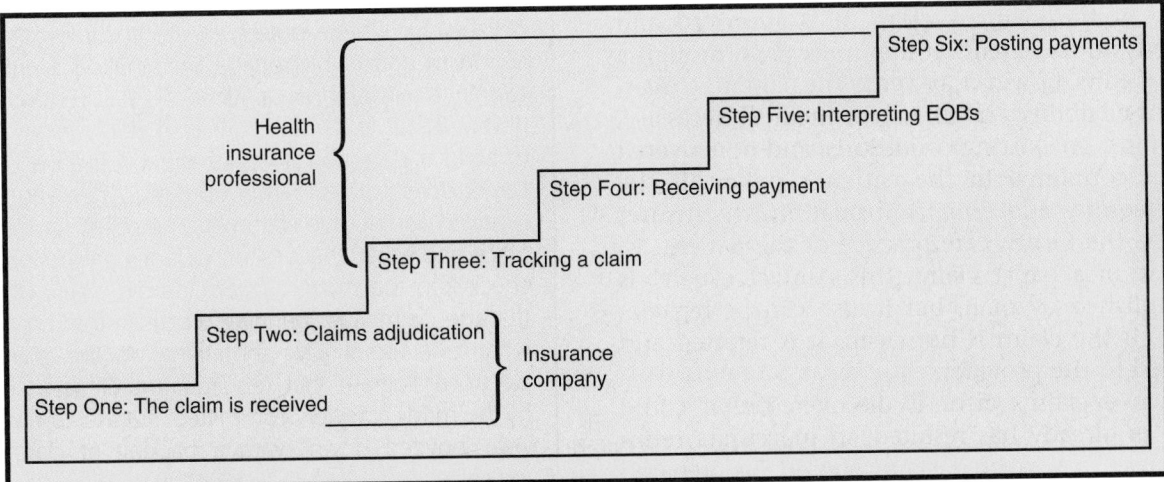

Fig. 11-4 Steps of the claim process. *EOBs*, explanations of benefits.

BOX 11-3   General Guidelines for Optical Character Recognition Scanning

- Use only the original preprinted red and white CMS-1500 claim form. This form is designed specifically for OCR systems. The scanner cannot read black-and-white (copied, carbon, faxed, or laser printer–generated) claim forms.
- Do not use red ink pens, highlighters, sticky notes, stickers, correction fluid, or tape anywhere on the claim form. The red ink or highlighter would not be picked up in the scanning process and would black out information.
- Do not write or use stamps or stickers that say "Rebill," "Tracer," or "Second Submission" on claim form.
- Use standard fonts that are 10 to 12 characters per inch. Do not mix character fonts on the same claim form. Do not use italics or script. Handwritten entries should be avoided.
- Use upper case (capital letters) for all alpha characters.
- Do not use punctuation marks, slashes, dashes, or any special characters anywhere on the claim form.
- Use black printer ribbon, ink-jet, or laser printer cartridges. Ensure that ink is not too light or faded.
- Ensure that all claim information is entirely contained within the proper field on the claim form and on the same horizontal plane. Misaligned data would delay processing and may be missed.
- If corrections need to be made, reprinting the claim is preferred. Correction fluid should not be used.

Step Two: Claims Adjudication

After the data are entered into the payer's computer system, if the claim is clean, it is approved and proceeds on to be paid. It first must pass through a series of edits, however, to verify the patient's coverage and eligibility and check for medical necessity, exclusions, preexisting conditions, and noncovered services contained in the patient's policy. If the claim requires additional information, the insurer contacts the health care practice or the patient. In the case of a paper claim, this contact usually is accomplished by mail, but it also can be by telephone. If the claim is not clean, it is rejected and returned to the provider.

When a claims error is discovered that could result, or already has resulted, in inaccurate reimbursement, a corrected claim should be prepared and submitted. The health insurance professional

should mark the corrected claim as a "corrected billing" and "not a duplicate claim." It also is advisable to include a note describing the error, plus any additional documentation necessary to support the correction. Some practices use a claims correction form (Fig. 11-5) for submitting corrected claims. The form is filled out, attached to a corrected claim, and resubmitted to the payer.

HIPAA TIP

A new transaction currently being developed by HIPAA will allow payers to request additional information to support claims. This transaction will use Logical Observation Identifiers Names and Codes (LOINC) to request the clinical information that is required to process health care claims.

Step Three: Tracking Claims

The health care practice should have a mechanism in place for tracking claims. Typically, it takes a paper claim 4 to 6 weeks to complete the entire claims process; however, this time varies by carrier and geographic location. Sometimes a claim may be clean, but some question arises, which results in a delay. Carefully tracking the progress of claims alerts the health insurance professional to the claims that remain unpaid past the normal payment time.

If, at the end of a set time period, the claim is not paid, and no communication has been received explaining the delay, the health insurance professional should follow-up on the claim. Many offices use a form similar to the one in Fig. 11-6 for claims follow-up.

IMAGINE THIS!

Laurence Benson visits his family physician, Myron Peters, yearly for annual wellness examinations. Every 3 years, Dr. Peters orders an electrocardiogram for Myron as part of his routine examination. Normally, Laurence's insurance carrier, XYZ Health Indemnity, pays within 2 to 3 weeks. It is Dr. Peters' office policy to send a statement to the patient if the insurance carrier does not pay within 60 days. When Laurence received an overdue statement, he called Dr. Peters' office and asked the health insurance professional to check into the matter. When she did, she was told that the claim was "pending" because the individual who reviewed it saw something on the attached electrocardiogram that required further assessment by the medical review committee, but the committee was "bogged down" with a backlog of claims to review.

Claim Correction Form

Physician offices are encouraged to submit claims electronically. This form should be used in situations where the provider cannot submit corrected claims electronically or where electronic submissions would not adequately address the issue.

Submitted To:

Plan/Payer Name: _____   Date Submitted: _____

Plan/Payer Address: _____

City _____   State: _____   Zip: _____

Telephone: (_____) _____   Fax: (_____) _____   E-mail: _____

Patient Name: _____   D.OB.: _____
               First   M.I.   Last

Subscriber Name: _____   Date of Service: _____

Policy #: _____   Group #: _____   Original Claim #: _____

Submitted From:

Provider Name: _____   TIN or ID #: _____

Contact: _____   Telephone: (_____) _____   Ext. _____

Fax: (_____) _____   E-mail: _____

THE FOLLOWING WAS CORRECTED ON THIS CLAIM:

❏ The patient's policy/group number was incorrect. The correct number(s) are shown above.

❏ The correct CPT code is _____ instead of _____

❏ Wrong date of service was filed. The correct date is _____

❏ Visits were denied based on the diagnosis given. Proper diagnosis code is _____ instead of _____

❏ Visit: ❏ Procedure: denied as over carrier's utilization limits. Please see attached letter to justify extensions of these limits.

❏ Carrier indicated that the patient is covered by another plan that is Primary. This is incorrect. Patient indicates you are Primary.

❏ The secondary carrier is: _____   ❏ There is no secondary carrier.

❏ The procedure was denied as medically not necessary. Documentation to support the medical necessity of this service is attached.

❏ Our clerk: ❏ Carrier's clerk: failed to enter correct number of times (units) procedure was performed. Correct units are as follows:

    D.O.S.: _____   Code: _____   Units: _____   Charge Total $: _____

❏ Multiple Surgical Procedures:

    ❏ Carrier failed to approve any procedure at 100%.   ❏ Carrier approved incorrect procedure at 100%.

    Carrier should have approved code _____   @ 100%/50% instead of _____

    Carrier should have approved code _____   @ 100%/50% instead of _____

    Carrier should have approved code _____   @ 100%/50% instead of _____

❏ Modifiers should be attached to code(s)

	Code	Code		Code	Code
❏ -50	_____	_____	❏ -51	_____	_____
❏ -58	_____	_____	❏ -59	_____	_____
❏ -79	_____	_____	❏ -GA	_____	_____
❏ __			❏ __	_____	_____

❏ The following E/M visit was denied as included in the global surgical fee. In fact, the service was a significant separately identifiable service provided above and beyond the procedure and submitted with appropriate E/M modifier. Please reconsider with attached documentation:

    Code: _____   with modifier(s): ❏ -24 ❏ -25   Charge $: _____

❏ UPIN information for code _____ was omitted. Physician name: _____   UPIN: _____

❏ Plan specific provider I.D. omitted. The I.D. # is _____

❏ CLIA number was omitted. The CLIA number is _____

❏ The place of service was incorrect. The place of service should be _____

❏ The service was rendered at the physician's physical location listed in Box 32 of the claim form.

❏ Failed to attach EOB from Primary carrier. The EOB is attached to this form.

❏ Failed to enter correct information on indicated line of claim form.

    Line #: _____   Correct Information: _____

❏ Other reason for claim correction: _____

❏ Comment: _____

June 2003

Fig. 11-5 Example of a claims correction form.

Prompt Payment Tracking Form

Practice/Physician Information (complaint by)

Name: _____

Address: _____

City, Zip _____

Phone: _____   Fax: _____

E-Mail: _____

Information Checklist

Please provide copies of the following:

☐ The claim form submitted to insurance company

☐ Electronic claim receipt if applicable

☐ Correspondence from the insurance company (EOBs, requests for additional information, etc.)

☐ Details of written/oral contacts with insurance company regarding this claim

☐ Other pertinent information

Note: Mark out all confidential patient information, such as name, date of birth or social security number.

Insurance Company and Claim Information

Company: _____

Date(s) of Services: _____

Submitted via: ☐ Paper   ☐ Electronic

Original Submission Date: _____

Phone: _____

Claims Rep (if known): _____

Action by Insurance Company

Date of Initial Response from Ins. Co.: _____

☐ Denied ☐ Requested Additional Information ☐ Reduced Payment ☐ Other (see attached)

Insurance Company Response: _____

_____

_____

Current Status of Claim: _____

_____

_____

Fig. 11-6   Example of a claims tracking form.

STOP AND THINK

Re-read Imagine This! concerning Dr. Peters. How might Dr. Peters' health insurance professional modify her routine to avoid future problems similar to the one experienced by Mr. Benson?

Creating a Suspension File System

For offices filing paper claims, some sort of claims tracking system is recommended, such as a **suspension file**. A suspension file is a series of files set up chronologically and labeled according to the number of days since the claim was submitted. Claims in a file labeled "current" might be 30 days

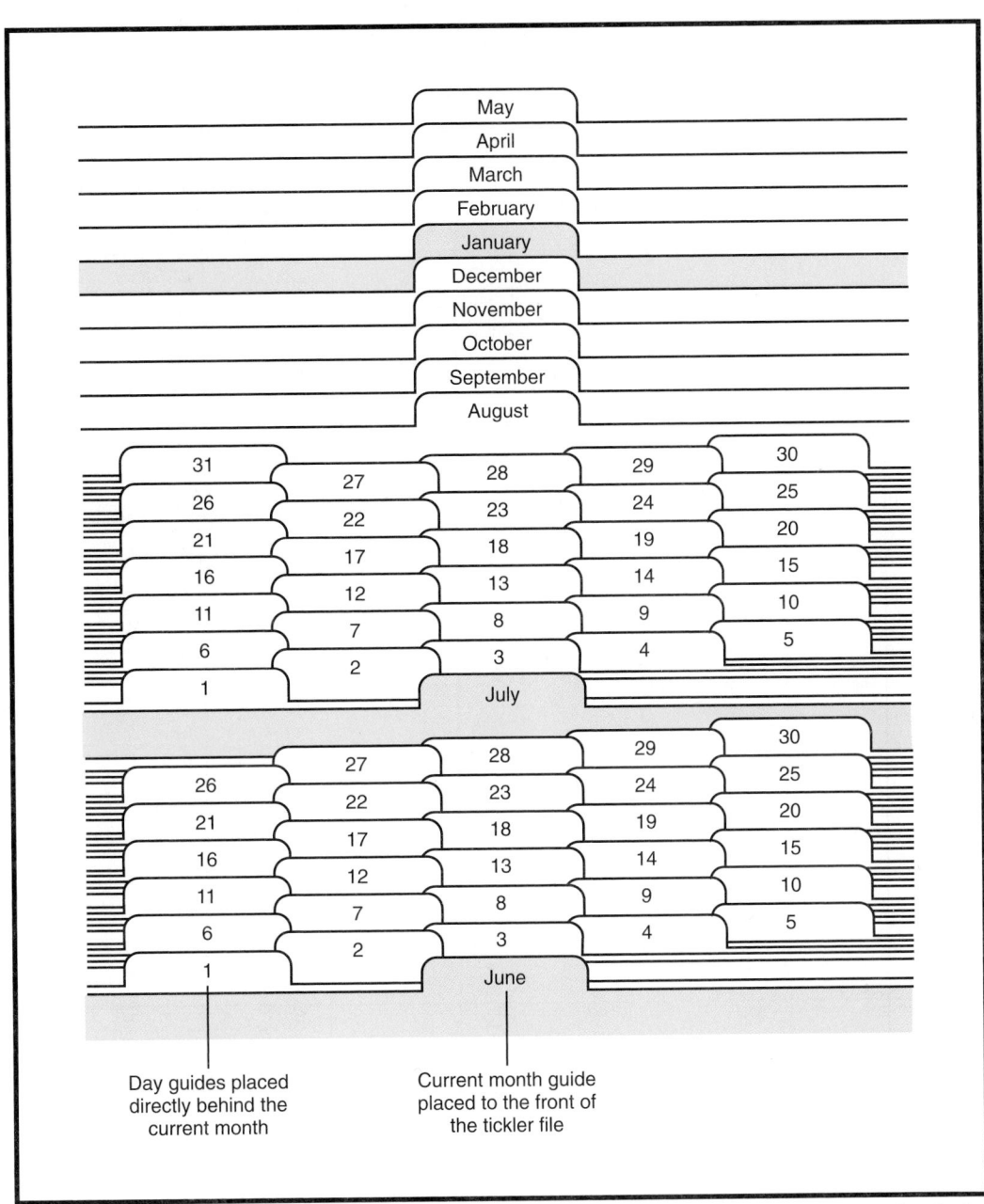

Fig. 11-7 Suspension file. *(From Fordney M:* Insurance handbook for the medical office, *10th ed, St Louis, 2008, Saunders.)*

or less; a second series might be labeled "claims over 30 days," and so forth. Another type of follow-up system that works well is the one pictured in Fig. 11-7, in which claims are filed according to the date they are submitted.

Claim copies should be removed systematically. Paid claims can be filed in a permanent folder or binder, under each major payer. If payment has not been received, some sort of follow-up procedure can be initiated. Claims follow-up should be given a high priority and become a regularly scheduled part of the health insurance professional's work week.

Experienced health insurance professionals who deal with Medicare and Medicaid carriers recom-

mend making inquiries in writing or using the forms specifically created for follow-up. Inquiries to commercial carriers often are handled more efficiently by a telephone call. If a claim has been rejected for a simple reason, without notification, a quick phone call is time well spent. In the case of resubmission, always attach a note with the date, the contact person's name, and a description of the conversation. Keep a copy of all correspondence as documented proof of response.

Creating an Insurance Claims Register System
An alternative to the suspension file is to record claims information on a columnar form known as

INSURANCE CLAIMS REGISTER

Filing Date	Chart Number	Patient's Name	Name & Address Where Claim Submitted	Amount Billed	Amount Paid	Difference	Status or Comment
10/6	1221	Matthew Kramer	First Insurance 1st Avenue Newark, NJ 12345	$525			10/21 busy 10/30 busy 11/6 busy
10/6	1350	Luke Myers	Better Insurance 3rd Avenue New York City, NY 02110	$1200	$700	$500	Requester Review 10/30
10/6	1098	Christi Wilson	County Farm Ins 6th Avenue New Era, IA 45678	$125	$50	$75	$75 deductible. Bill Patient
10/6	1352	Rose Larson	Last Insurance 7th Avenue New Hope, MS 56789	$1500	0		Sent to Medical Review 10/30

Fig. 11-8 Example of an insurance claims register.

an **insurance claims register** or **log** (Fig. 11-8). When a claim is submitted, the health insurance professional records the filing date, the patient's name and chart number, the name and address of the payer, and the amount billed. As payments are received, the original copy of the claim form is removed from the follow-up file and compared with the explanation of benefits (EOB). The amount paid is recorded in the applicable column along with any difference from the amount billed as shown on the log sheet. Any notations, such as "claim sent to review" or "claim rejected for additional information," should be recorded in the status column along with the date the notice was received. If a claim is resubmitted, that date also should be recorded on the log.

Step Four: Receiving Payment

The insurer sends the payment for services and the EOB—sometimes called a remittance advice (RA)—back to the provider's office. (Whether or not there is a payment, there is always an EOB or RA.) If the practice submits claims electronically, the EOB or RA also may be in an electronic format. Each EOB should be checked thoroughly to ensure that the payment is consistent with the fee schedule or contracted amount from the insurance company (Table 11-1). Claims that have been denied or rejected for any reason or that have been reduced in payment should be reviewed to determine the source of the denial or payment reduction. It then must be decided whether to pursue the claim further.

TABLE 11-1   Common Payment Errors

Result	Reason
A service is reduced	The adjudicator may have downcoded the claim for lack of documentation
	The CPT code was converted to an RVS code that did not directly correlate with CPT
Reimbursement is made at a much reduced rate	Possibly a data entry error. Compare the CPT code submitted with the code paid
Low reimbursement	Precertification was not completed
	Insufficient documentation to establish medical necessity
Multiple units are paid as one unit	The insurer "missed" a number in the unit column
Reimbursement for a procedure or service suddenly decreases	This could mean a recalculation of the allowable fee or an error. Phone the payer
Payment is not received	Claim is lost or "caught in the system." Begin your inquiry
Multiple procedures were not paid	The insurance company either ignored the additional procedures or lumped them in with the primary procedure

Republished with permission of Ingenix. Copyright © 2007.

Step Five: Interpreting Explanation of Benefits

The EOB is the document sent by the insurance carrier to the provider and the patient explaining how the claim was adjudicated. The EOB is the key to knowing how much of the claim was paid, how much was not, and why—in other words, adjudicated. Sometimes, understanding what this document means can be challenging, however. Every payer has a different EOB format. The EOB has a unique vocabulary, such as "applied to deductible," "above usual and customary," "patient co-pay," and "allowable." Often codes are used, and the health insurance professional must determine what each code means. Deciphering the EOB language and codes reveals the following:

- Date received
- Date processed
- Amount of billed charges
- Charges allowed by the carrier
- How much of the claim was applied to patient deductible
- How much of the patient's annual deductible has been met
- Why a service was reduced or denied

Knowing how to read the EOB is important because it aids in collecting full reimbursement, including any balance owed by the patient. Fig. 11-9 shows an EOB from a commercial insurance company and an explanation of what each code means.

Troubleshooting Explanation of Benefits

As discussed, an EOB explains the outcome of the claim that was submitted for payment processing. If the payment was reduced or rejected, the EOB itemizes the reason for doing so. By reading the EOB and following the instructions, the health insurance professional is able to analyze the situation. If an error has been made on the claim, and it is correctable, it should be done so in a timely manner. If it is believed that the insurance carrier made the error, it should be reported immediately.

Initially, there are several things to evaluate when looking over an EOB that indicates no payment or a reduced payment. The first thing is to compare the totals billed on the EOB and the CMS-1500 form. If they do not match, it is a good indication that the insurer missed a procedure. If the totals match, but the number of line items (actual procedure codes performed) do not, more than likely the insurer bundled one procedure into another, without listing them as "duplicate."

The odds are that if a claim is reduced or rejected, the problem lies with the provider's office. This is not always the case, however, and the health insurance professional should be vigilant in analyzing the EOB. One billing professional suggests keeping copies of sample EOB files for procedures the medical practice performs regularly for each payer. This way, a payment discrepancy stands out when compared with the file. This "example" file can be used for appealing claims, as long as all patient identification is deleted.

EXPLANATION OF BENEFITS

EMPLOYEE BENEFIT PLAN ADMINISTRATION SERVICES

EMPLOYER/GROUP NAME	SOUTHEAST IOWA SCHOOLS		DATE PREPARED	08–06–06
PLAN/LOCATION NUMBER	10000000 14008020 02		SOCIAL SECURITY I.D. NUMBER	
EMPLOYEE/MEMBER NAME	BEIK JANET I		CONTROL #	8470.0
PATIENT NAME	BEIK JANET I		EOB #	9808060048

JANET I BEIK
545 IOWA CITY RD
SOMEWHERE IA 00506

SOUTHEAST IOWA SCHOOLS
SOMEWHERE IA 00506

PROVIDER NAME and TYPE OF SERVICE	DATES FROM/THRU	AMOUNT CHARGED	AMOUNT COVERED	EXPL. CODE	COVERED AT 100 %	COVERED AT %	COVERED AT %
HAYS, ANDERSON, DIAGNOSTIC LABORATORY	06–22–98	15.00	15.00	099 514	15.00		
ADJUSTMENTS TO BENEFITS	TOTAL →	15.00	15.00		15.00		
			Less Deductible				
			Balance		15.00		
			Benefit %		AT 100%	AT %	AT %
			Plan Benefits		15.00		
			Total Benefit		15.00		

099   THIS PREFERRED PROVIDER ACCEPTS THE "AMOUNT COVERED" AND HAS AGREED NOT TO
099   BILL PATIENTS FOR MORE THAN DEDUCTIBLES, CO-PAYS, & NONCOVERED CHARGES.
514   THIS WORKSHEET WAS PROCESSED BY JENNIFER

DEDUCTIBLE SATISFIED: 1000.00

PAYMENTS HAVE BEEN ISSUED TO THE FOLLOWING BASED ON ABOVE EXPENSES.

HAYS, ANDERSON   15.00

Fig. 11-9 Example of explanation of benefits.

IMAGINE THIS!

Dr. Edwin Carter, a podiatrist, performed three arthroplasties on Priscilla Fortune's toes at $500 each procedure. When the EOB was received, the total charge was $1500, but there were only two codes of 28285 listed. This meant that Ms. Fortune's insurance carrier had bundled two of the procedures into one, but the fee schedule was considered for only one. To clear things up, Wayne Thomas, Dr. Carter's health insurance professional, had to contact the insurer and explain that there were three distinct procedures performed on three individual toes and not two, as the carrier had assumed.

Downcoding

Downcoding by an insurance company occurs when claims are submitted with outdated, deleted, or nonexistent CPT codes. When this happens, the payer assigns a substitute code it thinks best fits the services performed. Often, the health care practice does not agree with the choice because the substituted code results in a lesser payment. Similar problems occur when an insurer's payment system is based on CPT codes, and an RVS (Relative Value System) code is submitted that does not directly translate to CPT. When these claims are reviewed by a claims adjuster, he or she assigns a valid CPT code. Coding accurately and knowing which coding systems payers use help to avoid these downcoding problems.

If the claims adjuster changes a valid procedure code that was submitted on the claim, the health insurance professional should contact the claims adjuster and ask for the reason. If the contact is by mail, documentation that supports the code submitted should be included. In some cases, a procedure is denied because the insurer states that it is considered "integral to the main procedure." In other cases, a modifier that was submitted on the claim was dropped, or the claim was subject to a **correct code initiative** edit. Correct code initiative edits are the result of the National Correct Coding Initiative (NCCI), which develops correct coding methods for CMS. The edits are intended to reduce overpayments that result from improper coding. If the denial was due to a correct code initiative edit, documentation supporting why the procedure was distinct and not related to another procedure must be submitted.

Step Six: Posting Payments

After the EOB has been reconciled with the patient's account, the health insurance professional or other staff member posts the payment received from the insurance carrier to the patient ledger and bills the patient for any applicable outstanding co-payments or deductible amounts. Participating providers cannot balance bill, but nonparticipating providers for commercial claims are allowed to bill the patient for any balance the insurance carrier does not pay. It is against the law to waive Medicare co-payments unless financial hardship has been established and documented. Fig. 11-10 illustrates a payment entry on a patient ledger.

Time Limits

As stated previously, claims should be submitted to the insurance carrier as soon as possible, ideally within 30 days or sooner of the conclusion of treatment. Claims for patients who receive ongoing treatment typically are submitted on a periodic basis—every 15 to 30 days, depending on the policy of the health care practice. Most third-party payers have time limits for when claims can be submitted to be considered for payment.

Many third-party payers do not pay a claim if the time limit for claim submission has been exceeded. Not all payers deny late claims, but instead levy a fine or penalty because of lateness or "past timely filing" status. The time limit in which to file a claim varies from carrier to carrier and often depends on various circumstances, such as the following:

- Whether the provider of the services participates (or is contracted) with the insurer
- Whether the provider of services does not participate (or is not contracted) with the insurer
- The method in which the claim was submitted for payment (i.e., electronic or paper)
- The type of provider who is billing for services (e.g., physician, hospital)
- When coordination of benefits apply

Generally, an insurer allows a maximum of 1 year from the date of service for submitting a claim; however, this is not always the case because some commercial carriers allow 180 days. If there is any question about time limits, the health insurance professional should contact the carrier. It is a good idea to include each major payer's time limits in the same file containing their claims submission guidelines.

Most insurance companies also have a time limit for filing appeals. The time limit varies from carrier to carrier, and it is important that the health insurance professional keep this information on file so that it is readily available when and if needed.

The health insurance professional should establish a routine for completing and submitting insurance claims, such as at the end of every week or on the 15th and 30th of each month. How often claims are submitted varies depending on the following:

- The size of the practice
- Office staffing
- The type of claim (e.g., workers' compensation, supplemental security income, Medicare)
- How the claims are submitted (electronically or paper)
- Whether claims are sent directly or a clearinghouse is used
- The major carriers involved

STATEMENT

Westlake Medical Clinic
2604 Spindle Center
Cherokee, XY 23133
231-555-1212

Stanley P. Grady
1234 Old Colony Road
Calamus City, XY 23232

DATE	REFERENCE	DESCRIPTION	CHARGES	CREDITS PYMNTS.	ADJ.	BALANCE
2004		BALANCE FORWARD →				26 00
1/10	Stanley	99214, ROA	135 00	8 00		153 00
3/21	Stanley	99214, ROA	135 00	8 00		280 00
5/18	Stanley	99214, ROA	135 00	8 00		407 00
5/20		XYZ Ins. Claim				
6/24		XYZ Ins. Ck 319116		324 00		83 00
6/24		Contr. Adj XYZ			50 00	33 00

B40BC-2   PLEASE PAY LAST AMOUNT IN BALANCE COLUMN →

Fig. 11-10 Example of a patient ledger card with entries.

WHAT DID YOU LEARN?

1. What is typically the first thing that happens to a claim when it is received by the insurer?
2. If the insurer determines a claim is "unclean," what happens to it?
3. Name the two suggested methods for tracking claims.
4. List four common payment errors.
5. Why is it important for the health insurance professional to know how to interpret EOBs?

IMAGINE THIS!

Maise Smyth is employed as a billing and insurance clerk for family practice physician, Dr. Isaac Finnes, at the Gulf Coast Medical Clinic. Dr. Finnes sees approxi- mately 25 patients a day. The clinic is not yet com- puterized, so all of the claims are submitted on paper. To accomplish this challenging workload, Maise has set up a routine for submitting preparation. At the end of each day, she sorts the health records by insurer name. The following is Maise's schedule for claims preparation:

Monday—Blue Cross and Blue Shield
Tuesday—Medicare and Medicaid
Wednesday—TRICARE/CHAMPVA
Thursday—Magna Insurance (a major carrier in the area)
Friday—all miscellaneous carriers/claims follow-up

By the end of the day on Friday, all claims for patients seen that week have been prepared and submitted. Because there are only a few miscella- neous carriers, Maise has time on Friday afternoon to do any necessary claims tracking.

PROCESSING SECONDARY CLAIMS

Occasionally, patients may be covered under two insurance plans. When this happens, the health insurance professional may have to prepare and submit a primary claim and a **secondary claim**. The insurer that pays first is the primary payer, and that payer receives the first claim. The insurance company that pays after the primary carrier is referred to as the secondary insurer. This second carrier receives a claim after the primary carrier pays its monetary obligations.

As mentioned previously, the health insurance professional must determine which coverage is primary and which is secondary. If it is not immediately obvious which payer is primary, the health insurance professional should first ask the patient. If the patient does not know, a telephone call to one of the insurance companies should answer the question quickly and easily. If there is a second insurance policy, it is important to check "yes" in Block 11d on the CMS-1500 form and complete Blocks 9 through 9d (Fig. 11-11).

Occasionally, a patient and spouse (or parent) are covered under two separate employer group policies, resulting in what is referred to as **coordination of benefits**. When a coordination of benefits situation exists, the health insurance professional should

- verify which payer is primary and which is secondary and
- send a copy of the EOB from the primary payer along with the claim to the secondary carrier (if the EOB is not included, the claim is likely to be rejected or delayed pending coordination of benefits determination).

The rule of thumb for dependent children covered under more than one policy is as follows: The payer whose subscriber has the earlier birthday in the calendar year generally is primary. This is referred to as the **birthday rule**. In the case of divorce, the birthday rule may not apply. The custodial parent's

policy may be primary, depending on the arrangement ordered by the Court.

Medicare Secondary Payer claims are claims that are submitted to another insurance company before they are submitted to Medicare. When a Medicare beneficiary has other insurance coverage that is primary to Medicare, the other insurer's payment information must be included on the claim that is submitted to Medicare; otherwise, Medicare may deny payment for the services. The health insurance professional should check the current guidelines of the specific payer in questions when a secondary policy is involved. See Chapter 5 for more information on submitting Medicare Secondary Payer claims.

STOP AND THINK

Fran and Ted Washburn and their two children have been coming to Gulf Coast Clinic on a regular basis for nearly 2 years. Shortly before the last office visit, Fran and Ted divorced; Ted changed jobs and moved to a different address in a nearby town. Fran and Ted are both employed, and each is covered under a separate employer group policy. Ted's date of birth is 09/06/65 and Fran's is 08/16/66. Which parent's policy should be considered primary?

WHAT DID YOU LEARN?

1. What is a secondary claim?
2. What document typically must accompany a secondary claim?
3. Explain what is meant by the "birthday rule."

APPEALS

An appeal, as defined in insurance language, is the process of calling for a review of a decision made by a third-party carrier. Providers of service and patients have the right to appeal a rejected insurance claim or a payment made that the provider or patient (or both) believes is incorrect.

Incorrect Payments

Before appealing a payment or a claim, whether with Medicare or a private commercial insurer, the health insurance professional should notify the insurer in writing that there has been an error. Many payers have a set time limit for claim appeals and often print it on their EOB.

A basic rule for appealing a claim is always to include a copy of the original claim, EOB or RA, and any additional documentation necessary to provide

9. OTHER INSURED'S NAME (Last Name, First Name, Middle Initial)
GARCIA SAM T

a. OTHER INSURED'S POLICY OR GROUP NUMBER
123456

b. OTHER INSURED'S DATE OF BIRTH   SEX
MM DD YY
11 03 1978   M [X]   F [ ]

c. EMPLOYER'S NAME OR SCHOOL NAME
ACME DRYGOODS INC

d. INSURANCE PLAN NAME OR PROGRAM NAME
CERTIF EMPLOYEE BENEFITS

Fig. 11-11 Section of CMS-1500 form showing Blocks 9 through 9d.

evidence for the appeal. Cover letters also are effective for appeals and provide the claims reviewer all of the necessary information regarding the reason for the appeal. If the payer does not respond to an appeal, the health insurance professional can pursue other alternatives, such as contacting the state's insurance commissioner and sending a clear, well-documented account of the discrepancy. See the websites listed at the end of this chapter for links to individual state insurance departments.

Denied Claims

If the health insurance professional believes a claim has been wrongly denied, an appeal can be filed. The appeal process differs from carrier to carrier; however, appeals generally must be in writing and initiated within a specified number of days—usually 30 to 60. The appeal letter should identify the claim and the reason the health insurance professional believes the claim should be approved.

The appeal usually is sent directly to the carrier along with any written comments, documents, records, or other information relating to the claim, even if they were not submitted with the original claim. The carrier typically reviews the appeal within 30 calendar days. Sometimes the insurance carrier's review committee allows the provider (or a representative) to present the case in person or over the telephone, which allows the individual or committee members conducting the review to ask questions to clarify the reason that the provider (or the provider's representative) thinks the claim is valid. The outcome of the appeal is determined, and the provider is notified verbally or in writing of the decision. This decision is usually final; however, some carriers allow second-level or even third-level appeals. The health insurance professional should consult the individual carrier's guidelines regarding the steps to take when initiating an appeal.

If the claim remains unpaid after all levels of appeal are exhausted, there are still some options open. If there have been repeated problems with a

particular carrier, the state insurance commission can be contacted and the problem case outlined in a letter. A second option is to file a complaint with HIPAA. Also, it may be important to get the patient involved because he or she often can make helpful contributions.

Appealing a Medicare Claim

The Medicare program has a multilevel appeal process in place to challenge denied or underpaid claims. There are five different levels of the Medicare appeals process:

- Level I—appeal request
- Level II—hearing
- Level III—administrative law judge (ALJ) hearing
- Level IV—appeals council hearing
- Level V—judicial review

Level I: Appeal Request

The Medicare appeal process begins when either the health care provider or the beneficiary disagrees with the carrier's determination as explained on the EOB or RA. If the claim was assigned, only the provider can initiate the review. If the claim was unassigned, the beneficiary usually initiates the review or can stipulate in writing that the physician is authorized to act on his or her behalf.

The review request must come within 120 days from the date of the original determination for Part A appeals and 120 days for Part B appeals. A Part B appeal can be submitted on the HCFA-1964 Request for Review Form (Fig. 11-12). If a fully completed HCFA-1964 Request for Review Form is not used to express disagreement with the initial determination, a written appeal request must contain the following information:

- Beneficiary name
- Medicare health insurance claim number
- Name and address of provider/supplier of item/service
- Date of initial determination
- Date of service for which the initial determination was issued
- Which item, if any, or service is at issue in the appeal

The health insurance professional should forward the request to the local fiscal intermediary or carrier and clearly mark it "review" to avoid denial as a duplicate claim. As with any review, always include a copy of the claim, the EOB or RA, and any information that would aid in the review determination (e.g., a statement that the payment error was

---

HIPAA TIP

HIPAA provides an online health plan complaint form so that health care providers and their staff members can report administrative and payment disputes with health insurers and third-party payers. The form is designed to collect information from physicians on health plan and third-party payer noncompliance with the provisions of the HIPAA Transaction and Code Set Standards.

DEPARTMENT OF HEALTH AND HUMAN SERVICES
HEALTH CARE FINANCING ADMINISTRATION

FORM APPROVED
OMB NO. 0938-0033

REQUEST FOR REVIEW OF PART B MEDICARE CLAIM
Medical Insurance Benefits – Social Security Act

NOTICE – Anyone who misrepresents or falsifies essential information requested by this form may upon conviction subject to fine and imprisonment under Federal Law.

1. Carrier's Name and Address	2. Name of Patient
	3. Health Insurance Claim Number

4. I do not agree with the determination you made on my claim as described on my Explanation of Medicare Benefits dated:

5. MY REASONS ARE: (Attach a copy of the Explanation of Medicare Benefits, or describe the service, date of service, and physician's name. NOTE: If the date on the Explanation of Medicare Benefits mentioned in Item 4 is more than six months ago, include your reason for not making this request earlier.)

6. Describe illness or injury:

7. ☐ I have additional evidence to submit. (Attach such evidence to this form.)
    ☐ I do not have additional evidence.

COMPLETE ALL OF THE INFORMATION REQUESTED. SIGN AND RETURN THE FIRST COPY AND ANY ATTACHMENTS TO THE CARRIER NAMED ABOVE. IF YOU NEED HELP, TAKE THIS AND YOUR NOTICE FROM THE CARRIER TO A SOCIAL SECURITY OFFICE, OR TO THE CARRIER. KEEP THE DUPLICATE COPY OF THIS FORM FOR YOUR RECORDS.

8. SIGNATURE OF EITHER THE CLAIMANT OR HIS REPRESENTATIVE

Claimant	Representative	
Address	Address	
City, State and Zip Code	City, State and Zip Code	
Telephone Number	Date	Telephone Number	Date

Form HCFA-1964 (9/91)

CARRIER COPY

Fig. 11-12   Request for Review of Part B Medicare Claim.

due to a clerical mistake or any documentation to support payment at the appropriate level, such as chart notes, operative report, or hospital records).

Level II: Fair Hearing

If the claim has gone through the basic review steps, and the health insurance professional still disagrees with the payer's determination, a Request for Hearing—Part B Medicare Claim form may be filed. To qualify for a fair hearing, the amount in question must be at least $100. Medicare allows a practice to "batch" claims with the same problem and procedure to equal the required $100 base. The hearing must be requested within 6 months of the date the informal review decision was made. The request must be in writing and sent to the Medicare Hearing Officer or Coordinator. A request for a fair hearing can be pursued in three ways:

1. **Hearing on record**—a hearing officer investigates all aspects of the claim, but the physician does not testify unless oral testimony is determined to be necessary. A hearing on record is often the most productive fair hearing procedure. The physician is advised of the officer's decision, and a copy of the decision is forwarded to the local Medicare carrier for appropriate action.
2. **Telephone hearing**—the provider (or his or her representative) presents the case to a hearing officer. Before the scheduled hearing, the physician is provided with information in the hearing officer's file. The provider is advised of the decision, and a copy is forwarded to the Medicare carrier for action.
3. **Personal hearing**—when the provider believes a hearing is best done in person, the Medicare hearing officer may agree to schedule a face-to-face meeting to discuss the case. Complete and well-organized records help present the best case possible.

Fig. 11-13 shows the form used to request a hearing on Part B Medicare claims.

Level III: Administrative Law Judge Review

To pursue the third level of appeal, the claim must have completed the fair hearing process, the dollar amount in question must be at least $500, and the appeal must be requested within 60 days of the fair hearing judgment.

Level IV: Departmental Appeals Board Review

If the provider (or beneficiary) is dissatisfied with the ALJ's decision, he or she may request a review by the Departmental Appeals Board (DAB). There are no requirements at this level regarding the amount of money in controversy. The request for a DAB review must be submitted within 60 days of receipt of the ALJ's decision and should specify the issues and findings by the ALJ being contested.

Level V: Judicial Review in United States District Court

After a decision by the DAB, if $1000 or more is still in controversy, a judicial review before a U.S. District Court judge can be considered. The provider must request a U.S. District Court hearing within 60 days of receipt of the DAB's decision. Medicare's appeals process was amended in 2002.

WHAT DID YOU LEARN?

1. If a payer does not respond to an appeal, what alternative does the health insurance professional have?
2. Who initiates an appeal on unassigned Medicare claims?
3. What is the time limit for a Medicare review request?
4. Name the three ways a fair hearing request may be pursued.

SUMMARY CHECK POINTS

 The six keys to successful claims are as follows:

- Verify patient information—It is important to keep patient information and a signed release of information current to generate clean claims, process them expeditiously, and minimize claim delay or denial because of misinformation. Also, if there is a second insurance carrier, primary status must be determined.
- Obtain necessary pre-authorization and pre-certification—Most insurance carriers have a rule that when a patient is to be hospitalized or undergo certain procedures or diagnostic studies, pre-authorization or precertification

REQUEST FOR HEARING
PART B MEDICARE CLAIM
Medical Insurance Benefits - Social Security Act

NOTICE—Anyone who misrepresents or falsifies essential information requested by this form may upon conviction be subject to fine and imprisonment under Federal Law.

CARRIER'S NAME AND ADDRESS

1 NAME OF PATIENT

2 HEALTH INSURANCE CLAIM NUMBER

3 I disagree with the review determination on my claim, and request a hearing before a hearing officer of the insurance carrier named above.

MY REASONS ARE: (Attach a copy of the Review Notice. NOTE: If the review decision was made more than 6 months ago, include your reason for not making this request earlier.)

4 CHECK ONE OF THE FOLLOWING

☐ I have additional evidence to submit.
(Attach such evidence to this form or forward it to the carrier within 10 days.)

☐ I do not have additional evidence.

CHECK **ONLY ONE** OF THE STATEMENTS BELOW:

☐ I wish to appear in person before the Hearing Officer.

☐ I do not wish to appear and hereby request a decision on the evidence before the Hearing Officer.

5 EITHER THE CLAIMANT OR REPRESENTATIVE SHOULD SIGN IN THE APPROPRIATE SPACE BELOW

SIGNATURE OR NAME OF CLAIMANT'S REPRESENTATIVE

CLAIMANT'S SIGNATURE

ADDRESS

ADDRESS

CITY, STATE, AND ZIP CODE

CITY, STATE, AND ZIP CODE

TELEPHONE NUMBER | DATE

TELEPHONE NUMBER | DATE

(Claimant should not write below this line)

- -

ACKNOWLEDGMENT OF REQUEST FOR HEARING

Your request for a hearing was received on _____ . You will be notified of the time and place of the hearing at least 10 days before the date of the hearing.

SIGNED

DATE

Form CMS-1965 (05/03)

Fig. 11-13   Request for Hearing Part B Medicare Claim.

must be acquired beforehand. If this is not done, the claim is likely to be denied. Medicare does not require pre-authorization for medically necessary services.

- Documentation—The health care provider must document accurate and appropriate information in the patient's health record to substantiate the procedures and diagnoses listed on the claim form.
- Follow payer guidelines—Because every third-party payer has slightly different guidelines for completing and submitting claims, the health insurance professional should create and maintain a file for each payer's current guidelines and follow those guidelines to the letter when preparing claims.
- Proofread the claim to avoid errors—It is important to proofread paper claims carefully before submitting them. Most errors that result in denial are simple mistakes, such as typos, transpositions, or omissions, resulting from carelessness and failure to double check each entry on the claim form.
- Submit a clean claim—The ultimate goal in the health care insurance process is to submit a clean claim, meaning all of the necessary, correct information appears on the claim. Clean claims typically are processed quickly.

☑ The claim process includes several steps:
- When the claim is received by the third-party payer, the claim is dated, attachments (if any) are confirmed, and the claim is processed through an OCR scanner.
- The claim passes through a series of edits and is compared with the patient's policy to verify coverage, eligibility, medical necessity, exclusions, preexisting conditions, and noncovered services. If the claim is "clean," it is approved and proceeds on for payment, if payment is due. If there is a problem with the claim, the provider is notified by mail or by telephone.
- At the end of a set time period (4 to 6 weeks for paper claims), if a claim is not paid, and no communication has been received explaining the delay, the claim needs to be followed up. The health care facility should have a mechanism in place for "tracking" claims so that no claim "falls through the cracks." This tracking mechanism could be a suspension filing system or an insurance claims log system.
- Whether or not a payment is made against a claim, there is always an EOB. Each EOB should be checked to ensure that no error has been made by the insurance carrier. If the claim is denied, or there has been a payment reduction, a decision must be made whether or not to appeal.
- Interpreting the EOB is the "key" to understanding how the claim was adjudicated. Accurately deciphering an EOB aids in collecting full reimbursement, including any balance owed by the patient.
- After the EOB has been reconciled, the payment is posted to the patient's account ledger. Participating providers of commercial claims cannot balance bill beyond deductibles and co-payments; nonparticipating providers can. Medicare co-payments cannot be waived, unless a financial hardship case has been established.

☑ Time limits for submitting claims vary with insurance carriers; however, most allow 1 year after the date of service. It is important to follow specific payer guidelines because some demand claims submission within 90 days. The health insurance professional should endeavor to file all claims in a timely manner for the benefit of the practice and the patient.

☑ The most important consideration with patients who are covered under more than one insurance policy is to establish which one is primary. After that, complete the claim for the primary carrier, checking "yes" in Block 11d on the CMS-1500 form and completing Blocks 9 through 9d. Usually, the process for sending a claim to the secondary carrier is to include the EOB from the primary carrier with the claim. It is important to check the guidelines of the secondary carrier for submission rules.

☑ The first step in appealing a denied claim (or a claim in which the payment has been reduced) is to notify the insurance carrier. Most payers have time limits for appealing claims and for submitting claims—typically 30 to 60 days. The health insurance professional should check the payer-specific guidelines for appealing claims. If all efforts of appeal are exhausted without success, and the health insurance professional is certain the claim is valid, a remaining option is to contact the state insurance commissioner's office.

☑ The Medicare program has a multilevel appeals process in place to challenge the determination on a claim.
- *Level I: appeal request*—A party who is dissatisfied with an initial Medicare coverage

determination may request that the carrier review the determination. The request for an appeal must be filed within the time limit allowed. The request also must meet the requirements for the contents of an appeal request.

- *Level II: hearing*—If the claim has gone through the basic review steps, and the issue is still unresolved, a fair hearing request form (Request for Hearing—Part B Medicare Claim form) may be filed with the time limit specified in the Medicare guidelines. A fair hearing can be conducted one of three ways: (1) hearing on record, (2) telephone hearing, or (3) personal hearing.
- *Level III: ALJ hearing*—The following criteria must be met when requesting an ALJ hearing: (1) The ALJ hearing must be requested in writing, and (2) the amount in controversy must be $500 or more (appeals may be combined to meet the $500 limit).
- *Level IV: DAB review*—If the provider (or beneficiary) is dissatisfied with the ALJ's decision, he or she may request a review by the DAB. There are no requirements regarding the amount of money in controversy. The request for a DAB review must be submitted within 60 days of receipt of the ALJ's decision and should specify the issues and findings by the ALJ being contested.
- *Level V: judicial review in U.S. District Court*—If $1000 or more is still in controversy after the decision by the DAB, a judicial review before a U.S. District Court judge is the last level. The provider/beneficiary must request a U.S. District Court hearing within 60 days of receipt of the DAB's decision.

Closing Scenario

Zoey and Kristin felt confident that what they had learned about health care billing and filing insurance claims would give them a solid foundation for an "at-home" career. Learning the keys to successful claims was an important concept in the overall health insurance process. If a claim was not clean, the bottom line was that submitting it was a waste of time, effort, and money for all parties involved. Understanding what happens to a claim after it reaches the payer's office also was interesting and enlightening for these two students. Until now, where the claim went after it left the health care office and what was done with it were basically mysteries to them, and the term "adjudication" was simply another perplexing word with ambiguous meaning. After completing Chapter 11, they both had a clear understanding of the entire claim process and meaning of adjudication became clear.

Appealing claims, especially Medicare claims, also was a learning experience. Zoey and Kristin already were aware that learning the intricacies associated with Medicare could be demanding, but becoming educated with the various levels of appeal and studying the forms lessened their apprehension. Overall, Zoey and Kristin knew they were on their way to an exciting and rewarding home career.

WEBSITES TO EXPLORE

- For more information on HIPAA, log on to
  http://www.cms.hhs.gov/hipaa

- For general information on claims processing, log on to
  http://www.ama-assn.org

- For links to individual state insurance offices, log on to
  http://www.naic.org/state_web_map.htm

- To learn more about the Medicare appeals process, check the following websites:
  http://www.cms.hhs.gov
  http://www.gpoaccess.gov/fr/index.html
  http://www.cms.hhs.gov/medlearn
  http://www.medicare.gov

Chapter Review

Assessment

Multiple Choice

Directions: *In the questions/statements presented, choose the response that **best** answers/completes the stem, and circle the letter that precedes it.*

1. The claims process begins when ___C___.
   A. the patient/provider encounter is concluded
   B. the CMS-1500 form has been completed and submitted
   C. the patient first contacts the office for an appointment
   D. the patient's record is placed on the health insurance professional's desk

2. The health insurance professional should reverify patient information ___C___.
   A. monthly
   B. at least once a year
   C. each time the patient visits the office
   D. it is not necessary to reverify patient information

3. In the case of a minor child of a divorced couple who is covered under both parents' group health care plans, the health insurance professional should ___A___.
   A. determine which carrier is primary
   B. have the patient fill out two patient information forms
   C. submit CMS-1500 forms to both carriers simultaneously
   D. check with the office manager to avoid submitting a "dirty" claim

4. Many medical practices include a section (often positioned at the bottom of the form) for the patient to sign an _____.
   A. authorization to release information
   B. agreement to pay the bill in full
   C. authorization to pay with a credit card
   D. authorization to use a personal check

5. Services that typically require pre-authorization or precertification include _____.
   A. laboratory tests
   B. emergency department services
   C. routine "wellness" examinations
   D. inpatient hospitalization

6. After a claim is completed, to help reduce claims rejection and delay, it is good practice *first* to have the claim ___B___.
   A. signed
   B. proofread
   C. photocopied
   D. recorded on the insurance claim log

7. The most important document in the medical insurance process is the ___C___.
   A. patient information form
   B. insurance claim form
   C. encounter form
   D. the ledger card

8. The number that is assigned by the Internal Revenue Service (IRS) and used as the employer identifier standard for all electronic health care transactions is the _D_.
   A. group number
   B. Social Security number (SSN)
   C. provider identification number (PIN)
   D. employer identification number (EIN)

9. After the claim has been received by a third-party payer, it is reviewed, and the carrier makes payment decisions. This process is referred to as _A_.
   A. adjudication
   B. judgment ruling
   C. claims processing
   D. decision making

10. When the insurance carrier receives a paper claim, it is dated, and the claim is processed through a(an) _B_.
    A. visual imaging tomographer (VIT)
    B. optical character recognition (OCR) scanner
    C. character verification regulator (CVR)
    D. computerized claim optimizer (CCO)

11. A series of files set up chronologically and labeled according to the number of days since a claim was submitted is referred to as a(an) _D_.
    A. tracking file
    B. insurance claims register
    C. general ledger file
    D. suspension file

12. A columnar form on which insurance claims are tracked is a(an) _D_.
    A. tracking file
    B. suspension file
    C. general ledger file
    D. insurance claims register

13. The document sent by the insurance carrier to the provider/patient explaining how the claim was adjudicated is called a(an) _C_.
    A. insurance claims register
    B. adjudication document
    C. EOB
    D. payment tracking form

14. The key to knowing how much of the claim was paid, how much was not, and why is the _____.
    A. EOB
    B. EIN
    C. ROA
    D. PIN

15. When a carrier assigns a substitute code because a claim was submitted with outdated, deleted, or nonexistent CPT codes, it is called _C_.
    A. fraud
    B. upcoding
    C. downcoding
    D. crosswalking

16. *Ideally*, insurance claims should be submitted to the insurance carrier within ___A___.
    A. 30 days
    B. 60 days
    C. 90 days
    D. 1 year

17. If there is any question as to time limits for filing claims, the health insurance professional should contact the ___A___.
    A. Department of Health and Human Services (HHS)
    B. office manager
    C. physician
    D. carrier

18. The insurance company that pays after the primary carrier is referred to as the ___C___.
    A. subsequent payer
    B. secondary insurer
    C. preferred provider
    D. health maintenance organization

19. In the case of dual coverage, if it is not immediately obvious which payer is primary, the health insurance professional first should ask ___A___.
    A. the patient
    B. the employer
    C. the office manager
    D. the insurance carrier

20. If there is a second insurance policy, it is important to check "yes" in ___C___.
    A. block 1a
    B. block 9
    C. block 11d
    D. block 27

21. When a patient and spouse (or parent) are covered under two separate group policies, it results in what is commonly referred to as ___B___.
    A. double coverage
    B. coordination of benefits
    C. primary versus secondary coverage
    D. a patient cannot be covered under two separate group policies

22. Claims that are submitted to another insurance company *before* they are submitted to Medicare are called ___B___ ___A___
    A. Medicare Secondary Payer (MSP) claims
    B. coordination of benefits claims
    C. payer of last resort claims
    D. crossover claims

23. The process of calling for a review of a decision made by a third-party carrier is referred to as a(an) ___B___.
    A. appeal
    B. claims review
    C. adjudication
    D. correct coding edit

24. The Medicare appeal process begins when ___D___.
    A. the patient/provider encounter is concluded
    B. the Medicare claim is rejected
    C. disagreement arises with the carrier's payment determination
    D. the patient telephones the provider with a complaint

25. A Medicare review request for Part B appeals must come within __B__.
    A. 30 days
    B. 60 days
    C. 120 days
    D. 1 year

26. After the Medicare appeal has gone through the first step, the provider/beneficiary may file a(an) __?__.
    A. corrected claim
    B. small claims suit
    C. request for hearing
    D. administrative law judge review

True/False

Directions: *Place a "T" in the blank preceding each of the following statements if it is true; place an "F" if it is false.*

_____ 1. Ultimately, it is the patient's responsibility to know when and how to notify the insurance company for pre-authorization or precertification.

__T__ 2. Medicare (fee-for-service) does not need prior authorization to provide covered services.

_____ 3. It is the health insurance professional's responsibility to document the appropriate health-related comments in the patient's health record.

_____ 4. It is poor judgment for the health insurance professional to double-check the codes the health care provider puts on the encounter form.

_____ 5. All major government payers have the same guidelines for completing the CMS-1500 claim form.

_____ 6. The medical practice should have a mechanism in place for tracking claims.

_____ 7. Claims follow-up does not warrant high priority in a busy medical office.

_____ 8. When dealing with Medicare and Medicaid, health insurance professionals should submit claims inquiries in writing.

_____ 9. The third-party payer sends an EOB only if a payment accompanies the document.

_____ 10. EOBs can be in electronic or paper format.

_____ 11. When an insurance claim is denied, the health insurance professional cannot pursue the claim further.

_____ 12. Often, if a claim is reduced or rejected, the problem lies with the provider's office.

_____ 13. Coding accurately and knowing which coding systems payers use helps avoid payment errors on claims.

_____ 14. If the claims adjuster changes a valid procedure code that was submitted on the claim, the health insurance professional must accept the change.

_____ 15. Correct code initiative edits are intended to reduce overpayments that result from improper coding.

_____ 16. All participating (PAR) providers are allowed to bill the patient for any balance the insurance carrier does not pay.

_____ 17. The provider cannot waive Medicare co-payments unless financial hardship has been established and documented.

_____ 18. All third-party payers have a 30-day time limit for claims to be submitted if they are to be considered for payment.

_____ 19. All government payers (e.g., Medicare, Medicaid, TRICARE/CHAMPVA) have the same time limit for submitting claims.

_____ 20. The time limit for filing appeals varies from carrier to carrier.

_____ 21. When a patient has other insurance coverage primary to Medicare, the other insurer's payment information must be included on the Medicare claim.

_____ 22. When a patient is dual eligible (Medicare/Medicaid), there is an automatic crossover from Medicaid to Medicare.

_____ 23. Only the provider has the right to appeal a rejected insurance claim.

_____ 24. Many payers have a set time limit for claim appeals.

_____ 25. If after all levels of appeal are exhausted the claim remains unpaid, there are no other options.

Short Answer/Fill-in-the-Blank

1. List the six keys to successful claims processing.

_____

_____

_____

_____

_____

2. Explain the rationale for photocopying the front and the back of a patient's health insurance identification card.

_____

3. If any attachments accompany a claim, list the information that should appear on each document.

_____

_____

_____

4. Explain in detail what the health insurance professional should do when a claims error is discovered that could result, or already has resulted, in inaccurate reimbursement.

_____

_____

_____

5. List six items typically found on an EOB (remittance advice [RA]).

_____

_____

_____

_____

_____

_____

6. List six things that influence how often medical facilities submit insurance claims.

_____

_____

_____

_____

_____

_____

7. List two important things the health insurance professional should do when a coordination of benefits situation exists.

_____

_____

8. List and explain the basic rules for appealing a claim.

_____

_____

_____

9. List and explain the five different levels of the Medicare appeals process.

LEVEL I   APPEALING REQUEST

LV II   HEARING

LV III   ADMINISTRATIVE LAW JUDGE HEARING

LV IV   APPEALS COUNCIL HEARING

LEVEL V   JUDICIAL REVIEW

10. List the six informational items that a Medicare appeal request must contain.

_____

_____

_____

_____

_____

_____

Critical Thinking Activities

A. A major U.S. university conducted an experiment wherein patients went online and answered a series of questions about their health history before their medical encounter. The purpose of this study was to "assess the feasibility and reliability of a Web-based, self-administered, patient assessment system as compared with a standard, interviewer-administered approach." Discuss the pros and cons of such a system.

B. What is the difference, if any, between pre-authorization and precertification?

C. Write a short paragraph on the importance of documentation in a patient's health record.

Case Studies

A. Fig. 11-14 shows an insurance ID card. After studying the card, answer the following questions.

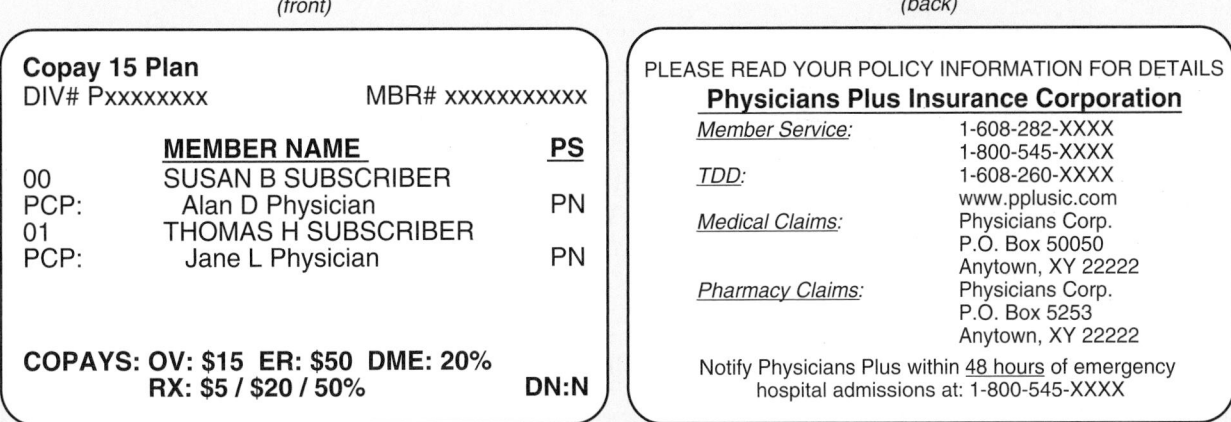

Fig. 11-14   Insurance ID card for S. Subscriber.

1. Who is the subscriber?

2. Do the subscriber and the dependent have the same primary care provider (PCP)?

3. If yes, what is their PCP's name? If no, list the subscriber and the dependent along with the name of each member's PCP.

4. If Thomas had an office visit for which he was charged $75, how much should he pay at the time of the service?

5. Susan was in an accident and was treated in the emergency department and released on the same day. The charges for this encounter totaled $2354. What was Susan's share?

6. Susan was confined to a wheelchair for 6 weeks after her accident. The cost of the wheelchair was $896. How much of this charge did Physicians Plus Insurance Corp. pay?

7. Susan was given a prescription for a pain medication. If the pharmacist gave her the generic form of the drug, the cost would be $26.50; the cost of the brand name would be $67. What would Susan's savings be if she accepted the generic drug?

8. Susan's accident occurred at 7:43 p.m. on 10/14/20XX, and she was treated in the emergency department on the same date (she was not admitted as an inpatient from the emergency department). She did not report the accident to Physicians Plus until 4 p.m. on 10/17/20XX. Will Physicians Plus pay this claim?

B. Wanda Fortune's ledger card is shown in Fig. 11-15. Fig. 11-16 shows an EOB from her insurance carrier (TRICARE). Post the information from the EOB onto Ms. Fortune's ledger card. (Assume that the TRICARE payment was received on 8/01/20XX.)

Note: Ms. Fortune's cost share is 25% of the TRICARE approved amount.

TRICARE
SPONSOR: George M.
SS#   321-44-5555
DOB   4/16/77

STATEMENT

BROADMOOR MEDICAL CLINIC
4353 Pine Ridge Drive
Milton, XY 12345-0001
Telephone: 555-656-7890

BENEFICIARY:
Wanda Mae
SS# 321-44-6600
DOB 11/02/80

GEORGE M. FORTUNE
566 LONGMEADOW
MILTON, XY 12345

| DATE 20XX | PROFESSIONAL SERVICE DESCRIPTION | CHARGE | CREDITS | | CURRENT BALANCE |
			PAYMENTS	ADJUSTMENTS	
1/08	OV EST (99213)	45 00			45 00
"	Comp Met Pane (88054)	20 00			65 00
"	Auto Hemo (85025)	12 00			77 00
1/09	TRICARE Submitted				

Due and payable within 10 days.   Pay last amount in balance column ⇧

Fig. 11-15   Ledger ID for Wanda (George) Fortune.

TRICARE EXPLANATION OF BENEFITS

PGBA or WPS
TRICARE Claims Administrator for Your Region

This is a statement of the action taken on your TRICARE Claim. Keep this notice for your records.

Prime Contractor

Date of Notice:	August 02, 2000
Sponsor SSN:	321-44-5555
Sponsor Name:	George M. Fortune
Beneficiary Name:	Wanda Mae Fortune

Benefits were payable to:

Wanda Mae Fortune
566 Longmeadow
Milton, XY 12345

BROADMOOR MEDICAL CLINIC
4353 PINE RIDGE DRIVE
MILTON XY 12345-0001

Claim Number: 919533693-00-00

Services Provided By Date of Services		Services Provided		Amount Billed	TRICARE Approved	See Remarks
PROVIDER OF MEDICAL CARE						
07/08/20XX	1	Office/outpatient visit, est	(99213)	$ 45.00	$ 38.92	1
07/08/20XX	1	Comprehen metabolic panel	(88054)	20.00	19.33	1
07/08/20XX	1	Automated hemogram	(85025)	12.00	12.00	1
Totals:				**$ 77.00**	**$ 70.25**	

Claim Summary		Beneficiary Liability Summary		Benefit Period Summary		
				Fiscal Year Beginning:		
Amount billed:	77.00	Deductible	0.00	October 01, 20XX		
TRICARE Approved:	70.25	Copayment:	0.00		Individual	Family
Non-Covered: 14*	6.75	Cost Share	17.56	Deductible:	150.00	150.00
Paid by Beneficiary:	0.00			Catastrophic Cap:		
Other Insurance:	0.00			**Enrollment Year Beginning:**		
Paid to Provider:	52.69			**December 01, 20XX**		
Paid to Beneficiary:	0.00				Individual	Family
Check Number:				POS Deductible:	300.00	600.00
				Prime Cap:		856.32

Fig. 11-16 TRICARE explanation of benefits for Fortune.

C. Joann Carlyle was seen by Todd Hamblin, a dermatologist at Broadmoor Medical Clinic, for removal of a xanthoma growth beneath each of her eyes. After the procedure, Dr. Hamblin instructed Evelyn Tanner, his health insurance professional, to bill the procedures as follows:

Excision lesion, right cheek	11442	$430
Intermediate repair, right cheek	12051	$360
Excision lesion, left cheek	11442	$430
Intermediate repair, left cheek	12051	$360
TOTAL		$1580

Fig. 11-17 illustrates how Evelyn completed Block 24 of the CMS-1500 form. Assume that Ms. Carlyle had met her deductible for the year, and Dr. Hamblin is a PAR provider for Ms. Carlyle's insurance carrier. Her co-insurance was 90/10 for outpatient hospital surgical procedures; however, the insurance carrier paid only $711 (90% of one excision and 90% of one repair) and denied the second procedure and repair.

24. A. DATE(S) OF SERVICE From MM DD YY	To MM DD YY	B. PLACE OF SERVICE	C. EMG	D. PROCEDURES, SERVICES, OR SUPPLIES (Explain Unusual Circumstances) CPT/HCPCS	MODIFIER	E. DIAGNOSIS POINTER	F. $ CHARGES	G. DAYS OR UNITS	H. EPSDT Family Plan	I. ID. QUAL.	J. RENDERING PROVIDER ID. #
1 01 12 XX	01 12 XX	22		11442		1	430 00	1		NPI	009229011
2 01 12 XX	01 12 XX	22		12051		1	360 00	1		NPI	009229011
3 01 12 XX	01 12 XX	22		11442		1	430 00	1		NPI	009229011
4 01 12 XX	01 12 XX	22		12051		1	360 00	1		NPI	009229011
5										NPI	
6										NPI	

25. FEDERAL TAX I.D. NUMBER SSN EIN	26. PATIENT'S ACCOUNT NO.	27. ACCEPT ASSIGNMENT? (For govt. claims, see back)	28. TOTAL CHARGE	29. AMOUNT PAID	30. BALANCE DUE
42 1898989 ☐ X	052599	X YES ☐ NO	$ 1580 00	$	$

Fig. 11-17 Block 24 of CMS-1500 form for Ms. Carlyle.

1. Why were the second excision and repair denied?

2. What, if anything, can Evelyn do to collect the insurance payment for the second procedure and repair?

3. If Evelyn submits a corrected claim, how should Block 24 be filled out?

4. If Evelyn does nothing and sends a statement to Ms. Carlyle for the balance, what recourse, if any, does Ms. Carlyle have?

Internet Exploration

A. Log on to the Internet, and using the search words "Understanding an EOB" (or similar words), explore various websites that offer information on how to interpret and understand an EOB.

B. Log on to the Internet at **http://www.ama-assn.org/amednews/2000/12/25/bisa1225.htm** and read the article "Downcoding, denial of claims by insurers are facts of life for many doctors: An American Medical Association survey finds that most physicians have had these kinds of troubles with their claims from insurance companies," by Cheryl Jackson, *AMNews* staff, Dec. 25, 2000. If you cannot find this article, use the search word "downcoding" to find alternative articles on this topic.

C. The Internet has a wealth of information for filing appeals—especially appeals for Medicare claims. Search the Web (using the **medicare.gov** and the Centers for Medicare and Medicaid Services websites or search words such as "filing a Medicare appeal") to learn more about this process.

Erin WILEY
_____
Student Name (print)

Mrs TABER
_____
Instructor's Name (print)

_____
Date

MEDICAL ASSISTANT
CORE SKILLS COMPETENCY GRADE SHEET

Core Skills	Points Earned	Points Possible	Instructor's Signature	Date
1. Perform Proper Handwashing for Medical Asepsis		100		
2. Apply and Remove Clean, Disposable (Nonsterile) Gloves		100		
3. Measure Oral Body Temperature Using a Mercury-Free Glass Thermometer (5)		100		
4. Measure Body Temperature Using a Disposable Oral Thermometer (5)		60		
5. Measure Body Temperature Using a Tympanic Thermometer		125		
6. Measure Radial Pulse (5)		75		
7. Measure Respiratory Rate (5)		50		
8. Measure Blood Pressure (5)		175		
9. Prepare a Parenteral Medication from a Vial		115		
10. Administer an Intradermal Injection (2)		245		
11. Administer a Subcutaneous Injection (2)		175		
12. Administer an Intramuscular Injection to an Adult (2)		210		
13. Administer an Intramuscular Injection Using the Z-Track Technique (2) **NOTE: 8th or 9th module students only**		215		
14. Perform Venipuncture Using the Evacuated-Tube Method (Collection of Multiple Tubes) (3)		250		
15. Perform Venipuncture Using the Syringe Method (1) **NOTE: 8th or 9th module students only**		255		
16. Perform Venipuncture Using the Butterfly Method (Collection of Multiple Evacuated Tubes) (1) **NOTE: 8th or 9th module students only**		250		

Core Skills	Points Earned	Points Possible	Instructor's Signature	Date
17. Charting		90		
18. Use *Physician's Desk Reference*		80		
19. Being a Professional		430		
	Total Points ÷ Earned	Total Points = Possible	Final Percentage	
		÷ 3100 =		
	Instructor's Signature		Date	

Numbers in ( ) indicate minimum practice requirements.

Student Name (print)   Instructor's Name (print)   Date

DOCUMENT EACH PATIENT IN PROPER CHARTING FORMAT.

VITAL SIGNS

	Date/Time	Patient	T	P	R	B/P	MA Signature
1.							
2.							
3.							
4.							
5.							

INJECTIONS

	Date/Time	Patient	Location	Reactions	MA Signature
INTRADERMAL					
1.					
2.					
SUBCUTANEOUS					
1.					
2.					
INTRAMUSCULAR (DELTOID)					
1.					
2.					
INTRAMUSCULAR (GLUTEAL/Z-TRACK) [8th or 9th module students only]					
1.					
2.					

VENIPUNCTURE

	Date/Time	Patient	Location	Reactions	MA Signature
EVACUATED-TUBE METHOD					
1.					
2.					
3.					
SYRINGE METHOD [8th or 9th module students only]					
1.					
BUTTERFLY METHOD [8th or 9th module students only]					
1.					

Student Name _____   Date _____

CHECKLIST: PERFORM PROPER HANDWASHING FOR MEDICAL ASEPSIS

TASK: Prevent the spread of pathogens by aseptically washing hands, following Standard Precautions.

CONDITIONS: Given the proper equipment and supplies, the student will be required to demonstrate the proper method of performing handwashing for medical asepsis.

EQUIPMENT AND SUPPLIES
- Liquid antibacterial soap
- Nailbrush or orange stick
- Paper towels
- Warm running water
- Regular waste container

STANDARDS: Complete the procedure within _____ minutes and achieve a minimum score of _____%.

Time began _____   Time ended _____

Steps	Possible Points	First Attempt	Second Attempt
1. Assemble all supplies and equipment.	5		
2. Remove rings and watch or push the watch up on the forearm.	5		
3. Stand close to the sink, without allowing clothing to touch the sink.	5		
4. Turn on the faucets, using a paper towel.	5		
5. Adjust the water temperature to warm—not hot or cold. Explain why proper water temperature is important.	10		
6. Discard the paper towel in the proper waste container.	5		
7. Wet hands and wrists under running water, and apply liquid antibacterial soap. Hands must be held lower than the elbows at all times. Hands must not touch the inside of the sink.	10		
8. Work soap into a lather by rubbing the palms together using a circular motion.	10		
9. Clean the fingernails with a nailbrush or an orange stick.	5		
10. Rinse hands thoroughly under running water, holding them in a downward position and allowing soap and water to run off the fingertips.	10		
11. Repeat the procedure if hands are grossly contaminated.	10		
12. Dry the hands gently and thoroughly using a clean paper towel. Discard the paper towel in proper waste container.	10		
13. Using a dry paper towel, turn the faucets off, clean the area around the sink, and discard the towel in regular waste container.	10		
Total Points Possible	100		

Comments: Total Points Earned _____   Instructor's Signature _____

Student Name _____   Date _____

CHECKLIST: APPLY AND REMOVE CLEAN, DISPOSABLE (NONSTERILE) GLOVES

TASK: Apply and remove disposable (nonsterile) gloves properly.

CONDITIONS: Given the proper equipment and supplies, the student will be required to apply and remove nonsterile disposable gloves.

EQUIPMENT AND SUPPLIES
- Alcohol-based hand rub
- Nonsterile disposable gloves
- Biohazardous waste container

STANDARDS: Complete the procedure within _____ minutes and achieve a minimum score of _____%.

Time began _____   Time ended _____

Steps	Possible Points	First Attempt	Second Attempt
Applying Gloves			
1. Assemble all supplies and equipment.	5		
2. Select the correct size and style of gloves according to office policy.	5		
3. Sanitize hands.	10		
4. Apply gloves and adjust them to ensure a proper fit.	5		
5. Inspect the gloves carefully for tears, holes, or punctures before and after application.	5		
Removing Gloves			
1. Grasp the outside of one glove with the first three fingers of the other hand, approximately 1 to 2 inches below the cuff.	10		
2. Stretch the soiled glove by pulling it away from the hand, and slowly pull the glove downward off the hand. Usually the dominant hand is ungloved first.	10		
3. After the glove is pulled free from the hand, ball it in the palm of the gloved hand.	10		
4. Remove the other glove by placing the index and middle fingers of the ungloved hand inside the glove of the gloved hand; turn the cuff downward. Be careful not to touch the outside of the soiled glove.	10		
5. Stretch the glove away from the hand and pull the cuff downward over the hand and over the balled-up glove, turning it inside out with the balled glove inside.	10		
6. Carefully dispose of the gloves in a marked biohazardous waste container.	10		
7. Sanitize hands.	10		
Total Points Possible	100		

Comments: Total Points Earned _____   Instructor's Signature _____

Student Name _____   Date _____

CHECKLIST: MEASURE ORAL BODY TEMPERATURE USING A MERCURY-FREE GLASS THERMOMETER

TASK: Accurately measure and record a patient's oral temperature.

CONDITIONS: Given the proper equipment and supplies, the student will be required to role-play with another student or an instructor the proper method for measuring an oral body temperature using a mercury-free glass thermometer.

EQUIPMENT AND SUPPLIES
- Mercury-free glass oral thermometer
- Thermometer sheath
- Disposable gloves
- Biohazardous waste container
- Pen
- Patient's medical record

STANDARDS: Complete the procedure within _____ minutes and achieve a minimum score of _____%.

Time began _____   Time ended _____

Steps	Possible Points	First Attempt	Second Attempt
1. Assemble all supplies and equipment.	5		
2. Sanitize hands.	5		
3. Greet and identify the patient.	5		
4. Explain the procedure to the patient.	5		
5. Determine if the patient has recently had a hot or cold beverage to drink or has smoked.	5		
6. Put on gloves and remove the thermometer from its holder, without touching the bulb end with your fingers.	5		
7. Inspect the thermometer for chips or cracks.	5		
8. Read the thermometer to ensure that the temperature is well below 96.0° F. Shake down thermometer as necessary.	5		
9. Cover the thermometer with a protective thermometer sheath.	5		
10. Ask the patient to open his or her mouth and place the probe tip under the tongue.	5		
11. Ask the patient to hold, not clasp, the thermometer between the teeth and to close the lips snugly around it to form an airtight seal.	5		
12. Leave the thermometer in place for a minimum of 3 minutes.	5		
13. Remove the thermometer and read the results.	10		

Steps	Possible Points	First Attempt	Second Attempt
14. Holding the thermometer by the stem, remove the protective sheath and discard in a biohazardous waste container.	5		
15. Sanitize the thermometer following the manufacturer's recommendations.	5		
16. Remove gloves and discard in biohazardous waste container.	5		
17. Return the thermometer to its storage container.	5		
18. Sanitize hands.	5		
19. Document the results in the patient's medical record.	5		
Total Points Possible	100		

Comments: Total Points Earned _____   Instructor's Signature _____

Student Name _____   Date _____

CHECKLIST: MEASURE BODY TEMPERATURE USING A DISPOSABLE ORAL THERMOMETER

TASK: Accurately measure and record a patient's oral temperature using a disposable thermometer.

CONDITIONS: Given the proper equipment and supplies, the student will be required to perform the proper method for measuring an oral temperature using a disposable oral thermometer.

EQUIPMENT AND SUPPLIES
- Disposable thermometer
- Disposable gloves
- Biohazardous waste container
- Pen
- Patient's medical record

STANDARDS: Complete the procedure within _____ minutes and achieve a minimum score of _____%.

Time began _____   Time ended _____

Steps	Possible Points	First Attempt	Second Attempt
1. Assemble all supplies and equipment.	5		
2. Sanitize hands.	5		
3. Greet and identify the patient.	5		
4. Explain the procedure to the patient.	5		
5. Put on disposable gloves.	5		
6. Open the thermometer packaging.	5		
7. Place the thermometer under the patient's tongue and wait 60 seconds.	5		
8. Remove the thermometer and read the results by looking at the colored dots.	5		
9. Discard the thermometer and gloves in a biohazardous waste container.	5		
10. Sanitize hands.	5		
11. Document results in the patient's medical record.	10		
Total Points Possible	60		

Comments: Total Points Earned _____   Instructor's Signature _____

Student Name _____   Date _____

CHECKLIST: MEASURE BODY TEMPERATURE USING A TYMPANIC THERMOMETER

TASK: Accurately measure and record a patient's temperature using a tympanic thermometer.

CONDITIONS: Given the proper equipment and supplies, the student will be required to role-play with another student the proper method for measuring the tympanic temperature using a tympanic thermometer.

EQUIPMENT AND SUPPLIES
- Tympanic thermometer
- Disposable probe cover
- Pen
- Patient's medical record
- Biohazardous waste container

STANDARDS: Complete the procedure within _____ minutes and achieve a minimum score of _____%.

Time began _____   Time ended _____

Steps	Possible Points	First Attempt	Second Attempt
1. Assemble all supplies and equipment.	5		
2. Sanitize hands.	5		
3. Greet and identify the patient.	5		
4. Explain the procedure to the patient.	5		
5. Remove the thermometer from the charger.	5		
6. Check to be sure the mode for interpretation of temperature is set to "oral" mode.	10		
7. Check the lens probe to be sure it is clean and not scratched.	5		
8. Turn on the thermometer.	5		
9. Insert the probe firmly into a disposable plastic probe cover.	5		
10. Wait for a digital "READY" display.	5		
11. With the hand that is not holding the probe, pull adult patient's ear up and back to straighten the ear canal. For a small child, pull the patient's ear down and back to straighten the ear canal.	10		
12. Insert the probe into the patient's ear and tightly seal the ear canal opening.	10		
13. Position the probe.	5		
14. Depress the activation button.	5		
15. Release the activation button and wait 2 seconds.	5		
16. Remove the probe from the ear and read the temperature.	5		

Steps	Possible Points	First Attempt	Second Attempt
17. Note the reading, making sure that the screen displays "oral" as the mode of interpretation.	5		
18. Discard the probe cover in a biohazardous waste container.	5		
19. Replace the thermometer on the charger base.	5		
20. Sanitize hands.	5		
21. Document results in the patient's medical record using ⓣ to indicate a tympanic temperature was obtained.	10		
Total Points Possible	125		

Comments: Total Points Earned _____   Instructor's Signature _____

Student Name _____   Date _____

CHECKLIST: **MEASURE RADIAL PULSE**

TASK: Accurately measure and record the rate, rhythm, and quality of a patient's pulse.

CONDITIONS: Given the proper equipment and supplies, the student will be required to role-play with another student or an instructor the proper method for measuring a patient's radial pulse.

EQUIPMENT AND SUPPLIES
- Watch with a second hand
- Patient's medical record
- Pen

STANDARDS: Complete the procedure within _____ minutes and achieve a minimum score of _____%.

Time began _____   Time ended _____

Steps	Possible Points	First Attempt	Second Attempt
1. Assemble all supplies and equipment.	5		
2. Sanitize hands.	5		
3. Greet and identify the patient.	5		
4. Explain the procedure to the patient.	5		
5. Observe the patient for any signs that may indicate an increase or a decrease in the pulse rate due to external conditions.	5		
6. Position the patient.	5		
7. Place the index and middle fingertips over the radial artery while resting the thumb on the back of the patient's wrist.	10		
8. Apply moderate, gentle pressure directly over the site until the pulse can be felt.	10		
9. Count the pulse for 60 seconds.	10		
10. Sanitize hands.	5		
11. Document the results in the patient's chart; include the pulse rate, rhythm, and volume.	10		
Total Points Possible	75		

Comments: Total Points Earned _____   Instructor's Signature _____

Student Name _____   Date _____

CHECKLIST: **MEASURE RESPIRATORY RATE**

TASK: Accurately measure and record a patient's respiratory rate.

CONDITIONS: Given the proper equipment and supplies, the student will be required to role-play with another student the proper method for measuring a patient's respiratory rate.

EQUIPMENT AND SUPPLIES
- Watch with a second hand
- Patient's medical record
- Pen

STANDARDS: Complete the procedure within _____ minutes and achieve a minimum score of _____%.

Time began _____   Time ended _____

Steps	Possible Points	First Attempt	Second Attempt
1. Assemble all supplies and equipment.	5		
2. Sanitize hands.	5		
3. Greet and identify the patient.	5		
4. Explain the procedure to the patient.	5		
5. Count each respiration for 30 seconds and multiply by 2. (If breathing pattern is irregular, count for 1 full minute.)	15		
6. Sanitize hands.	5		
7. Document the results in the patient's chart; include the respiratory rate, rhythm, and depth. Document any irregularities found.	10		
Total Points Possible	50		

Comments: Total Points Earned _____   Instructor's Signature _____

Student Name _____   Date _____

CHECKLIST: MEASURE BLOOD PRESSURE

TASK: Accurately measure and record a patient's blood pressure by palpation and auscultation.

CONDITIONS: Given the proper equipment and supplies, the student will be required to role-play with another student the proper method for measuring a patient's blood pressure.

EQUIPMENT AND SUPPLIES
- Stethoscope
- Aneroid sphygmomanometer in proper size for patient
- Alcohol wipe
- Patient's medical record
- Pen

STANDARDS: Complete the procedure within _____ minutes and achieve a minimum score of _____%.

Time began _____   Time ended _____

Steps	Possible Points	First Attempt	Second Attempt
1. Assemble all supplies and equipment.	5		
2. Sanitize hands.	5		
3. Greet and identify the patient.	5		
4. Explain the procedure to the patient.	5		
5. Position the patient comfortably in a sitting or supine position.	5		
6. Palpate the brachial artery.	10		
7. Position the blood pressure cuff; wrap the cuff snugly and evenly around the patient's arm and secure the end.	10		
8. Position the aneroid gauge for direct viewing at a distance of no more than 3 feet.	10		
9. Measure the systolic pressure by palpation.	15		
10. Deflate the cuff completely and wait at least 60 seconds before re-inflating.	10		
11. Clean the stethoscope.	5		
12. Place the earpieces of the stethoscope in your ears, with the earpieces directed slightly forward.	5		
13. Position the head of the stethoscope over the brachial artery of the arm.	5		
14. Close the valve to the manometer.	5		
15. Pump the cuff at a smooth rate to approximately 20 to 30 mm Hg above the palpated systolic pressure.	10		

Steps	Possible Points	First Attempt	Second Attempt
16. Loosen the thumbscrew slightly to open the valve and release the pressure on the cuff, slowly and steadily.	10		
17. Obtain the systolic reading.	10		
18. Continue to release the air from the cuff at a moderately slow rate.	5		
19. Listen for the disappearance of the Korotkoff sounds; obtain diastolic pressure.	10		
20. Release the air remaining in the cuff quickly by loosening the thumbscrew to open the valve completely.	5		
21. Remove the earpieces of the stethoscope from your ears, and remove the cuff from the patient's arm.	5		
22. Sanitize hands.	5		
23. Document the results in the patient's chart.	10		
24. Clean the earpieces and diaphragm with an alcohol wipe, and properly store the equipment.	5		
Total Points Possible	175		

Comments: Total Points Earned _____   Instructor's Signature _____

Student Name _____   Date _____

CHECKLIST: PREPARE A PARENTERAL MEDICATION FROM A VIAL

TASK: From a vial, measure the ordered medication dosage into a 3-mL hypodermic syringe for injection.

CONDITIONS: Given the proper equipment and supplies, the student will prepare a parenteral medication from a vial in a 3-mL syringe.

EQUIPMENT AND SUPPLIES
- Vial of medication as ordered by physician
- 70% isopropyl alcohol wipes
- 3-mL syringe for ordered dose
- Needle with safety device appropriate for site of injection
- 2 × 2-inch gauze squares
- Biohazardous waste container
- Patient's medical record

STANDARDS: Complete the procedure within _____ minutes and achieve a minimum score of _____%.

Time began _____   Time ended _____

Steps	Possible Points	First Attempt	Second Attempt
1. Sanitize hands.	5		
2. Verify the order, and assemble equipment and supplies.	5		
3. Check expiration date of the medication.	10		
4. Follow the "seven rights" of medication administration.	10		
5. Check the medication against the physician's order three times before administration.	10		
6. Check the patient's medical record for drug allergies or conditions that may contraindicate the injection.	10		
7. Calculate the correct dose to be given, as necessary.	10		
8. Prepare the vial, needle, and syringe.	5		
9. Draw the amount of air into the syringe for the amount of medication to be administered.	5		
10. Remove the cover from the needle and insert the needle into the vial.	10		
11. Inject the air into vial and fill the syringe with the medication.	10		
12. Remove any air bubbles and recap the needle as necessary.	10		
13. Compare the medication to the vial label, and return the medication to its proper storage.	5		
14. Sanitize hands.	10		
Total Points Possible	115		

Comments: Total Points Earned _____   Instructor's Signature _____

Student Name _____   Date _____

CHECKLIST: ADMINISTER AN INTRADERMAL INJECTION

TASK
- Identify the correct syringe, needle gauge, and length for an intradermal injection.
- Select and prepare an appropriate site for an intradermal injection.
- Demonstrate the correct technique to administer an intradermal injection.
- Document an intradermal injection correctly in the medical record.

CONDITIONS: Given the proper equipment and supplies, the student will prepare and administer an intradermal injection.

EQUIPMENT AND SUPPLIES
- Nonsterile disposable gloves
- Medication as ordered by physician
- Tuberculin syringe for ordered dose
- Needle with safety device (26 or 27 gauge, ⅜ inch to ½ inch)
- 2 × 2-inch sterile gauze
- 70% isopropyl alcohol wipes
- Written patient instructions for post testing as appropriate
- Sharps container
- Biohazardous waste container
- Patient's medical record

STANDARDS: Complete the procedure within _____ minutes and achieve a minimum score of _____%.

Time began _____   Time ended _____

Steps	Possible Points	First Attempt	Second Attempt
1. Sanitize hands.	5		
2. Verify the order, and assemble equipment and supplies.	5		
3. Check expiration date of the medication.	10		
4. Follow the "seven rights" of medication administration.	10		
5. Check the medication against the physician's order three times before administration.	10		
6. Check the patient's medical record for drug allergies or conditions that may contraindicate the injection.	10		
7. Calculate the dose to be given, if necessary.	15		
8. Follow the correct procedure for drawing the medication into syringe.	10		
9. Greet and identify the patient, and explain the procedure to the patient.	10		
10. Select an appropriate injection site and properly position the patient as necessary to expose the site adequately.	10		
11. Apply gloves.	5		

Steps	Possible Points	First Attempt	Second Attempt
12. Prepare the injection site.	10		
13. While the prepared site is drying, remove the cover from the needle.	10		
14. Pull the skin taut at the injection site.	10		
15. Inject the medication between the dermis and epidermis. Create a wheal.	10		
16. Withdraw the needle from the injection site at the same angle as it was inserted, and activate the safety device immediately.	10		
17. Dab the area with the gauze. Do not rub.	5		
18. Discard in the syringe sharps container. Remove gloves and discard in a biohazardous container.	5		
19. Sanitize the hands.	5		
20. Check the patient.	5		
21. Read or discuss with the patient the test results.	10		
22. Sanitize hands.	5		
23. Document the procedure.	10		
Mantoux Test			
24. Check to be sure test was given 48 to 72 hours earlier.	10		
25. After sanitizing the hands and applying nonsterile gloves, gently rub the test site with a finger and lightly palpate for induration.	10		
26. Using the tape that comes with the medication, measure the diameter of the area of induration from edge to edge.	10		
27. Record the area of induration and notify the health care provider of the measurement if not within the negative range.	10		
28. Record the reading in the medical record.	10		
Total Points Possible	245		

Comments: Total Points Earned _____   Instructor's Signature _____

Student Name _____   Date _____

CHECKLIST: ADMINISTER A SUBCUTANEOUS INJECTION

TASK
- Identify the correct syringe, needle gauge, and length for a subcutaneous injection.
- Select and prepare an appropriate site for a subcutaneous injection.
- Demonstrate the correct technique to administer a subcutaneous injection.
- Document a subcutaneous injection correctly in the medical record.

CONDITIONS: Given the proper equipment and supplies, the student will prepare and administer a subcutaneous injection.

EQUIPMENT AND SUPPLIES
- Nonsterile disposable gloves
- Medication as ordered by physician
- Appropriate syringe for ordered dose of medication
- Appropriate needle with safety device
- 2 × 2-inch sterile gauze
- 70% Isopropyl alcohol wipes
- Sharps container
- Biohazardous waste container
- Patient's medical record

STANDARDS: Complete the procedure within _____ minutes and achieve a minimum score of _____%.

Time began _____   Time ended _____

Steps	Possible Points	First Attempt	Second Attempt
1. Sanitize hands.	5		
2. Verify the order, and assemble equipment and supplies.	5		
3. Check expiration date of the medication.	10		
4. Follow the "seven rights" of medication administration.	10		
5. Check the medication against the physician's order three times before administration.	10		
6. Check the patient's medical record for drug allergies or conditions that may contraindicate the injection.	10		
7. Calculate the correct dose to be given, if necessary.	15		
8. Follow the procedure for drawing the medication into the syringe.	5		
9. Greet and identify the patient, and explain the procedure.	10		
10. Select an appropriate injection site and properly position the patient as necessary to expose the site.	10		
11. Apply gloves.	5		
12. Prepare the injection site.	10		

Steps	Possible Points	First Attempt	Second Attempt
13. While the prepared site is drying, remove the cover from the needle.	5		
14. Pinch the skin at the injection site and puncture the skin quickly and smoothly, making sure the needle is kept at a 45-degree angle.	10		
15. Aspirate the syringe to check for blood. If no blood is present, inject the medication.	10		
16. Place a gauze pad over the injection site and quickly withdraw the needle from the injection site at the same angle at which it was inserted.	10		
17. Massage the injection site, if appropriate.	5		
18. Discard the syringe and needle into a rigid biohazardous container.	5		
19. Remove gloves and discard in a biohazardous waste container.	5		
20. Sanitize the hands.	5		
21. Check on the patient.	5		
22. Document procedure.	10		
Total Points Possible	175		

Comments: Total Points Earned _____   Instructor's Signature _____

Student Name _____   Date _____

CHECKLIST: ADMINISTER AN INTRAMUSCULAR INJECTION TO AN ADULT

TASK
- Identify the correct syringe, needle gauge, and length for an adult intramuscular injection.
- Select and prepare an appropriate site for a pediatric intramuscular injection.
- Demonstrate the correct technique to administer an intramuscular injection.
- Document an intramuscular injection correctly in the medical record.

CONDITIONS: Given the proper equipment and supplies, the student will prepare and administer an intramuscular injection to an adult patient.

EQUIPMENT AND SUPPLIES
- Nonsterile disposable gloves
- Medication as ordered by physician
- Appropriate syringe for ordered medication dose
- Appropriate needle with safety device (21 or 25 gauge, 1 inch to 1½ inch)
- 2 × 2-inch sterile gauze
- 70% isopropyl alcohol wipes
- Sharps container
- Biohazardous waste container
- Patient's medical record

STANDARDS: Complete the procedure within _____ minutes and achieve a minimum score of _____%.

Time began _____   Time ended _____

Steps	Possible Points	First Attempt	Second Attempt
1. Sanitize hands.	5		
2. Verify the order, and assemble equipment and supplies.	5		
3. Follow the "seven rights" of medication administration.	10		
4. Check the medication against the physician's order three times before administration.	10		
5. Check the patient's medical record for drug allergies or conditions that may contraindicate the injection.	10		
6. Check expiration date of the medication.	10		
7. Calculate the correct dose to be given.	20		
8. Greet and identify the patient, and explain the procedure.	10		
9. Select an appropriate injection site by amount and density of medication. Properly position the patient as necessary to expose the site adequately.	10		
10. Apply gloves.	5		
11. Prepare the injection site.	10		
12. While the prepared site is drying, remove the cover from the needle.	10		

Steps	Possible Points	First Attempt	Second Attempt
13. Secure the skin at the injection site.	10		
14. Puncture the skin quickly and smoothly, making sure the needle is kept at a 90-degree angle.	10		
15. Aspirate the syringe.	10		
16. Inject medication using proper technique for density of medication.	10		
17. Place a gauze pad over the injection site and quickly withdraw the needle from the injection site at the same angle at which it was inserted. Activate the safety shield over the needle.	10		
18. Massage the injection site if appropriate for medication.	10		
19. Discard the syringe and needle into a sharps container.	5		
20. Remove gloves and discard in a biohazardous waste container.	5		
21. Sanitize the hands.	5		
22. Check on the patient.	10		
23. Document procedure.	10		
Total Points Possible	210		

Comments: Total Points Earned _____   Instructor's Signature _____

Student Name _____   Date _____

CHECKLIST: ADMINISTER AN INTRAMUSCULAR INJECTION USING THE Z-TRACK TECHNIQUE

TASK: Demonstrate the correct technique to administer an intramuscular injection using the Z-track technique.

CONDITIONS: Given the proper equipment and supplies, the student will prepare and administer an intramuscular injection using the Z-track technique.

EQUIPMENT AND SUPPLIES
- Nonsterile disposable gloves
- Medication order by physician
- Appropriate syringe for ordered dose
- Appropriate needle with safety device
- 2 × 2-inch sterile gauze
- 70% isopropyl alcohol wipes
- Biohazardous waste container
- Patient's medical record

STANDARDS: Complete the procedure within _____ minutes and achieve a minimum score of _____%.

Time began _____   Time ended _____

Steps	Possible Points	First Attempt	Second Attempt
1. Sanitize hands.	5		
2. Verify the order, and assemble equipment and supplies.	5		
3. Follow the "seven rights" of medication administration.	10		
4. Check the medication against the physician's order three times before administration.	10		
5. Check the patient's medical record for drug allergies or conditions that may contraindicate the injection.	10		
6. Check expiration date of the medication.	10		
7. Calculate the correct dose to be given.	20		
8. Follow the correct procedure for drawing the medication into syringe.	10		
9. Greet and identify the patient, and explain the procedure to the patient.	15		
10. Select an appropriate injection site and properly position the patient.	5		
11. Apply disposable gloves.	5		
12. Prepare the injection site.	5		
13. While the prepared site is drying, remove the cover from the needle.	5		

Steps	Possible Points	First Attempt	Second Attempt
14. Secure the skin at the injection site by pushing the skin away from the injection site.	10		
15. Puncture the skin quickly and smoothly, making sure the needle is kept at a 90-degree angle.	10		
16. Continue to hold the tissue in place while aspirating and injecting the medication.	15		
17. Inject the medication.	10		
18. Withdraw the needle.	10		
19. Release the traction on the skin to seal the track as the needle is being removed. Activate safety shield over needle.	10		
20. Discard the syringe and needle into a rigid biohazardous container.	5		
21. Remove gloves and discard in a biohazardous waste container.	5		
22. Sanitize the hands.	5		
23. Check on the patient.	5		
24. Document the procedure.	5		
25. Clean the equipment and examination room.	10		
Total Points Possible	215		

Comments: Total Points Earned _____   Instructor's Signature _____

Student Name _____   Date _____

CHECKLIST: **PERFORM VENIPUNCTURE USING THE EVACUATED-TUBE METHOD (COLLECTION OF MULTIPLE TUBES)**

TASK: Obtain a venous blood specimen acceptable for testing using the evacuated-tube system.

CONDITIONS: Given the proper equipment and supplies, the student will be required to perform a venipuncture using the evacuated-tube system method of collection.

EQUIPMENT AND SUPPLIES
- Nonsterile disposable gloves
- Personal protective equipment (PPE) as required
- Tourniquet (latex-free)
- Evacuated tube holder
- Evacuated tube multidraw needle (21 or 22 gauge, 1 or 1½ inch) with safety guards
- Evacuated blood tubes for requested tests with labels (correct nonadditive or additive required for ordered test)
- Alcohol wipe
- Sterile 2 × 2-inch gauze pads
- Bandage (latex-free) or nonallergenic tape
- Sharps container
- Biohazardous waste container
- Laboratory requisition form
- Patient's medical record

STANDARDS: Complete the procedure within _____ minutes and achieve a minimum score of _____%.

Time began _____   Time ended _____

Steps	Possible Points	First Attempt	Second Attempt
1. Sanitize hands.	5		
2. Verify the order, and assemble equipment and supplies.	5		
3. Greet the patient, identify yourself, and confirm the patient's identity. Escort the patient to the proper room. Ask the patient to sit in phlebotomy chair.	5		
4. Confirm that the patient has followed the needed preparation (e.g., fasting).	10		
5. Explain the procedure to the patient.	5		
6. Prepare the evacuated tube system.	5		
7. Open the sterile gauze packet and place the gauze pad on the inside of its wrapper, or obtain sterile gauze pads from a bulk package.	10		
8. Position the remaining needed supplies for ease of reaching with nondominant hand. Place tube loosely in holder with label facing downward.	10		
9. Position and examine the arm to be used in the venipuncture.	10		
10. Apply the tourniquet.	10		
11. Apply gloves and PPE.	5		

Steps	Possible Points	First Attempt	Second Attempt
12. Thoroughly palpate the selected vein.	5		
13. Release the tourniquet.	5		
14. Prepare the puncture site using alcohol swabs.	10		
15. Reapply the tourniquet.	10		
16. Position the holder while keeping the needle covered, being certain to have control of holder. Uncover the needle.	10		
17. Position the needle so that it follows the line of the vein.	5		
18. Perform the venipuncture.	5		
19. Secure the holder. Push the bottom of the tube with the thumb of your nondominant hand so that the needle inside the holder pierces the rubber stopper of the tube. Follow the direction of the vein.	10		
20. Change tubes (minimum of two tubes) as required by test orders.	10		
21. Gently invert tubes that contain additives to be mixed with the specimen.	10		
22. While the blood is filling the last tube, release the tourniquet and withdraw the needle. Cover the needle with the safety shield.	10		
23. Apply direct pressure on the venipuncture site, and instruct the patient to raise the arm straight above the head and maintain pressure on the site for 1 to 2 minutes.	10		
24. Discard the contaminated needle and holder into the sharps container.	10		
25. Label the tubes as appropriate for lab.	10		
26. Place the tube into the biohazard transport bag.	5		
27. Check for bleeding at puncture site and apply a pressure dressing.	5		
28. Remove and discard the alcohol wipe and gloves.	5		
29. Sanitize the hands.	5		
30. Record the collection date and time on the laboratory requisition form, and place the requisition in the proper place in the biohazard transport bag.	10		
31. Ask and observe how the patient feels.	5		
32. Clean the work area using Standard Precautions.	5		
33. Document the procedure, indicating tests for which blood was drawn and the labs to which blood will be sent.	10		
Total Points Possible	250		

Comments: Total Points Earned _____   Instructor's Signature _____

Student Name _____   Date _____

CHECKLIST: PERFORM VENIPUNCTURE USING THE SYRINGE METHOD

TASK: Obtain a venous blood specimen acceptable for testing using the syringe method.

CONDITIONS: Given the proper equipment and supplies, the student will be required to perform a venipuncture using the syringe method of collection.

EQUIPMENT AND SUPPLIES
- Nonsterile disposable gloves
- Personal protective equipment (PPE) as required
- Tourniquet (latex-free)
- Test tube rack
- 10-cc (10-mL) syringe with 21- or 22-gauge needle and safety guards
- Proper evacuated blood tubes for tests ordered
- Alcohol wipe
- Sterile 2 × 2-inch gauze pads
- Bandage (latex-free) or nonallergenic tape
- Sharps container
- Biohazardous waste container
- Laboratory requisition form
- Patient's medical record

STANDARDS: Complete the procedure within _____ minutes and achieve a minimum score of _____%.

Time began _____   Time ended _____

Steps	Possible Points	First Attempt	Second Attempt
1. Sanitize hands.	5		
2. Verify the order. Assemble equipment and supplies.	5		
3. Greet the patient, identify yourself, and confirm the patient's identity. Escort the patient to the room for the blood draw. Position the patient in phlebotomy chair or on examination table.	5		
4. Confirm any necessary preparation has been accomplished (e.g., fasting). Explain the procedure to the patient.	5		
5. Prepare the needle and syringe, maintaining syringe sterility. Break the seal on the syringe by moving the plunger back and forth several times. Loosen the cap on the needle and check to make sure that the hub is screwed tightly onto the syringe.	15		
6. Place the evacuated tubes to be filled in a test tube rack on a work surface in order of fill.	15		
7. Open the sterile gauze packet and place the gauze pad on the inside of its wrapper, or obtain sterile gauze pads from a bulk package.	5		
8. Position and examine the arm to be used in the venipuncture.	10		
9. Apply gloves and PPE.	5		

Steps	Possible Points	First Attempt	Second Attempt
10. Thoroughly palpate the selected vein.	10		
11. Release the tourniquet.	10		
12. Prepare the puncture site and reapply tourniquet.	10		
13. If drawing from the hand, ask the patient to make a fist or bend the fingers downward. Pull the skin taut with your thumb over the top of the patient's knuckles.	15		
14. Position the syringe and grasp the syringe firmly between the thumb and the underlying fingers.	10		
15. Follow the direction of the vein and insert the needle in one quick motion at about a 45-degree angle.	10		
16. If drawing from AC vein, with your nondominant hand pull the skin taut beneath the intended puncture site to anchor the vein. Thumb should be 1 to 2 inches below and to the side of the vein.	15		
17. Position the syringe and grasp the syringe firmly between the thumb and the underlying fingers.	10		
18. Follow the direction of the vein and insert the needle in one quick motion at about a 15-degree angle.	10		
19. Perform the venipuncture. If flash does not occur, gently pull back on the plunger. Do not move the needle. If blood still does not enter the syringe, slowly withdraw the needle, secure new supplies, and retry the draw.	10		
20. Anchor the syringe, and gently continue pulling back on the plunger until the required amount of blood is in the syringe.	10		
21. Release the tourniquet.	5		
22. Remove the needle and cover the needle with safety shield.	10		
23. Apply direct pressure on the venipuncture site, and instruct the patient to raise the arm straight above the head. Instruct the patient to maintain pressure on the site for 1 to 2 minutes.	5		
24. Transfer the blood to the evacuated tubes as soon as possible.	10		
25. Properly dispose of the syringe and needle.	10		
26. Label the tubes and place into biohazard transport bag.	10		
27. Check for bleeding at venipuncture site and place a pressure dressing.	10		
28. Remove and discard the alcohol wipe and gloves.	5		
29. Sanitize the hands.	5		
30. Record the collection date and time on the laboratory requisition form, and place the requisition in the biohazard transport bag.	10		

Steps	Possible Points	First Attempt	Second Attempt
31. Ask and observe how the patient feels.	5		
32. Clean the work area using Standard Precautions.	5		
33. Document the procedure.	10		
Total Points Possible NOTE: Awards points for Steps 13-14-15 OR 16-17-18, not both	255		

Comments: Total Points Earned _____   Instructor's Signature _____

Student Name _____   Date _____

CHECKLIST: PERFORM VENIPUNCTURE USING THE BUTTERFLY METHOD (COLLECTION OF MULTIPLE EVACUATED TUBES)

TASK: Obtain a venous blood specimen acceptable for testing using the butterfly method.

CONDITIONS: Given the proper equipment and supplies, the student will perform a venipuncture using the butterfly method of collection.

EQUIPMENT AND SUPPLIES
- Nonsterile disposable gloves
- Personal protective equipment (PPE) as required
- Tourniquet (latex-free)
- Test tube rack
- Winged-infusion set with Luer adapter and safety guard
- Multidraw needle (22 to 25 gauge) and tube holder, or 10-cc (10-mL) syringe
- Evacuated blood tubes for requested tests with labels (correct nonadditive or additive required for ordered tests)
- Alcohol wipe
- Sterile 2 × 2-inch gauze pads
- Bandage (latex-free) or nonallergenic tape
- Sharps container
- Biohazardous waste container
- Laboratory requisition form
- Patient's medical record

STANDARDS: Complete the procedure within _____ minutes and achieve a minimum score of _____%.

Time began _____   Time ended _____

Steps	Possible Points	First Attempt	Second Attempt
1. Sanitize hands.	5		
2. Verify the order. Assemble equipment and supplies.	5		
3. Greet the patient, identify yourself, and confirm the patient's identity. Escort the patient to the proper room for venipuncture.	5		
4. Ask the patient to have a seat in the phlebotomy chair or on the examination table.	5		
5. Confirm any necessary preparation has been followed (e.g., fasting). Explain the procedure to the patient.	10		
6. Prepare the winged infusion set. Attach the winged infusion set to either a syringe or an evacuated tube holder.	15		
7. Open the sterile gauze packet and place the gauze pad on the inside of its wrapper, or obtain sterile gauze pads from a bulk package.	5		
8. Position and examine the arm to be used in the venipuncture.	10		
9. Apply the tourniquet.	10		
10. Apply gloves and PPE.	5		
11. Thoroughly palpate the selected vein.	10		

Steps	Possible Points	First Attempt	Second Attempt
12. Release the tourniquet.	10		
13. Prepare the puncture site and reapply the tourniquet.	5		
14. If drawing from the hand, ask the patient to make a fist or bend the fingers downward. Pull the skin taut with your thumb over the top of the patient's knuckles.	10		
15. Remove the protective shield from the needle of the infusion set, being sure the bevel is facing up. Position needle over vein to be punctured.	10		
16. Perform the venipuncture. With your nondominant hand, pull the skin taut beneath the intended puncture site to anchor the vein. Thumb should be 1 to 2 inches below and to the side of the vein. Follow the direction of the vein and insert the needle in one quick motion at about a 15-degree angle.	20		
17. After penetrating the vein, decrease the angle of the needle to 5 degrees until a "flash" of blood appears in the tubing.	5		
18. Secure the needle for blood collection.	10		
19. Insert the evacuated tube into the tube holder or gently pull back on the plunger of the syringe. Change tubes as required by the test ordered.	10		
20. Release the tourniquet and remove the needle.	10		
21. Apply direct pressure on the venipuncture site, and instruct the patient to raise the arm straight above the head. Maintain pressure on the site for 1 to 2 minutes, with the arm raised straight above the head.	10		
22. If a syringe was used, transfer the blood to the evacuated tubes as soon as possible.	10		
23. Dispose of the winged infusion set.	5		
24. Label the tubes and place the tube into the biohazard transport bag.	5		
25. Check for bleeding and place a bandage over the gauze to create a pressure dressing.	5		
26. Remove and discard the alcohol wipe and gloves.	5		
27. Sanitize the hands.	5		
28. Record the collection date and time on the laboratory requisition form, and place the requisition in the biohazard transport bag.	10		
29. Ask and observe how the patient feels.	5		
30. Clean the work area using Standard Precautions.	5		
31. Document the procedure.	10		
Total Points Possible	250		

Comments: Total Points Earned _____   Instructor's Signature _____

Student Name _____   Date _____

CHECKLIST: CHARTING

TASK: Create new medical records, organize contents, interview patients, and document subjective and objective data.

CONDITIONS: Given the proper equipment and supplies, the students will be required to create new medical records by labeling them correctly and organizing sample forms and/or reports within each appropriately. The student will then role-play with another student or an instructor to demonstrate how to interview a patient. Finally, using the list of common charting abbreviations (as directed) from the student handbook, the student will record the "patient's" chief complaint (subjective data) as well as every procedure in this module using the sample documentation provided on the procedure competency checklists (objective data).

EQUIPMENT AND SUPPLIES
- File folders
- Blank file labels
- Color-coded year labels
- Alphabetical labels
- Medical alert labels
- Other labels as appropriate
- Sample forms and/or reports
- Sample documentation (on procedure competency checklists)

STANDARDS: Complete the procedure within _____ minutes and achieve a minimum score of _____%.

Time began _____   Time ended _____

Steps	Possible Points	First Attempt	Second Attempt
1. Assemble all equipment and supplies.	5		
2. Create a file label (patient name).	5		
3. Attach other labels as appropriate (year, initials, medical alert).	5		
4. Organize preprinted forms appropriately within the folder.	10		
5. Review medical history form with the patient (subjective data).	10		
6. Record chief complaint (in patient's own words/subjective data).	10		
7. Document all procedures on appropriate forms using correct terminology and abbreviations (objective data).	10		
8. Record all information legibly.	10		
9. Maintain HIPAA privacy guidelines.	10		
10. Maintain professional qualities as defined.	10		
11. Clean area when finished.	5		
Total Points Possible	90		

Comments: Total Points Earned _____   Instructor's Signature _____

Student Name _____   Date _____

CHECKLIST: USE *PHYSICIAN'S DESK REFERENCE*

TASK: Demonstrate understanding of *Physician's Desk Reference's* organization by creating a fact sheet for each drug listed on a prepared document.

CONDITIONS: Given proper equipment and supplies, the student will be required to identify the trade and generic names for each listed drug, its classification, one indication for its use, one contraindication for its use, its usual dosage and administration, and any possible side effects.

EQUIPMENT AND SUPPLIES
- *Physician's Desk Reference*
- List of drugs (on following pages)
- Pen or pencil

STANDARDS: Complete the procedure within _____ minutes and achieve a minimum score of _____%.

Time began _____   Time ended _____

Steps	Possible Points	First Attempt	Second Attempt
1. Assemble all equipment and supplies.	5		
2. Create a fact sheet for each medication listed on the prepared drug list (see next page) to include the following:			
• Trade name, generic name, and drug classification	10		
• Identify indications for assigned medications	10		
• Identify contraindications for assigned medications	10		
• Identify dosage and administration of assigned medications	10		
• Identify side effects of assigned medications	10		
3. Display professional abilities through penmanship.	10		
4. Clean area.	5		
5. Proofread and correct your work and submit to your instructor. Demonstrate professionalism throughout procedure and accept constructive feedback with a problem-solving attitude.	10		
Total Points Possible	80		

Comments: Total Points Earned _____   Instructor's Signature _____

WORK PRODUCT FOR
USE PHYSICIAN'S DESK REFERENCE

Drug	Generic Name	Classification	Indication(s)	Contraindication(s)	Dosage and Administration	Side Effects
Lipitor						
	atenolol					
Zithromax						
Norvasc						

Continued

Drug	Generic Name	Classification	Indication(s)	Contraindication(s)	Dosage and Administration	Side Effects
	alprazolam					
Zoloft						
Toprol-XL						
Zyrtec						

Levoxyl	Ambien	Allegra	Fosamax

Continued

Drug	Generic Name	Classification	Indication(s)	Contraindication(s)	Dosage and Administration	Side Effects
	prednisone					
Neurontin						
Paxil						
Plavix						

Trimox	Amaryl	Concerta	Avapro

Student Name _____   Date _____

CHECKLIST: BEING A PROFESSIONAL

TASK: Complete a self-survey checklist to increase your awareness of areas needing improvement before entering the job market.

CONDITIONS: Using the checklist as a tool, assess your professional characteristics, abilities and image. Discuss expectations with your instructor.

EQUIPMENT AND SUPPLIES
- Checklist and pen/pencil

STANDARDS: Complete the procedure within _____ minutes and achieve a minimum score of _____%.

Time began _____   Time ended _____

Steps	Possible Points	Student	Instructor
PROFESSIONAL CHARACTERISTICS			
1. Dependability			
a. I am punctual.	10	5	
b. I am efficient.	5	5	
c. I am reliable.	10	5	
2. Loyalty			
a. I turn in quality work.	10	10	
b. I complete work on time.	10	5	
c. I display consistent work habits.	10	10	
d. I accept decisions.	5	5	
e. I display ethical behavior.	15	15	
3. Positive attitude			
a. I am enthusiastic.	10	10	
b. I set goals.	10	10	
c. I seek out learning opportunities.	10	10	
d. I am a team player.	10	10	
e. I accept constructive criticism.	5	5	
f. I adapt to change.	5	5	
g. I complete assignments on time.	10	5	

Steps	Possible Points	Student	Instructor
4. Integrity			
a. I am trustworthy.	15	15	
b. I keep information confidential.	10	10	
c. I make ethical decisions.	15	15	
5. Diplomacy			
a. I use tact when dealing with classmates.	10	10	
b. I display courtesy and empathy when appropriate.	10	10	
6. Confidence			
a. I display leadership.	10	10	
b. I make decisions based on consensus.	5	5	
c. I prioritize assignments.	5	5	
PROFESSIONAL ABILITIES			
7. Competence			
a. I complete assignments on time.	10	10	
b. I request assistance when unfamiliar with assignment and/or instructions.	15	15	
8. Dexterity			
a. I display quality manual skills.	10	10	
b. I am able to assist with lifting or positioning.	10	10	
9. Effective communication			
a. I use correct grammar.	10	10	
b. I spell correctly.	10	10	
c. I have good penmanship.	5	5	
10. Nonverbal communication			
a. I smile when communicating with others.	10	10	
PROFESSIONAL IMAGE			
11. Personal hygiene			
a. I bathe or shower, use deodorant, and brush my teeth every morning.	20	20	

Steps	Possible Points	Student	Instructor
12. Grooming			
a. My hair is neat and off my face and collar. I don't use extreme hair colors or highlights or any ornaments or decorations in my hair.	10	10	
b. My fingernails are clean and short. I don't use colored nail polish or artificial nails.	10	10	
c. If I use makeup and/or wear perfume/after shave, it is minimal.	10	10	
d. I wear minimal jewelry, no more than a wedding ring, a wristwatch, and/or a single pair of nondangling earrings. I do not have any visible body piercings except perhaps for earrings.	10	10	
13. Dress			
a. I wear a uniform that is clean, pressed, in good condition, and that fits properly over appropriate undergarments.	20	20	
b. I wear clean stockings without holes or tears.	10	10	
c. I wear clean and polished closed-toe shoes (not Crocs) with clean laces.	10	10	
14. Professional appearance			
a. I don't chew gum.	10	10	
b. I don't smell like cigarette smoke.	10	10	
c. I don't slouch.	5	5	
d. If I have tattoos, they are hidden from view.	10	10	
Total Points Possible	430		

Comments: Total Points Earned _____   Instructor's Signature _____

Student Name (print): _Erin Wiley_

Instructor's Name (print): _Mrs Taber_

Date: _____

MEDICAL ASSISTANT
MODULE H
PROCEDURE COMPETENCY GRADE SHEET

Module H Skills	Points Earned	Points Possible	Instructor's Signature	Date
1. Complete an Encounter Form and Ledger Card		50		7/29/11
2. Complete a CMS-1500 Form		100		7/29/11
3. Interpret an Explanation of Benefits		30		
4. Complete a Pre-authorization Form		30		
5. Complete a Precertification Form		28		
6. Complete a Medicaid Simple Claim		45		
7. Post Payments from Medicaid Remittance Advice		35		
8. Complete a Medicare-Only Claim		35		
9. Complete a Medicare/Medicaid Claim		50		
10. Assign Diagnostic Codes		30		
11. Code Procedures and Services		20		
12. Code Office Visits (E/M Codes)		30		
13. Complete a CMS-1500 Claim: TRICARE Standard Coverage Only		50		
14. Complete a CMS-1500 Claim: Medicare and CHAMPVA		50		
15. Complete a Workers' Compensation Claim		50		
16. Complete an Attending Physician's Statement for a Workers' Compensation Claim		30		
17. Complete Supplemental Security Income Claim		35		

Module H Skills	Points Earned	Points Possible	Instructor's Signature	Date
18. Compose a Patient Termination Letter		40		
19. Determine Primary Coverage		75		
	Total Points ÷ Points = Earned Possible		Final Percentage	
	÷ 813 =			
	Instructor's Signature		Date	

Student Name _____ Date _____

CHECKLIST: COMPLETE AN ENCOUNTER FORM AND LEDGER CARD

TASK: Analyze the information provided and correctly complete an encounter form and ledger card.

CONDITIONS: Complete an encounter form and ledger card using the work product on the following pages.

EQUIPMENT AND SUPPLIES
- Ledger form/pen
- Patient information form (Fig. B-1)
- ID card (Fig. B-2),
- Encounter form (Fig. B-3)
- Ledger card (Fig. B-4)

STANDARDS: Complete the procedure within _____ minutes and achieve a minimum score of _____%.

Time began _____ Time ended _____

Steps	Possible Points	First Attempt	Second Attempt
Carefully read and study the applicable documents.	0	0	
Encounter Form **1.** Calculate the total charge of all services checked, and enter the amount under "TODAY'S FEE."	10	10	
2. Still using the encounter form and assuming the patient paid the co-insurance, calculate the amount paid, and enter it under "AMT. REC'D."	10	10	
Ledger Card **3.** Complete the ledger card by listing each procedure/service separately. Post today's payment, and calculate the balance due.	30	30	
Total Points Possible	50	50	

Comments: Total Points Earned _____ Instructor's Signature _____

Registration Data

1. Your Name   Ebers   Karen   S   Sex ☐ Male   Date of Birth 01/28/2002
   (Last)   (First)   (Middle)   ☒ Female

2. Social Security #: 222-99-0000   Marital Status: Ⓢ M D Se W

3. Address: 14276 Valley View Lane   4. SSS-756-1234
            (Street)   (Phone)
   Hopkins,   XY   98765
   (City)   (State)   (Zip)

5. Employer: Sunrise Care Center (mother)   Occupation: dietitian

   Employer Address: 189 West Elm St.   SSS-756-3321
                                         (Work Phone)
   Hopkins, XZ 98765

   Spouse: N/A   Employer: ____   Occupation: ____

   Employer Address: ____   (Work Phone)

6.
Other Household Members	Date of Birth	Relationship
Tricia Lambert	03/18/72	mother
Adam Ebers	11/04/99	brother
	/ /	
	/ /	
	/ /	

7. Medical Insurance Information

	Ins. Company Name	Policy No.	Policy Holder	Sgl.	Fmly.	Primary	Sec.
( )	BCBS	XYZ511-11-0022	mother	☐	☒	☐	☐
( )				☐	☐	☐	☐
( )				☐	☐	☐	☐

(Type of Coverage)

8. Person to Contact in an Emergency Tricia Lambert Relationship to you mother
   Their Work Phone 756-3321   Their Home Phone 756-1234

9. Party with primary responsibility for payment: ☐ Self   ☒ Other
   Name Tricia Lambert   Relationship to you mother
   Address (see above)   Home Phone ____

For Office Use Only

Date Completed ____   Account No. ____   Patient No. ____

Household Status   ☐ Head of Household

☐ Spouse   ☐ Child   ☐ Other: ____

Head of Household Name ____

Fig. B-1   Registration data sheet (for Karen Ebers).

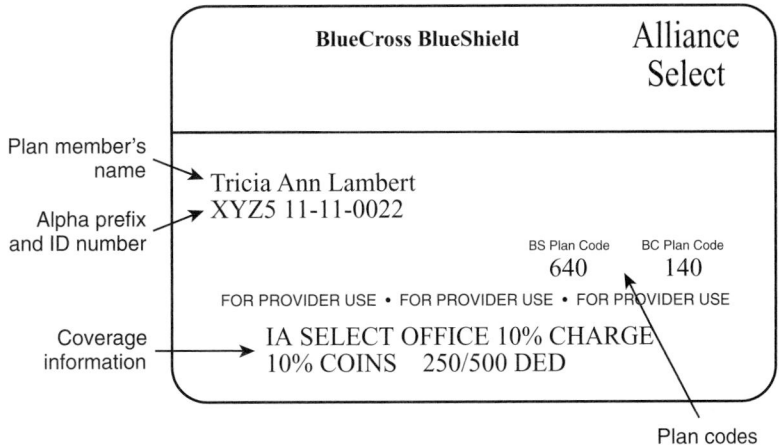

Plan member's name

Alpha prefix and ID number

Coverage information

Plan codes

Fig. B-2 ID card (for Tricia Ann Lambert).

BROADMOOR MEDICAL CLINIC

PRACTICE # 0 4

ACCT. #: 11122	DATE OF SERVICE: 10-07-20XX	CATEGORY:	DIAGNOSIS: V 20.1
PATIENT'S NAME: Ebers, Karen S.		HEALTHCARE PROVIDER: Dr. Marilou Lucero	

CPT	✔	DESCRIPTION	FEE	CPT	✔	DESCRIPTION	FEE	CPT	✔	DESCRIPTION	FEE
OFFICE VISIT - NEW PATIENT				**IMMUNIZATIONS**				**INJECTIONS (CONT'D.)**			
99201		Focused		90701		DtaP		J3410		Vistaril	
99202		Expanded		90632		Hep A (Adult)		J3420		Vitamin B12	
99203		Detailed		90633		Hep A (Ped)		J2000		Xylocaine	
99204		Comprehensive		90744		Hep B (Ped)		**PROCEDURES**			
99205		Complex		90746		Hep B (Adult)		46600		Anoscopy	
OFFICE VISIT - ESTABLISHED PATIENT				90737		Hib		92551	✔	Audio Screening	35.00
99211		Minimal		90657		Influenza		11730		Avulsion Nail, Partial or	
99212		Focused		90707		MMR				Complete, Single	
99213		Expanded		90732		Pneumococcal		11200		Rem. of Skin Tags up to 15	
99214		Detailed		90718		Td		11201		Each Additional 10	
99215		Comprehensive		90703	✔	Tetanus Toxoid	20.00	10060		I & D Simple Abscess	
				90716		Varicella		10120		Removal FB Skin	
PHYSICAL EXAM - NEW PATIENT								11740		I & D Subung. Hematoma	
99381		Age Under 1 Year		**INJECTIONS**				58310		IUD Removal	
99382		Age 1 - 4 Years		J1200		Benadryl up to 50 mg		94010		Spirometry	
99383	✔	Age 5 - 11 Years	125.00	J0540		Bicillin up to 1,200,000 mg		A4570		Splint	
99384		Age 12 - 17 Years		J0690		Cefazolin Sodium 250 mg		99173	✔	Vision Screening	40.00
99385		Age 18 - 39 Years		J0704		Celestone		**LABORATORY**			
99386		Age 40 - 64 Years		J0780		Compazine		82270		Blood Occult	
99387		Age 65+ Years		J1100		Decadron		85680		TB Intradermal	
				J0970		Delestrogen		81000		Urine Dip Stick	
PHYSICAL EXAM - ESTABLISHED PATIENT				J1050		Depo Provera		84703		Serum Pregnancy Test	
99391		Age Under 1 Year		J1510		Gamma Globulin		87082		Strep Screen	
99392		Age 1 - 4 Years		J3301		Kenalog					
99393		Age 5 - 11 Years		J1940		Kasix		36415		Venipuncture	
99394		Age 12 - 17 Years		J2550		Phenergan		99000		Handling	
99395		Age 18 - 39 Years		J3490		Rocephin					
99396		Age 40 - 64 Years		J1070		Testosterone		**MISCELLANEOUS**			
99397		Age 65+ Years		J3250		Tigan					
				J1885		Torodol					

ICD-9 ☐ DIAGNOSIS			
CARDIOLOGY	388.30 ☐ Tinnitus Nos	787.0 ☐ Nausea And Vomiting	733.00 ☐ Osteoporosis
794.31 ☐ Abn Ekg	463. ☐ Tonsillitis, Acute	533.90 ☐ Peptic Ulcer Nos	845.00 ☐ Sprain: Ankle
786.50 ☐ Chest Pain, Nos	474.0 ☐ Tonsillitis, Chronic	569.3 ☐ Rectal Bleeding	847.2 ☐ Sprain: Back
780.4 ☐ Dizziness And Giddiness	**FEMALE / GYNECOLOGY**	**GENITO-URINARY**	847.0 ☐ Sprain: Cervical
787.1 ☐ Heartburn	795.0 ☐ Abn Pap Smear-Cervix	585. ☐ Chronic Renal Failure	840.9 ☐ Sprain: Shoulder
272.0 ☐ Hypercholesterolem	793.8 ☐ Abn Findings-Breast	595.0 ☐ Cystitis Acute	729.81 ☐ Swelling of Limb
272.4 ☐ Hyperlipidemia Nec/Nos	626.0 ☐ Amenorrhea	788.1 ☐ Dysuria	726.00 ☐ Tendonitis
401.1 ☐ Hyptertension Benign	611.72 ☐ Breast Mass/Lump	599.7 ☐ Hematuria	**NEUROLOGY**
401.9 ☐ Hypertension Nos	616.0 ☐ Cervicitis	601.0 ☐ Prostatitis Acute	784.0 ☐ Headache
401.0 ☐ Hypertension, Malig.	V25.09 ☐ Contracep. Mgmt.	599.0 ☐ UTI	346.9 ☐ Migraine Nos
785.1 ☐ Palpitations	625.3 ☐ Dysmenorrhea	**HEMATOLOGY**	724.3 ☐ Sciatica
ENDOCRINE	626.4 ☐ Menstruation, Irreg.	790.6 ☐ Abn Blood Chemistry Nec	307.81 ☐ Tension Headache
250.01 ☐ IDDM Controlled	625.2 ☐ Menstruation, Excessive	285.9 ☐ Anemia Nos	780.4 ☐ Vertigo
250.03 ☐ IDDM Uncontrolled	614.9 ☐ Pelvic Inflam Dis	280.1 ☐ Anemia, Iron Def	**OPHTHALMOLOGY**
250.02 ☐ NIDDM Uncontrolled	V22.2 ☐ Preg State, Incidental	**INFECTIOUS**	373.00 ☐ Blepharitis Nos
250.00 ☐ NIDDM Controlled	616.10 ☐ Vaginitis	616.3 ☐ Abcess: Bartholin Gland	372.30 ☐ Conjunctivitis
251.2 ☐ Hypoglycemia	**PHYSICAL EXAM**	682.9 ☐ Abcess: Skin	918.1 ☐ Corneal Abrasion
244.9 ☐ Hypothyroidism	V20.1 ☑ Well Child	780.6 ☐ Fever: Unkn. Origin	**PULMONARY / RESPIRATORY**
242.90 ☐ Hyperthyroidism	V72.84 ☐ Pre-Op Exam	**IMMUNOLOGY - ALLERGIES**	493.9 ☐ Asthma Nos
EAR, NOSE,THROAT	**GASTRO-INTESTINAL**	995.3 ☐ Allergic Reaction Nos	466.0 ☐ Bronchitis Acute
386.30 ☐ Labyrinthitis Nos	789.06 ☐ Abnormal Pain, Epigastric	477.0 ☐ Allergy, Hay Fever	490. ☐ Bronchitis Nos
382.9 ☐ Otitis Media, Ac./Chr.	794.3 ☐ Abn. Liver Function Study	042. ☐ Human ImmunoVirus Dis.	486. ☐ Pneumonia
462. ☐ Pharyngitis Acute	578.1 ☐ Blood in Stool	**ORTHOPEDICS**	786.2 ☐ Cough
477.9 ☐ Rhinitis, Allergic	564.0 ☐ Constipation	716.90 ☐ Arthritis Unspec.	786.0 ☐ Dyspnea/Resp Abn
461.9 ☐ Sinusitis, Ac Nos	787.91 ☐ Diarrhea	724.5 ☐ Backache Nos	487. ☐ Influenza
473.9 ☐ Sinusitis, Chronic	562.11 ☐ Diverticulitis	727.3 ☐ Bursitis Nec	786.52 ☐ Painful Respiration
528.0 ☐ Stomatitis	530.81 ☐ Esophageal Reflux	354.0 ☐ Carpal Tunnel Syndrome	786.09 ☐ S O B
034.0 ☐ Strep Throat	535.5 ☐ Gastritis/Duodenitis Nos	719.40 ☐ Joint Pain-Unspec.	465.9 ☐ URI
	455.6 ☐ Hemorrhoids	729.1 ☐ Myalgia And Myositis Nos.	079.9 ☐ Viral Syndrome

PSYCH / MENTAL HEALTH		
303.9 ☐ Alcoholism		
300.00 ☐ Anxiety State Nos		
300.00 ☐ Depression		
SKIN / DERMATOLOGIC		
706.1 ☐ Acne Nec		
691. ☐ Dermatitis, Atopic		
692. ☐ Dermatitis, Contact		
110.1 ☐ Dermatophytosis, Nail		
691.0 ☐ Diaper Rash		
054.9 ☐ Herpes Simplex Nos		
053.9 ☐ Herpes Zoster Nos		
054.19 ☐ Herpes Genital Nec		
684. ☐ Impetigo		
703.0 ☐ Ingrowing Nail		
215.9 ☐ Nevus		
110.1 ☐ Onychomycosis		
696.1 ☐ Psoriasis		
706.2 ☐ Sebaceous Cyst		
708.8 ☐ Urticaria Nec		
078.1 ☐ Warts, Viral		
OTHER - MISC.		
780.7 ☐ Malaise and Fatigue		
780.2 ☐ Syncope		
WRITE - IN		

INSTRUCTIONS:	RETURN APPOINTMENT:	PAID	PREV. BAL. — 0 —
	1 year	☐ CASH	
	___ Days ___ Weeks ___ Months (PRN)	☐ CHECK	TODAY'S FEE 220.00
	15 ___ 30 ___ 45	☐ CR. CD.	AMT. REC'D.

Fig. B-3 Encounter form (for Karen Ebers).

BCBS XYZ 511110022
$250; 90/10 10% COINS
A/C #11122

STATEMENT

BROADMOOR MEDICAL CLINIC
4353 Pine Ridge Drive
Milton, XY 12345-0001
Telephone: 555-656-7890

Tricia   03/18/1972
Adam   11/04/1999
Karen   04/28/2002

TRICIA LAMBERT
14276 VALLEY VIEW LANE
HOPKINS, XY 98765

20XX

DATE	PROFESSIONAL SERVICE DESCRIPTION	CHARGE	CREDITS		CURRENT BALANCE
			PAYMENTS	ADJUSTMENTS	
10/07	99383 WCX-NP (KAREN)	125 —			125 —
10/07	90703 TT INJ (KAREN	20 —			145 ~~170~~ —
10/07	92551 AUD SCR ES (KAREN)	35 —			180 —
10/07	99173 VIS. SC (KAREN	40 —			220 —
10/07	POA CK# 1234		22 00		198 00

Due and payable within 10 days.   **Pay last amount in balance column** ⇧

Fig. B-4   Ledger card (for Tricia Ann Lambert).

Student Name _____   Date _____

CHECKLIST: COMPLETE A CMS-1500 FORM

TASK: Apply third-party guidelines and use information provided to complete an insurance claim form.

CONDITIONS: Complete a CMS-1500 form using the information provided below and from the completed encounter form (for Karen Ebers) and ledger card (for Tricia Ann Lambert) from the previous checklist.

Broadmoor Medical Clinic
4353 Pine Ridge Drive
Milton, XY 12345-0001
Clinic NPI X100XX1000
Telephone: 555-656-7890

Clinic EIN # 42-1898989
Dr. R.G. Jones NPI 1234567890
Dr. Marilou Lucero NPI 2907511822
Group # GRW0000
Date claim 1 day after examination

EQUIPMENT AND SUPPLIES
- CMS-1500 form (Fig. B-5)
- Pen
- Patient information form
- ID card
- Encounter form (use completed Fig. B-3)
- Ledger card (use completed Fig. B-4)

STANDARDS: Complete the procedure within _____ minutes and achieve a minimum score of _____%.

Time began _____   Time ended _____

Steps	Possible Points	First Attempt	Second Attempt
1. Carefully read and study the applicable documents.	0		
2. Using the Blue Cross and Blue Shield template from F-5, generate a clean claim for Karen Ebers' office visit.	100		
Total Points Possible	100		

Comments: Total Points Earned _____   Instructor's Signature _____

1500

HEALTH INSURANCE CLAIM FORM
APPROVED BY NATIONAL UNIFORM CLAIM COMMITTEE 08/05

(Handwritten note, top right:) NOTE ** WRITE SAME

(Left margin notes:)
NOTE ** SIGNATURE ON FILE

NOTE ** JUST WRITE M.D

(Right margin note:) NOTE LEAVE BLANK

PICA		PICA

1. MEDICARE (Medicare #) ☐ / MEDICAID (Medicaid #) ☐ / TRICARE CHAMPUS (Sponsor's SSN) ☐ / CHAMPVA (Member ID#) ☐ / GROUP HEALTH PLAN (SSN or ID) ☒ / FECA BLK LUNG (SSN) ☐ / OTHER (ID) ☐ **1a. INSURED'S I.D. NUMBER** (For Program in Item 1): XYZ511-11-0022

2. PATIENT'S NAME (Last Name, First Name, Middle Initial): EBERS, KAREN S

3. PATIENT'S BIRTH DATE: 07 28 2007 **SEX**: M ☐ F ☒

4. INSURED'S NAME (Last Name, First Name, Middle Initial): LAMBERT TRICIA

5. PATIENT'S ADDRESS (No., Street): 14276 VALLEY VIEW LN

6. PATIENT RELATIONSHIP TO INSURED: Self ☐ Spouse ☐ Child ☒ Other ☐

7. INSURED'S ADDRESS (No., Street): 14276 VALLEY VIEW LANE

CITY: HOPKINS **STATE**: XY

8. PATIENT STATUS: Single ☒ Married ☐ Other ☐ / Employed ☐ Full-Time Student ☒ Part-Time Student ☐

CITY: HOPKINS **STATE**: XY

ZIP CODE: 98765 **TELEPHONE** (Include Area Code): (555) 756-1234

ZIP CODE: 98765 **TELEPHONE** (Include Area Code): (555) 756 1234

9. OTHER INSURED'S NAME (Last Name, First Name, Middle Initial):

10. IS PATIENT'S CONDITION RELATED TO:

11. INSURED'S POLICY GROUP OR FECA NUMBER:

a. OTHER INSURED'S POLICY OR GROUP NUMBER:

a. EMPLOYMENT? (Current or Previous): YES ☐ NO ☒

a. INSURED'S DATE OF BIRTH: 03 18 72 **SEX**: M ☐ F ☒

b. OTHER INSURED'S DATE OF BIRTH: MM DD YY **SEX**: M ☐ F ☐

b. AUTO ACCIDENT?: YES ☐ NO ☒ PLACE (State)

b. EMPLOYER'S NAME OR SCHOOL NAME: SUNRISE CARE CENTER

c. EMPLOYER'S NAME OR SCHOOL NAME:

c. OTHER ACCIDENT?: YES ☐ NO ☒

c. INSURANCE PLAN NAME OR PROGRAM NAME: BCBS

d. INSURANCE PLAN NAME OR PROGRAM NAME:

10d. RESERVED FOR LOCAL USE:

d. IS THERE ANOTHER HEALTH BENEFIT PLAN?: YES ☐ NO ☒ *If yes,* return to and complete item 9 a-d.

READ BACK OF FORM BEFORE COMPLETING & SIGNING THIS FORM.

12. PATIENT'S OR AUTHORIZED PERSON'S SIGNATURE I authorize the release of any medical or other information necessary to process this claim. I also request payment of government benefits either to myself or to the party who accepts assignment below.
SIGNED: *Tricia Lambert* DATE: 10/07/2011

13. INSURED'S OR AUTHORIZED PERSON'S SIGNATURE I authorize payment of medical benefits to the undersigned physician or supplier for services described below.
SIGNED: *Tricia Lambert*

14. DATE OF CURRENT: ILLNESS (First symptom) OR INJURY (Accident) OR PREGNANCY(LMP): 10 07 2011

15. IF PATIENT HAS HAD SAME OR SIMILAR ILLNESS. GIVE FIRST DATE MM DD YY:

16. DATES PATIENT UNABLE TO WORK IN CURRENT OCCUPATION FROM TO:

17. NAME OF REFERRING PROVIDER OR OTHER SOURCE: DR. MARILOU LUCERO MD **17a.** **17b. NPI** 2907511822

18. HOSPITALIZATION DATES RELATED TO CURRENT SERVICES FROM TO:

19. RESERVED FOR LOCAL USE:

20. OUTSIDE LAB?: YES ☐ NO ☒ **$ CHARGES**:

21. DIAGNOSIS OR NATURE OF ILLNESS OR INJURY (Relate Items 1, 2, 3 or 4 to Item 24E by Line)
1. V20.1
2.
3.
4.

22. MEDICAID RESUBMISSION CODE / ORIGINAL REF. NO.:

23. PRIOR AUTHORIZATION NUMBER:

24. A. DATE(S) OF SERVICE From MM DD YY	To MM DD YY	B. PLACE OF SERVICE	C. EMG	D. PROCEDURES, SERVICES, OR SUPPLIES CPT/HCPCS	MODIFIER	E. DIAGNOSIS POINTER	F. $ CHARGES	G. DAYS OR UNITS	H. EPSDT Family Plan	I. ID. QUAL.	J. RENDERING PROVIDER ID. #
1	10 07 XX	10 07 XX	11		99383			125 —			NPI	2907511822
2	10 07 XX	10 07 XX			90703			20 —			NPI	2907511822
3	10 07 XX	10 07 XX			92551			25 —			NPI	2907511822
4	10 07 XX	10 07 XX			99173			40 —			NPI	2907511822
5											NPI	
6											NPI	

25. FEDERAL TAX I.D. NUMBER: 42 1898989 **SSN EIN**: ☐ ☒

26. PATIENT'S ACCOUNT NO.: 11172

27. ACCEPT ASSIGNMENT? (For govt. claims, see back): YES ☒ NO ☐

28. TOTAL CHARGE: $ 220 —

29. AMOUNT PAID: $ 22 —

30. BALANCE DUE: $ 198 —

31. SIGNATURE OF PHYSICIAN OR SUPPLIER INCLUDING DEGREES OR CREDENTIALS (I certify that the statements on the reverse apply to this bill and are made a part thereof.)
SIGNED: MARILOU LUCERO *Marilou Lucero* MD DATE 10/07/XX

32. SERVICE FACILITY LOCATION INFORMATION: BROADMOOR MEDICAL CLINIC 4353 PINE RIDGE DRIVE MILTON XY 12345
a. X100XX1000 b.

33. BILLING PROVIDER INFO & PH #: BROADMOOR MEDICAL CLINIC 4353 PINE RIDGE DRIVE MILTON XY 12345
a. X100XX1000 b.

NUCC Instruction Manual available at: www.nucc.org

APPROVED OMB-0938-0999 FORM CMS-1500 (08/05)

Fig. B-5 Blank CMS-1500 form (for Karen Ebers).

Student Name _____   Date _____

CHECKLIST: INTERPRET AN EXPLANATION OF BENEFITS

TASK: Analyze an EOB form and correctly interpret the results.

CONDITIONS: Student will interpret an EOB on the following page.

EQUIPMENT AND SUPPLIES
- Pen
- EOB form Blue Cross and Blue Shield claim (Fig. B-6)

STANDARDS: Complete the procedure within _____ minutes and achieve a minimum score of _____%

Time began _____   Time ended _____

Steps	Possible Points	First Attempt	Second Attempt
1. Carefully read and study the EOB document provided in Fig. B-6.	0		
2. Using the ledger card generated on Fig. B-4, post the insurance payment rec'd 10/30.	10		
3. Calculate the amount that must be adjusted off.	10		
4. Calculate the amount still owed by the patient (the last figure in the column "Current Balance" should reflect the amount the patient owes).	10		
Total Points Possible	30		

Comments: Total Points Earned _____   Instructor's Signature _____

EXPLANATION OF BENEFITS   (THIS IS NOT A BILL)

This is your Explanation of Health Care Benefits. This statement shows how we applied your coverage to claim(s) submitted to us. If you have any questions, please call our Customer Service Department at 555-666-0000 or 800-222-1111 weekdays between the hours of 8 a.m. and 5 p.m.

Insured Name: Tricia Ann Lambert   ID # XYZ511110022
               14276 Valley View Lane
               Hopkins, XY 98765   Patient: Karen S. Ebers

Service Date(s): 10-07-20XX   Provider: Broadmoor Medical Clinic

Billed Charges	Provider Savings	Amount Insurance Paid	Amount Patient Owes
$220.00	$28.50	$136.45	$55.05

CLAIM DETAILS

Billed Charge	125.00	20.00	35.00	40.00
Allowed Charge	111.00	17.50	23.00	-- *
Copayment (–)	11.00	1.75	2.30	-- *
Deductible (–)	-- **	-- **	-- **	-- **
Sub-Total	100.00	15.75	20.70	40.00
Insurance Paid	100.00	15.75	20.70	--

Group Number	Claim Number	Account Number	Provider Number	Date Received	Date Processed
000GRW0000	000050505011	1818181XZ	00234543	10-10-20XX	10-11-20XX

NOTES:

*D – Patient has met yearly deductible

**L – Contract Limitation(s)

A check in the amount of $136.45 **has been mailed to your provider.**

Fig. B-6 Explanation of benefits for Tricia Lambert. *(Courtesy the Blue Cross Blue Shield Association.)*

Student Name _____   Date _____

CHECKLIST: COMPLETE A PRE-AUTHORIZATION FORM

TASK: Obtain pre-authorization from a patient's HMO for requested services or procedures.

CONDITIONS: Student will complete a pre-authorization/admission form from the information provided on the following pages.

EQUIPMENT AND SUPPLIES
- Pen/typewriter
- Envision HMO pre-authorization request form (Fig. B-7)
- Patient registration data form (Fig. B-8)
- Blank pre-authorization/admission form (Fig. B-9)

STANDARDS: Complete the procedure within _____ minutes and achieve a minimum score of _____%.

Time began _____   Time ended _____

Steps	Possible Points	First Attempt	Second Attempt
1. Carefully read and study the above-named forms, then correctly complete the pre-authorization form; 1 point is awarded for each correctly completed blank on the form.	0		
2. Patient information	3		
3. Provider information	8		
4. Physician information	6		
5. Procedure information	10		
6. Student used a pen/wrote legibly	3		
Total Points Possible	30		

Comments: Total Points Earned _____   Instructor's Signature _____

ENVISION HMO

PRE-AUTHORIZATION REQUEST FORM

PATIENT INFORMATION

Last Name: Scoval   First Name: Dorothy M

DOB: 10/16/1961   Member #: 123456789   Group #: S6XXZ

PRE-AUTHORIZATION REQUEST INFORMATION

Please list *both* procedure/product code *and* narrative description:

CPT/HCPCS Code(s): 27407   Durable Medical Equipment: ☐ Rental ☐ Purchase

Description: Repair, primary, torn anterior
cruciate ligament (Ⓛ knee) CPT 27407

Date of Service: 12-23-20XX   Length of Stay (if applicable): 24-48 hrs

Place of Service or Vendor Name: Broadmoor Medical Center

Assistant Surgeon Requested? ☐ Yes ☒ No   Please list *both* diagnosis(es) code *and* narrative description:

1. ICD-9 Code: 717.83

   Description: Sprain/tear anterior cruciate ligament Ⓛ knee

2. ICD-9 Code: _____

   Description: _____

Ordering Physician/Provider: John Langley, MD   Office Location: Suite 416 So. Vine
                              FIRST *AND* LAST NAMES PLEASE   SSS-988-6604
                                                                        Milton, X Y 12345

Referring Physician/Provider: Francis Tompkins, MD
                              FIRST *AND* LAST NAMES PLEASE; REQUIRED FOR PRIME PLANS FAX SSS-987-6540

Date: 11-14-20XX Contact Person: Celia Reeves   Phone: SSS-987-6543

Please note: Incomplete forms will delay the pre-authorization process.
Requests received after 3:00 p.m. are processed the next working day.

PacificSource responds to pre-authorization requests within 2 working days.
A determination notice will be mailed to the requesting provider, facility, and patient.

Please attach pertinent chart notes as appropriate.

FOR INTERNAL OFFICE USE ONLY:

STATUS: APPROVED / DENIED / PENDING / EXPLANATION   ENVISION Phone No.

DATE: 11-15-20XX ACUITY: UKN INITIALS: JIB   800-223-0000

Reason/Status R Code S6   S Code 114   Px Auth #004X39SRM
                            Hosp Auth #HSP003111

Field 11 Notes See pt record   LOS Approved F.W. Samules

☑ Chart notes filed with preauthorization

Notes Authorization numbers expire after 60 days

Field 10 Facility Copy 416 Suite 9 Bldg 4

Fig. B-7 Pre-authorization request form (Scoval).

Registration Data

1. Your Name Scoval Dorothy M   Sex ☐ Male   Date of Birth 10/16/1961
   (Last)   (First)   (Middle)   ☒ Female

2. Social Security #: 123-45-6789   Marital Status: Ⓢ M D Se W

3. Address: 320 Pine Grove   4. SSS-342-1110
   (Street)   (Phone)
   Milton   X Y   12345
   (City)   (State)   (Zip)

5. Employer: Kemper Engineering Inc   Occupation: Eng. Asst.
   Employer Address: 63 Highway 6West   SSS-342-6780
                                              (Work Phone)
   Spouse: ___   Employer: ___   Occupation: ___
   Employer Address: ___
                                              (Work Phone)

6.   Other Household Members   Date of Birth   Relationship
     _____   ____/____/____   _____
     _____   ____/____/____   _____
     _____   ____/____/____   _____
     _____   ____/____/____   _____
     _____   ____/____/____   _____

7. Medical Insurance Information

Ins. Company Name	Policy No.	Policy Holder	Sgl.	Fmly.	Primary	Sec.
Envision HMO	123456789	Self	☒	☐	☐	☐
			☐	☐	☐	☐
			☐	☐	☐	☐

Type of Coverage

8. Person to Contact in an Emergency Henry Barton Relationship to you brother
   Their Work Phone ___   Their Home Phone SSS-342-1177

9. Party with primary responsibility for payment: ☒ Self ☐ Other
   Name _____   Relationship to you _____
   Address _____   Home Phone _____

For Office Use Only

Date Completed _____   Account No. _____   Patient No. _____

Household Status ☐ Head of Household
      ☐ Spouse ☐ Child ☐ Other: _____
      Head of Household Name _____

Fig. B-8 Registration data sheet (Scoval).

PRE-AUTHORIZATION/ADMISSION FORM

Orders must be faxed to appropriate department. History and Physicals are required on all invasive procedures with conscious sedation. **If you have any questions, please call 555-992-XXXX.**

PATIENT INFORMATION

Patient Name: _____ SSN: _____ DOB: _____

PROVIDER INFORMATION

Policy Holder's Name: _____ SSN: _____

Policy Holder's Employer: _____ Employer's Phone Number: _____

Name of Health Plan: _____ Health Plan Phone Number: _____

Policy/ID#: _____ Group #: _____

PHYSICIAN INFORMATION

Physician Contact Person: _____ Coordinator's Phone Number: _____

Fax Number: _____ Primary Care Physician: _____

Requesting Physician: _____ Requesting Physician's Phone Number: _____

PROCEDURE INFORMATION

Procedure: _____ CPT Code: _____

Diagnosis: _____

Department(s) Involved *(Please check all appropriate areas.)*

OR _____ GI _____ RAD _____ Cath _____ CP _____ Women's Center _____ Day Surgery _____

Date of Procedure: _____ Authorized by: _____

Physician's Authorization Number: _____ Expiration Date: _____
Hospital Authorization Number: _____ Expiration Date: _____
Inpatient: _____ Outpatient: _____ Approximate Length of Stay: _____

Comments: _____
_____

Fig. B-9 Pre-authorization/admission form (Scoval).

Student Name _____   Date _____

CHECKLIST: **COMPLETE A PRECERTIFICATION FORM**

TASK: Obtain precertification from a patient's HMO for requested services or procedures.

CONDITIONS: Student will complete a precertification form (Fig. B-10) for the upper gastrointestinal series from the information provided in the case study in Fig. B-11. This is an outpatient procedure (length of stay is less than 24 hours). H & P and laboratory reports are to be attachments submitted with the precertification form. (Note: Student will be the "office contact person.")

EQUIPMENT AND SUPPLIES
- Pen
- Envision HMO precertification request form (Fig. B-10)
- Case study (Fig. B-11)

STANDARDS: Complete the procedure within _____ minutes and achieve a minimum score of _____%.

Time began _____   Time ended _____

Steps	Possible Points	First Attempt	Second Attempt
1. Carefully read and study the information provided, then complete the precertification form; 1 point is awarded for each correctly completed blank on the form.	0		
2. Patient information	7		
3. Hospital information	3		
4. Physician information	4		
5. Procedure information	8		
6. Diagnostic information	3		
7. Student used a pen/wrote legibly	3		
Total Points Possible	28		

Comments: Total Points Earned _____   Instructor's Signature _____

ENVISION HMO

REQUEST FOR INITIAL PRECERTIFICATION REVIEW
PHONE: 555-992-XXXX/FAX: 555-992-XXXX

Date: _____   Outpatient _____   Inpatient _____

Patient's Name _____ Member # _____ Group # _____

Patient's Address _____ DOB _____

Hospital Name _____ Phone # _____

Hospital Address _____

Physician Name _____ Phone # _____

Physician Address _____

Office Contact Person _____

Admission Date _____   Anticipated Length of Stay _____

Admitting DX/ICD-9 Code _____

Surgery/CPT Code _____ Date of Surgery _____

Related HX/Current Signs/Symptoms _____

_____

_____

_____

_____

Lab Findings _____

X-Ray/Diagnostic Findings _____

Current Medications/Freq. _____

Plan of Treatment: _____

_____

_____

FOR ENVISION USE ONLY: Date Received _____ by (initials) Date Referred for Review _____

Rev. Initials _____   Reference ID # _____   Date of PX Notification _____   Office Contact _____

Fig. B-10 Request for initial precertification review (Oliver).

Case Study: Before performing certain diagnostic tests, it is customary to contact the patient's insurance carrier to make sure the procedure/service will be covered under his or her policy. This is referred to as *precertification*, which differs from pre-authorization. This case study involves notifying the patient's insurance carrier of a planned diagnostic procedure.

Date: 4/19/20XX

Patient Name: Justin C. Oliver   DOB: 7/22/67   Record # OL72267
916 No. Court   SS # 666-77-8888
Milton, XY 12345

Patient is in the office today with continuing complaints of severe heartburn. He has been seen in the office by me on several occasions prior to this for treatment of GERD. He is currently on Naprosyn 500 mg BID with food PRN and Prevacid 15 mg one daily. He was advised on his last visit that if his stomach keeps bothering him with this heartburn, we may need to do a UGI or other testing. He is back in the office today requesting this procedure. He will be going to Envision Laboratory tomorrow for a CBC, CMP, lipid panel, and possibly a TSH. We will request a UGI to be performed at Broadmoor Medical Center on 4/22 and will see him back in 1 week.

Diagnosis: GERD 530.81   CPT Code for Upper Gastrointestinal (UGI) Series 91032

(s) Dennis R. Mulligan, MD   Broadmoor Medical Center
4353 Pine Ridge Drive, Suite 233   4500 Pine Ridge Drive
Milton, XY 12345   Milton, XY 12345
Phone: 555-876-5433
Fax: 555-876-5400

ENVISION HMO

Justin C. Oliver   07/22/1967   For Inpatient Pre-authorization
Name   Date of Birth   Telephone: 800-223-0000
123654998   01/17/2000   92LMQ   FAX   555-445-5555
Member No.   Effective Date   Grp Code
Dennis R. Mulligan, MD   555-544-6601
Primary Care Physician   Telephone No.
GHJKL   Copays   Office Visit $5
Pharmacy Code   ER/Outpatient $10
                              Inpatient $15

Fig. B-11   Case study (Oliver).

Student Name _____   Date _____

CHECKLIST: **COMPLETE A MEDICAID SIMPLE CLAIM**

TASK: Apply Medicaid guidelines and use information provided to complete an insurance claim form.

CONDITIONS: Student will complete a Medical "simple" claim and ledger card using the information provided.

EQUIPMENT AND SUPPLIES
- Patient Record NO. 052547 (Fig. B-12)
- CMS-1500 claim form
- Blank ledger card

STANDARDS: Complete the procedure within _____ minutes and achieve a minimum score of _____%.

Time began _____   Time ended _____

Steps	Possible Points	First Attempt	Second Attempt
1. Carefully read and study Patient Record No. 052547.	0		
2. Complete all blocks required for a Medicaid simple claim.	30		
3. Generate a ledger card; post date of office visit, CPT code/ description, fee, and balance.	14		
4. Note Medicaid claim submission.	1		
5. Proofread claim for accuracy.	0		
Total Points Possible	45		

Comments: Total Points Earned _____   Instructor's Signature _____

Patient Record No. 052547

Name: Charles T. Brown   Birth Date: 07/30/2000   Sex: M

Address: 55 N. Winston Dr.   City/State/Zip: Middletown, XT 12345

Employer/Occupation: student

Employer Address/Phone No.: _____

Responsible Party (Spouse/Parent/Guardian): Marvel Brown   Phone: 555-334-3344

Relationship to Patient: father   (Same address)

Occupation/Employer: janitor – Washington Heights Apartments

Employer Address/Phone No.: 3939 Belview Ct., Middletown, XT 12345

Primary Insurance: BCBS**   Subscriber: Marvel Brown

Policy No.: _____ Group No.: _____ Effective Date: _____

Other Insurance: _____ Subscriber: _____

Policy No.: QKZ111006666 Group No.: _____ Effective Date: _____

Medicare No.: _____ Medicaid No.: 5748392   SSN: _____

Name/NPI of Referring Provider: _____

Referring Provider's Address/Phone No.: _____

PROGRESS NOTES

11/09/20XX

CC   Charles is a new patient in the office today with complaints of pain
                and swelling in the R ankle. Applying weight on the ankle causes the
                pain to increase. He reports that he "crashed into another player"
                during soccer practice at the YMCA today.

PX   See patient's health record. X-ray revealed no fracture.

ASSESSMENT Sprain, R ankle (845.00)

PLAN   Charles was referred to Dr. Jamie Richards in the Orthopedic Clinic
                for treatment. *M. Lucero*

Charges: 99202 OV New PT $65.00
                73600 X-ray R ankle   40.00

**Pt not covered under father's BCBS plan.

Fig. B-12 Medical record (Brown).

Student Name _____   Date _____

CHECKLIST: **POST PAYMENTS FROM MEDICAID REMITTANCE ADVICE**

TASK: Analyze information provided and accurately post payments.

CONDITIONS: Student will post payments from a Medicaid RA on ledger cards for five patients.

EQUIPMENT AND SUPPLIES
- Pen
- RA NO. 433900 (Fig. B-13) from XT Department of Human Services
- Five patient ledger cards (Figs. B-14 through B-18)

STANDARDS: Complete the procedure within _____ minutes and achieve a minimum score of _____%.

Time began _____   Time ended _____

Steps	Possible Points	First Attempt	Second Attempt
1. Carefully read and study remittance advice #433900; note the Medicaid patients in this clinic must pay 10% co-pay for office visits on the day they are seen.	0		
2. Remittance advice and Medicaid check was received on 11/28/20XX.	0		
3. Correctly post payments on the ledger cards for the following patients:	—		
I. M. Jones	8		
C. T. Brown	8		
J. L. Doe	8		
E. Martin	8		
Juan Ruiz	3		
4. Proofread each ledger card for accuracy.	0		
Total Points Possible	35		

Comments: Total Points Earned _____   Instructor's Signature _____

XT DEPARTMENT OF HUMAN SERVICES
MEDICAID MANAGEMENT INFORMATION SYSTEM

REMITTANCE ADVICE

RA No. 433900
MMIS Ck No. 0098887

TO: HARPER, DANIEL, MD   PROVIDER NO.   12345678   REPORT SEQ NUMBER: 3   DATE: 11/24/20XX
606 BRIDGE STREET   POLICY/BILLING   800-555-0987   R/S NUMBER   987654343   PAGE 1
MIDDLETOWN, XT 12345

PATIENT NAME/ID NO. SERVICE DATES FROM TO	PERF PROV NO.	DAYS QTY	PROC CODE	PROCEDURE DESCRIPTION	AMOUNT BILLED	AMOUNT ALLOWED	COPAY	PAID AMOUNT	EOB CODES
PAID OR DENIED CLAIMS									
JONES, I.M./44637620011 110620XX 110720XX	81234123 81234123	1 1	99202 99214	OFFICE/OP VISIT–NEW PT OFFICE/OP VISIT–ESTABL PT	55.00 170.00	49.50 152.00	5.50 17.00	44.00 134.50	12 12
BROWN, C.T./44637112001 110920XX	12345678	1	99202 73600	OFFICE/OP VISIT–NEW PT XRAY Ⓡ ANKLE	65.00 40.00	49.50 38.00	6.50 4.00	44.00 36.00	12 12
DOE, J.L./44637220887 11/11/20XX	12345678	1	99218	INITIAL OBSERVATION CARE	110.00	110.00	N/A	110.00	14
MARTIN, E./4463771124 11/15/20XX 11/15/20XX 11/15/20XX	12345678 81234123 81234123	1 1 1	99215 99175 99401	OFFICE/OP VISIT–NEW PT IPECAC/SIM ADMIN FOR IND EMESIS COUNSELLING/RISK FX (15 MIN)	225.00 35.00 50.00	212.00 35.00 25.00	22.50 N/A 5.00	189.50 35.00 20.00	12 14 13
RUIZ, JUAN/446375566 11/19/20XX	81234123	1	96900	ACTINOTHERAPY (UV)	25.00	0.00	2.50	0.00	15
TOTALS					775.00	671.00	63.00	613.00	

EOB CODES:
12 Service paid at the maximum amount allowed by Medical Assistance Reimbursement policies
13 Service paid at 50% of amount allowed by Medical Assistance Reimbursement policies
14 Service paid at 100% by Medical Assistance Reimbursement policies
15 Service not allowed by Medical Assistance Reimbursement policies

Fig. B-13 Medicaid remittance advice.

STATEMENT

BROADMOOR MEDICAL CLINIC

4353 Pine Ridge Drive
Milton, XY 12345-0001
Telephone: 555-656-7890

INGA M. JONES
600 LINCOLN WAY
MIDDLETOWN, XT 12345

DATE 20XX	PROFESSIONAL SERVICE DESCRIPTION	CHARGE	CREDITS		CURRENT BALANCE
			PAYMENTS	ADJUSTMENTS	
11/06	99202 OV NP	55 00	5 50		49 50
11/07	99214 OV EST PT	170 00	17 00		202 50
11/08	Medicaid claim				

Due and payable within 10 days.   **Pay last amount in balance column** ⇧

Fig. B-14 Ledger card (Jones).

STATEMENT   Charles T.

BROADMOOR MEDICAL CLINIC
4353 Pine Ridge Drive
Milton, XY 12345-0001
Telephone: 555-656-7890

MARVEL BROWN
55 NORTH WINSTON DR.
MIDDLETOWN, XT 12345

| DATE 20XX | PROFESSIONAL SERVICE DESCRIPTION | CHARGE | CREDITS | | CURRENT BALANCE |
			PAYMENTS	ADJUSTMENTS	
11/09	99202 Charles OV NP	65 00	6 50		58 50
11/09	73600 x-ray ® ankle	40 00	4 00		94 50
11/10	Medicaid claim				

Due and payable within 10 days.   **Pay last amount in balance column** ⇧

Fig. B-15   Ledger card (Brown).

STATEMENT

BROADMOOR MEDICAL CLINIC
4353 Pine Ridge Drive
Milton, XY 12345-0001
Telephone: 555-656-7890

JERAMIAH L. DOE
14 HILLCREST CIRCLE
MIDDLETOWN XT 12345

| DATE 20XX | PROFESSIONAL SERVICE DESCRIPTION | CHARGE | CREDITS | | CURRENT BALANCE |
			PAYMENTS	ADJUSTMENTS	
11/11	99218 Init Obs. Care	110 00			110 00
11/12	Medicaid claim				

Due and payable within 10 days.   Pay last amount in balance column ⇧

Fig. B-16 Ledger card (Doe).

STATEMENT

BROADMOOR MEDICAL CLINIC
4353 Pine Ridge Drive
Milton, XY 12345-0001
Telephone: 555-656-7890

MRS. ELOISE C. MARTIN
543 MAPLE STREET
MIDDLETOWN, XT 12345

DATE 20XX	PROFESSIONAL SERVICE DESCRIPTION	CHARGE	CREDITS				CURRENT BALANCE	
			PAYMENTS		ADJUSTMENTS			
11/15	99215 OV NP	225 00	22 50				202 50	
11/15	99175 Ipecac Adm.	35 00	—				237 50	
11/15	99401 Couns./Risk FX	50 00	5 00				282 50	
11/16	Medicaid claim							

Due and payable within 10 days.   Pay last amount in balance column ⇧

Fig. B-17   Ledger card (Martin).

STATEMENT

BROADMOOR MEDICAL CLINIC
4353 Pine Ridge Drive
Milton, XY 12345-0001
Telephone: 555-656-7890

JUAN RUIZ
1500 SOUTH 9TH ST.
MIDDLETOWN, XT 12345

DATE 20XX	PROFESSIONAL SERVICE DESCRIPTION	CHARGE	CREDITS PAYMENTS	ADJUSTMENTS	CURRENT BALANCE
11/19	96900 Actinotherapy	25 00	2 50		22 50
11/20	Medicaid claim				

Due and payable within 10 days. **Pay last amount in balance column** ⇧

Fig. B-18 Ledger card (Ruiz).

Student Name _____   Date _____

CHECKLIST: **COMPLETE A MEDICARE-ONLY CLAIM**

TASK: Apply Medicare guidelines and use information provided to complete an insurance claim form.

CONDITIONS: Student will complete a Medicare-only claim using the information in the boxes below and in Patient Record No. 052547.

SPECIAL NOTES
1. The providers at Broadmoor Medical Clinic are PARs.
2. All patients have a current release of information on file.
3. All claims are assigned.
4. Names and addresses of FIs or carriers are listed below.

Names and Addresses of FIs and/or Insurance Carriers	
Medicare FI/Carrier	TRISTATE MEDICARE CARRIER PO BOX 8885A ZENOBIA, ZT 5555-8885
Blue Cross/Blue Shield	BLUE CROSS AND BLUE SHIELD OF XTRA PO BOX 1212 DUBUQUE, XT 44444-1212
Medicaid FI	MEDICAID FISCAL INTERMEDIARY PO BOX 4692J PORT HURON, XY 5111-0002

Provider Block	
Broadmoor Medical Clinic 4353 Pine Ridge Drive Milton, XY 12345-0001 Telephone: 555-656-7890 Clinic NPI X100XX1000	Clinic EIN No. 42-1898989 Dr. R. L. Jones NPI 1234567890 Dr. Marilou Lucero NPI 2907511822 Date claims 1 day after encounter

EQUIPMENT AND SUPPLIES
- Patient Record No. 052547 (Fig. B-19)
- CMS-1500 claim form

STANDARDS: Complete the procedure within _____ minutes and achieve a minimum score of _____%.

Time began _____   Time ended _____

Steps	Possible Points	First Attempt	Second Attempt
1. Carefully read and study Patient Record No. 052547.	0		
2. Complete all blocks required for a Medicaid claim.	35		
3. Proofread claim for accuracy.	0		
Total Points Possible	35		

Comments: Total Points Earned _____   Instructor's Signature _____

Patient/Insurance Information	Billing Information
Vivian R. Ross	Record No. 052547
DOB: 04/15/1952; widow	02/03/20XX; 99203—$81.00
688 Plum Street	02/03/20XX; 73560—$98.00
Middletown, XT 12345	Diagnosis: Knee Pain (719.46)
555-455-6009	Attending Physician: Marilou Lucero, M.D.
Med. No. 200-00-2222D	
No secondary insurance	

Fig. B-19

Student Name _____   Date _____

CHECKLIST: **COMPLETE A MEDICARE/MEDICAID CLAIM**

TASK: Apply Medicare/Medicaid guidelines and use information provided to complete an insurance claim form.

CONDITIONS: Student will complete a Medicare/Medicaid claim using the information in the boxes below and in patient Record No. 052549.

SPECIAL NOTES
1. The providers at Broadmoor Medical Clinic are PARs.
2. All patients have a current release of information of file.
3. All claims are assigned.
4. Names and addresses of FIs or carriers are listed below.

Names and Addresses of FIs and/or Insurance Carriers	
Medicare FI/Carrier	TRISTATE MEDICARE CARRIER PO BOX 8885A ZENOBIA, ZT 5555-8885
Blue Cross/Blue Shield	BLUE CROSS AND BLUE SHIELD OF XTRA PO BOX 1212 DUBUQUE, XT 44444-1212
Medicaid FI	MEDICAID FISCAL INTERMEDIARY PO BOX 4692J PORT HURON, XY 5111-0002

Provider Block	
Broadmoor Medical Clinic 4353 Pine Ridge Drive Milton, XY 12345-0001 Telephone: 555-656-7890 Clinic NPI X100XX1000	Clinic EIN No. 42-1898989 Dr. R. L. Jones NPI 1234567890 Dr. Marilou Lucero NPI 2907511822 Date claims 1 day after encounter

EQUIPMENT AND SUPPLIES
- Patient Record No. 052549 (Fig. B-20)
- CMS-1500 claim form

STANDARDS: Complete the procedure within _____ minutes and achieve a minimum score of _____%.

Time began _____   Time ended _____

Steps	Possible Points	First Attempt	Second Attempt
1. Carefully read and study Patient Record No. 052549.	0		
2. Complete all blocks required for a Medicaid claim.	50		
3. Proofread claim for accuracy.	0		
Total Points Possible	50		

Comments: Total Points Earned _____   Instructor's Signature _____

Patient/Insurance Information	Billing Information
Dorothy R. Stevens (single)	Record No. 052549
DOB: 02/26/1939	02/03/20XX; 99213—$75.00.
2934 Valley View	02/03/20XX; 82270—$25.00
Middletown, XT 12345	02/03/20XX; 81000—$15.00
555-478-9011	02/04/20XX; 90732—$10.00
Medicare No. 134-55-6666D	Diagnosis: Hypertension, benign (401.1)
Medicaid No. 22334567HIJ	Palpitations (785.1)
	Heartburn (727.1)
	Attending Physician: R. L. Jones, M.D.

Fig. B-20

Student Name _____   Date _____

CHECKLIST: **ASSIGN DIAGNOSTIC CODES**

TASK: Assign the proper International Classfication of Disease (ICD-9-CM) code based on medical documentation to the highest degree of specificity.

CONDITIONS: Student will study the 10 dieases/conditions listed on the instruction sheet in Fig. B-21, after which he or she will underline the main term and apply the steps for diagnostic coding to locate the correct ICD-9-CM code (to the greatest level of specificity).

EQUIPMENT AND SUPPLIES
- Pen/typewriter
- Current ICD-9-CM manual
- Instruction sheet (see Fig. B-21)

STANDARDS: Complete the procedure within _____ minutes and achieve a minimum score of _____%.

Time began _____   Time ended _____

Steps	Possible Points	First Attempt	Second Attempt
1. Carefully read and study the instruction sheet in Fig. B-21.	0		
2. Determine and underline the main term for each of the 10 diseases or conditions listed.	10		
3. Apply the seven steps to accurate diagnostic coding, and assign the correct code (to the greatest specificity) to each of the 10 diagnoses.	20		
4. Proofread your answers for accuracy.	0		
Total Points Possible	30		

Comments: Total Points Earned _____   Instructor's Signature _____

Instructions: (1) Determine the main term in each of the following diagnoses and underline it. (2) Using the seven steps to accurate diagnostic coding, code each disease/condition to its greatest specificity.

NOTE: Never code from Volume 2 alone. Find the main term in the Index to Diseases, then turn to the Tabular Section and code to the greatest specificity. Remember: Codes can have up to 5 digits.

1. urinary incontinence   _____

2. multiple vesicovaginal fistula of bladder   _____

3. carcinoma of prostate   _____

4. prepyloric gastric ulcer   _____

5. hypertension, benign essential   _____

6. two infected rectal polyps   _____

7. acute tonsillitis   _____

8. acute cephalgia   _____

9. nasal laceration   _____

10. deviated septum   _____

Fig. B-21   Coding exercise.

Student Name _____   Date _____

CHECKLIST: CODE PROCEDURES AND SERVICES

TASK: Assign the proper Current Procedural Terminology (CPT) code to the highest degree of specificity based on medical documentation for auditing and medical billing purposes.

CONDITIONS: Student will identify the main term in each of 10 procedural events by underlining it and then correctly code these same procedures.

EQUIPMENT AND SUPPLIES
- Pen/typewriter
- Current CPT manual
- List of procedures to code

STANDARDS: Complete the procedure within _____ minutes and achieve a minimum score of _____%.

Time began _____   Time ended _____

Steps	CPT Code	Possible Points	First Attempt	Second Attempt
1. Colonoscopy with biopsy		2		
2. Chest x-ray, single view, frontal		2		
3. Lipid panel		2		
4. HDL cholesterol		2		
5. Strep test, rapid		2		
6. ECG with interpretation		2		
7. Simple suture (face), local anesthetic		2		
8. Bilateral mammography		2		
9. Destruction, flat wart		2		
10. Partial splenectomy		2		
Total Points Possible		20		

Comments: Total Points Earned _____   Instructor's Signature _____

Student Name _____   Date _____

CHECKLIST: **CODE OFFICE VISITS (E/M CODES)**

TASK: Assign the proper E/M code for each scenario based on the information provided.

CONDITIONS: Student will study the scenarios in Box B-1 and code each encounter using E/M codes from the CPT manual.

EQUIPMENT AND SUPPLIES
- Pen/typewriter
- Current CPT manual
- Instruction sheet in Box B-1

STANDARDS: Complete the procedure within _____ minutes and achieve a minimum score of _____%.

Time began _____   Time ended _____

Steps	Possible Points	First Attempt	Second Attempt
1. Carefully read and study the case studies in Box B-1.	0		
2. Correctly identify the proper E/M code for each of these scenarios:	—		
E/M Code			
Scenario 1:	5		
Scenario 2:	5		
Scenario 3:	5		
Scenario 4:	5		
Scenario 5:	5		
Scenario 6:	5		
Total Points Possible	30		

Comments: Total Points Earned _____   Instructor's Signature _____

BOX B-1

1. Heidi Andrews, an 8-year-old girl, presents as a new patient to Broadmoor Medical Clinic with a severe skin rash. History and examination are problem focused; decision making is straightforward.

2. Forrest Gunther, an established patient with a history of chronic sinusitis, presents with sinus drainage, sore throat, severe nasal congestion, cough, and fever of 100.1° F. History and examination are problem focused; medical decision making is low complexity.

3. Elena Rodriguez presents with a benign lesion on her right leg. Although this patient has not been seen in the clinic before, she says she has had the mole for several years. The problem is low to moderate severity, and Dr. Jones spends 20 minutes face-to-face with Ms. Rodriguez.

4. Loris Hiller, an 82-year-old man, comes to the clinic for a follow-up examination. He is a controlled diabetic, but he has other health problems, including diabetic retinopathy, hypertension, glaucoma, and chronic obstructive pulmonary disease. History and examination are detailed with moderate-complexity medical decision making. Dr. Lucero spends 25 minutes with Mr. Hiller.

5. Melinsa Delarosa, a 55-year-old woman, was admitted for observation because of chest pains to Broadmoor Medical Center and discharged the same day. The key components are comprehensive history and examination with moderate-complexity medical decision making.

6. Dr. Jones admits 15-month-old Brittany Lanz to Broadmoor Medical Center. Brittany has been experiencing recurring episodes of respiratory distress with greenish-yellow nasal discharge, cough with wheezing, and fever of 103.6° F. Her mother reports a decrease in appetite and irritability with intermittent ear pulling. A comprehensive history is taken with a complete multisystem examination. Because of multiple diagnosis and management options plus an excessive amount of data to be reviewed in the health record, the medical decision making is high complexity.

Student Name _____   Date _____

CHECKLIST: COMPLETE A CMS-1500 CLAIM: TRICARE STANDARD COVERAGE ONLY

TASK: Apply TRICARE guidelines and use information provided to complete an insurance claim form.

CONDITIONS: Student will complete a CMS-1500 claim form for a patient with TRICARE Standard (only) using the information in the box below and in Patient Record No. 052555.

<table>
<tr><th colspan="2">Provider Block</th></tr>
<tr>
<td>Broadmoor Medical Clinic
4353 Pine Ridge Drive
Milton, XY 12345-0001
Clinic NPI X100XX1000
Telephone: 555-466-3422</td>
<td>Clinic EIN No. 42-1898989
Dr. R. L. Jones NPI 1234567890
Dr. Marilou Lucero NPI 2907511822
Date claims 1 day after encounter</td>
</tr>
</table>

EQUIPMENT AND SUPPLIES
- Patient Record No. 052555 (Fig. B-22)
- CMS-1500 claim form

STANDARDS: Complete the procedure within _____ minutes and achieve a minimum score of _____%.

Time began _____   Time ended _____

Steps	Possible Points	First Attempt	Second Attempt
1. Carefully read and study Patient Record No. 052555.	0		
2. Complete all blocks required for a TRICARE claim.	50		
3. Proofread claim for accuracy.	0		
Total Points Possible	50		

Comments: Total Points Earned _____   Instructor's Signature _____

Patient/Insurance Information	Billing Information
Marie I. Carson	Record No. 052555
DOB: 08/29/1975	11/16/20XX; 99395—$150.00
2334 Apple Tree Cove	11/16/20XX; 85025—$40.00
Middletown, XT 12345	11/16/20XX; 36415—$15.00
555-466-3422	11/16/20XX; 88142—$35.00
ID # 111-22-3333	Diagnosis: Annual physical examination (V70.0)
Relationship to sponsor: Spouse	Attending Physician: Marilou Lucero, M.D.
Employer: Unemployed	
Sponsor Name: Alan V. Carson; USMC/AD	
Sponsor's Address: APO 47349A, NY, NY, 22222	
Sponsor's DOB: 03/18/1972	
Sponsor's ID # 111010122	

Fig. B-22

Student Name _____   Date _____

CHECKLIST: COMPLETE A CMS-1500 CLAIM: MEDICARE AND CHAMPVA

TASK: Apply Medicare and CHAMPVA guidelines and use information provided to complete an insurance claim form.

CONDITIONS: Student will complete a CMS-1500 claim form for a patient with Medicare and CHAMPVA coverage using the information in the box below and in Patient Record No. 052558.

Provider Block	
Broadmoor Medical Clinic 4353 Pine Ridge Drive Milton, XY 12345-0001 Clinic NPI X100XX1000 Telephone: 555-466-3422	Clinic EIN No. 42-1898989 Dr. R. L. Jones NPI 1234567890 Dr. Marilou Lucero NPI 2907511822 Date claims 1 day after encounter

EQUIPMENT AND SUPPLIES
- Patient Record No. 052558 (Fig. B-23)
- CMS-1500 claim form

STANDARDS: Complete the procedure within _____ minutes and achieve a minimum score of _____%.

Time began _____   Time ended _____

Steps	Possible Points	First Attempt	Second Attempt
1. Carefully read and study Patient Record No. 052558.	0		
2. Complete *all* blocks required for a Medicare/CHAMPVA claim.	50		
3. Proofread claim for accuracy.	0		
Total Points Possible	50		

Comments: Total Points Earned _____   Instructor's Signature _____

Patient/Insurance Information	Billing Information
Dora L. Michaels	Record No. 052558
DOB: 10/23/1941	11/21/20XX; 74400-26—$140.00
29 Orchard Meadows	11/21/20XX; 71020-26—$55.00
Middletown, XT 12345	11/21/20XX; 76770-26—$108.00
555-444-6666	Diagnosis: Bladder neck obstruction (596.0)
ID # 222-11-4567	Diagnosis: Respiratory distress (786.09)
Medicare ID # 222-11-4567B	Attending Physician: R.L. Jones, M.D.
Sponsor name: Alvin Michaels; DOB: 02/18/1937	POS: 22
Sponsor SSN: 220-00-0001	
Sponsor service status: USMC	
Relationship to sponsor: Spouse	
Employer: Unemployed	

Fig. B-23

Student Name _____   Date _____

CHECKLIST: COMPLETE A WORKERS' COMPENSATION CLAIM

TASK: Apply workers' compensation guidelines and use information provided to complete an insurance claim form.

CONDITIONS: Student will complete a workers' compensation claim using the information in the box below and in Patient Record No. 052560.

Provider Block	
Broadmoor Medical Clinic 4353 Pine Ridge Drive Milton, XY 12345-0001 Telephone: 555-656-7890	Clinic EIN No. 42-1898989 Dr. R. L. Jones NPI 1234567890 Dr. Marilou Lucero NPI 2907511822 Date claims 1 day after encounter

EQUIPMENT AND SUPPLIES
- Patient Record No. 052560 (Fig. B-24)
- CMS-1500 claim form

STANDARDS: Complete the procedure within _____ minutes and achieve a minimum score of _____%.

Time began _____   Time ended _____

Steps	Possible Points	First Attempt	Second Attempt
1. Carefully read and study Patient Record No. 052560.	0		
2. Complete *all* blocks required for a workers' compensation claim.	50		
3. Proofread claim for accuracy.	0		
Total Points Possible	50		

Comments: Total Points Earned _____   Instructor's Signature _____

Patient/Insurance Information	Billing Information
Julia Elenstein	Record No. 052560
DOB: 04/11/1984	Claim # 83104900HJX
1800 Aspen Circle	"First Report of Injury" Date: 11/23/20XX
Milton, XY 12345	11/23/20XX; 99203—$130.00
555-551-1115	11/24/20XX; 73030—$55.00
SSN: 333-33-0000	Diagnosis: 831.00
Employer: Milton Basket Works	Unable to work from 11/23/20XX through 12/21/20XX
Address: 2799 Industrial Complex, Milton, XY 12345	Attending physician: R.L. Jones, M.D.
555-566-9988	
Occupation: Sorter/Packer	
Primary Insurance: BCBS XYZ333330000	
Group # 1414 XL	

Fig. B-24

Student Name _____   Date _____

CHECKLIST: COMPLETE AN ATTENDING PHYSICIAN'S STATEMENT FOR A WORKERS' COMPENSATION CLAIM

TASK: Review and interpret the information provided and correctly complete the attending physician's statement form.

CONDITIONS: Student will complete an attending physician's statement using the information in Patient Record No. 052561 and chart notes.

EQUIPMENT AND SUPPLIES
- Pen/typewriter
- Patient Record No. 052561 (Fig. B-25)
- Chart notes (Fig. B-26)
- Attending physician's statement form (Fig. B-27)

STANDARDS: Complete the procedure within _____ minutes and achieve a minimum score of _____%.

Time began _____   Time ended _____

Steps	Possible Points	First Attempt	Second Attempt
1. Carefully read and study Patient Record No. 052561.	0		
2. Complete *all* applicable blanks on the attending physician's form.	30		
3. Proofread claim for accuracy.	0		
Total Points Possible	30		

Comments: Total Points Earned _____   Instructor's Signature _____

Patient/Insurance Information	Billing Information
Frank E. Messmer	Record No. 052561
DOB: 01/16/1953	11/23/20XX; 99202—$140.00
601 Butternut Lane	DX: 959.19
Milton, XY 12345	Attending physician: R.L. Jones, M.D.
555-521-2226	
SSN: 321-00-5555	
Employer: Milton Creamery	
555-521-2226	
Occupation: Bottler	

Fig. B-25

CHART NOTES   Record # 052561

11/23/20XX   Frank E. Messmer   DOB: 01/16/1953

HX   This 53-year-old white male presents to the clinic today for chief complaint of a sharp pain in the left groin after loading a truck at his place of work yesterday. His work is repetitious, and patient recalls lifting something "the wrong way" after which he felt "sort of a dull pain." Patient states this has never occurred before. He denies bulging in the area of the lower abdomen, scrotal swelling, or scrotal pain. Patient denies urgency, frequency, or dysuria.
PAIN ASSESSMENT: Scale 0-10, 3-4 involving the left groin area.
ALLERGIES: NKA
CURRENT MEDS: None

PE   NAD. Ambulatory. Appears well
VS: BP: 116/80   P: 82   R: 18   WT: 193#
ENT: TMs: Clear bilaterally without inflammation, bulging, or retraction
NOSE: Clear
SINUS: Nontender to palpation and percussion
THROAT: Clear without tonsillar enlargement, inflammation, or exudates
NECK: Supple, not rigid, without adenopathy or thyropathy
LUNGS: CTA all fields with good breath sounds heard throughout. No wheezes or rales. Normal vocal fremitus without egophony change. Respiratory excursion is symmetric and equal.
ABDOMEN: Soft with active bowel sounds in all quadrants. No hepatosplenomegaly or palpable masses. No involuntary guarding or rebound tenderness. Patient has a mild palpable pain on the left side of the groin along the inguinal ligament. There is no obvious bulging.
GU EXAM: Testes are descended bilaterally, normal size, shape, and consistency without nodularity. Cord structure is normal, nontender. There is no swelling. Patient was checked for hernia, and none was noted, though there is some mild laxity in the left inguinal ring. Penis is without urethral discharge, circumcised, no lesions.

IMP.   Left inguinal groin strain with no evidence of hernia at this time.

PLAN Recommended no work for 1 week. When he returns to work, he should decrease his activity to lifting no greater than 10-15 pounds. This decreased activity should continue until his return visit in 2 weeks. I also counseled patient on signs/symptoms of hernias, and if he notes any changes, he should return for follow up at that time.
Routine follow up 2 wk.

R. L. Jones

R. L. Jones, MD/xxx

Fig. B-26 Chart notes for Messmer.

OFFICE OF STATE EMPLOYER
ATTENDING PHYSICIAN'S STATEMENT

Name: _Frank E. Messmer_   Social Security #: _321-00-SSSS_   Medical Record # _052561_
    First Name   Middle Name   Last Name
Address: _601 Butternut Lane, Milton   XY   12345_
    Street #   Street   City   State   Zip
Current Department: _Bottling_   Agency: _N/A_

I hereby authorize any agency of the State of Michigan insurance company, prepayment organization, employer, hospital, or physician, to release all information with respect to myself or any of my dependents which may have a bearing on the benefits payable under this or any other plan providing benefits or services. I certify that the information furnished by me in support of this claim is true and correct.

Date _11/23/20XX_   Employee's Signature _Frank E Messmer_

History

When did symptoms first appear or accident happen?   Mo. _____ Day _____ Year _____
Date doctor authorized patient to cease work because of disability?   Mo. _____ Day _____ Year _____
Has patient ever had same or similar condition?   ❑ Yes ❑ No
If yes, state when and describe

Present Condition

Subjective symptoms _____

Is the condition due to injury or sickness arising out of the patient's employment? ❑ Yes ❑ No If "yes" please explain. _____

Objective findings. (Include results of current X-rays, EKGs, or any other special tests). _____

Is patient...Ambulatory? ❑ Bed Confined? ❑ House Confined? ❑ Hospital Confined? ❑ Contagious? ❑ On Narcotic Medication? ❑

Restrictions/limitations

Diagnosis

Diagnosis _____   ICD 9 _____
Name of Hospital _____   Anticipated Length of Hospitalization _____
Surgical Procedure _____   Date of Surgery _____
If Pregnancy, date of LMC _____   EDC Date _____   Delivery Date _____

Treatment

Date of first visit for this period of disability   Month _____ Day _____ Year _____
Frequency of visits   ❑ Weekly   ❑ Monthly   ❑ Other _____
When did you last examine/treat the patient?   Month _____ Day _____ Year _____
Date of next scheduled visit   Month _____ Day _____ Year _____
Progress . . . . Recovered ❑   Improved ❑   Unimproved ❑   Retrogressed ❑

Extent Of Disability

	FOR ANY OCCUPATION	FOR USUAL OCCUPATION
Is patient now totally disabled?	❑ Yes ❑ No	❑ Yes ❑ No
If no, when was patient able to go to work?	Month ____ Day ____ Year ____	Month ____ Day ____ Year ____
If yes, when do you think patient will be able to resume any work?	Month ____ Day ____ Year ____	Month ____ Day ____ Year ____
	Never ❑	Never ❑

If yes, is patient a suitable candidate for a return to work program? ❑ Yes ❑ No If yes, please complete the appropriate return to work assessment form.
Is the patient competent to endorse the checks and direct the proceeds thereof? ❑ Yes   ❑ No

Print Name _____ Street Address _____ City or Town _____ State _____ Zip Code _____

Signature (Attending Physician/Mental/Health Provider) _____ Date _____ Degree _____ Telephone Number _____

Fig. B-27 Attending physician's statement for Messmer.

Student Name _____   Date _____

CHECKLIST: COMPLETE SUPPLEMENTAL SECURITY INCOME CLAIM

TASK: Analyze the information provided and correctly complete an SSI application.

CONDITIONS: Student will complete an SSI disability application using the information in Patient Record No. 052530 and chart notes.

EQUIPMENT AND SUPPLIES
- Pen/typewriter
- Patient Record No. 052530 (Fig. B-28)
- Chart notes (Fig. B-29)
- Attending physician's statement form (Fig. B-30)

STANDARDS: Complete the procedure within _____ minutes and achieve a minimum score of _____%.

Time began _____   Time ended _____

Steps	Possible Points	First Attempt	Second Attempt
1. Carefully read and study Patient Record No. 052530.	0		
2. Complete all applicable blanks on the attending physician's form.	35		
3. Proofread claim for accuracy.	0		
Total Points Possible	35		

Comments: Total Points Earned _____   Instructor's Signature _____

Patient/Insurance Information	Billing Information
Lynette Kay Burns	Record No. 052530
DOB: 05/06/1961	11/26/20XX; 99455-32—$225.00
156 Castle Courts	Diagnosis: 278.01, 401.1, 112.3, 311
Milton, XY 12345	Attending physician: M. Lucero, M.D.
No telephone	
SSN 456-65-4321	
Employer: Unemployed	
Primary insurance: None	

Fig. B-28

CHART NOTES

PATIENT NAME: Lynette K. Burns   DOB: 05/06/1961

DATE OF EXAM: 11/26/20XX   RECORD NO.   052530

S: Lynette presents today at the request of the Social Security Administration. She has applied for disability based on her morbid obesity. I have been asked by the SSA to do a physical exam. Lynette is a longtime pt of mine. I have been managing her chronic diseases since 4/6/1995.

> FH: Non-contributory
> SH: Single, does not smoke; drinks 1 or 2 beers a wk
> PMH: HTN, arthritis, morbid obesity, depression
> MEDS: Prozac/HCTZ

O: BP 142/105, P 90, R 19, W 355, H 5'2". Patient appears to not be in distress. On asking her questions she does not show good eye contact; her affect is flat. She seems more depressed today than usual. Abd is obese but soft. Heart RRR, Lungs CTA. Skin: there is a candidiasis infection under her breast. She has a Grade I-II stasis ulcer on her R ankle. Pt has bilateral varicose veins due to poor circulation. Pt becomes SOB when she walks less than 100 yards and she becomes tachycardic. She has chronic complaint of knee, ankle, and back pain. Legs show mild edema. She has arthritis of the knees, and today on exam they show crepitus bilaterally. Patient is unable to bend or stoop. She cannot stand for prolonged periods of time and needs rest in between.

A: Physical exam, requested by State of XY.

1. Morbid obesity
2. HTN, elevated
3. Candidiasis, skin of breast
4. Depression

P: I have been educating and working with Lynette since 1995, trying to get her motivated for weight loss and exercise program consisting of walking. She has tried a walking program of walking less than 100 yards the first week, then increasing her distance as tolerated week by week. She is encouraged to walk to help increase her tolerance. She has been on an 1800-cal. diet and low salt diet with no success. She is instructed to continue with her Prozac 20 mg d, and HCTZ 25 mg d for her leg edema and HTN. Rtn 1 mo.

Marilou Lucero

M. Lucero, MD/xx

CPT: 99455-32
DX: 278.01, 401.1, 112.3, 311

Fig. B-29   Chart notes for Burns.

APPLICATION FOR SSI DISABILITY

MEDICAL PROVIDER'S STATEMENT

1. PATIENT'S NAME: _____   DATE OF BIRTH: _____ / _____ / _____
    _____(First)_____(Middle)_____(Last)_____   MM   DD   YYYY

2. CURRENT MEDICAL CONDITION(s):

    PRIMARY DIAGNOSIS: _____   ICD-9 CM CODE: _____

    SECONDARY DIAGNOSIS: _____   ICD-9 CM CODE: _____

3. DATE THAT SYMPTOMS FIRST APPEARED OR ACCIDENT HAPPENED: _____ / _____ / _____
                                                               (Month) (Day) (Year)

4. DATE THAT PATIENT FIRST CONSULTED YOU FOR THIS CONDITION: _____ / _____ / _____
                                                               (Month) (Day) (Year)

5. DATE YOU LAST TREATED THE PATIENT: _____ / _____ / _____
                                          (Month) (Day) (Year)

6. IS THIS CONDITION RELATED TO PATIENT'S EMPLOYMENT?   YES ☐   NO ☐

7. WAS PATIENT REFERRED TO YOU BY ANOTHER PRACTITIONER? YES ☐   NO ☐
    (If "yes," please provide the name and address of that practitioner): _____

    _____

8. OBJECTIVE FINDINGS *(Include x-rays, lab results and clinical findings. If pregnancy, also give LMP and EDC):* _____

    _____

    _____

9. HAS PATIENT BEEN HOSPITALIZED? YES ☐   NO ☐ *(if "yes," provide reason, hospital name and*
    dates of confinement): _____

10. NATURE OF TREATMENT CURRENTLY BEING PROVIDED OR PLANNED: *(Include surgery and medications*
    prescribed if applicable):

    _____

11. HAVE YOU REFERRED THE PATIENT TO ANOTHER PRACTITIONER? YES ☐ NO ☐ *(If "yes," please provide the*
    name and address of all applicable physicians or practitioners): _____

    _____

12. IN YOUR OPINION IS THE PATIENT ABLE TO WORK AT THIS TIME?   YES ☐   NO ☐
    IF "NO," WHEN DO YOU EXPECT THAT THE
    PATIENT WILL BE ABLE TO PERFORM SOME WORK?   _____ / _____ / _____
                                                  (Month) (Day) (Year)

13. IS THERE ANY TYPE OF JOB MODIFICATION OR ACCOMMODATION THAT WOULD
    ENABLE THE PATIENT TO WORK AT THIS TIME? YES ☐ NO ☐ *(If "yes," please describe):* _____

Fig. B-30 Application for Supplemental Security income benefits (Burns).

14.   BASED ON OBJECTIVE FINDINGS AND YOUR MEDICAL OPINION:

a) THE PATIENT WAS TOTALLY DISABLED FROM: ___/___/___ THROUGH: ___/___/___
                                            (Mo.) (Day) (Year)   (Mo.) (Day) (Year)

b) THE PATIENT WAS PARTIALLY DISABLED FROM: ___/___/___ THROUGH: ___/___/___
                                            (Mo.) (Day) (Year)   (Mo.) (Day) (Year)

15.   LIST ALL CURRENT RESTRICTIONS AND LIMITATIONS YOU HAVE PLACED ON THE
      PATIENT'S WORK AND PERSONAL ACTIVITIES DUE TO HIS OR HER MEDICAL
      CONDITION (If none, indicate "NONE"): _____

      _____

      _____

16.   HAS THE PATIENT BEEN RELEASED FROM YOUR CARE? YES ☐ NO ☐

      IF "YES," DATE RELEASED   IF "NO," DATE OF NEXT SCHEDULED
      FROM YOUR CARE: TREATMENT OR EVALUATION:

      ___/___/___   ___/___/___
      (MO) (DAY) (YEAR)   (MO)   (DAY)   (YEAR)

ANY PERSON WHO KNOWINGLY AND WITH THE INTENT TO DEFRAUD ANY INSURANCE COMPANY OR OTHER PERSON FILES AN APPLICATION FOR INSURANCE OR STATEMENT OF CLAIM CONTAINING ANY MATERIALLY FALSE INFORMATION, OR CONCEALS FOR THE PURPOSE OF MISLEADING, INFORMATION CONCERNING ANY FACT MATERIAL THERETO, COMMITS A FRAUDULENT INSURANCE ACT, WHICH IS A CRIME AND SUBJECTS SUCH PERSON TO CRIMINAL AND CIVIL PENALTIES.

MEDICAL PROVIDER'S DECLARATION AND SIGNATURE

I declare that the answers on this statement are complete and true to the best of my knowledge and belief. I understand that periodic updates (including providing copies of medical records when requested) will be required in the event of a continuing claim.

_____   _____   (___) _____
PROVIDER'S NAME/SPECIALTY   TAX ID/SOCIAL SECURITY #   TELEPHONE NUMBER
   (PLEASE PRINT)

_____   _____ _____ _____
STREET ADDRESS   CITY   STATE   ZIP CODE

_____   _____
PROVIDER'S SIGNATURE   DATE SIGNED

Please return completed forms to:

State of XY Services
Attn: Disability Department
PO Box 22333
Crescent City, XY 21112

Fig. B-30, cont'd

Student Name _____   Date _____

CHECKLIST: COMPOSE A PATIENT TERMINATION LETTER

TASK: Create a termination letter for a patient using guidelines established by the state medical society.

CONDITIONS: Student will compose a letter terminating a patient's care because of nonpayment of fees, as discussed in the scenario in Box B-2.

EQUIPMENT AND SUPPLIES
- Pen/typewriter/computer
- Textbook
- Paper
- Information in Box B-2

STANDARDS: Complete the procedure within _____ minutes and achieve a minimum score of _____%.

Time began _____   Time ended _____

Steps	Possible Points	First Attempt	Second Attempt
Read the scenario in Box B-2, and compose a letter of termination; remember to follow all of the legal requirements discussed in the text.	—		
1. Format	—		
Date and Inside Address	2		
Subject Line	2		
Salutation	2		
Body	3		
Complimentary Close and Signature	2		
References and Enclosure Lines	2		
Special Notations	2		
2. Complete (brief, but contains all necessary information; courteous; and offers alternative care).	25		
Total Points Possible	40		

Comments: Total Points Earned _____   Instructor's Signature _____

BOX B-2

Patricia Henderson, 1111 Spruce Avenue, Milton, XY 12345, owes Broadmoor Medical Clinic $465 for professional services rendered beginning in April 2004 through June 2006. Mrs. Henderson has not made any payments since September 2004, and all letters and telephone calls have proved unsuccessful in collecting this account. Dr. Jones has instructed you to send Mrs. Henderson a letter informing her that he no longer can treat her for her chronic asthma because of her refusal to pay her bill.

Student Name _____   Date _____

CHECKLIST: DETERMINE PRIMARY COVERAGE

TASK: Analyze the information provided, select the correct third-party provider, and complete an insurance claim form.

CONDITIONS: Student will study the information in Fig. B-31, determine the primary carrier, and complete a claim using the information in Patient Record No. 052567.

EQUIPMENT AND SUPPLIES
- Pen/typewriter
- Patient Record No. 052567 (Fig. B-31)
- CMS-1500 claim form

STANDARDS: Complete the procedure within _____ minutes and achieve a minimum score of _____%.

Time began _____   Time ended _____

Steps	Possible Points	First Attempt	Second Attempt
1. Carefully read and study Patient Record No. 052567.	0		
2. Determine the primary carrier.	10		
3. Correctly complete *all* blocks required for the appropriate claim.	65		
4. Proofread the claim for accuracy.	0		
Total Points Possible	75		

Comments: Total Points Earned _____   Instructor's Signature _____

Determine Primary Insurer; Complete Claim	
Broadmoor Medical Clinic	Clinic EIN# 42-1898989
4353 Pine Ridge Drive	Dr. R. L. Jones NPI 1234567890
Milton, XY 12345-0001	Dr. Marilou Lucero ID NPI 2907511822
Clinic NPI X100XX1000	
Telephone: 555-656-7890	Date claims one day after encounter

Patient/Insurance Information

Truman Ross Beckler	DOB: 08/29/1946
430 Cedar Drive	
Middletown, XT 12345	PH 555-672-4207
555-452-0334	SS # 321-44-5511
Medicare	321445511X
Unix Benefits Inc.	198442000LJ
Vera T. Beckler	DOB 05/02/1950
Employer: ALCAT Industries	

Billing Information

Record No. 052567

07/08/20XX	99213	$145.00
07/08/20XX	93000	60.00
07/08/20XX	85025	22.00

Diagnosis: Abdominal Pain (789.06)

Attending Physician: R. L. Jones, MD

Notes: Mr. Beckler is retired and has both Medicare Parts A and B. He also has full health care coverage under his wife's employer group health plan (Unix Benefits Inc.)

Notes: Assume the date of current onset of illness was the same day of the encounter. Date the primary claim one day after the encounter, and date the secondary claim one day after the primary payer's EOB is received.

Fig. B-31 Patient record information for Beckler.

BCBS XYZ 511110022
$250; 90/10 10% COINS
A/C #11122

STATEMENT

BROADMOOR MEDICAL CLINIC
4353 Pine Ridge Drive
Milton, XY 12345-0001
Telephone: 555-656-7890

Tricia   03/18/1972
Adam   11/04/1999
Karen   04/28/2002

20XX

DATE	PROFESSIONAL SERVICE DESCRIPTION	CHARGE		CREDITS				CURRENT BALANCE	
				PAYMENTS		ADJUSTMENTS			

Due and payable within 10 days.   **Pay last amount in balance column**

BCBS XYZ 511110022
$250; 90/10 10% COINS
A/C #11122

STATEMENT

BROADMOOR MEDICAL CLINIC
4353 Pine Ridge Drive
Milton, XY 12345-0001
Telephone: 555-656-7890

Tricia   03/18/1972
Adam   11/04/1999
Karen 04/28/2002

20XX

| DATE | PROFESSIONAL SERVICE DESCRIPTION | CHARGE | | CREDITS | | | CURRENT BALANCE | |
				PAYMENTS	ADJUSTMENTS			

Due and payable within 10 days.   **Pay last amount in balance column**

BCBS XYZ 511110022
$250; 90/10 10% COINS
A/C #11122

STATEMENT

BROADMOOR MEDICAL CLINIC
4353 Pine Ridge Drive
Milton, XY 12345-0001
Telephone: 555-656-7890

Tricia   03/18/1972
Adam   11/04/1999
Karen   04/28/2002

20XX

DATE	PROFESSIONAL SERVICE DESCRIPTION	CHARGE	CREDITS				CURRENT BALANCE	
			PAYMENTS		ADJUSTMENTS			

Due and payable within 10 days.   **Pay last amount in balance column**

BCBS XYZ 511110022
$250; 90/10 10% COINS
A/C #11122

STATEMENT

BROADMOOR MEDICAL CLINIC
4353 Pine Ridge Drive
Milton, XY 12345-0001
Telephone: 555-656-7890

Tricia   03/18/1972
Adam   11/04/1999
Karen 04/28/2002

20XX

DATE	PROFESSIONAL SERVICE DESCRIPTION	CHARGE		CREDITS				CURRENT BALANCE	
				PAYMENTS		ADJUSTMENTS			

Due and payable within 10 days.

Pay last amount in balance column

BCBS XYZ 511110022
$250; 90/10 10% COINS
A/C #11122

STATEMENT

BROADMOOR MEDICAL CLINIC

4353 Pine Ridge Drive
Milton, XY 12345-0001
Telephone: 555-656-7890

Tricia   03/18/1972
Adam   11/04/1999
Karen 04/28/2002

20XX

| DATE | PROFESSIONAL SERVICE DESCRIPTION | CHARGE | | CREDITS | | | CURRENT BALANCE | |
				PAYMENTS	ADJUSTMENTS			

Due and payable within 10 days.

Pay last amount in balance column

1500

HEALTH INSURANCE CLAIM FORM

APPROVED BY NATIONAL UNIFORM CLAIM COMMITTEE 08/05

↑ CARRIER →

| | PICA | | | | | | | | PICA | |

1. MEDICARE (Medicare #) **MEDICAID** (Medicaid #) **TRICARE CHAMPUS** (Sponsor's SSN) **CHAMPVA** (Member ID#) **GROUP HEALTH PLAN** (SSN or ID) **FECA BLK LUNG** (SSN) **OTHER** (ID)

1a. INSURED'S I.D. NUMBER (For Program in Item 1)

2. PATIENT'S NAME (Last Name, First Name, Middle Initial)

3. PATIENT'S BIRTH DATE MM DD YY   **SEX** M ☐ F ☐

4. INSURED'S NAME (Last Name, First Name, Middle Initial)

5. PATIENT'S ADDRESS (No., Street)

6. PATIENT RELATIONSHIP TO INSURED Self ☐ Spouse ☐ Child ☐ Other ☐

7. INSURED'S ADDRESS (No., Street)

CITY   **STATE**

8. PATIENT STATUS Single ☐ Married ☐ Other ☐

CITY   **STATE**

ZIP CODE   **TELEPHONE** (Include Area Code) ( )

Employed ☐ Full-Time Student ☐ Part-Time Student ☐

ZIP CODE   **TELEPHONE** (Include Area Code) ( )

9. OTHER INSURED'S NAME (Last Name, First Name, Middle Initial)

10. IS PATIENT'S CONDITION RELATED TO:

11. INSURED'S POLICY GROUP OR FECA NUMBER

a. OTHER INSURED'S POLICY OR GROUP NUMBER

a. EMPLOYMENT? (Current or Previous) YES ☐ NO ☐

a. INSURED'S DATE OF BIRTH MM DD YY   **SEX** M ☐ F ☐

b. OTHER INSURED'S DATE OF BIRTH MM DD YY   **SEX** M ☐ F ☐

b. AUTO ACCIDENT? YES ☐ NO ☐   **PLACE** (State)

b. EMPLOYER'S NAME OR SCHOOL NAME

c. EMPLOYER'S NAME OR SCHOOL NAME

c. OTHER ACCIDENT? YES ☐ NO ☐

c. INSURANCE PLAN NAME OR PROGRAM NAME

d. INSURANCE PLAN NAME OR PROGRAM NAME

10d. RESERVED FOR LOCAL USE

d. IS THERE ANOTHER HEALTH BENEFIT PLAN? YES ☐ NO ☐ *If yes*, return to and complete item 9 a-d.

READ BACK OF FORM BEFORE COMPLETING & SIGNING THIS FORM.
12. PATIENT'S OR AUTHORIZED PERSON'S SIGNATURE I authorize the release of any medical or other information necessary to process this claim. I also request payment of government benefits either to myself or to the party who accepts assignment below.

SIGNED _____   DATE _____

13. INSURED'S OR AUTHORIZED PERSON'S SIGNATURE I authorize payment of medical benefits to the undersigned physician or supplier for services described below.

SIGNED _____

↑ PATIENT AND INSURED INFORMATION ↓

14. DATE OF CURRENT: MM DD YY ◄ ILLNESS (First symptom) OR INJURY (Accident) OR PREGNANCY(LMP)

15. IF PATIENT HAS HAD SAME OR SIMILAR ILLNESS. GIVE FIRST DATE MM DD YY

16. DATES PATIENT UNABLE TO WORK IN CURRENT OCCUPATION FROM MM DD YY TO MM DD YY

17. NAME OF REFERRING PROVIDER OR OTHER SOURCE   17a.   17b. NPI

18. HOSPITALIZATION DATES RELATED TO CURRENT SERVICES FROM MM DD YY TO MM DD YY

19. RESERVED FOR LOCAL USE

20. OUTSIDE LAB? YES ☐ NO ☐   **$ CHARGES**

21. DIAGNOSIS OR NATURE OF ILLNESS OR INJURY (Relate Items 1, 2, 3 or 4 to Item 24E by Line)

1. |___.___   3. |___.___
2. |___.___   4. |___.___

22. MEDICAID RESUBMISSION CODE   **ORIGINAL REF. NO.**

23. PRIOR AUTHORIZATION NUMBER

24. A. DATE(S) OF SERVICE From MM DD YY To MM DD YY	B. PLACE OF SERVICE	C. EMG	D. PROCEDURES, SERVICES, OR SUPPLIES (Explain Unusual Circumstances) CPT/HCPCS	MODIFIER	E. DIAGNOSIS POINTER	F. $ CHARGES	G. DAYS OR UNITS	H. EPSDT Family Plan	I. ID. QUAL.	J. RENDERING PROVIDER ID. #
1										NPI
2										NPI
3										NPI
4										NPI
5										NPI
6										NPI

25. FEDERAL TAX I.D. NUMBER SSN ☐ EIN ☐

26. PATIENT'S ACCOUNT NO.

27. ACCEPT ASSIGNMENT? (For govt. claims, see back) YES ☐ NO ☐

28. TOTAL CHARGE $

29. AMOUNT PAID $

30. BALANCE DUE $

31. SIGNATURE OF PHYSICIAN OR SUPPLIER INCLUDING DEGREES OR CREDENTIALS (I certify that the statements on the reverse apply to this bill and are made a part thereof.)

SIGNED _____ DATE _____

32. SERVICE FACILITY LOCATION INFORMATION

a. NPI b.

33. BILLING PROVIDER INFO & PH # ( )

a. NPI b.

↑ PHYSICIAN OR SUPPLIER INFORMATION ↓

NUCC Instruction Manual available at: www.nucc.org

APPROVED OMB-0938-0999 FORM CMS-1500 (08/05)

1500

HEALTH INSURANCE CLAIM FORM

APPROVED BY NATIONAL UNIFORM CLAIM COMMITTEE 08/05

PICA

CARRIER ⟶

PICA

1. MEDICARE MEDICAID TRICARE CHAMPVA GROUP FECA OTHER	1a. INSURED'S I.D. NUMBER (For Program in Item 1)

MEDICARE (Medicare #) MEDICAID (Medicaid #) TRICARE CHAMPUS (Sponsor's SSN) CHAMPVA (Member ID#) GROUP HEALTH PLAN (SSN or ID) FECA BLK LUNG (SSN) OTHER (ID)

2. PATIENT'S NAME (Last Name, First Name, Middle Initial)

3. PATIENT'S BIRTH DATE   SEX
MM   DD   YY   M   F

4. INSURED'S NAME (Last Name, First Name, Middle Initial)

5. PATIENT'S ADDRESS (No., Street)

6. PATIENT RELATIONSHIP TO INSURED
Self   Spouse   Child   Other

7. INSURED'S ADDRESS (No., Street)

CITY   STATE

8. PATIENT STATUS
Single   Married   Other

CITY   STATE

ZIP CODE   TELEPHONE (Include Area Code)
(   )

Employed   Full-Time Student   Part-Time Student

ZIP CODE   TELEPHONE (Include Area Code)
(   )

9. OTHER INSURED'S NAME (Last Name, First Name, Middle Initial)

10. IS PATIENT'S CONDITION RELATED TO:

11. INSURED'S POLICY GROUP OR FECA NUMBER

a. OTHER INSURED'S POLICY OR GROUP NUMBER

a. EMPLOYMENT? (Current or Previous)
YES   NO

a. INSURED'S DATE OF BIRTH   SEX
MM   DD   YY   M   F

b. OTHER INSURED'S DATE OF BIRTH   SEX
MM   DD   YY   M   F

b. AUTO ACCIDENT?   PLACE (State)
YES   NO

b. EMPLOYER'S NAME OR SCHOOL NAME

c. EMPLOYER'S NAME OR SCHOOL NAME

c. OTHER ACCIDENT?
YES   NO

c. INSURANCE PLAN NAME OR PROGRAM NAME

d. INSURANCE PLAN NAME OR PROGRAM NAME

10d. RESERVED FOR LOCAL USE

d. IS THERE ANOTHER HEALTH BENEFIT PLAN?
YES   NO   If yes, return to and complete item 9 a-d.

READ BACK OF FORM BEFORE COMPLETING & SIGNING THIS FORM.
12. PATIENT'S OR AUTHORIZED PERSON'S SIGNATURE I authorize the release of any medical or other information necessary to process this claim. I also request payment of government benefits either to myself or to the party who accepts assignment below.

SIGNED _____   DATE _____

13. INSURED'S OR AUTHORIZED PERSON'S SIGNATURE I authorize payment of medical benefits to the undersigned physician or supplier for services described below.

SIGNED _____

PATIENT AND INSURED INFORMATION ⟶

14. DATE OF CURRENT: ILLNESS (First symptom) OR INJURY (Accident) OR PREGNANCY(LMP)
MM   DD   YY

15. IF PATIENT HAS HAD SAME OR SIMILAR ILLNESS. GIVE FIRST DATE   MM   DD   YY

16. DATES PATIENT UNABLE TO WORK IN CURRENT OCCUPATION
MM   DD   YY   MM   DD   YY
FROM   TO

17. NAME OF REFERRING PROVIDER OR OTHER SOURCE

17a.
17b. NPI

18. HOSPITALIZATION DATES RELATED TO CURRENT SERVICES
MM   DD   YY   MM   DD   YY
FROM   TO

19. RESERVED FOR LOCAL USE

20. OUTSIDE LAB? $ CHARGES
YES   NO

21. DIAGNOSIS OR NATURE OF ILLNESS OR INJURY (Relate Items 1, 2, 3 or 4 to Item 24E by Line)

1. |___ . ___| 3. |___ . ___|
2. |___ . ___| 4. |___ . ___|

22. MEDICAID RESUBMISSION CODE   ORIGINAL REF. NO.

23. PRIOR AUTHORIZATION NUMBER

24. A. DATE(S) OF SERVICE		B. PLACE OF SERVICE	C. EMG	D. PROCEDURES, SERVICES, OR SUPPLIES (Explain Unusual Circumstances)		E. DIAGNOSIS POINTER	F. $ CHARGES	G. DAYS OR UNITS	H. EPSDT Family Plan	I. ID. QUAL.	J. RENDERING PROVIDER ID. #
From MM DD YY	To MM DD YY			CPT/HCPCS	MODIFIER						
1										NPI	
2										NPI	
3										NPI	
4										NPI	
5										NPI	
6										NPI	

25. FEDERAL TAX I.D. NUMBER   SSN EIN

26. PATIENT'S ACCOUNT NO.

27. ACCEPT ASSIGNMENT? (For govt. claims, see back)
YES   NO

28. TOTAL CHARGE
$

29. AMOUNT PAID
$

30. BALANCE DUE
$

31. SIGNATURE OF PHYSICIAN OR SUPPLIER INCLUDING DEGREES OR CREDENTIALS (I certify that the statements on the reverse apply to this bill and are made a part thereof.)

SIGNED _____   DATE _____

32. SERVICE FACILITY LOCATION INFORMATION

a. NPI   b.

33. BILLING PROVIDER INFO & PH # (   )

a. NPI   b.

PHYSICIAN OR SUPPLIER INFORMATION ⟶

NUCC Instruction Manual available at: www.nucc.org

APPROVED OMB-0938-0999 FORM CMS-1500 (08/05)

1500

HEALTH INSURANCE CLAIM FORM

APPROVED BY NATIONAL UNIFORM CLAIM COMMITTEE 08/05

PICA

PICA

1. MEDICARE ☐ (Medicare #) MEDICAID ☐ (Medicaid #) TRICARE CHAMPUS ☐ (Sponsor's SSN) CHAMPVA ☐ (Member ID#) GROUP HEALTH PLAN ☐ (SSN or ID) FECA BLK LUNG ☐ (SSN) OTHER ☐ (ID) | 1a. INSURED'S I.D. NUMBER (For Program in Item 1)

2. PATIENT'S NAME (Last Name, First Name, Middle Initial) | 3. PATIENT'S BIRTH DATE MM DD YY SEX M ☐ F ☐ | 4. INSURED'S NAME (Last Name, First Name, Middle Initial)

5. PATIENT'S ADDRESS (No., Street) | 6. PATIENT RELATIONSHIP TO INSURED Self ☐ Spouse ☐ Child ☐ Other ☐ | 7. INSURED'S ADDRESS (No., Street)

CITY | STATE | 8. PATIENT STATUS Single ☐ Married ☐ Other ☐ | CITY | STATE

ZIP CODE | TELEPHONE (Include Area Code) ( ) | Employed ☐ Full-Time Student ☐ Part-Time Student ☐ | ZIP CODE | TELEPHONE (Include Area Code) ( )

9. OTHER INSURED'S NAME (Last Name, First Name, Middle Initial) | 10. IS PATIENT'S CONDITION RELATED TO: | 11. INSURED'S POLICY GROUP OR FECA NUMBER

a. OTHER INSURED'S POLICY OR GROUP NUMBER | a. EMPLOYMENT? (Current or Previous) YES ☐ NO ☐ | a. INSURED'S DATE OF BIRTH MM DD YY SEX M ☐ F ☐

b. OTHER INSURED'S DATE OF BIRTH MM DD YY SEX M ☐ F ☐ | b. AUTO ACCIDENT? PLACE (State) YES ☐ NO ☐ | b. EMPLOYER'S NAME OR SCHOOL NAME

c. EMPLOYER'S NAME OR SCHOOL NAME | c. OTHER ACCIDENT? YES ☐ NO ☐ | c. INSURANCE PLAN NAME OR PROGRAM NAME

d. INSURANCE PLAN NAME OR PROGRAM NAME | 10d. RESERVED FOR LOCAL USE | d. IS THERE ANOTHER HEALTH BENEFIT PLAN? YES ☐ NO ☐ If yes, return to and complete item 9 a-d.

READ BACK OF FORM BEFORE COMPLETING & SIGNING THIS FORM.
12. PATIENT'S OR AUTHORIZED PERSON'S SIGNATURE I authorize the release of any medical or other information necessary to process this claim. I also request payment of government benefits either to myself or to the party who accepts assignment below.

SIGNED _____ DATE _____ | 13. INSURED'S OR AUTHORIZED PERSON'S SIGNATURE I authorize payment of medical benefits to the undersigned physician or supplier for services described below.

SIGNED _____

14. DATE OF CURRENT: MM DD YY ◄ ILLNESS (First symptom) OR INJURY (Accident) OR PREGNANCY(LMP) | 15. IF PATIENT HAS HAD SAME OR SIMILAR ILLNESS. GIVE FIRST DATE MM DD YY | 16. DATES PATIENT UNABLE TO WORK IN CURRENT OCCUPATION MM DD YY FROM MM DD YY TO

17. NAME OF REFERRING PROVIDER OR OTHER SOURCE | 17a. | 18. HOSPITALIZATION DATES RELATED TO CURRENT SERVICES MM DD YY FROM MM DD YY TO
| 17b. NPI |

19. RESERVED FOR LOCAL USE | 20. OUTSIDE LAB? YES ☐ NO ☐ | $ CHARGES

21. DIAGNOSIS OR NATURE OF ILLNESS OR INJURY (Relate Items 1, 2, 3 or 4 to Item 24E by Line) | 22. MEDICAID RESUBMISSION CODE ORIGINAL REF. NO.

1. |___.___ | 3. |___.___ | 23. PRIOR AUTHORIZATION NUMBER

2. |___.___ | 4. |___.___ |

24. A. DATE(S) OF SERVICE From MM DD YY To MM DD YY	B. PLACE OF SERVICE	C. EMG	D. PROCEDURES, SERVICES, OR SUPPLIES (Explain Unusual Circumstances) CPT/HCPCS	MODIFIER	E. DIAGNOSIS POINTER	F. $ CHARGES	G. DAYS OR UNITS	H. EPSDT Family Plan	I. ID. QUAL.	J. RENDERING PROVIDER ID. #
1										NPI
2										NPI
3										NPI
4										NPI
5										NPI
6										NPI

25. FEDERAL TAX I.D. NUMBER SSN ☐ EIN ☐ | 26. PATIENT'S ACCOUNT NO. | 27. ACCEPT ASSIGNMENT? (For govt. claims, see back) YES ☐ NO ☐ | 28. TOTAL CHARGE $ | 29. AMOUNT PAID $ | 30. BALANCE DUE $

31. SIGNATURE OF PHYSICIAN OR SUPPLIER INCLUDING DEGREES OR CREDENTIALS (I certify that the statements on the reverse apply to this bill and are made a part thereof.)

SIGNED _____ DATE _____ | 32. SERVICE FACILITY LOCATION INFORMATION

a. NPI b. | 33. BILLING PROVIDER INFO & PH # ( )

a. NPI b.

NUCC Instruction Manual available at: www.nucc.org | APPROVED OMB-0938-0999 FORM CMS-1500 (08/05)

CARRIER

PATIENT AND INSURED INFORMATION

PHYSICIAN OR SUPPLIER INFORMATION

1500

HEALTH INSURANCE CLAIM FORM

APPROVED BY NATIONAL UNIFORM CLAIM COMMITTEE 08/05

CARRIER

PICA		PICA

1. MEDICARE (Medicare #)   MEDICAID (Medicaid #)   TRICARE CHAMPUS (Sponsor's SSN)   CHAMPVA (Member ID#)   GROUP HEALTH PLAN (SSN or ID)   FECA BLK LUNG (SSN)   OTHER (ID)

1a. INSURED'S I.D. NUMBER   (For Program in Item 1)

2. PATIENT'S NAME (Last Name, First Name, Middle Initial)

3. PATIENT'S BIRTH DATE MM DD YY   SEX   M   F

4. INSURED'S NAME (Last Name, First Name, Middle Initial)

5. PATIENT'S ADDRESS (No., Street)

6. PATIENT RELATIONSHIP TO INSURED   Self   Spouse   Child   Other

7. INSURED'S ADDRESS (No., Street)

CITY   STATE

8. PATIENT STATUS   Single   Married   Other

CITY   STATE

ZIP CODE   TELEPHONE (Include Area Code) ( )

Employed   Full-Time Student   Part-Time Student

ZIP CODE   TELEPHONE (Include Area Code) ( )

9. OTHER INSURED'S NAME (Last Name, First Name, Middle Initial)

10. IS PATIENT'S CONDITION RELATED TO:

11. INSURED'S POLICY GROUP OR FECA NUMBER

a. OTHER INSURED'S POLICY OR GROUP NUMBER

a. EMPLOYMENT? (Current or Previous)   YES   NO

a. INSURED'S DATE OF BIRTH MM DD YY   SEX M F

b. OTHER INSURED'S DATE OF BIRTH MM DD YY   SEX M F

b. AUTO ACCIDENT?   PLACE (State)   YES   NO

b. EMPLOYER'S NAME OR SCHOOL NAME

c. EMPLOYER'S NAME OR SCHOOL NAME

c. OTHER ACCIDENT?   YES   NO

c. INSURANCE PLAN NAME OR PROGRAM NAME

d. INSURANCE PLAN NAME OR PROGRAM NAME

10d. RESERVED FOR LOCAL USE

d. IS THERE ANOTHER HEALTH BENEFIT PLAN?   YES   NO   If yes, return to and complete item 9 a-d.

READ BACK OF FORM BEFORE COMPLETING & SIGNING THIS FORM.
12. PATIENT'S OR AUTHORIZED PERSON'S SIGNATURE I authorize the release of any medical or other information necessary to process this claim. I also request payment of government benefits either to myself or to the party who accepts assignment below.

SIGNED _____ DATE _____

13. INSURED'S OR AUTHORIZED PERSON'S SIGNATURE I authorize payment of medical benefits to the undersigned physician or supplier for services described below.

SIGNED _____

PATIENT AND INSURED INFORMATION

14. DATE OF CURRENT: MM DD YY   ILLNESS (First symptom) OR INJURY (Accident) OR PREGNANCY(LMP)

15. IF PATIENT HAS HAD SAME OR SIMILAR ILLNESS. GIVE FIRST DATE MM DD YY

16. DATES PATIENT UNABLE TO WORK IN CURRENT OCCUPATION FROM MM DD YY   TO MM DD YY

17. NAME OF REFERRING PROVIDER OR OTHER SOURCE   17a.   17b. NPI

18. HOSPITALIZATION DATES RELATED TO CURRENT SERVICES FROM MM DD YY   TO MM DD YY

19. RESERVED FOR LOCAL USE

20. OUTSIDE LAB?   YES   NO $ CHARGES

21. DIAGNOSIS OR NATURE OF ILLNESS OR INJURY (Relate Items 1, 2, 3 or 4 to Item 24E by Line)
1. ___.___   3. ___.___
2. ___.___   4. ___.___

22. MEDICAID RESUBMISSION CODE   ORIGINAL REF. NO.

23. PRIOR AUTHORIZATION NUMBER

24. A. DATE(S) OF SERVICE From MM DD YY To MM DD YY	B. PLACE OF SERVICE	C. EMG	D. PROCEDURES, SERVICES, OR SUPPLIES (Explain Unusual Circumstances) CPT/HCPCS MODIFIER	E. DIAGNOSIS POINTER	F. $ CHARGES	G. DAYS OR UNITS	H. EPSDT Family Plan	I. ID. QUAL.	J. RENDERING PROVIDER ID. #
1								NPI	
2								NPI	
3								NPI	
4								NPI	
5								NPI	
6								NPI	

25. FEDERAL TAX I.D. NUMBER   SSN EIN

26. PATIENT'S ACCOUNT NO.

27. ACCEPT ASSIGNMENT? (For govt. claims, see back)   YES   NO

28. TOTAL CHARGE $

29. AMOUNT PAID $

30. BALANCE DUE $

31. SIGNATURE OF PHYSICIAN OR SUPPLIER INCLUDING DEGREES OR CREDENTIALS (I certify that the statements on the reverse apply to this bill and are made a part thereof.)

SIGNED _____ DATE _____

32. SERVICE FACILITY LOCATION INFORMATION

a. NPI   b.

33. BILLING PROVIDER INFO & PH # ( )

a. NPI   b.

PHYSICIAN OR SUPPLIER INFORMATION

NUCC Instruction Manual available at: www.nucc.org

APPROVED OMB-0938-0999 FORM CMS-1500 (08/05)

1500

HEALTH INSURANCE CLAIM FORM

APPROVED BY NATIONAL UNIFORM CLAIM COMMITTEE 08/05

PICA
PICA

1. MEDICARE (Medicare #)   MEDICAID (Medicaid #)   TRICARE CHAMPUS (Sponsor's SSN)   CHAMPVA (Member ID#)   GROUP HEALTH PLAN (SSN or ID)   FECA BLK LUNG (SSN)   OTHER (ID) | 1a. INSURED'S I.D. NUMBER   (For Program in Item 1)

2. PATIENT'S NAME (Last Name, First Name, Middle Initial) | 3. PATIENT'S BIRTH DATE MM | DD | YY   SEX M☐ F☐ | 4. INSURED'S NAME (Last Name, First Name, Middle Initial)

5. PATIENT'S ADDRESS (No., Street) | 6. PATIENT RELATIONSHIP TO INSURED   Self☐ Spouse☐ Child☐ Other☐ | 7. INSURED'S ADDRESS (No., Street)

CITY   STATE | 8. PATIENT STATUS   Single☐ Married☐ Other☐ | CITY   STATE

ZIP CODE   TELEPHONE (Include Area Code) (   ) | Employed☐ Full-Time Student☐ Part-Time Student☐ | ZIP CODE   TELEPHONE (Include Area Code) (   )

9. OTHER INSURED'S NAME (Last Name, First Name, Middle Initial) | 10. IS PATIENT'S CONDITION RELATED TO: | 11. INSURED'S POLICY GROUP OR FECA NUMBER

a. OTHER INSURED'S POLICY OR GROUP NUMBER | a. EMPLOYMENT? (Current or Previous)   YES☐ NO☐ | a. INSURED'S DATE OF BIRTH MM | DD | YY   SEX M☐ F☐

b. OTHER INSURED'S DATE OF BIRTH MM | DD | YY   SEX M☐ F☐ | b. AUTO ACCIDENT?   PLACE (State)   YES☐ NO☐ | b. EMPLOYER'S NAME OR SCHOOL NAME

c. EMPLOYER'S NAME OR SCHOOL NAME | c. OTHER ACCIDENT?   YES☐ NO☐ | c. INSURANCE PLAN NAME OR PROGRAM NAME

d. INSURANCE PLAN NAME OR PROGRAM NAME | 10d. RESERVED FOR LOCAL USE | d. IS THERE ANOTHER HEALTH BENEFIT PLAN?   YES☐ NO☐   *If yes*, return to and complete item 9 a-d.

READ BACK OF FORM BEFORE COMPLETING & SIGNING THIS FORM.
12. PATIENT'S OR AUTHORIZED PERSON'S SIGNATURE I authorize the release of any medical or other information necessary to process this claim. I also request payment of government benefits either to myself or to the party who accepts assignment below.

SIGNED _____   DATE _____

13. INSURED'S OR AUTHORIZED PERSON'S SIGNATURE I authorize payment of medical benefits to the undersigned physician or supplier for services described below.

SIGNED _____

14. DATE OF CURRENT: MM | DD | YY   ILLNESS (First symptom) OR INJURY (Accident) OR PREGNANCY(LMP) | 15. IF PATIENT HAS HAD SAME OR SIMILAR ILLNESS. GIVE FIRST DATE MM | DD | YY | 16. DATES PATIENT UNABLE TO WORK IN CURRENT OCCUPATION   FROM MM | DD | YY   TO MM | DD | YY

17. NAME OF REFERRING PROVIDER OR OTHER SOURCE   17a.   17b. NPI | 18. HOSPITALIZATION DATES RELATED TO CURRENT SERVICES   FROM MM | DD | YY   TO MM | DD | YY

19. RESERVED FOR LOCAL USE | 20. OUTSIDE LAB?   YES☐ NO☐ $ CHARGES

21. DIAGNOSIS OR NATURE OF ILLNESS OR INJURY (Relate Items 1, 2, 3 or 4 to Item 24E by Line)
1. L___ . ___   3. L___ . ___
2. L___ . ___   4. L___ . ___

22. MEDICAID RESUBMISSION CODE   ORIGINAL REF. NO.

23. PRIOR AUTHORIZATION NUMBER

24. A. DATE(S) OF SERVICE		B.	C.	D. PROCEDURES, SERVICES, OR SUPPLIES	E.	F.	G.	H.	I.	J.
From MM DD YY	To MM DD YY	PLACE OF SERVICE	EMG	(Explain Unusual Circumstances) CPT/HCPCS | MODIFIER	DIAGNOSIS POINTER	$ CHARGES	DAYS OR UNITS	EPSDT Family Plan	ID. QUAL.	RENDERING PROVIDER ID. #
1										NPI
2										NPI
3										NPI
4										NPI
5										NPI
6										NPI

25. FEDERAL TAX I.D. NUMBER   SSN☐ EIN☐ | 26. PATIENT'S ACCOUNT NO. | 27. ACCEPT ASSIGNMENT? (For govt. claims, see back) YES☐ NO☐ | 28. TOTAL CHARGE $ | 29. AMOUNT PAID $ | 30. BALANCE DUE $

31. SIGNATURE OF PHYSICIAN OR SUPPLIER INCLUDING DEGREES OR CREDENTIALS (I certify that the statements on the reverse apply to this bill and are made a part thereof.)

SIGNED _____   DATE _____

32. SERVICE FACILITY LOCATION INFORMATION
a. NPI   b.

33. BILLING PROVIDER INFO & PH # (   )
a. NPI   b.

NUCC Instruction Manual available at: www.nucc.org

APPROVED OMB-0938-0999 FORM CMS-1500 (08/05)

1500

HEALTH INSURANCE CLAIM FORM

APPROVED BY NATIONAL UNIFORM CLAIM COMMITTEE 08/05

| | PICA | | | | | | | | PICA | |

1. MEDICARE   MEDICAID   TRICARE CHAMPUS   CHAMPVA   GROUP HEALTH PLAN   FECA BLK LUNG   OTHER   1a. INSURED'S I.D. NUMBER   (For Program in Item 1)

(Medicare #)   (Medicaid #)   (Sponsor's SSN)   (Member ID#)   (SSN or ID)   (SSN)   (ID)

2. PATIENT'S NAME (Last Name, First Name, Middle Initial)   3. PATIENT'S BIRTH DATE MM DD YY   SEX   M   F   4. INSURED'S NAME (Last Name, First Name, Middle Initial)

5. PATIENT'S ADDRESS (No., Street)   6. PATIENT RELATIONSHIP TO INSURED   Self   Spouse   Child   Other   7. INSURED'S ADDRESS (No., Street)

CITY   STATE   8. PATIENT STATUS   Single   Married   Other   CITY   STATE

ZIP CODE   TELEPHONE (Include Area Code)   (   )   Employed   Full-Time Student   Part-Time Student   ZIP CODE   TELEPHONE (Include Area Code)   (   )

9. OTHER INSURED'S NAME (Last Name, First Name, Middle Initial)   10. IS PATIENT'S CONDITION RELATED TO: 11. INSURED'S POLICY GROUP OR FECA NUMBER

a. OTHER INSURED'S POLICY OR GROUP NUMBER   a. EMPLOYMENT? (Current or Previous)   YES   NO   a. INSURED'S DATE OF BIRTH MM DD YY   SEX   M   F

b. OTHER INSURED'S DATE OF BIRTH MM DD YY   SEX   M   F   b. AUTO ACCIDENT?   PLACE (State)   YES   NO   b. EMPLOYER'S NAME OR SCHOOL NAME

c. EMPLOYER'S NAME OR SCHOOL NAME   c. OTHER ACCIDENT?   YES   NO   c. INSURANCE PLAN NAME OR PROGRAM NAME

d. INSURANCE PLAN NAME OR PROGRAM NAME   10d. RESERVED FOR LOCAL USE   d. IS THERE ANOTHER HEALTH BENEFIT PLAN?   YES   NO   If yes, return to and complete item 9 a-d.

READ BACK OF FORM BEFORE COMPLETING & SIGNING THIS FORM.
12. PATIENT'S OR AUTHORIZED PERSON'S SIGNATURE I authorize the release of any medical or other information necessary to process this claim. I also request payment of government benefits either to myself or to the party who accepts assignment below.

SIGNED _____   DATE _____

13. INSURED'S OR AUTHORIZED PERSON'S SIGNATURE I authorize payment of medical benefits to the undersigned physician or supplier for services described below.

SIGNED _____

14. DATE OF CURRENT: MM DD YY   ILLNESS (First symptom) OR INJURY (Accident) OR PREGNANCY(LMP)   15. IF PATIENT HAS HAD SAME OR SIMILAR ILLNESS. GIVE FIRST DATE MM DD YY   16. DATES PATIENT UNABLE TO WORK IN CURRENT OCCUPATION MM DD YY   FROM   TO MM DD YY

17. NAME OF REFERRING PROVIDER OR OTHER SOURCE   17a.   17b. NPI   18. HOSPITALIZATION DATES RELATED TO CURRENT SERVICES MM DD YY   FROM   TO MM DD YY

19. RESERVED FOR LOCAL USE   20. OUTSIDE LAB?   YES   NO $ CHARGES

21. DIAGNOSIS OR NATURE OF ILLNESS OR INJURY (Relate Items 1, 2, 3 or 4 to Item 24E by Line)

1. L___ . ___   3. L___ . ___

2. L___ . ___   4. L___ . ___

22. MEDICAID RESUBMISSION CODE   ORIGINAL REF. NO.

23. PRIOR AUTHORIZATION NUMBER

24. A. DATE(S) OF SERVICE From MM DD YY To MM DD YY	B. PLACE OF SERVICE	C. EMG	D. PROCEDURES, SERVICES, OR SUPPLIES (Explain Unusual Circumstances) CPT/HCPCS MODIFIER	E. DIAGNOSIS POINTER	F. $ CHARGES	G. DAYS OR UNITS	H. EPSDT Family Plan	I. ID. QUAL.	J. RENDERING PROVIDER ID. #
1								NPI	
2								NPI	
3								NPI	
4								NPI	
5								NPI	
6								NPI	

25. FEDERAL TAX I.D. NUMBER   SSN EIN   26. PATIENT'S ACCOUNT NO.   27. ACCEPT ASSIGNMENT? (For govt. claims, see back)   YES   NO   28. TOTAL CHARGE $ 29. AMOUNT PAID $ 30. BALANCE DUE $

31. SIGNATURE OF PHYSICIAN OR SUPPLIER INCLUDING DEGREES OR CREDENTIALS (I certify that the statements on the reverse apply to this bill and are made a part thereof.)   32. SERVICE FACILITY LOCATION INFORMATION   33. BILLING PROVIDER INFO & PH # (   )

SIGNED _____ DATE _____   a. NPI   b.   a. NPI   b.

NUCC Instruction Manual available at: www.nucc.org   APPROVED OMB-0938-0999 FORM CMS-1500 (08/05)

PATIENT AND INSURED INFORMATION

PHYSICIAN OR SUPPLIER INFORMATION

1500

HEALTH INSURANCE CLAIM FORM

APPROVED BY NATIONAL UNIFORM CLAIM COMMITTEE 08/05

CARRIER →

| | | PICA | | | | | | | | PICA | | |

1. MEDICARE   MEDICAID   TRICARE CHAMPUS   CHAMPVA   GROUP HEALTH PLAN   FECA BLK LUNG   OTHER   1a. INSURED'S I.D. NUMBER   (For Program in Item 1)
(Medicare #)   (Medicaid #)   (Sponsor's SSN)   (Member ID#)   (SSN or ID)   (SSN)   (ID)

2. PATIENT'S NAME (Last Name, First Name, Middle Initial)   3. PATIENT'S BIRTH DATE   MM DD YY   SEX   M   F   4. INSURED'S NAME (Last Name, First Name, Middle Initial)

5. PATIENT'S ADDRESS (No., Street)   6. PATIENT RELATIONSHIP TO INSURED   Self   Spouse   Child   Other   7. INSURED'S ADDRESS (No., Street)

CITY   STATE   8. PATIENT STATUS   Single   Married   Other   CITY   STATE

ZIP CODE   TELEPHONE (Include Area Code)   (   )   Employed   Full-Time Student   Part-Time Student   ZIP CODE   TELEPHONE (Include Area Code)   (   )

9. OTHER INSURED'S NAME (Last Name, First Name, Middle Initial)   10. IS PATIENT'S CONDITION RELATED TO: 11. INSURED'S POLICY GROUP OR FECA NUMBER

a. OTHER INSURED'S POLICY OR GROUP NUMBER   a. EMPLOYMENT? (Current or Previous)   YES   NO   a. INSURED'S DATE OF BIRTH   MM DD YY   SEX   M   F

b. OTHER INSURED'S DATE OF BIRTH   MM DD YY   SEX   M   F   b. AUTO ACCIDENT?   PLACE (State)   YES   NO   b. EMPLOYER'S NAME OR SCHOOL NAME

c. EMPLOYER'S NAME OR SCHOOL NAME   c. OTHER ACCIDENT?   YES   NO   c. INSURANCE PLAN NAME OR PROGRAM NAME

d. INSURANCE PLAN NAME OR PROGRAM NAME   10d. RESERVED FOR LOCAL USE   d. IS THERE ANOTHER HEALTH BENEFIT PLAN?   YES   NO   If yes, return to and complete item 9 a-d.

READ BACK OF FORM BEFORE COMPLETING & SIGNING THIS FORM.
12. PATIENT'S OR AUTHORIZED PERSON'S SIGNATURE I authorize the release of any medical or other information necessary to process this claim. I also request payment of government benefits either to myself or to the party who accepts assignment below.

SIGNED _____   DATE _____

13. INSURED'S OR AUTHORIZED PERSON'S SIGNATURE I authorize payment of medical benefits to the undersigned physician or supplier for services described below.

SIGNED _____

PATIENT AND INSURED INFORMATION

14. DATE OF CURRENT: MM DD YY   ◄ ILLNESS (First symptom) OR INJURY (Accident) OR PREGNANCY(LMP)   15. IF PATIENT HAS HAD SAME OR SIMILAR ILLNESS. GIVE FIRST DATE   MM DD YY   16. DATES PATIENT UNABLE TO WORK IN CURRENT OCCUPATION   MM DD YY   FROM   MM DD YY   TO

17. NAME OF REFERRING PROVIDER OR OTHER SOURCE   17a.   17b. NPI   18. HOSPITALIZATION DATES RELATED TO CURRENT SERVICES   MM DD YY   FROM   MM DD YY   TO

19. RESERVED FOR LOCAL USE   20. OUTSIDE LAB?   YES   NO $ CHARGES

21. DIAGNOSIS OR NATURE OF ILLNESS OR INJURY (Relate Items 1, 2, 3 or 4 to Item 24E by Line)
1. |___.___   3. |___.___
2. |___.___   4. |___.___

22. MEDICAID RESUBMISSION CODE   ORIGINAL REF. NO.

23. PRIOR AUTHORIZATION NUMBER

24. A. DATE(S) OF SERVICE						B. PLACE OF SERVICE	C. EMG	D. PROCEDURES, SERVICES, OR SUPPLIES (Explain Unusual Circumstances)		E. DIAGNOSIS POINTER	F. $ CHARGES	G. DAYS OR UNITS	H. EPSDT Family Plan	I. ID. QUAL.	J. RENDERING PROVIDER ID. #
	From			To					CPT/HCPCS	MODIFIER					
	MM	DD	YY	MM	DD	YY									
1														NPI	
2														NPI	
3														NPI	
4														NPI	
5														NPI	
6														NPI	

25. FEDERAL TAX I.D. NUMBER   SSN EIN   26. PATIENT'S ACCOUNT NO.   27. ACCEPT ASSIGNMENT? (For govt. claims, see back)   YES   NO   28. TOTAL CHARGE $ 29. AMOUNT PAID $ 30. BALANCE DUE $

31. SIGNATURE OF PHYSICIAN OR SUPPLIER INCLUDING DEGREES OR CREDENTIALS (I certify that the statements on the reverse apply to this bill and are made a part thereof.)

SIGNED _____   DATE _____

32. SERVICE FACILITY LOCATION INFORMATION   a. NPI   b.

33. BILLING PROVIDER INFO & PH #   (   )   a. NPI   b.

PHYSICIAN OR SUPPLIER INFORMATION

NUCC Instruction Manual available at: www.nucc.org   APPROVED OMB-0938-0999 FORM CMS-1500 (08/05)

1500

HEALTH INSURANCE CLAIM FORM

APPROVED BY NATIONAL UNIFORM CLAIM COMMITTEE 08/05

[ ][ ] PICA

CARRIER →

PICA [ ][ ]

1. MEDICARE   MEDICAID   TRICARE CHAMPUS   CHAMPVA   GROUP HEALTH PLAN   FECA BLK LUNG   OTHER

[ ] (Medicare #)   [ ] (Medicaid #)   [ ] (Sponsor's SSN)   [ ] (Member ID#)   [ ] (SSN or ID)   [ ] (SSN)   [ ] (ID)

1a. INSURED'S I.D. NUMBER   (For Program in Item 1)

2. PATIENT'S NAME (Last Name, First Name, Middle Initial)

3. PATIENT'S BIRTH DATE
MM | DD | YY   SEX
M [ ]   F [ ]

4. INSURED'S NAME (Last Name, First Name, Middle Initial)

5. PATIENT'S ADDRESS (No., Street)

6. PATIENT RELATIONSHIP TO INSURED
Self [ ]   Spouse [ ]   Child [ ]   Other [ ]

7. INSURED'S ADDRESS (No., Street)

CITY   STATE

8. PATIENT STATUS
Single [ ]   Married [ ]   Other [ ]

Employed [ ]   Full-Time Student [ ]   Part-Time Student [ ]

CITY   STATE

ZIP CODE   TELEPHONE (Include Area Code)
(   )

ZIP CODE   TELEPHONE (Include Area Code)
(   )

9. OTHER INSURED'S NAME (Last Name, First Name, Middle Initial)

10. IS PATIENT'S CONDITION RELATED TO:

11. INSURED'S POLICY GROUP OR FECA NUMBER

a. OTHER INSURED'S POLICY OR GROUP NUMBER

a. EMPLOYMENT? (Current or Previous)
[ ] YES   [ ] NO

a. INSURED'S DATE OF BIRTH
MM | DD | YY   SEX
M [ ]   F [ ]

b. OTHER INSURED'S DATE OF BIRTH
MM | DD | YY   SEX
M [ ]   F [ ]

b. AUTO ACCIDENT?   PLACE (State)
[ ] YES   [ ] NO

b. EMPLOYER'S NAME OR SCHOOL NAME

c. EMPLOYER'S NAME OR SCHOOL NAME

c. OTHER ACCIDENT?
[ ] YES   [ ] NO

c. INSURANCE PLAN NAME OR PROGRAM NAME

d. INSURANCE PLAN NAME OR PROGRAM NAME

10d. RESERVED FOR LOCAL USE

d. IS THERE ANOTHER HEALTH BENEFIT PLAN?
[ ] YES   [ ] NO   *If yes*, return to and complete item 9 a-d.

READ BACK OF FORM BEFORE COMPLETING & SIGNING THIS FORM.

12. PATIENT'S OR AUTHORIZED PERSON'S SIGNATURE I authorize the release of any medical or other information necessary to process this claim. I also request payment of government benefits either to myself or to the party who accepts assignment below.

SIGNED _____   DATE _____

13. INSURED'S OR AUTHORIZED PERSON'S SIGNATURE I authorize payment of medical benefits to the undersigned physician or supplier for services described below.

SIGNED _____

PATIENT AND INSURED INFORMATION →

14. DATE OF CURRENT: ILLNESS (First symptom) OR
MM | DD | YY   INJURY (Accident) OR
PREGNANCY(LMP)

15. IF PATIENT HAS HAD SAME OR SIMILAR ILLNESS.
GIVE FIRST DATE   MM | DD | YY

16. DATES PATIENT UNABLE TO WORK IN CURRENT OCCUPATION
FROM   MM | DD | YY   TO   MM | DD | YY

17. NAME OF REFERRING PROVIDER OR OTHER SOURCE

17a.
17b. NPI

18. HOSPITALIZATION DATES RELATED TO CURRENT SERVICES
FROM   MM | DD | YY   TO   MM | DD | YY

19. RESERVED FOR LOCAL USE

20. OUTSIDE LAB? $ CHARGES
[ ] YES   [ ] NO

21. DIAGNOSIS OR NATURE OF ILLNESS OR INJURY (Relate Items 1, 2, 3 or 4 to Item 24E by Line)

1. |___.___
2. |___.___
3. |___.___
4. |___.___

22. MEDICAID RESUBMISSION
CODE   ORIGINAL REF. NO.

23. PRIOR AUTHORIZATION NUMBER

24. A. DATE(S) OF SERVICE From	To		B. PLACE OF SERVICE	C. EMG	D. PROCEDURES, SERVICES, OR SUPPLIES (Explain Unusual Circumstances) CPT/HCPCS	MODIFIER	E. DIAGNOSIS POINTER	F. $ CHARGES	G. DAYS OR UNITS	H. EPSDT Family Plan	I. ID. QUAL.	J. RENDERING PROVIDER ID. #
MM DD YY	MM DD YY											
1											NPI	
2											NPI	
3											NPI	
4											NPI	
5											NPI	
6											NPI	

25. FEDERAL TAX I.D. NUMBER   SSN EIN
[ ] [ ]

26. PATIENT'S ACCOUNT NO.

27. ACCEPT ASSIGNMENT?
(For govt. claims, see back)
[ ] YES   [ ] NO

28. TOTAL CHARGE $

29. AMOUNT PAID $

30. BALANCE DUE $

31. SIGNATURE OF PHYSICIAN OR SUPPLIER INCLUDING DEGREES OR CREDENTIALS
(I certify that the statements on the reverse apply to this bill and are made a part thereof.)

SIGNED _____   DATE _____

32. SERVICE FACILITY LOCATION INFORMATION

a. NPI   b.

33. BILLING PROVIDER INFO & PH #   (   )

a. NPI   b.

PHYSICIAN OR SUPPLIER INFORMATION →

NUCC Instruction Manual available at: www.nucc.org

APPROVED OMB-0938-0999 FORM CMS-1500 (08/05)

1500

HEALTH INSURANCE CLAIM FORM

APPROVED BY NATIONAL UNIFORM CLAIM COMMITTEE 08/05

CARRIER

☐☐☐ PICA

PICA ☐☐☐

1. MEDICARE	MEDICAID	TRICARE CHAMPUS	CHAMPVA	GROUP HEALTH PLAN	FECA BLK LUNG	OTHER	1a. INSURED'S I.D. NUMBER (For Program in Item 1)
☐ (Medicare #)	☐ (Medicaid #)	☐ (Sponsor's SSN)	☐ (Member ID#)	☐ (SSN or ID)	☐ (SSN)	☐ (ID)	

2. PATIENT'S NAME (Last Name, First Name, Middle Initial)

3. PATIENT'S BIRTH DATE MM | DD | YY   SEX M ☐ F ☐

4. INSURED'S NAME (Last Name, First Name, Middle Initial)

5. PATIENT'S ADDRESS (No., Street)

6. PATIENT RELATIONSHIP TO INSURED Self ☐ Spouse ☐ Child ☐ Other ☐

7. INSURED'S ADDRESS (No., Street)

CITY   STATE

8. PATIENT STATUS Single ☐ Married ☐ Other ☐

CITY   STATE

ZIP CODE   TELEPHONE (Include Area Code) ( )

Employed ☐ Full-Time Student ☐ Part-Time Student ☐

ZIP CODE   TELEPHONE (Include Area Code) ( )

9. OTHER INSURED'S NAME (Last Name, First Name, Middle Initial)

10. IS PATIENT'S CONDITION RELATED TO:

11. INSURED'S POLICY GROUP OR FECA NUMBER

a. OTHER INSURED'S POLICY OR GROUP NUMBER

a. EMPLOYMENT? (Current or Previous) ☐ YES ☐ NO

a. INSURED'S DATE OF BIRTH MM | DD | YY   SEX M ☐ F ☐

b. OTHER INSURED'S DATE OF BIRTH MM | DD | YY   SEX M ☐ F ☐

b. AUTO ACCIDENT? ☐ YES ☐ NO   PLACE (State) ☐

b. EMPLOYER'S NAME OR SCHOOL NAME

c. EMPLOYER'S NAME OR SCHOOL NAME

c. OTHER ACCIDENT? ☐ YES ☐ NO

c. INSURANCE PLAN NAME OR PROGRAM NAME

d. INSURANCE PLAN NAME OR PROGRAM NAME

10d. RESERVED FOR LOCAL USE

d. IS THERE ANOTHER HEALTH BENEFIT PLAN? ☐ YES ☐ NO   If yes, return to and complete item 9 a-d.

READ BACK OF FORM BEFORE COMPLETING & SIGNING THIS FORM.
12. PATIENT'S OR AUTHORIZED PERSON'S SIGNATURE I authorize the release of any medical or other information necessary to process this claim. I also request payment of government benefits either to myself or to the party who accepts assignment below.

SIGNED _____ DATE _____

13. INSURED'S OR AUTHORIZED PERSON'S SIGNATURE I authorize payment of medical benefits to the undersigned physician or supplier for services described below.

SIGNED _____

PATIENT AND INSURED INFORMATION

14. DATE OF CURRENT: MM | DD | YY   ILLNESS (First symptom) OR INJURY (Accident) OR PREGNANCY(LMP)

15. IF PATIENT HAS HAD SAME OR SIMILAR ILLNESS. GIVE FIRST DATE MM | DD | YY

16. DATES PATIENT UNABLE TO WORK IN CURRENT OCCUPATION FROM MM | DD | YY TO MM | DD | YY

17. NAME OF REFERRING PROVIDER OR OTHER SOURCE

17a.
17b. NPI

18. HOSPITALIZATION DATES RELATED TO CURRENT SERVICES FROM MM | DD | YY TO MM | DD | YY

19. RESERVED FOR LOCAL USE

20. OUTSIDE LAB? ☐ YES ☐ NO $ CHARGES

21. DIAGNOSIS OR NATURE OF ILLNESS OR INJURY (Relate Items 1, 2, 3 or 4 to Item 24E by Line)

1. |___.___| 3. |___.___|

2. |___.___| 4. |___.___|

22. MEDICAID RESUBMISSION CODE   ORIGINAL REF. NO.

23. PRIOR AUTHORIZATION NUMBER

24. A. DATE(S) OF SERVICE		B. PLACE OF SERVICE	C. EMG	D. PROCEDURES, SERVICES, OR SUPPLIES (Explain Unusual Circumstances)		E. DIAGNOSIS POINTER	F. $ CHARGES	G. DAYS OR UNITS	H. EPSDT Family Plan	I. ID. QUAL.	J. RENDERING PROVIDER ID. #
From MM DD YY	To MM DD YY			CPT/HCPCS	MODIFIER						
1										NPI	
2										NPI	
3										NPI	
4										NPI	
5										NPI	
6										NPI	

25. FEDERAL TAX I.D. NUMBER   SSN ☐ EIN ☐

26. PATIENT'S ACCOUNT NO.

27. ACCEPT ASSIGNMENT? (For govt. claims, see back) ☐ YES ☐ NO

28. TOTAL CHARGE $

29. AMOUNT PAID $

30. BALANCE DUE $

31. SIGNATURE OF PHYSICIAN OR SUPPLIER INCLUDING DEGREES OR CREDENTIALS (I certify that the statements on the reverse apply to this bill and are made a part thereof.)

SIGNED _____ DATE _____

32. SERVICE FACILITY LOCATION INFORMATION

a. NPI   b.

33. BILLING PROVIDER INFO & PH # ( )

a. NPI   b.

PHYSICIAN OR SUPPLIER INFORMATION

NUCC Instruction Manual available at: www.nucc.org

APPROVED OMB-0938-0999 FORM CMS-1500 (08/05)

1500

HEALTH INSURANCE CLAIM FORM

APPROVED BY NATIONAL UNIFORM CLAIM COMMITTEE 08/05

| | PICA | | | | | | | PICA | |

| 1. MEDICARE | MEDICAID | TRICARE CHAMPUS | CHAMPVA | GROUP HEALTH PLAN | FECA BLK LUNG | OTHER | 1a. INSURED'S I.D. NUMBER (For Program in Item 1) |

(Medicare #)   (Medicaid #)   (Sponsor's SSN)   (Member ID#)   (SSN or ID)   (SSN)   (ID)

2. PATIENT'S NAME (Last Name, First Name, Middle Initial)

3. PATIENT'S BIRTH DATE   MM   DD   YY   SEX   M   F

4. INSURED'S NAME (Last Name, First Name, Middle Initial)

5. PATIENT'S ADDRESS (No., Street)

6. PATIENT RELATIONSHIP TO INSURED   Self   Spouse   Child   Other

7. INSURED'S ADDRESS (No., Street)

CITY   STATE

8. PATIENT STATUS   Single   Married   Other

CITY   STATE

ZIP CODE   TELEPHONE (Include Area Code)   (   )

Employed   Full-Time Student   Part-Time Student

ZIP CODE   TELEPHONE (Include Area Code)   (   )

9. OTHER INSURED'S NAME (Last Name, First Name, Middle Initial)

10. IS PATIENT'S CONDITION RELATED TO:

11. INSURED'S POLICY GROUP OR FECA NUMBER

a. OTHER INSURED'S POLICY OR GROUP NUMBER

a. EMPLOYMENT? (Current or Previous)   YES   NO

a. INSURED'S DATE OF BIRTH   MM   DD   YY   SEX   M   F

b. OTHER INSURED'S DATE OF BIRTH   MM   DD   YY   SEX   M   F

b. AUTO ACCIDENT?   PLACE (State)   YES   NO

b. EMPLOYER'S NAME OR SCHOOL NAME

c. EMPLOYER'S NAME OR SCHOOL NAME

c. OTHER ACCIDENT?   YES   NO

c. INSURANCE PLAN NAME OR PROGRAM NAME

d. INSURANCE PLAN NAME OR PROGRAM NAME

10d. RESERVED FOR LOCAL USE

d. IS THERE ANOTHER HEALTH BENEFIT PLAN?   YES   NO   If yes, return to and complete item 9 a-d.

READ BACK OF FORM BEFORE COMPLETING & SIGNING THIS FORM.

12. PATIENT'S OR AUTHORIZED PERSON'S SIGNATURE I authorize the release of any medical or other information necessary to process this claim. I also request payment of government benefits either to myself or to the party who accepts assignment below.

SIGNED _____   DATE _____

13. INSURED'S OR AUTHORIZED PERSON'S SIGNATURE I authorize payment of medical benefits to the undersigned physician or supplier for services described below.

SIGNED _____

14. DATE OF CURRENT: MM   DD   YY   ILLNESS (First symptom) OR INJURY (Accident) OR PREGNANCY(LMP)

15. IF PATIENT HAS HAD SAME OR SIMILAR ILLNESS. GIVE FIRST DATE   MM   DD   YY

16. DATES PATIENT UNABLE TO WORK IN CURRENT OCCUPATION   MM   DD   YY   FROM   TO   MM   DD   YY

17. NAME OF REFERRING PROVIDER OR OTHER SOURCE

17a.
17b. NPI

18. HOSPITALIZATION DATES RELATED TO CURRENT SERVICES   MM   DD   YY   FROM   TO   MM   DD   YY

19. RESERVED FOR LOCAL USE

20. OUTSIDE LAB?   YES   NO $ CHARGES

21. DIAGNOSIS OR NATURE OF ILLNESS OR INJURY (Relate Items 1, 2, 3 or 4 to Item 24E by Line)

1.
2.
3.
4.

22. MEDICAID RESUBMISSION CODE   ORIGINAL REF. NO.

23. PRIOR AUTHORIZATION NUMBER

24. A. DATE(S) OF SERVICE						B. PLACE OF SERVICE	C. EMG	D. PROCEDURES, SERVICES, OR SUPPLIES (Explain Unusual Circumstances) CPT/HCPCS MODIFIER	E. DIAGNOSIS POINTER	F. $ CHARGES	G. DAYS OR UNITS	H. EPSDT Family Plan	I. ID. QUAL.	J. RENDERING PROVIDER ID. #
From MM	DD	YY	To MM	DD	YY									
1													NPI	
2													NPI	
3													NPI	
4													NPI	
5													NPI	
6													NPI	

25. FEDERAL TAX I.D. NUMBER   SSN   EIN

26. PATIENT'S ACCOUNT NO.

27. ACCEPT ASSIGNMENT? (For govt. claims, see back)   YES   NO

28. TOTAL CHARGE $

29. AMOUNT PAID $

30. BALANCE DUE $

31. SIGNATURE OF PHYSICIAN OR SUPPLIER INCLUDING DEGREES OR CREDENTIALS (I certify that the statements on the reverse apply to this bill and are made a part thereof.)

SIGNED _____   DATE _____

32. SERVICE FACILITY LOCATION INFORMATION

a. NPI   b.

33. BILLING PROVIDER INFO & PH #   (   )

a. NPI   b.

NUCC Instruction Manual available at: www.nucc.org

APPROVED OMB-0938-0999 FORM CMS-1500 (08/05)

CARRIER

PATIENT AND INSURED INFORMATION

PHYSICIAN OR SUPPLIER INFORMATION

Prescription drugs
    in CHAMPVA, 298
    in Medicaid, 119
    in Medicare, 151–152
    table in ICD-9, 210–211, 212f
Preventive care
    HMOs and, 79
    in Medicare supplemental plans,
        154t
Primary care manager (PCM), in
    TRICARE, 285–286
Primary care physician (PCP)
    consultations and, 86
    as gatekeeper, 90
    in PPOs, 77
    referrals and, 86
Primary coverage, determination of
    checklist, 537–543
Prior approval, in Medicaid, 127
Prior authorization, in CMS-1500
    form, 17
Privacy. See also Health Insurance
        Portability and Accountability
        Act (HIPAA)
    HMOs and, 80
    patients and, 358
Private insurance, 40, 42–44
PRO. See Peer review organization
    (PRO)
Problem-focused history, 253
Problem patients, billing and,
    371–372
Procedural coding. See CPT coding
Procedure(s)
    in CMS-1500 form, 18
    unnecessary in HMOs, 80
Procedure Competency Checklists,
    479–554
Professional office setting, 356–357
Professional services, in CHAMPVA,
    299t
Program of All-Inclusive Care for the
    Elderly (PACE), 118, 152
Progress reports, in workers'
    compensation, 329, 331f
Prolonged services, in E/M coding,
    256, 259
Prompt rebilling, 368
Proofreading, 5–6, 6f, 20, 395
Prospective payment system (PPS),
    188
Protected health information, 332
Provider(s)
    CHAMPVA, 300
    managed care and, 90–91
    qualifications of, 81
    rendering in CMS-1500 form, 19
    requesting payment in CMS-1500
        form, 20
    small, 6
Provider-sponsored organization
    (PSO), Medicare, 159

Psychiatric facility, as place of
    service, 18t, 305t
Psychiatric residential center, as place
    of service, 18t, 305t
Public health clinic, as place of
    service, 18t, 305t
Purchased services, in CMS-1500
    form, 17

Q
Qualification, provider, 81
Qualified Disabled and Working
    Individuals, in Medicare, 122
Qualified Individuals Program, 122
Quality improvement organizations,
    188
Quality review study, 186–189

R
RA. See Remittance advice (RA)
Radial pulse checklist, 441
RCs. See Reserve components (RCs)
Reasonable and customary fee, 42
Rebilling, prompt, 368
Reciprocity, Medicaid and, 125
Records management, Medicaid, 129
Reduced services, in E/M coding,
    259
Referrals
    vs. consultations, 86
    definition of, 86
    in HMOs, 78
    in managed care, 86, 87f–88f
    obtaining, 86
    in PPOs, 77
Referring Provider, in original vs.
    new forms, 2
Regional directors, in TRICARE, 283
Register system, insurance claims,
    401–402
Regulation
    of HMOs, 78
    managed care, 80–82, 89
Regulation Z, 370
Rehabilitation, in workers'
    compensation, 322, 326
Rehabilitation facility, as place of
    service, 18t, 305t
Rejected claims, vs. denied, 396
Relative Value Committee, 242
Release of information authorization
    in CMS-1500 form, 14–15, 16f
    in HIPAA, 361–363
    in patient information form, 7, 8f
Remittance advice (RA), 126–127,
    128f, 176–178, 179f–181f
Remittance notice. See Explanation of
    benefits (EOB)
Remittance remark codes, 178
Remote assignment, in TRICARE, 286
Renal disease facility, as place of
    service, 18t, 305t

Rendering Provider, in CMS-1500
    form, 19
Replacement claims, 17
Reporting injury, in workers'
    compensation, 323, 324f–325f
Reserve components (RCs), in
    TRICARE, 285
Resource-based relative value system,
    165
Respect, appointment times and, 357
Respiratory rate checklist, 443
Respite care, in CHAMPVA, 299t
Restricted coverage, in HMOs, 80
Resubmission, of Medicaid claims,
    123
Retention, of Medicaid records, 129
Review of system (ROS), in E/M
    coding, 253
Right of access, 361
Right of correction, 361
ROS. See Review of system (ROS)

S
Savings accounts, in Medicare, 150
SCHIP. See State Children's Health
    Insurance Program (SCHIP)
Secondary claims
    Medicaid, 126t
    processing of, 407
Secondary coverage, commercial
    claims with, 52–54
Secondary payer
    Medicaid as, 14
    Medicare, 154, 156f–157f, 166,
        171, 407
Section, in CPT coding, 248
Selection of providers, in managed
    care, 78f
Self-insurance, 43
Self-pay patients, 370
Self-referring, 158
Semicolon, in CPT coding, 247–248
Service(s)
    in CMS-1500 form, 18
    mandated in Medicaid, 115
    optional in Medicaid, 115–116
Service dates, in CMS-1500 form, 17
Service Facility Location Information,
    in new vs. original forms, 2
Short-term disability insurance, 333
Signature
    of patient in CMS-1500 form,
        14–15
    of provider in CMS-1500 form, 19
Signature on file, in CMS-1500 form,
    14–15
Significant, separately identifiable
    evaluation services, in E/M
    coding, 259
Sign-in sheets, 13
Signs, coding of, 220–221, 222
Similar illness, in CMS-1500 form, 15